CONDENSED PYRIDAZINE AND PYRAZINE RINGS
(Cinnolines, Phthalazines, and Quinoxalines)

This is the fifth volume published in the series
THE CHEMISTRY OF HETEROCYCLIC COMPOUNDS

THE CHEMISTRY OF HETEROCYCLIC COMPOUNDS

A SERIES OF MONOGRAPHS

ARNOLD WEISSBERGER, *Consulting Editor*

CONDENSED PYRIDAZINE
AND PYRAZINE RINGS
(Cinnolines, Phthalazines, and Quinoxalines)

J. C. E. SIMPSON
Late Member of Scientific Staff
Medical Research Council
England

1953
INTERSCIENCE PUBLISHERS, INC., NEW YORK
INTERSCIENCE PUBLISHERS LTD., LONDON

INTERSCIENCE PUBLISHERS, INC., 250 Fifth Avenue, New York 1, N. Y.

For Great Britain and Northern Ireland:
Interscience Publishers Ltd., 2a Southampton Row, London, W. C. 1

PRINTED IN THE UNITED STATES OF AMERICA BY MACK PRINTING CO., EASTON, PA.

The Chemistry of Heterocyclic Compounds

The chemistry of heterocyclic compounds is one of the most complex branches of organic chemistry. It is equally interesting for its theoretical implications, for the diversity of its synthetic procedures, and for the physiological and industrial significance of heterocyclic compounds.

A field of such importance and intrinsic difficulty should be made as readily accessible as possible, and the lack of a modern detailed and comprehensive presentation of heterocyclic chemistry is therefore keenly felt. It is the intention of the present series to fill this gap by expert presentations of the various branches of heterocyclic chemistry. The subdivisions have been designed to cover the field in its entirety by monographs which reflect the importance and the interrelations of the various compounds, and accommodate the specific interests of the authors.

I am deeply sorry that the author of this volume will not see the completed book. Dr. Simpson died on February 7, 1952, while his manuscript was being set in print.

Dr. Simpson's friend and colleague, Dr. C. M. Atkinson, volunteered to take over the author's burden in the production of the book, and I want to thank him most sincerely for his generous help. He has also supplied the obituary of Dr. Simpson, printed on the following pages, which we hope will help to make the book a lasting memorial to its author.

Research Laboratories   ARNOLD WEISSBERGER
Eastman Kodak Company
Rochester, New York

J. C. E. SIMPSON
1908—1952

James Charles Edward Simpson was born on August 14, 1908, in Cheshire, where his father was Vicar of Liscard and later Residentiary Canon of Chester Cathedral. He received his education at St. Edward's School, Oxford, and proceeded to the University of Liverpool, where he was graduated in 1929 and was awarded the Leverhulme Chemistry Prize and the Campbell Brown Fellowship.

Under the direction of Professor (now Sir Ian) Heilbron, Simpson's first researches provided a number of contributions to the elucidation of the structure of ergosterol. After two years' work he obtained the Ph. D. degree, and in 1933 he went as a Commonwealth Fund Fellow to the Rockefeller Institute, New York, where he collaborated with Dr. W. A. Jacobs in proving the presence of the steroid skeleton in the digitalis sapogenins.

In 1935, Simpson became an assistant lecturer at King's College, London, and published from there a series of contributions on the isolation and chemistry of various triterpenes; in this field he was one of the first workers to apply the chromatographic technique to the separation of mixtures. Four years later he took up a temporary lectureship in the Durham Division of the University of Durham, where his interest in heterocyclic chemistry first found expression in studies on cinnoline derivatives. This work, which was linked initially to a wartime program on potential antimalarials, but contained much fundamental work on the scope and mechanism of cinnoline syntheses, established Simpson as the authority on this ring system and led to his recognition in the wider field of related nitrogenous heterocyclic compounds. In 1945 he was awarded the D. Sc. degree of the University of Liverpool and moved as I. C. I. Fellow to the Chemotherapy Department of the Liverpool School of Tropical Medicine. Collaboration with the director, at that time Dr. E. M. Lourie, on the application of cinnolines and related heterocyclic types to the chemotherapy of trypanosomiasis was most successful, and this happy partnership continued after 1949 when Simpson joined the Department of Chemistry at Manchester

J. C. E. Simpson

University as director of a Medical Research Council Group for Research on Chemotherapy. The chemical work during this period consisted of the synthesis of compounds which might be regarded as simple analogs of the trypanocidal phenanthridinium salts, and afforded an opportunity to study the properties of a group of related heterocyclic compounds. This program was being extended to test further a derived hypothesis, of proven usefulness, on the structural features required by trypanocidal compounds in this group, at the time of Simpson's death.

Apart from his research communications, Simpson contributed to reviews of heterocyclic chemistry and carried out editorial work for the Bureau of Abstracts. He was concerned always at the multiplication of labor involved in the separate literature surveys of research workers and he agreed readily to write this volume. As a memorial to him it cannot, of course, show his contributions to the field of natural products and it does not reflect his wider chemical horizon, but it represents well his insistence on the accurate classification of data.

He was well known for his energetic devotion to research and for his zealous approach as a teacher. A similar enthusiasm characterized his pastimes, which included fell-walking and playing tennis or badminton. He was an active member of choral societies and the early interest in campanology which he formed at Liscard developed during his life to such an extent that his intellectual and physical prowess were recognized throughout England.

Department of Organic Chemistry   C. M. ATKINSON
University of Manchester

Now at Chelsea Polytechnic
London, England

PREFACE

Although the chapters of this volume are numbered continuously, the subject matter falls naturally into three distinct sections: (*1*) cinnolines and (*2*) phthalazines—both formed by condensation of a pyridazine nucleus with an aromatic ring, and (*3*) quinoxalines, which represent the fusion of a pyrazine with an aromatic ring.

This book has been written with the objective of ensuring continuity with, and expansion from, Meyer-Jacobson's *Lehrbuch der organischen Chemie*, Volume II, 3, and in order to avoid the creation of possible gaps the literature has been fully covered from 1917 up to the end of 1948. Adequate reference is also made to the 1949 literature, and in many instances details of compounds there described have been included in the tables. Throughout the book the emphasis is on a critical presentation, so far as is reasonably possible, of the facts, rather than on a mere compilation of data. However, the treatment given to cinnolines and phthalazines differs slightly from that given to quinoxalines by reason of the fact that, twenty-five years ago, the chemistry of cinnoline and, to some extent, of phthalazine derivatives also, was very largely undeveloped, whereas that of quinoxaline compounds rested on a much broader basis of established fact and has already been reviewed, so far as the early literature is concerned, in Meyer-Jacobson's *Lehrbuch*. In this volume, therefore, references to the quinoxaline literature earlier than 1917, though numerous, are incidental; the accounts of cinnoline and phthalazine chemistry, on the other hand, are intended to be exhaustive. This selective treatment of quinoxaline chemistry applies particularly to those chapters dealing with compounds containing three or more fused rings.

Mention should be made of one or two conventions that have been adopted. Heterocyclic rings for which alternative formulations are possible by reason of tautomerism (for example, rings substituted in appropriate positions by amino and hydroxyl groups) are written in the form which approximates most closely the aromatic state; this procedure has been followed purely for reasons of simplicity of classification, and no indication is thereby implied that a given compound exists in the form shown rather than in the alternative imino- or keto-dihydro modification. Where substituents in the tables have been represented by cyclic formulas no effort has been made to show fully bonded (aromatic) structures but this can be assumed where representation is not clearly a reduced form (alicyclic). Colors of bases are not mentioned unless deeper than "almost colorless" or "very pale yellow"; and by the same token no mention is made of the colors of picrates which are merely "yellow." The keys to the various tables are not intended to furnish full experimental detail, but are usually so worded as to indicate in outline the conditions required to prepare a given compound. Standard British nomenclature has been used throughout this volume.

The following condensed mixed heterocyclics are included in the present volume: For condensed cinnolines and phthalazines, the choice has been based essentially on the *Ring Index*, and includes all compounds in which the cinnoline or phthalazine nucleus is intact and also those in which one CH group in the benzene ring of these nuclei is replaced by N. Compounds in which a CH group of these nuclei is replaced by other hetero elements are excluded. The same principles govern the selection of condensed quinoxalines, with the further exclusion of phenazines, condensed phenazines, and their aza analogs. In all these compounds, the intact quinoxaline nucleus is preserved.

Much of the work entailed in the preparation of this book was carried out at the Liverpool School of Tropical Medicine, and the author is greatly indebted to Dr. E. M. Lourie, then Director of the Warrington Yorke Department of Chemotherapy, for the secretarial facilities which were so willingly made available to him.

Medical Research Council   J. C. E. SIMPSON
Group for Research in Chemotherapy
Department of Organic Chemistry
University of Manchester
September, 1950

Contents

J. C. E. Simpson, 1908–1952.................................... vi

Preface.. ix

PART I. Cinnolines

I. General Introduction to Cinnoline Derivatives. Preparation and Properties of Cinnoline........................... 3

1. General Introduction to Cinnoline Derivatives................ 3
2. Preparation and Properties of Cinnoline..................... 4

II. 4-Aryl-, 4-Acyl-, and 4-Carboxycinnolines 6

1. 4-Arylcinnolines.. 6
2. 4-Acylcinnolines.. 11
3. 4-Carboxycinnolines (Cinnoline-4-carboxylic Acids)............ 11

III. 4-Methylcinnolines... 13

IV. 4-Hydroxycinnolines.. 16

1. Methods of Preparation................................... 16
   A. Richter Synthesis...................................... 16
   B. Pfannstiel and Janecke Synthesis........................ 17
   C. Borsche Synthesis..................................... 17
2. Properties... 23
   A. 4-Hydroxycinnolines Other Than 4-Hydroxycinnoline-3-carboxylic Acids................................... 23
   B. 4-Hydroxycinnoline-3-carboxylic Acids 24

V. 4-Chloro-, 4-Alkoxy-, and 4-Phenoxycinnolines.............. 29

1. 4-Chlorocinnolines.. 29
2. 4-Alkoxycinnolines....................................... 31
3. 4-Phenoxycinnolines...................................... 32

VI. 4-Aminocinnolines.. 35

1. Primary Amino Compounds............................... 35
2. Secondary Amino Compounds............................. 36
   A. 4-Arylaminocinnolines................................. 36
   B. 4-Dialkylaminoalkylaminocinnolines..................... 36
   C. 4-Hydroxylamino-7-acetylcinnolineoxime................. 38

VII. Cinnoline Quaternary Salts................................. 39

   A. Preparation... 39
   B. Structure... 39
   C. Reactions... 43

VIII. Reduced Cinnolines................................... 46

  1. Reduced Cinnolines with Nonoxygenated Rings............. 46
    A. Dihydrocinnolines..................................... 46
    B. Tetrahydrocinnolines................................. 47
    C. Hexahydrocinnolines.................................. 48
  2. Reduced Cinnolines with Oxygenated Rings.................. 48
    A. Reduced 3- and 4-Hydroxycinnolines..................... 48
    B. 1-Methyl-4-keto-1,4-dihydrocinnolines.................. 48
    C. Methyl 4-Keto-4,6-dihydrocinnolyl-6-nitronates............ 49
    D. 3-Acetoxy-2-aryl-6-keto-2,6-dihydrocinnolines............. 49
    E. 2-Phenyl-3-keto-4-hydroxy-2,3,5,6,7,8-hexahydrocinnoline.... 51

  IX. Cinnolines Containing Additional Fused Rings.............. 52

  1. 3,4-Benzocinnolines....................................... 52
  2. Tetrahydro-3,4-benzocinnolines............................ 57
  3. Other Cinnolines with Additional Aromatic Rings............. 57
  4. Cinnolines Containing Bridged Rings........................ 61
  5. Cinnolines Containing Fused Heterocyclic Rings.............. 62

PART II. Phthalazines

  X. Phthalazines Unsubstituted in the Hetero Ring 69

  1. Phthalazine.. 69
  2. 5,6-Dihydroxyphthalazine................................. 71

XI. 1-Alkyl-, 1-Aryl-, and 1,4-Diarylphthalazines.............. 72

  1. 1-Alkyl- and 1-Arylphthalazines........................... 72
  2. 1,4-Diarylphthalazines.................................... 76

XII. 1-Hydroxyphthalazines................................. 78

    A. Preparation... 78
    B. Properties.. 78

XIII. Alkyl, Aryl, and Acyl Derivatives of 4-(1-)Hydroxyphthalazines 84

  1. O-Derivatives... 84
  2. N-Derivatives (3-Substituted-4-keto-3,4-dihydrophthalazines)... 85
    A. Compounds without a 1-Substituent; 3-Aryl-, 3-Alkyl-, and
        3-Aralkyl-4-keto-3,4-dihydrophthalazines.............. 85
    B. Compounds with a 1-Substituent........................ 95
  3. Derivatives of Unknown Structure.......................... 96

XIV. 1-Hydroxy-3-aryl-3,4-dihydrophthalazine-4-acetic Acids ... 106

    A. Preparation... 106
    B. Properties.. 108

XV. 3-Aryl-1-ketophthalazines............................. 119

    A. Preparation... 119
    B. Properties and Reactions............................. 126

XVI. Methylated Derivatives of 3-Aryl-1-ketophthalazines 130

    1. Derivatives of Compounds Containing a Hydrogen Atom at C_4. . 130
       A. 1-Methoxy-4-alkoxy-3-aryl-3,4-dihydrophthalazines 130
       B. 1-Methoxy-3-arylphthalazinium Perchlorates 133
    2. Derivatives of Compounds Containing a Methyl Group at C_4:
       1-Methoxy-3-aryl-4-methylene-3,4-dihydrophthalazines 133

XVII. 1,4-Dihydroxyphthalazines 140

       A. Preparation 140
       B. Properties 143
       C. Chemiluminescence of Phthalazine Derivatives 153

XVIII. Monoalkyl and Monoacyl Derivatives of 1,4-Dihydroxyphthal-azines 157

    1. *O*-Derivatives 157
    2. *N*-Derivatives (1-Hydroxy-3-substituted-4-keto-3,4-dihydro-
       phthalazines) 158
       A. Compounds Containing No Substituent in the Benzene Ring 158
       B. Compounds Containing a Substituent in the Benzene Ring. . . 162
    3. Derivatives of Unknown Structure 165

XIX. Dialkyl and Diacyl Derivatives of 1,4-Dihydroxyphthalazines. . 168

    1. 1,4-Derivatives 168
    2. 1,3-Derivatives (1-Alkoxy- and 1-Acetoxy-3-substituted-4-keto-
       3,4-dihydrophthalazines) 169
       A. Preparation 169
       B. Properties 170
       C. Structure of Alkoxy Compounds 173
    3. 2,3-Derivatives 175
    4. Derivatives of Unknown Structure 176

XX. 1-Halogeno- and 1,4-Dihalogenophthalazines 178

    1. 1-Halogenophthalazines 178
    2. 1,4-Dihalogenophthalazines 179

XXI. 1-Aminophthalazines 183

XXII. Reduced Phthalazines 186

    1. 3,4-Dihydrophthalazines 186
    2. 1,2,3,4-Tetrahydrophthalazines 189

XXIII. Condensed Phthalazines and Azaphthalazines 191

    1. 1′,2′-3,4-Benziminazolo-3,4-dihydrophthalazines 191
    2. Compounds Prepared from 1,4-Diketones 192
    3. Miscellaneous Compounds 196
    4. Azaphthalazines 198

PART III. Quinoxalines

XXIV. Preparation of Quinoxalines from Primary Aromatic o-Diamines and 1,2-Dicarbonyl Compounds.................... 203

XXV. Quinoxalines Unsubstituted in the Hetero Ring 228

    Quinoxaline.. 228
    6,6'-Diquinoxalyl..................................... 229

XXVI. Quinoxaline N-Oxides................................... 232

    A. Preparation....................................... 232
    B. Properties.. 232

XXVII. 2-Hydroxy- and 2,3-Dihydroxyquinoxalines.................. 235

    1. 2-Hydroxyquinoxalines............................. 235
    A. Compounds Containing No Additional Substituent in the Hetero Ring... 235
    B. Compounds Containing an Additional (C_3) Substituent in the Hetero Ring.................................... 236
    Methylation of Hydroxyquinoxalines.................... 241
    2. 2,3-Dihydroxyquinoxalines......................... 242

XXVIII. Quinoxaline-2-aldehydes............................... 246

    A. Preparation....................................... 246
    B. Properties.. 246
    C. 3-Hydroxyquinoxaline-2-aldehyde.................... 246

XXIX. Quinoxaline-2-carboxylic and -2,3-dicarboxylic Acids......... 250

    1. Quinoxaline-2-carboxylic Acids..................... 250
    2. Quinoxaline-2,3-dicarboxylic Acids.................. 254

XXX. 2-Chloro- and 2,3-Dichloroquinoxalines..................... 258

    1. 2-Chloroquinoxalines.............................. 258
    2. 2,3-Dihalogenoquinoxalines......................... 260
    A. 2,3-Dichloroquinoxalines........................... 260
    B. 2,3-Dibromoquinoxaline............................ 261

XXXI. 2-Amino- and 2,3-Diaminoquinoxalines 263

    1. 2-Aminoquinoxalines.............................. 263
    A. Primary Amino Compounds......................... 263
    B. Secondary Amino Compounds....................... 264
    C. 2-Sulfonamidoquinoxalines......................... 265
    D. Tertiary Amino Compound.......................... 265
    2. Diaminoquinoxalines.............................. 265
    A. Diprimary Amino Compounds....................... 265
    2,3-Diaminoquinoxaline............................. 265
    2,3-Diaminoquinoxaline-6-arsonic Acid................. 267
    B. Primary-Secondary Amino Compounds................ 267
    C. Disecondary Amino Compounds..................... 269

Contents

XXXII. 2-Alkoxy-, 2,3-Dialkoxy-, and 2,3-Diaryloxyquinoxalines...... 270

   1. 2-Alkoxyquinoxalines... 270
   2. 2,3-Dialkoxy- and 2,3-Diaryloxyquinoxalines.................. 271

XXXIII. 2-Methyl- and 2,3-Dimethylquinoxalines.................... 273

   1. 2-Methylquinoxalines 273
   2. 2,3-Dimethylquinoxalines................................... 277

XXXIV. Quinoxaline Quaternary Salts............................... 286

   A. Preparation... 286
   B. Properties.. 288
   C. Decomposition by Alkali................................. 290
   D. Quinoxaline Cyanines................................... 290

XXXV. Formation of Quinoxalines from Compounds Containing a Furan Ring 293

   1. Conversion of 5-Hydroxy-2,5-diphenyl-4-keto-4,5-dihydrofurans and Related Compounds into Quinoxalines............... 293
   2. Conversion of Coumaran-3-ones into Quinoxalines............. 296
      A. 2-Hydroxy- and 2-Bromocoumaran-3-ones................. 296
      B. Coumaran-2,3-diones..................................... 298

XXXVI. 2-Polyhydroxyalkylquinoxalines........................... 300

   1. Synthesis... 300
   2. Properties and Reactions................................... 302
      A. General... 302
      B. Decomposition by Alkali................................. 304
      C. Reactions with Phenylhydrazine.......................... 306

XXXVII. Reduced Quinoxalines.................................... 310

   1. 1,2- and 1,4-Dihydroquinoxalines........................... 310
      A. Compounds Containing No Hydroxyl or Carbonyl Group in the Hetero Ring.................................... 310
      B. Compounds Containing a Hydroxyl or Carbonyl Group in the Hetero Ring.. 310
         (a) 1-Substituted-2-keto-1,2-dihydroquinoxalines........... 310
         (b) 1,2- and 1,4-Dihydroquinoxalines Having Hydroxyl Groups at C_2 or C_3.............................. 318
   2. 1,2,3,4-Tetrahydroquinoxalines............................. 325
      A. 1,2,3,4-Tetrahydroquinoxalines Containing No Oxygen Atom Attached to the Hetero Ring....................... 325
      Preparation... 325
      Properties.. 326
      Stereoisomerism of 1,2,3,4-Tetrahydroquinoxalines........ 326
      1,4-Endoalkylene-1,2,3,4-tetrahydroquinoxalines.......... 326
      B. 1,2,3,4-Tetrahydroquinoxalines Containing an Oxygen Atom Attached to the Hetero Ring....................... 329

XXXVIII. Condensed Quinoxalines.................................... 332

    1. Quinoxalines Condensed with Carbocyclic Rings............... 332
        A. 5,6-Benzoquinoxalines................................. 332
        B. 5,6,7,8-Dibenzoquinoxalines............................ 338
        C. Glucazidone and Derivatives........................... 338
        D. Other Condensed Quinoxalines.......................... 341
    2. Quinoxalines Condensed with Nitrogenous Heterocyclic Rings... 346
        A. Pyrroloquinoxalines................................... 346
        B. Pyridoquinoxalines.................................... 348
        C. Pyrazoloquinoxalines (Flavazoles)...................... 348
        D. Glyoxalinoquinoxalines................................ 353
        E. Triazoloquinoxalines.................................. 353
        F. Pyridazoquinoxalines.................................. 354

XXXIX. Azaquinoxalines.. 356

**Appendix I. Ultraviolet Absorption Spectra of Cinnoline and Quinoxaline
    Derivatives**.. 358

**Appendix II. Basic Strengths of Cinnoline, Phthalazine, and Quinoxaline
    Derivatives** 363

**Appendix III. Antibacterial and Parasiticidal Activities of Cinnoline and
    Quinoxaline Derivatives**................................ 364

Index 367

PART I

Cinnolines

General Introduction to Cinnoline Derivatives. Preparation and Properties of Cinnoline

1. General Introduction to Cinnoline Derivatives

So far as is known, no derivative of cinnoline occurs in nature. The cinnoline ring system was discovered in 1883 by von Richter,[1] who, in the course of experiments designed to convert o-nitrophenylpropiolic acid into o-hydroxyacetophenone, found that the diazonium chloride derived from o-aminophenylpropiolic acid was transformed on heating into a nitrogenous derivative (Eq. 1). The new ring system so formed was named cinnoline

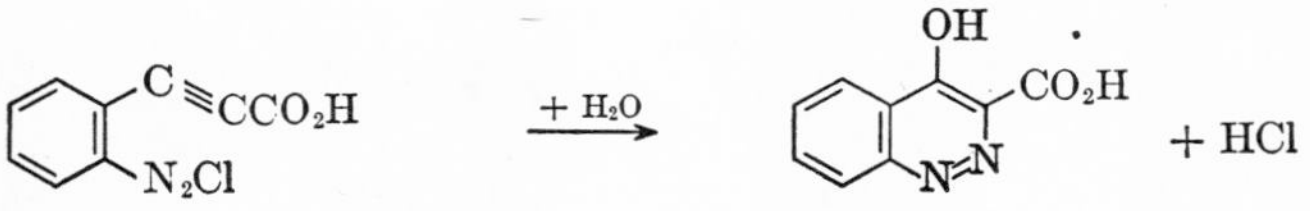

$$\text{(1)} \qquad + \text{HCl}$$

(*R.I.* 976) from analogy with quinoline. In the following year, Widman[2] prepared 4-methylcinnoline-7-carboxylic acid by diazotization of 1-methyl-1,2'-amino-4'-carboxyphenylethylene (Eq. 2). In 1909, Stoermer

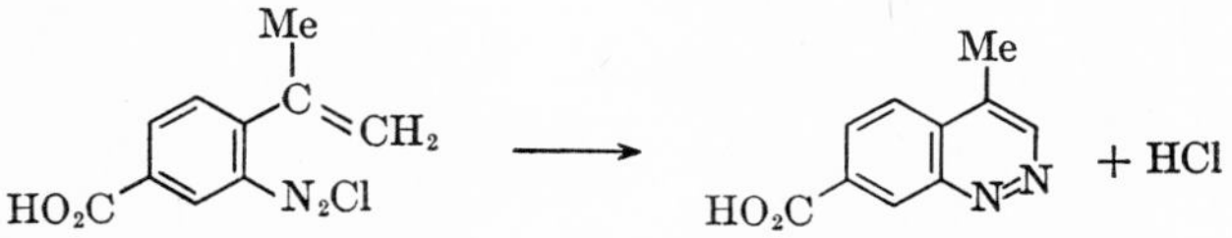

$$\text{(2)} \qquad + \text{HCl}$$

and his co-workers[3,4] found that this reaction could also be used to prepare 4-arylcinnolines.

No further work was carried out in this field until 1941, when Borsche and Herbert[5] found that diazotized 5-nitro-2-aminoacetophenone slowly cyclized on standing, yielding 6-nitro-4-hydroxycinnoline (Eq. 3). In

$$\text{(3)} \qquad + \text{HX}$$

3

point of time, this observation may be said to have ushered in a new chapter in the chemistry of cinnolines, as, during the last few years, knowledge of this group of compounds has expanded considerably.   The three reactions described above have been shown to be general synthetic routes, and the third reaction, leading to 4-hydroxycinnolines, has in particular been widely explored.

It is convenient to draw a sharp distinction between true cinnolines and a miscellaneous group of compounds which, although formally classifiable as cinnolines, contain additional rings fused to the cinnoline nucleus. The reasons for this distinction are: (1) such compounds are not prepared by the typical methods of cinnoline ring closure;   (2) the characteristic reactions of true cinnoline derivatives frequently cannot be shown by cinnolines carrying additional fused rings owing to the fact that positions important for cinnoline reactivity (e.g., C_3, C_4) may be positions of ring fusion;   and (3) these condensed cinnolines can, on occasion, be regarded equally logically as condensed phthalazines.   The chapters which follow are therefore concerned with true cinnoline derivatives, and miscellaneous condensed cinnolines are grouped together in Chapter IX.

2. Preparation and Properties of Cinnoline

Cinnoline (I), the parent compound of the heterocyclic group to which it gives its name, may be prepared by two methods.   The first of these, due to Busch and Rast,[6] consists in the reduction of 4-chlorocinnoline (II)

(I)   (II)   (III)   (IV)

with iron and 15% sulfuric acid to 1,2-dihydrocinnoline (III), which yields cinnoline on oxidation with mercuric oxide.   The second method, devised by Jacobs et al.,[7] involves the synthesis of cinnoline-4-carboxylic acid (IV), which is then decarboxylated in benzophenone at 155–165°.   Of the two methods, the latter is preferable as a preparative route.

Cinnoline is a pale yellow solid of geraniumlike odor which is soluble in water.   It crystallizes from ether with 1 molecule of solvent, and then melts at 24–25°C.[6];   the solvent-free base melts at 39°C.[6] [37–38°C.[7]]. It tends to liquefy[7] on exposure to air at 20–25°.   The base forms stable salts;   the hydrochloride melts at 156–160°C.[6] (154–156°C.[7]) and sublimes at 110–115°/3 mm.[7]; the picrate, yellow prisms from alcohol, has m.p. 196–196.5°C.[7] (190°C.[6]); and the methiodide, dark reddish-brown crystals, melts at 168–170.5° (dec.)[7] [168°C.[6]]. The chloroplatinate, m.p. 280° (dec.), and aurichloride, m.p. 146°, are also described.[6] Busch and Rast[6] state that cinnoline is a strong base, but this statement was clearly based on qualitative impressions, and recent quantitative work has established that the base is actually fairly weak ($pK_a = 2.51$ at 21–22° in 50% aqueous alcohol[8]; 2.70 at 20° in water[9]).

Cinnoline is distinctly toxic, and also shows appreciable antibacterial action against *Escherichia coli*.[6]

References

1. von Richter, *Ber.*, **16**, 677 (1883).
2. Widman, *Ber.*, **17**, 722 (1884).
3. Stoermer and Fincke, *Ber.*, **42**, 3115 (1909).
4. Stoermer and Gaus, *Ber.*, **45**, 3104 (1912).
5. Borsche and Herbert, *Ann.*, **546**, 293 (1941).
6. Busch and Rast, *Ber.*, **30**, 521 (1897).
7. T. L. Jacobs, Winstein, Henderson, and Spaeth, *J. Am. Chem. Soc.*, **68**, 1310 (1946).
8. Keneford, Morley, Simpson, and Wright, *J. Chem. Soc.*, **1949**, 1356.
9. Albert, Goldacre, and J. Phillips, *J. Chem. Soc.*, **1948**, 2240.

CHAPTER II

4-Aryl-, 4-Acyl-, and 4-Carboxy-cinnolines

1. 4-Arylcinnolines

A. Synthesis. The first recorded examples of the synthesis of 4-arylcinnolines are by Stoermer and Fincke,[1] who found that diazotization of o-aminoarylethylenes (I; R_1 = aryl; R_2 = H or Me) effected reaction

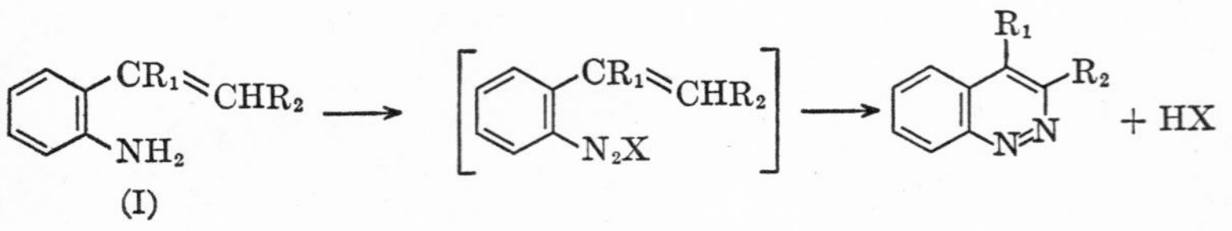

$$\text{(I)} \qquad\qquad\qquad\qquad\qquad\qquad\qquad + HX \qquad (1)$$

(1), which is precisely the same reaction that was first observed many years earlier by Widman,[2] who prepared 4-methylcinnoline-7-carboxylic acid (II), and in consequence the reaction has come to be known as the

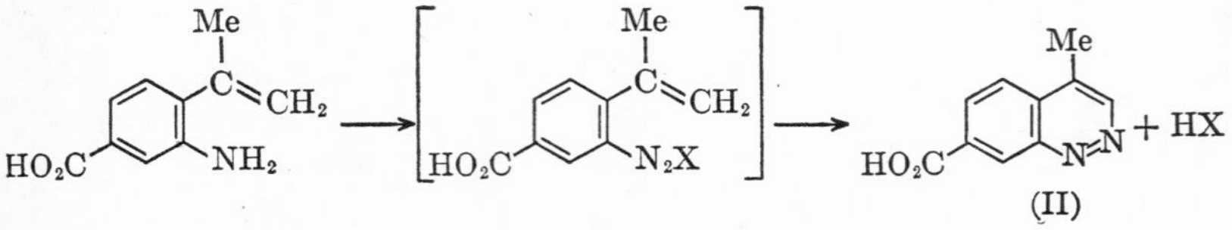

$$\qquad\qquad\qquad\qquad\qquad\qquad\qquad\qquad\qquad\qquad + HX \qquad (2)$$
$$\text{(II)}$$

Widman-Stoermer synthesis (2). A list of the known 4-arylcinnolines is given in Table II-1.

Recent investigations of the scope and mechanism of the reaction[3,4,16] have shown that it proceeds successfully when R_1 is aryl or methyl and R_2 is alkyl, aryl, or aralkyl, but that it fails in cases so far investigated when R_1 is hydrogen or carboxyl (R_2 being aryl, α-pyridyl, or α-quinolyl). The reaction is usually very rapid, and it is seemingly independent of the geometrical configuration of the groups around the ethylenic linkage. It is concluded from these results[5] that the ring closure is more or less ionic in character, and that it is induced by polarization of the diazonium salt of (I) as indicated below. The essential requisite which enables this polarization to be set up is, clearly, that R_1 must be an electron-donating group

6

$$(3)$$

(Eq. 3).   According to this mechanism, the coordination of the anionoid C_β with the cationoid diazonium grouping should be retarded if R_2 has sufficient electron-absorbing powers.   In agreement with this conclusion, it has been found that, whereas (I; $R_1 = R_2 = $ Ph) yields 3,4-diphenyl-cinnoline almost quantitatively, the reaction with (I; $R_1 = $ Ph; $R_2 = \alpha\text{-}C_{10}H_7$) gives, in addition to the expected cinnoline, 2-phenylchrysene (III).[6]   This hydrocarbon arises through the agency of a competing Pschorr reaction, and is formed because an α-naphthyl residue on the β-carbon atom

(III)

of the diazotized aminoethylene is more effective than a similarly placed phenyl group in absorbing the lone electron pair from C_β, thus militating against the cinnoline ring closure.

B. Properties.   No detailed study of the chemistry of 4-arylcinnolines has yet been made.   In general, 4-arylcinnolines are, qualitatively, weak bases, although some compounds are soluble in dilute acids,[1] and the basic strength seems to be enhanced by a 3-methyl or a 3-benzyl group. Usually they react as monoacid bases, but abnormal salts are also known. Thus 4-phenylcinnoline forms a hydrochloride, m.p. 130° (dec.), a hydro-bromide, m.p. 202–204°, a hydriodide (dec. 150°), a nitrate, m.p. 156–157°, a picrate, m.p. 156–158°, a chloroaurate (melts gradually above 158°), and a chloroplatinate, m.p. $> 300°$; but it also yields a basic hydriodide (B_2HI), m.p. 93–95°, an acid sulfate, m.p. 181–182°, a chloro-aurate (BHCl)$_2$AuCl$_3$, m.p. 145–147°, and an argentonitrate, BAgNO$_3$, m.p. 260° (dec.).[1]   4-p-Anisylcinnoline forms a normal hydrochloride, m.p. 215°, a picrate, m.p. 150°, a nitrate, m.p. 151–152°, a chloroaurate, m.p. 120° (dec.), and a chloroplatinate (dec. 200°), an acid sulfate, m.p. 211° (dec.), and an argentonitrate, BAgNO$_3$ (dec. 250°).[10]   3-Methyl-4-phenylcinnoline gives a chloroplatinate (dec. 180°)[1]; and 4-p-hydroxy-phenylcinnoline yields a chloroplatinate (dec. 252°), an acid sulfate, m.p. 210°, and a sodium salt, m.p. 85°.[10]

TABLE II-1.* 4-Arylcinnolines

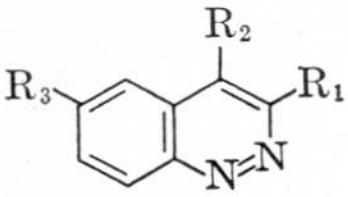

R₁	R₂	R₃	Prep.a	M.p., °C.	Remarks	Ref.
H	Ph	H	A	67–67.5	Yellow cryst.	1
H	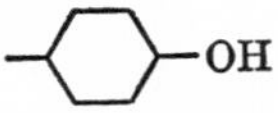 ⟨C₆H₄⟩-OH	H	B	230, 234–235	Yellow prisms	8,10
H	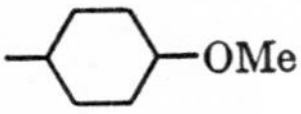 ⟨C₆H₄⟩-OMe	H	A	85	Yellow needles	10
H	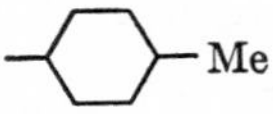 ⟨C₆H₄⟩-Me	H	A	58–59	Yellow cryst.	1
H	2′-Pyridyl	H	A	128–129	Picrate, m.p. 201–203°	16
H	Ph	Br	A	143.5–144.5	Yellow needles	3
H	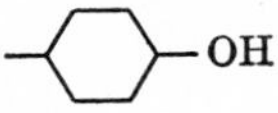 ⟨C₆H₄⟩-OH	Cl	A	257–259 (dec.)	Yellow plates	3
H	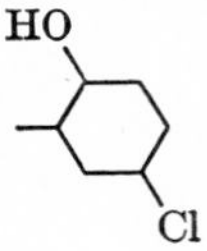 HO-⟨C₆H₃⟩-Cl	Cl	A	260–261 (dec.)	Golden needles	3
Me	Ph	H	A	134–136 135–136	Yellow cryst.	1,4
Me	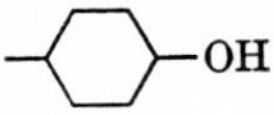 ⟨C₆H₄⟩-OH	H	B	241–242	Yellow prisms	8
Me	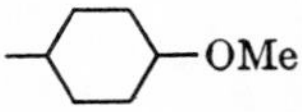 ⟨C₆H₄⟩-OMe	H	A	131–133	Yellow leaflets	4
CH₂Ph	Ph	H	A	116.5–118	Pale yellow needles	6
Ph	Ph	H	A,C	149–150	Yellow rhombs	6,17
Ph	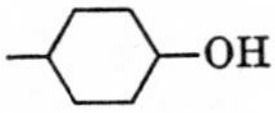 ⟨C₆H₄⟩-OH	H	B	283–286	—	8
Ph	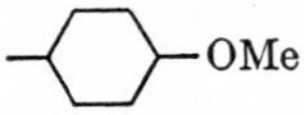 ⟨C₆H₄⟩-OMe	H	A	169–170.5	Yellow needles	4
1′-C₁₀H₇	Ph	H	A	178–179	Yellow cryst.	6
2′-Pyridyl	Ph	H	A	—	Picrate, m.p. 194–196°	16

TABLE II-1.   4-Arylcinnolines (continued)

R₁	R₂	R₃	Prep.[a]	M.p., °C.	Remarks	Ref.
2′-Pyridyl	 ⬡—OMe	H	A	157–158	Yellow tablets	16
2′-Quinolyl	 ⬡—OMe	H	A	151–152	Yellow tablets	16

* In this and in all other tables, plain hexagons are used to indicate substituent aryl groups.
[a] A, by the Widman-Stoermer reaction.   B, by demethylation of the corresponding anisylcinnoline with hydrobromic acid.   C, from benzil monophenylhydrazone by cyclodehydration with 75–80% (w/w) aqueous sulfuric acid.

TABLE II-2. 4-Arylcinnoline N-oxides

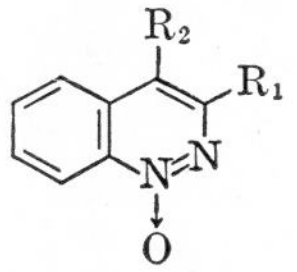

R₁	R₂	Color and cryst. form	M.p., °C.	Ref.
Me	Ph	Straw-colored needles	124–125	8
Me	 ⬡—OMe	Blades	161	8
CH₂Ph	Ph	Needles	110–111 (clear at 130)	8
Ph	Ph	Yellow needles	196–198 (clear at 202)	8
Ph	 ⬡—OMe	Light brown blades	176–177	8

Quaternary salt formation occurs fairly readily in five cases so far examined, viz., 4-phenyl-, 4-phenyl-3-methyl-, 4-p-anisyl-, 4-p-hydroxyphenyl-, and 3-phenyl-4-p-hydroxyphenylcinnoline[1,7,10] (see Chapter VII).

The formation of N-oxides is also a characteristic property of 4-arylcinnolines,[8] as shown in Table II-2; these oxides are produced by oxidation of the cinnolines with hydrogen peroxide in acetic acid, but, unlike quinoxaline di-N-oxides, which are similarly formed (Chapter XXVI), they show no peroxidic properties. The oxidation is considered to occur at N₁ and not at N₂ by reason of the fact that the basic center of 4-substituted cinnolines is probably N₁[7] (see Chapter VII). On nitration, 4-phenyl-3-methylcinnoline N-oxide yields, somewhat unexpectedly, four isomeric mononitro derivatives (m.p. 256–257°, 235–238°, 218–219°, and 198–199°), the orientations of which are unknown.

On oxidation with hot aqueous permanganate, 4-phenylcinnoline yields the acid (IV),[1] and the analogs (V) and (VI) are produced by similar oxidation of 3-methyl-4-phenyl- and 4-p-anisyl-cinnoline.[1,10] Degradation of (VI) ultimately yields pyridazine.[10]

(IV)   (V)   (VI)

The most interesting known property of 4-arylcinnolines is their behavior on reduction with sodium and alcohol, whereby they are converted into the corresponding 3-arylindoles. Table II-3 gives a list of cinnolines of which the behavior under these conditions has been investigated.[8] It will be noted that 4-methylcinnolines undergo the same reaction; the ring contraction is thus characteristic of cinnolines carrying a hydrocarbon substituent at C_4, but it seems possible that substitution of both C_3 and C_4 by aryl groups has an inhibitory effect. Two cases have also been recorded of the conversion of cinnolines into indoles in acid reducing media; 4-phenylcinnoline gives 3-phenylindole when refluxed for 2 hours with 33% aqueous acetic acid and amalgamated zinc, and 3-hydroxycinnoline gives oxindole when refluxed 1 hour with red phosphorus and hydriodic acid (d 1.7); but no indole derivative could be obtained from 4-hydroxycinnoline.[9]

TABLE II-3. Conversion of 4-Substituted Cinnolines into Indoles

Cinnoline	Ammonia evolved (% of theoretical)	Products
4-Phenyl-3-methyl	—	3-Phenyl-2-methylindole + unchanged cinnoline
4-p-Anisyl-3-methyl	58	3-p-Anisyl-2-methylindole
4-p-Hydroxyphenyl-3-methyl	55	3-p-Hydroxyphenyl-2-methylindole + unchanged cinnoline
4-p-Hydroxyphenyl	53	3-p-Hydroxyphenylindole + unchanged cinnoline
4-p-Anisyl	15	Resin
3-Phenyl-4-p-anisyl	3	Unidentified mixture
3-Phenyl-4-p-hydroxyphenyl	1	Unchanged cinnoline + unidentified material
4-Methyl	65	Skatole + unchanged cinnoline
7-Chloro-4-methyl	60	Skatole + 4-methylcinnoline
6-Chloro-4-methyl	57	Skatole + unidentified material

2. 4-Acylcinnolines

4-Acetylcinnoline (I), m.p. 100–101°, is prepared from ethyl cinnoline-4-carboxylate (*vide infra*) by condensation with ethyl acetate, followed by acid hydrolysis of the intermediate keto ester (II) (m.p. 81.5–82°)[11]; it forms an oxime, m.p. 165–165.5° (corr.).

4-1'-Keto-6'-benzamido-n-hexylcinnoline (III), m.p. 115–116.5° (corr.), is formed by a similar condensation of ethyl cinnoline-4-carboxylate with ethyl ω-benzamidocaproate, followed by hydrolysis.[11]

4-Chloroacetylcinnoline (IV), m.p. 95–100° (dec.), results from interaction of diazomethane with the acid chloride of cinnoline-4-carboxylic acid, followed by treatment with hydrogen chloride and basification of the hydrochloride of IV.[11]

3,4-Dibenzoylcinnoline (V) is prepared by oxidation of VI (Chapter IX) with nitric acid in acetic acid; it forms brown crystals, m.p. 163°, which give a blue coloration with concentrated sulfuric acid.[12] Reactions of this compound are described in Chapter IX.

3,4-Di(thiobenzoyl)cinnoline (VII), which forms yellow crystals, m.p. 206–207° (dec.), is prepared by refluxing compound V with alcoholic ammonium sulfide.[13]

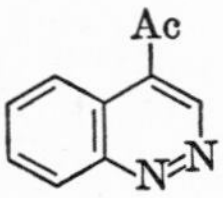

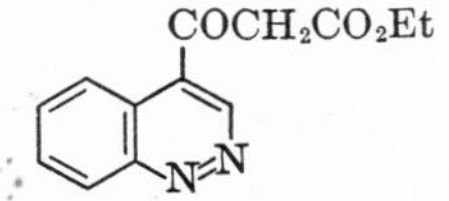

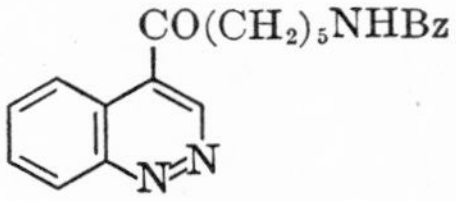

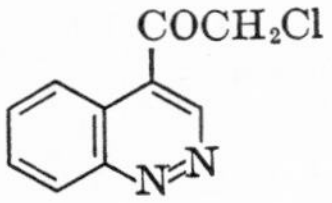

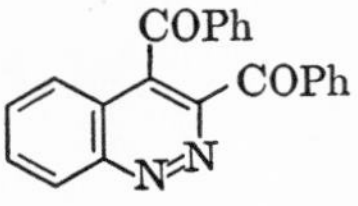

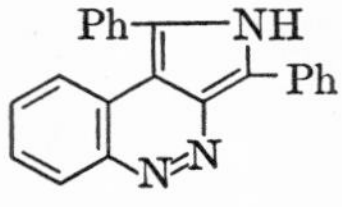

3. 4-Carboxycinnolines (Cinnoline-4-carboxylic Acids)

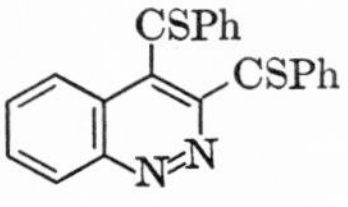

Cinnoline-4-carboxylic acid (I) is prepared by oxidation of 4-styryl-cinnoline (Chapter III) with permanganate in aqueous pyridine. It melts at 195–196° (dec., corr.) and gives an ethyl ester, m.p. 48.5–49.5°.[11] When heated in benzophenone at 155–165° it is smoothly converted into cinnoline,[11] a small amount of 4,4'-dicinnolyl (II) (m.p. 237–238°) being formed as a by-product.[14]

3-Phenylcinnoline-4-carboxylic acid (III) is formed by the action of hot aqueous sodium hydroxide on N-benzylideneaminoisatin (IV)[15]; it forms yellow plates, m.p. 244° (dec.).

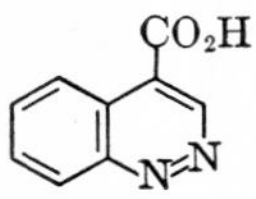

(I) 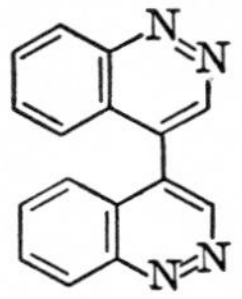   (II) 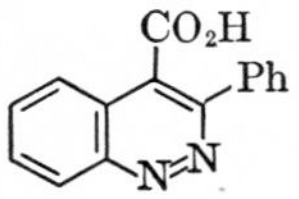   (III) 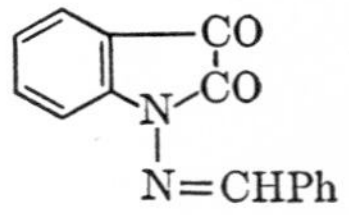   (IV)

References

1. Stoermer and Fincke, *Ber.*, **42**, 3115 (1909).
2. Widman, *Ber.*, **17**, 722 (1884).
3. Simpson and Stephenson, *J. Chem. Soc.*, **1942**, 353.
4. Simpson, *J. Chem. Soc.*, **1946**, 673.
5. Schofield and Simpson, *J. Chem. Soc.*, **1945**, 520.
6. Simpson, *J. Chem. Soc.*, **1943**, 447.
7. Simpson, *J. Chem. Soc.*, **1947**, 1653.
8. Atkinson and Simpson, *J. Chem. Soc.*, **1947**, 1649.
9. Neber, Knöller, Herbst, and Trissler, *Ann.*, **471**, 113 (1929).
10. Stoermer and Gaus, *Ber.*, **45**, 3104 (1912).
11. T. L. Jacobs, Winstein, R. B. Henderson, and Spaeth, *J. Am. Chem. Soc.*, **68**, 1310 (1946).
12. F. Angelico, *Zentr. I*, 445 (1909) [*Atti Accad. Lincei, Classe sci. fis. mat. nat.* [5], **17**, II, 655 (1908)].
13. F. Angelico and C. Labisi, *Zentr. I*, 2095 (1910) [*Gazz. chim. ital.*, **40**, I, 411 (1910)].
14. Morley, *J. Chem. Soc.*, **1951**, 1971.
15. Stollé and Becker, *Ber.*, **57**, 1123 (1924).
16. Schofield, *J. Chem. Soc.*, **1949**, 2408.
17. B. P. Moore, *Nature*, **163**, 918 (1949).

CHAPTER III

4-Methylcinnolines

4-Methylcinnolines afford an excellent illustration of the fact (*cf.* Chapter I) that cinnoline chemistry has been largely neglected until recent years. 4-Methylcinnoline-7-carboxylic acid (I), prepared by Widman[1] in

(I)	(II)	(III)	(IV)

1884, was one of the earliest cinnoline derivatives to be described, but more than sixty years elapsed before any further study of its properties was made and some of its analogs were prepared. The acid (I) is not suitable for the study of the characteristic reactions of 4-methylcinnolines, as its synthesis starts with the expensive cuminal (II), the final step being the diazotization and cyclization of the amino acid (III). Recently, however, it has been found[2,3] that 2-aminoarylethylenes (IV; R = H, 4-Cl, or 5-Cl) are easily prepared from the appropriate methyl anthranilates or *o*-aminoacetophenones, and these amines, like (III), readily yield the corresponding 4-methylcinnolines. Table III-1 shows the physical properties of the 4-methylcinnolines which have been described so far.

4-Methylcinnoline and its analogs are usually prepared by the Widman-Stoermer reaction, which was described in some detail in the preceding chapter. It may be noted here that the compounds (IV) contain the electron-releasing methyl group on the α-carbon atom of the aminoethylene, and the fact that such compounds undergo the reaction is in line with the mechanism previously discussed. The rapidity of the reaction is in general rather less than in the synthesis of 4-arylcinnolines, but decidedly greater than that of the reaction which gives rise to 4-hydroxycinnolines (Chapter IV).

From a limited study of the reactions of 4-methylcinnolines one fact of fundamental importance to cinnoline chemistry has emerged, namely that N_1 is the basic nitrogen in these compounds.[2] Quaternary salts are formed with ease (see Chapter VII), and as the methyl group in these salts

TABLE III-1. 4-Methylcinnolines

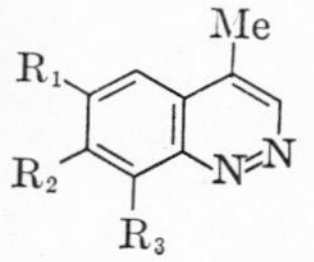

R₁	R₂	R₃	Prep.[a]	M.p., °C.	Remarks	Ref.
H	H	H	A	72.5–74, 74–75	Yellow needles	2,3
H	H	Cl	A,B	126–127	Yellow needles	5
H	H	NO₂	C	138–139 (dec.)	Yellow plates	5
H	H	NH₂	D	126–127	Orange prisms	5
H	Cl	H	A	119–120	Yellow leaflets	2
H	CO₂H	H	A	230 (dec.), 251–253 (dec.)	—	1,2
H	CO₂Et	H	E	117	Golden plates	2
Cl	H	H	A	136–137	—	2

[a] A, by Widman-Stoermer reaction. B, from the amine by diazotization and Sand-meyer reaction. C, by nitration of 4-methylcinnoline. D, from the nitro com-pound by reduction with stannous chloride in concentrated hydrochloric acid at 50°. E, from the acid by esterification.

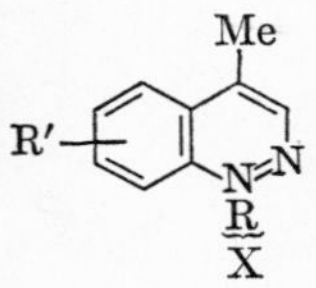

(V) 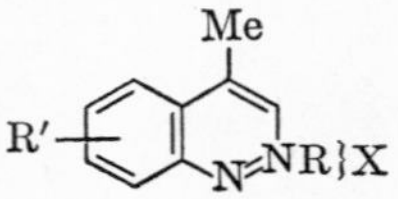   (VI) 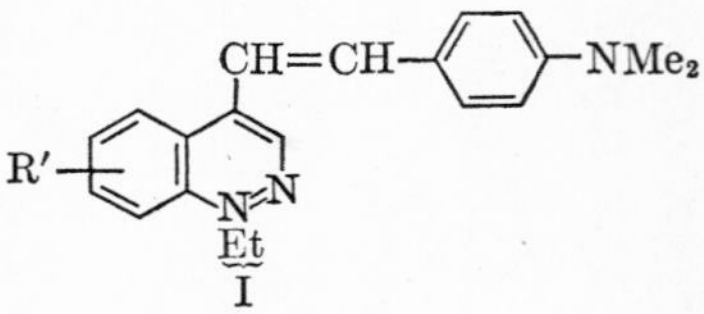   (VII)

shows considerable activity it follows that the salts are correctly represented as (V) and not as (VI). The reactivity of the methyl group in (V) was established by condensation with p-dimethylaminobenzaldehyde, whereby p-dimethylaminostyryl-1-ethylcinnolinium iodides (as VII) are formed. The methyl group of the unquaternized base also shows activity, for con-densation of 4-methylcinnoline with boiling benzaldehyde in presence of zinc chloride yields 4-styrylcinnoline (VIII), m.p. 121.5–122.5°,[3] which on oxidation gives cinnoline-4-carboxylic acid (Chapter II, Section 3).

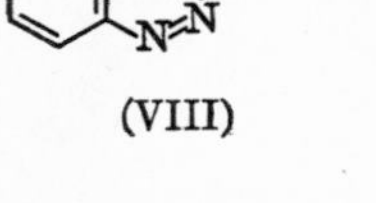

(VIII)

As noted in Chapter II, 4-methylcinnoline and its 6- and 7-chloro derivatives yield skatole on reduction with sodium and alcohol.[4] Nitration of 4-methylcinnoline occurs at C_8, yielding 8-nitro-4-methylcinnoline.[5]

References

1. Widman, *Ber.*, **17**, 722 (1884).
2. Atkinson and Simpson, *J. Chem. Soc.*, **1947**, 808.
3. T. L. Jacobs, Winstein, Henderson, and Spaeth, *J. Am. Chem. Soc.*, **68**, 1310 (1946).
4. Atkinson and Simpson, *J. Chem. Soc.*, **1947**, 1649.
5. Schofield and Swain, *J. Chem. Soc.*, **1949**, 1367.

CHAPTER IV

4-Hydroxycinnolines

4-Hydroxycinnolines* constitute the most important class of cinnoline derivatives and (in comparison with other members of this heterocyclic group) have been investigated in considerable detail. Table IV-1 lists the known 4-hydroxycinnolines.

1. Methods of Preparation

A. Richter Synthesis. This synthesis originated in 1883 with the discovery that 4-hydroxycinnoline-3-carboxylic acid (I) results from cyclization of diazotized o-aminophenylpropiolic acid (Eq. 1). No further

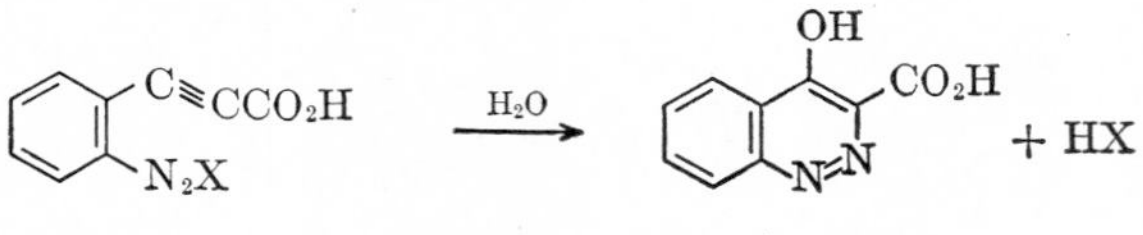

(1)

(I)

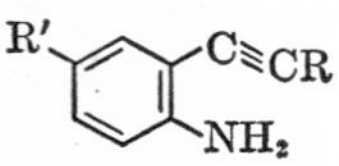

(II)

use was made of this reaction until 1945, when the original synthesis was improved into a practical method for preparing (I),[2] and it is now regarded as a general route to 6-substituted-4-hydroxycinnoline-3-carboxylic acids.[2,28] 4-Hydroxycinnolines may be similarly prepared[2,28] from (II; R = H or Ph), but the synthesis fails with (II; R = 2'-pyridyl).[28] The mechanism of this synthesis has been discussed,[2,3,28] and there are strong grounds for believing that the polarization depicted in the annexed formula (R = H or CO_2H) induces coordination of the anionoid C_β with the diazonium group-

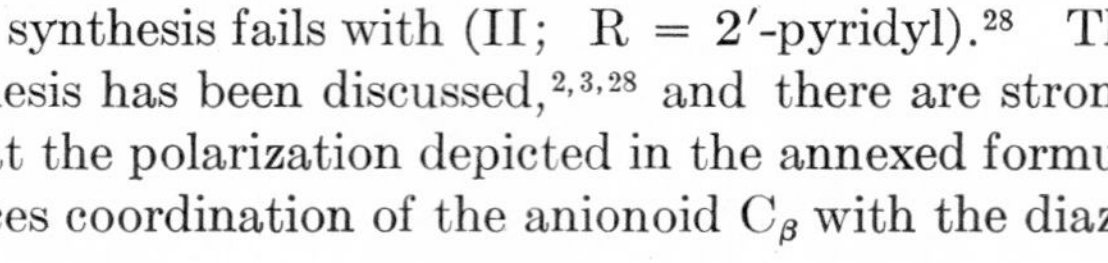

(2)

* 3-Hydroxycinnoline has been prepared,[25,26] but a detailed description is unfortunately not available.

ing, with accompanying entry of hydroxyl ion (Eq. 2). The resemblance between this mechanism and that of the Widman-Stoermer reaction (Chapter II) is obvious.

B. Pfannstiel and Janecke Synthesis. These authors[4] find that 6-chloro-2-hydrazinobenzoic acid yields 5-chloro-3-phenyl-4-hydroxycinnoline in small amount when it is refluxed with benzaldehyde (4-

chloroindazolone is simultaneously formed) (Eq. 3). However, there is no other example on record of the formation of a 4-hydroxycinnoline by this method.

C. Borsche Synthesis. The first example of this synthesis was discovered in 1941 by Borsche and Herbert,[5] who observed that 5-nitro-2-aminoacetophenone on diazotization undergoes a slow cyclization at room temperature to 6-nitro-4-hydroxycinnoline (Eq. 4). This reaction has

subsequently been found to be a valuable general method for preparing 4-hydroxycinnoline and its analogs; it has, in consequence, received considerable attention, and a variety of 3-, 5-, 6-, 7-, and 8-substituted 4-hydroxycinnolines have been prepared,[3,6-14,29,30] as indicated in Table IV-1.

The reaction has several points of interest. Cinnoline formation is favored by the presence of electron-attractive substituents at C_3 or C_5 in the 2-aminoacetophenone.[3,10] If the cyclization is effected in dilute acid medium, the yield of hydroxycinnoline is low unless such substituents are present, owing to the preponderance of the competing reaction of phenol formation, but by working in concentrated hydrochloric acid at moderate temperatures the reaction can be successfully effected in the absence of electron-attractive substituents; indeed, the nucleus may even contain electron-donating substituents such as methyl.[11,12,15] It has been observed that the yield of hydroxycinnoline is favored by the avoidance of heating, as, although the reaction is then slow, phenolic decomposition of the diazonium salt is thus largely prevented.[10]

A further feature of the synthesis is that, in certain circumstances, group exchange is prone to occur. Thus, 4-chloro-5-nitro-2-aminoacetophenone gives either 7-chloro-6-nitro- or 6,7-dichloro-4-hydroxycinnoline according as the ring closure is effected in sulfuric or hydrochloric acid[8];

TABLE IV-1. 4-Hydroxycinnolines

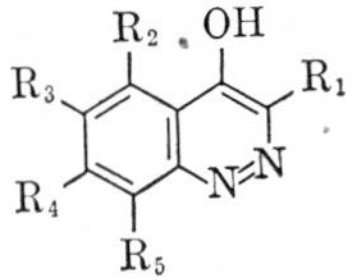

R_1	R_2	R_3	R_4	R_5	Prep,[a]	M.p., °C.	Remarks	Ref.
H	H	H	H	H	A	225, 233.5–234, 236 (corr.)	pK_a (as acid) = 9.53 in 50% aq. alc. at 21°. Ac deriv, m.p. 127–128°	1,2,10, 27
H	H	H	H	Cl	A	198–199	—	3
H	H	H	H	Br	A	193–194	—	3
H	H	H	H	NO₂	A	184–186, 185.5–186.5	Yellow needles	2,6
H	H	H	H	NH₂	C	290–291	Yellow needles. Ac₂ deriv., m.p. 282–283°	29
H	H	H	H	Me	A	220–221	—	12
H	H	H	Cl	H	A	276–277, 288 (corr.)	—	8,10
H	H	H	NO₂	H	A	295–296	Pale yellow needles. Ac deriv., m.p. 140–141°	29
H	H	H	NH₂	H	C,H	276–277	Ac₂ deriv., m.p. > 330°	29
H	H	H	NHAc	H	I	>330	—	29
H	H	H	Me	H	A	243.5–244.5	Ac deriv., m.p. 117–118°	12
H	H	H	Ac	H	A	242–243	Oxime, m.p. 294–295°, gives C₁₂H₁₁O₃N₃, m.p. 191–192°, when treated with hot conc. H₂SO₄ followed by Ac₂O	29
H	H	Cl	H	H	A,B,D	289.5–290, 294–295	Ac deriv., m.p., 150–160°	3,10, 19,28
H	H	Br	H	H	A,B,D	276–277, 286–287 (corr.)	—	3,10,28
H	H	I	H	H	A	300–301	—	10

R_1	R_2	R_3	R_4	R_5	Prep.[a]	M.p., °C.	Remarks	Ref.
H	H	NO_2	H	H	A	330–331, 338–340 (corr.), 343–344 (corr.)	Red-brown needles. Ac deriv., m.p. 147–148°	2,5,10
H	H	NH_2	H	H	C	275–276 (corr.)	Yellow needles	10
H	H	OMe	H	H	A	255–256	—	2
H	H	CN	H	H	A	284–285	Pale yellow needles	3
H	NO_2	H	H	H	A	304–305	Ac deriv., m.p. 185–186°	29
Cl	H	H	H	H	A	278–279	Ac deriv., m.p. 125–126°	11
Br	H	H	H	H	A	276–276.5	Ac deriv., m.p. 139–140°	11
NO_2	H	H	H	H	E	276.5–277.5	Light brown needles. Structure tentative	2,29,31
Me	H	H	H	H	A	241–242, 248–249 (corr.)	Ac deriv., m.p. 117–117.5°	9,10
Et	H	H	H	H	A	225–226	—	13
Ph	H	H	H	H	B	260–261	—	28
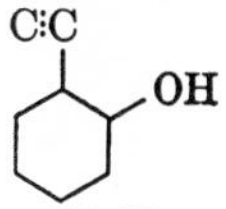 C:C (cyclohexanol)	H	H	H	H	B	224–225	Pale green needles. Prepd. from (o-$NH_2C_6H_4C$:C—)$_2$. Structure tentative	28
CO_2H	H	H	H	H	B	260–265 (dec.), 268–268.5 (dec.)	—	1,2
CO_2Et	H	H	H	H	G	191–192	Ac deriv, m.p. 82–83°	16
$(CH_2)_3$—CO_2H	H	H	H	H	A	201.5–202.5	—	13

Table continued

TABLE IV-1. 4-Hydroxycinnolines (continued)

R₁	R₂	R₃	R₄	R₈	Prep.ᵃ	M.p., °C.	Remarks	Ref.
H	H	H	Cl	Cl	A	253–254	—	7
H	H	H	Cl	NO₂	A	262–264 (dec.)	Yellow needles	8
H	H	H	Me	Cl	A	209–210	—	7
H	H	H	Me	NO₂	E	243–244 (dec.)	Yellow blades	12
H	H	H	—(CH₂)₃—	H	A	246–247	—	30
H	H	H	—(CH₂)₄—	H	A	276–277	—	30
H	H	Br	H	Br	A	247–247.5 (corr.)	—	10
H	H	Cl	Cl	H	A	333–334	Ac deriv., m.p. 148–149°	7
H	H	Cl	Me	H	A	271–272	—	7
H	H	Br	Me	H	A	273–274	—	7
H	H	NO₂	Cl	H	A	252–254 (dec.)	Bronze needles	8
H	H	NO₂	Me	H	A	250–251	Light brown rhombs	12
H	H	—OCH₂O—		H	D	dec. 316–318	Light brown needles	2
H	H	Me	Me	H	A	267–268	Ac deriv., m.p. 151–152°	30
H	H	—(CH₂)₃—		H	A	271–272	Ac deriv., m.p. 112–113°	30
H	H	—(CH₂)₄—		H	A	262–263	—	30
H	NO₂ or H	H or NO₂	H	Me	E	255–256	—	12
Cl	H	H	H	H	A	305–306	—	11
Cl	H	Cl	H	H	A	298.5–299.5	Ac deriv., m. p. 186–187°	30
Br	H	Cl	H	H	A	311–312	—	11
Me	H	Cl	H	NO₂	A	238–239	Yellow plates	9
Me	H	Cl	H	H	A	328–329	—	9
Me	H	Br	H	H	A	326–327, 331–332	—	9,10

R_1	R_2	R_3	R_4	R_5	Prep.[a]	M.p., °C.	Remarks	Ref.
Me	H	NO_2	H	H	A	>350 >360	Brown blades. Ac deriv., m.p. 194–194.5°	9,10
Ph	H	OMe	H	H	B	318–319	—	28
Ph	Cl	H	H	H	F	>300	—	4
CO_2H	H	Cl	H	H	B	263–264 (dec.)	—	28
CO_2H	H	Br	H	H	B	264 (dec.)	—	28
CO_2H	H	OMe	H	H	B	268 (dec.)	—	2
CO_2Et	H	OMe	H	H	G	233–234	Ac deriv., m.p. 152–153°	16
CH_2—CO_2Et	H	H	CO_2Et	H	A	168–171	—	14
Cl	H	Me	Me	H	A	314–315	Ac deriv., m.p. 196–197°	30
Cl	H	—$(CH_2)_3$—		H	A	>340	Ac deriv., m.p. 159–160°	30
Cl	H	—$(CH_2)_4$—		H	A	288–289	Ac deriv., m.p. 148–149°	30
CO_2H	H	—OCH_2O—		H	B	276–278 (dec.)	—	2
CH_2—CO_2H	H	OMe	OMe	H	A	327–330 (dec.)	—	3
CH_2—CO_2Et	H	OMe	OMe	H	A	293–294 (dec.)	—	3

[a] A, by the Borsche reaction; diazotization and ring closure are effected in dilute or concentrated hydrochloric or sulfuric acid, or in a mixture of acetic and sulfuric acids, depending on the individual case. B, by the Richter reaction (carried out in dilute hydrochloric or sulfuric acid, or in concentrated hydrochloric acid, according to individual cases). C, from the nitro compound by reduction with iron and boiling aqueous acetic acid. D, from the 3-carboxylic acid by decarboxylation in benzophenone at 210°. E, by nitration of the corresponding 4-hydroxy compound. F, by the Pfannstiel-Janecke synthesis (see text). G, by esterification of the 3-carboxylic acid. H, from the 7-acetamido compound and boiling 5 *N* hydrochloric acid. I, from 7-acetamido-4-hydroxycinnoline by the Schmidt reaction.

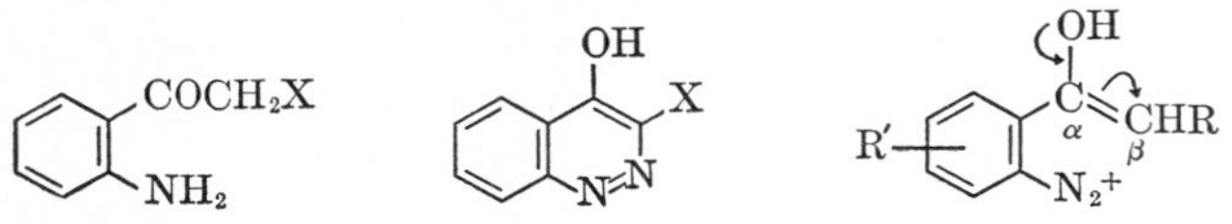

(III)   (IV)   (V)

and 4-chloro-3-nitro-2-aminoacetophenone[8] and 3-nitro-2-aminoaceto-phenone[12] behave similarly. Furthermore, ω-halogeno-o-aminoacetophe-nones (as III), which in sulfuric acid yield the expected 3-halogeno-4-hydroxycinnolines (as IV), give rise to analogs of (IV) in which an exchange of halogen atoms has occurred at C_3 if the cyclizations are performed in a different halogen acid from that corresponding to the original substituent of (III).[11] The conditions governing these group exchanges and the mechanism of the reaction are not known with certainty, but in the case of 4-chloro-3- and -5-nitro-2-aminoacetophenone it has been shown that the exchange occurs in the diazonium cation.[8]

The theoretical aspects of the Borsche synthesis have received a good deal of attention[3,10,11]; essentially, the reaction occurs by intramolecular cyclization of the species (V), a process which clearly indicates that there is a close relationship between the Borsche, the Widman-Stoermer, and the Richter syntheses. Ring closure of (V) will be favored by the cationoid reactivity of the diazonium grouping (hence the favorable influence observed for electron-attractive substituents at C_3 and C_5), and also by the development of anionoid reactivity at C_β (hence the importance of strong hydrochloric acid in promoting enolization of the C-acetyl group, especially in compounds in which the activity of the N_2 grouping is not increased by electron-attractive substituents). The following scheme has been advanced[11] as a comprehensive representation of the possible reactions of diazotized o-aminoacetophenones under the conditions of the Borsche synthesis. Cinnoline formation is represented as occurring via an acid-cata-

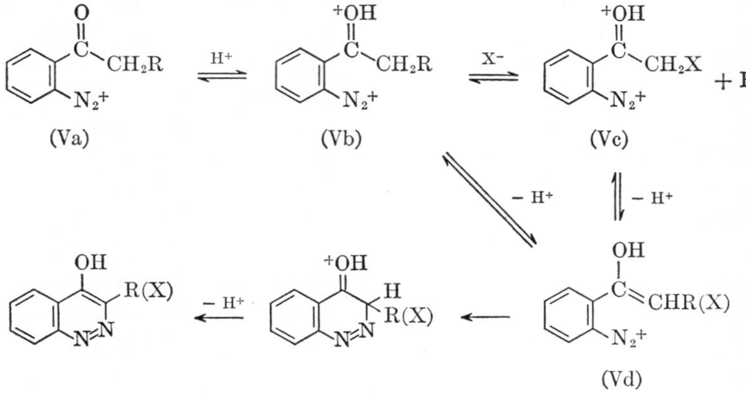

(Va)   (Vb)   (Vc)

(5)

(Vd)

lyzed enolization of the carbonyl group; this would normally produce the species (Vb), but could also give rise to (Vc), in the formation of which group interchange has occurred (analogous group exchanges involving the aromatic ring are not shown). The competing phenolic decomposition (also not shown) is considered to involve one or more of the species (Va–Vd) (Eq. 5).

2. Properties

A. 4-Hydroxycinnolines Other than 4-Hydroxycinnoline-3-carboxylic Acids. These 4-hydroxycinnolines show distinctly acid properties. They dissolve readily in dilute sodium hydroxide (5-chloro-3-phenyl-4-hydroxycinnoline is exceptional in being insoluble in this reagent[4]), and compounds containing powerfully negative groups in the 6-position (CN, NO$_2$) are also soluble in aqueous sodium carbonate.[2,3] 8-Chloro- and 8-bromo-4-hydroxycinnoline, in contrast to their 6-halogeno isomers, are soluble in dilute ammonia.[3] In contrast to 4-hydroxy-quinolines and -quinazolines, 4-hydroxycinnolines are readily acetylated, giving, presumably, 4-acetoxy compounds[2,7,9,11,12,16,30]; 8-substituted analogs, however, are resistant to boiling acetic anhydride in cases (8 NO$_2$, 8 Me) so far investigated,[2,6,9,12] and in the case of 8-nitro-4-hydroxycinnolines this inertness has been attributed to chelation, the compounds being represented as (VI; R = H and Me).[6,12]

(VI)   (VII)   (VIII)   (IX)

Treatment of 4-hydroxycinnolines with a mixture of phosphorus pentachloride and phosphoryl chloride yields the corresponding 4-chloro derivatives (as VII). These compounds are usually formed smoothly and in good yield, but on occasion group interchange may occur. 6-Bromo-4-hydroxycinnoline, for instance, yields 4-chloro-6-bromo- or 4,6-dichlorocinnoline, depending upon conditions[10,15]; 7-chloro-6-nitro-4-hydroxycinnoline gives 4,6,7-trichlorocinnoline[12]; and 3-bromo-4-hydroxycinnolines under suitable conditions give 3,4-dichlorocinnolines.[17]

4-Hydroxycinnolines are converted into 1-methyl-4-keto-1,4-dihydrocinnolines (as VIII)[2,18,19,29] by the action of methyl sulfate and sodium hydroxide. These compounds are mentioned in Chapter VIII, but two points may be noted here. First, O-methylation occurs, in addition to N-methylation, when 4-hydroxy-6,7-dimethoxycinnoline-3-acetic acid is so treated[20]; and, second, 6-nitro-4-hydroxycinnoline and its 3-methyl analog yield, in addition to the N-methyl derivatives, the methyl nitronates (IX; R = H and Me).[2,19]

Nitration of 4-hydroxycinnoline gives 6-nitro-4-hydroxycinnoline as main product,[2] together with small amounts of the 8-nitro isomer[2,6] and a third compound which may be the 3-nitro isomer.[2,31] 4-Hydroxy-7-methylcinnoline gives the 8-nitro derivative,[12] and 4-hydroxy-8-methylcinnoline yields 5- (or 7-) nitro-4-hydroxy-8-methylcinnoline.[12]

B. 4-Hydroxycinnoline-3-carboxylic Acids. The parent acid of this group (X; R = R′ = H) cannot be esterified under ordinary condi-

        (X)   (XI)   (XII)

tions, but with alcohol and fuming or 100% sulfuric acid it and the 6-methoxy analog (X; R = OMe; R′ = H) yield the corresponding ethyl esters (X; R = H and OMe; R′ = Et), which, like other 4-hydroxycinnolines, are appreciably acidic and also yield 4-acetoxy derivatives.[16] The action of diazomethane on (X; R = R′ = H) produces an ester-ether, m.p. 110°, which is either (XI) or (XII).[2] With acetic anhydride, (X; R = R′ = H) undergoes decarboxylation with formation of 4-acetoxycinnoline. The most convenient method of decarboxylating (X; R = R′ = H) and its analogs, however, is to heat the acid in benzophenone[2] at 210°.

The most characteristic property of (X; R = R′ = H) is its behavior —which appears to be highly specific for this type of compound—when heated with a mixture of pyridine and acetic anhydride. The reaction, which is not shown by 4-hydroxyquinoline-3-carboxylic acids or their esters, or by the esters (X; R = H or OMe; R′ = Et), has been studied in detail,[21] and the following are the main features.

When the acid (X; R = R′ = H), pyridine, and acetic anhydride, in the approximate ratio 2:9:13, are heated at 95°, a crystalline substance, m.p. 217°, of formula $C_{16}H_{11}O_3N_3$, is formed in good yield. This is formulated provisionally as a resonance hybrid of the three unperturbed structures (XIIIa–c), and is produced according to the equation $C_9H_6O_3N_2$ + C_5H_5N + $Ac_2O \rightarrow C_{16}H_{11}O_3N_3$ + $AcOH$ + H_2O (Eq. 6). (See footnote on page 26). This formulation of the reaction is based on analogy with the production of pseudo bases from quinolinium and pyridinium hydroxides,[22,24] *i.e.*, it is analogous to the tendency for a quinolinium cation to assume covalency with a weak anion, here derived from (X; R = R′ = H). Representation of the compound, m.p. 217° (hereafter referred to as the

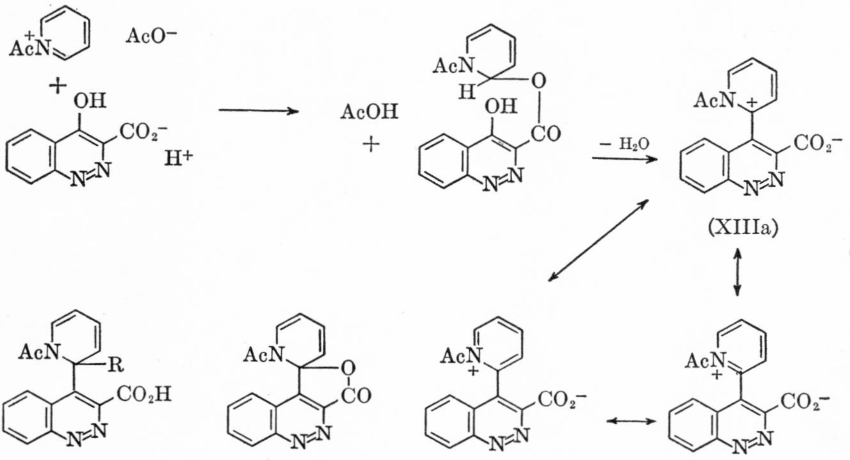

(XV)   (XIV)   (XIIIb)   (XIIIc)

"C_{16} zwitterion"), as (XIIIa–c) is consistent with its properties, which cannot be satisfactorily explained on the basis of the isomeric lactone structure (XIV). The C_{16}-zwitterion, for example, is readily soluble in cold aqueous sodium carbonate; and when it is refluxed with the lower alcohols, or with aniline in benzene, it yields a series of amphoteric adducts (XV; R = OMe, OEt, OPr$^\beta$, and NHPh).

Treatment of (XV; R = OMe) with sulfuric acid and either methyl or ethyl alcohol produces a bright yellow compound, m.p. 106–107°, of formula $C_{15}H_{13}O_3N_3$, and (XV; R = OEt) similarly yields with sulfuric acid and each of these alcohols the homolog $C_{16}H_{15}O_3N_3$, which melts at 140–141.5° and is also bright yellow in color. These two substances are bases, and are mostly simply formulated as (XVI; R = Me and Et); they are, however, insoluble in cold alkalis, so that (XVII; R = Me or Et) is an alternative possibility. The main interest in these reactions, however, is that they involve loss of the N-acyl group of the dihydropyridine ring of (XV; R = OMe); the analogy, referred to above, between the production of the C_{16}-zwitterion and the formation of the covalent "Reissert compounds" in the quinoline series is thus strengthened, because 1-benzoyl-2-cyano-1,2-dihydroquinoline (XVIII) (a typical "Reissert compound") on treatment with acid likewise loses the N-benzoyl group and yields quinaldinic acid (*via* the nitrile). The conversion of (XV; R = OMe and OEt) into (XVI; R = Me and Et) does not, of course, involve an aromatization of the dihydropyridine ring such as occurs in the conversion of (XVIII) into quinaldinic acid, but under other conditions (*vide infra*) such an aromatization does actually occur, so that the analogy with the "Reissert compounds" is thus complete.

A further reaction of the C_{16}-zwitterion [which, like those already mentioned, is more satisfactorily explained in terms of (XIIIa–c) than of (XIV)] is its conversion into a colorless base, m.p. 161.5–162.5°, of formula $C_{15}H_{13}O_2N_3$ (XIX). This transformation is effected by refluxing either a suspension of the C_{16}-zwitterion in water or a solution of it in ordinary (*i.e.*

(XVI)   (XVII)   (XVIII)   (XIX)

not anhydrous) pyridine. The base (XIX) is, however, most readily prepared by short-time refluxing of a mixture of 4-hydroxycinnoline-3-carboxylic acid, pyridine, and acetic anhydride, in the ratio 1:3:1. It is noteworthy that none of the base (XIX) is formed from the acid (X; R = R' = H) or from the C_{16}-zwitterion by the action of a mixture of pyridine and acetic anhydride containing a high proportion of the latter; the non-formation of (XIX) under these conditions is ascribed to a suppression of hydroxyl ion concentration.

The base (XIX) is rapidly attacked by hot dilute sodium hydroxide yielding several products, chief of which is a yellow base, m.p. 152.5–153.5°, of the formula $C_{13}H_9N_3,2H_2O$ (picrate, m.p. 207–208°; styphnate monohydrate, m.p. 203–204°; hydrochloride dihydrate, m.p. 219–221°). This base has been formulated as 4,2'-pyridylcinnoline (XX)*; it is an important degradation product, as it is produced from several of the compounds in this series as summarized in scheme 7. All these precursors of (XX) con-

(7)

tain a dihydropyridine ring which becomes aromatic, with loss of the *N*-substituent (H or Ac) during their conversion into (XX); these reactions

---

* This formulation is apparently incorrect, because 4,2'-pyridylcinnoline has recently been synthesized by a seemingly unambiguous route[32] and is not identical (Chapter II, Table II-1) with the base, m.p. 152.5–153.5°. Until further data are available, however, it is not possible to say to what extent the structures of the precursors and derivatives of this base are incorrect.

therefore complete the analogy (*vide supra*) between the C_{16}-zwitterion and the quinoline "Reissert compounds."

The other products formed by the alkaline degradation of (XIX) are acetic acid, 4-hydroxy-1-methyl-3,9,10-triazaphenanthrene (XXI), m.p. 187°, and 1-methyl-3,9,10-triazaphenanthrene-4-carboxylic acid (XXII), m.p. 170°. The latter readily loses carbon dioxide at its melting point yielding 1-methyl-3,9,10-triazaphenanthrene, m.p. 114°. These triaza-phenanthrene derivatives are considered to arise by fission of the dihydro-pyridine ring of (XIX) and subsequent recyclization; however, their structures are not proved.

(XIX) ⟶   or   ⟶   (XXI)

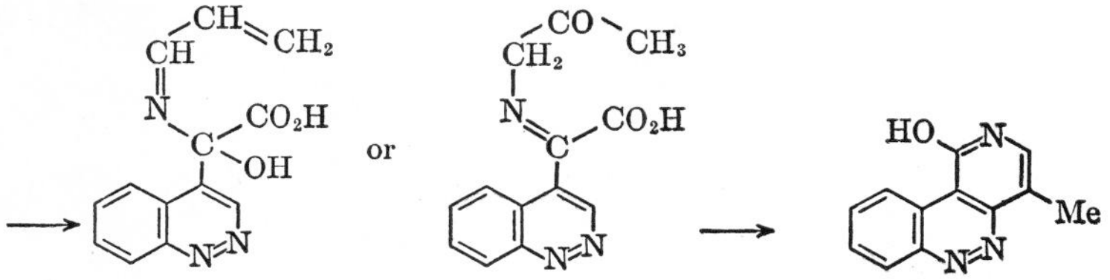

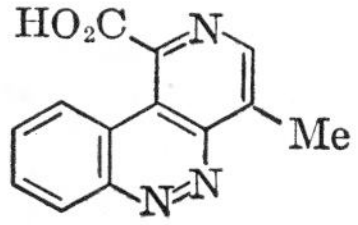

(XXII)

A somewhat unexpected property of the pyridylcinnoline (XX) is its susceptibility to oxidation. It is rapidly attacked by cold aqueous per-manganate, giving a good yield of a single product of formula $C_{12}H_9O_2N_3$. This substance, m.p. 146–147° (picrate, m.p. 172–174°), crystallizes from ethyl acetate in orange-red prisms, but from water as a mixture of white and red needles; it shows marked amphoteric properties and dissolves in cold aqueous sodium bicarbonate. It is provisionally formulated as (XXIII).

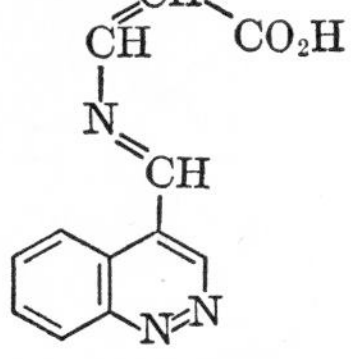

(XXIII) 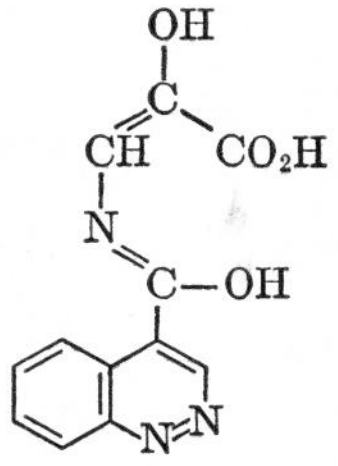   (XXIV) 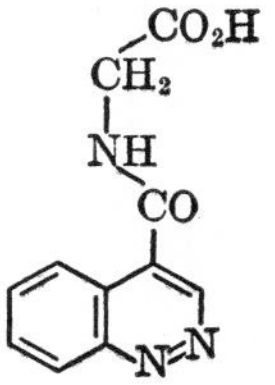   (XXV)

It is stable toward warm aqueous permanganate and boiling 2 N sodium hydroxide, but is gradually converted by boiling 5 N hydrochloric acid into a mixture of an orange-pink amphoteric compound, m.p. 195°, and a colorless weak ampholyte, m.p. 254°, which are tentatively represented as (XXIV) and (XXV).

The key reaction in the foregoing transformations, namely the formation of the C_{16}-zwitterion, is probably characteristic of 4-hydroxycinnoline-3-carboxylic acids as a class, because the initial stages of the reaction series have been reproduced[21] with 4-hydroxy-6-methoxycinnoline-3-carboxylic acid. Thus, when this acid is heated with pyridine and acetic anhydride (ratio 1:7:8) it is converted into a "zwitterion," m.p. (crude) 214–216° (dec.). Treatment of this with methyl alcohol yields a substance, m.p. 179–180°, the formula of which ($C_{18}H_{17}O_5N_3$) suggests that it is the analog of (XV; R = OMe). Furthermore, the action of boiling pyridine on the "zwitterion" produces a substance, m.p. 131.5–132.5°, with the formula $C_{16}H_{15}O_3N_3$, which evidently corresponds to the base (XIX).

References

1. Richter, *Ber.*, **16,** 677 (1883).
2. Schofield and Simpson, *J. Chem. Soc.*, **1945,** 512.
3. Schofield and Simpson, *J. Chem. Soc.*, **1945,** 520.
4. Pfannstiel and Janecke, *Ber.*, **75,** 1096 (1942).
5. Borsche and Herbert, *Ann.*, **546,** 293 (1941).
6. Simpson, *J. Chem. Soc.*, **1947,** 237.
7. Keneford and Simpson, *J. Chem. Soc.*, **1947,** 227.
8. Atkinson and Simpson, *J. Chem. Soc.*, **1947,** 232.
9. Keneford and Simpson, *J. Chem. Soc.*, **1948,** 354.
10. Leonard and Boyd, *J. Org. Chem.*, **11,** 419 (1946).
11. Schofield and Simpson, *J. Chem. Soc.*, **1948,** 1170.
12. Keneford, Morley, and Simpson, *J. Chem. Soc.*, **1948,** 1702.
13. Keneford and Simpson, *J. Chem. Soc.*, **1948,** 354.
14. Koelsch, *J. Org. Chem.*, **8,** 295 (1943).
15. Keneford and Simpson, *J. Chem. Soc.*, **1947,** 917.
16. Simpson, *J. Chem. Soc.*, **1946,** 1035.
17. Schofield and Swain, *J. Chem. Soc.*, **1950,** 384.
18. Simpson, *J. Chem. Soc.*, **1947,** 1653.
19. Keneford, Morley, Simpson, and Wright, *J. Chem. Soc.*, **1950,** 1104.
20. Simpson, *J. Chem. Soc.*, **1946,** 480.
21. Schofield and Simpson, *J. Chem. Soc.*, **1946,** 472.
22. Decker, *Ber.*, **25,** 443 (1892).
23. Hantzsch and Kalb, *Ber.*, **32,** 3119 (1899).
24. Reissert, *Ber.*, **38,** 1603 (1905).
25. P. W. Neber, G. Knöller, K. Herbst, and A. Trissler, *Ann.*, **471,** 113 (1929).
26. G. Bossel, *Inaug.-Diss.*, Tübingen, May, 1925, p. 31.
27. Keneford, Morley, Simpson, and Wright, *J. Chem. Soc.*, **1949,** 1356.
28. Schofield and Swain, *J. Chem. Soc.*, **1949,** 2393.
29. Schofield and Theobald, *J. Chem. Soc.*, **1949,** 2404.
30. Schofield, Swain, and Theobald, *J. Chem. Soc.*, **1949,** 2399.
31. Schofield and Swain, *J. Chem. Soc.*, **1949,** 1367.
32. Schofield, *J. Chem. Soc.*, **1949,** 2408.

CHAPTER V

4-Chloro-, 4-Alkoxy-, and 4-Phenoxycinnolines

1. 4-Chlorocinnolines

A. Preparation. These compounds are prepared from 4-hydroxy-cinnolines by the action of a mixture of phosphoryl chloride and phosphorus pentachloride[1-6] or of phosphoryl chloride alone,[6,15] usually at 100°. Normally the reaction is straightforward, and the products are isolated by dilution with ice water and basification, but Busch and Klett[1] observed that, in the preparation of 4-chlorocinnoline itself, a black by-product is formed when the diluted reaction medium is made alkaline. This behavior is confirmed by Leonard and Boyd[6] both in this reaction and also in the preparation of 4-chloro-6-bromocinnoline, but these authors find that the extent of the side reaction with 4-chlorocinnoline can be diminished by careful neutralization, instead of basification, of the acid solution. The normal reaction time is about 1 hour, but in the preparation of chloro compounds from 8-nitro-4-hydroxy-7-methyl- and 5- (or 7-) nitro-4 hydroxy-8-methyl-cinnoline it is necessary to limit the reaction time to about 5 minutes, as longer heating seriously reduces the yield.[5] Instances have been observed of the replacement of a nuclear substituent, as well as of the hydroxyl group, by chlorine during the reaction. Thus, at 100°, 6-bromo-4-hydroxycinnoline reacts normally,[3,6] but at 135–140° the product is 4,6-dichlorocinnoline[6]; 7-chloro-6-nitro-4-hydroxycinnoline gives only 4,6,7-trichlorocinnoline[5]; and the formation of 3,4-dichloro- from 3-bromo-4-hydroxy-cinnolines has been observed.[7] Table V-1 lists the known 4-chlorocinnolines; many of these compounds have not been analyzed owing to their reactivity (see below), but in such cases they have been characterized by the preparation of the corresponding 4-phenoxy- or 4-anilino-cinnolines.

B. Properties. 4-Chlorocinnolines are characterized as a group by their extreme reactivity; 4-chloroquinoline, which is commonly regarded as a classical illustration of a heterocyclic compound with a reactive chlorine atom, is a very stable compound when compared with most 4-chlorocinnolines.

Thus, Busch and Klett observed,[1] and it has recently been confirmed,[8]

TABLE V-1. 4-Chlorocinnolines

R_1	R_2	R_3	R_4	R_5	M.p., °C.	Remarks	Ref.
H	H	H	H	H	76–77, 78–79, 79	White or yellow needles	1,3,6
H	H	H	H	Cl	146–147	Yellow spikes	5
H	H	H	H	NO_2	167–169, 180 (dec.)	Yellow cryst.	5,15
H	H	H	H	Me	92–93	Pale green rods	5
H	H	H	Cl	H	143–144	—	3,6
H	H	H	NO_2	H	148–149	Yellow needles	15
H	H	H	Me	H	115–117	Yellow scales	5
H	H	H	Ac	H	147–148	Yellow needles	15
H	H	Cl	H	H	111–112, 113–114	Pale yellow needles	3,6
H	H	Br	H	H	127–128, 136–137	Pale yellow needles High- and low-melting forms are interconvertible	3,6
H	H	NO_2	H	H	135–137	Yellow plates	10
H	H	OMe	H	H	149–151	—	3
H	NO_2	H	H	H	170–171	Yellow cryst.	15
Me	H	H	H	H	99–100	—	4
Ph	H	H	H	H	119–120	Orange micro-cryst.	16
H	H	H	Cl	Cl	221–222	Pale green needles	2
H	H	H	Me	NO_2	210–211 (dec.)	Pale green blades	5
H	H	Cl	Cl	H	141.5–142.5	Pale yellow needles	2
H	H	Cl	Me	H	176–177	—	3
H	$\left\{\begin{array}{l} NO_2 \\ H \end{array}\right.$	H or H	$\left.\begin{array}{r} H \\ NO_2 \end{array}\right\}$	Me	130–131	Yellow-green prisms	5
Me	H	H	H	NO_2	180–181	Yellow prisms	4
Me	H	NO_2	H	H	146–147	Yellow needles	4

that 4-chlorocinnoline is converted into the 4-hydroxy compound merely by boiling with water. Hydrolysis in aqueous solution also occurs with 4-chloro-6-nitrocinnoline,[8] and 4,7-dichlorocinnoline, although moderately stable in hot aqueous solution, is hydrolyzed rapidly in hot very dilute acid.[8] 4-Chloroquinoline, on the other hand, is stable under much more drastic conditions.[8] In further illustration of this point are the observations that 4-chlorocinnoline can be titrated with aqueous silver nitrate,[1] and that brief refluxing with acetic anhydride converts it into 4-acetoxy-cinnoline.[9] As a result of their extreme reactivity, 4-chlorocinnolines tend to decompose on standing, sometimes quite rapidly[1,2,10]; it has been found that the decomposition product which is formed from 4,6,7-trichlorocinno-line on standing is probably the corresponding 4-hydroxy compound.[2]

Busch and Klett[1] prepared 4-anilino- and 4-*p*-toluidino-cinnoline by brief warming of 4-chlorocinnoline with the appropriate base; other examples, from recent literature, of the condensation of 4-chlorocinnolines with ammonia and primary aliphatic and aromatic amines will be found in Chapter VI. Busch and Klett[1] also prepared 4-ethoxycinnoline from the chloro compound and alcoholic sodium ethoxide by gentle warming, and a number of further examples of replacement reactions of this type have recently been described (*vide infra*). 4-Phenoxycinnolines are readily obtainable from the chloro compounds by warming either with a mixture of phenol and ammonium carbonate or with a solution of potassium hydroxide in molten phenol. Comparison of the conditions required for the conversion of 4-chlorocinnoline and 4-chloroquinoline into their respective methoxy and phenoxy analogs further exemplifies the reactivity of chlorocinnolines relative to that of chloroquinolines.[8]

The basic nature of 4-chlorocinnoline was recognized by Busch and Klett,[1] who describe a hydrochloride (m.p. 151°), a hydriodide, and a chloroplatinate. It is, however, a weak base, the pK_a value being 2.08 in 50% aqueous alcohol at 21–22°.[11]

Reduction of 4-chlorocinnoline with iron and 15% sulfuric acid yields a chlorine-free product regarded as 1,2-dihydrocinnoline,[12] whence cinnoline is obtainable by dehydrogenation with mercuric oxide.

2. 4-Alkoxycinnolines

Table V-2 shows the few compounds of this group that have been described in the literature. They are prepared from the 4-chloro compounds by treatment with sodium alkoxide in the appropriate alcohol, usually under reflux.

TABLE V-2. 4-Alkoxycinnolines

R	R_1	R_2	Color and cryst. form	M.p., °C.	Ref.
Me	H	H	Needles	127–128	10
Me	H	NO_2	Yellow needles	194–194.5	10
Me	H	Cl	Blades	169.5–170	14
Me	Me	NO_2	Golden needles	150–151	8
Et	H	H	Needles	106	1
				101–102	10

Like 4-chlorocinnolines, 4-alkoxycinnolines are of much lower melting point, and are much more soluble in organic solvents than the corresponding hydroxy compounds. 4-Methoxycinnoline is distinctly more basic in character than 4-hydroxycinnoline,[13] but is not a strong base, the respective pK_a values in 50% aqueous alcohol at 21–22° being 2.7 and 1.77.[11]

Treatment of 4-hydroxycinnoline-3-carboxylic acid with diazomethane gives a compound, m.p. 109–110°, which is either the 4-methoxy ester (I) or the N-methyl isomer (II).[10]   4-Hydroxy-6,7-dimethoxycinnoline-3-

(I)   (II)   (III)

(IV)

acetic acid, on treatment with methyl sulfate and alkali, followed by esterification with methanol and sulfuric acid, gives two isomeric ether-esters (III or IV; R = Me), m.p. 186–187° and 184–185° (or 188–189°); these compounds are readily hydrolyzed by dilute acid to the corresponding acids (III or IV; R = H), m.p. 261–262° (efferv.) and 244–245°. The acid, m.p. 244–245°, gives a hydrochloride, m.p. 252–253° (dec.) and is stable above its melting point; in contrast, the isomer, m.p. 261–262°, does not give a hydrochloride (in 2 N acid), but loses carbon dioxide at its melting point with formation of the 3-methyl derivative, m.p. 229–230°. Despite these differences, it has not been possible to determine which of the two series is to be represented by the 4-methoxy structures (as III).[13]

3. 4-Phenoxycinnolines

A. Preparation.   4-Phenoxycinnolines are prepared from 4-chlorocinnolines in either of two ways; (1) by heating the chloro compound with a solution of rather more than one equivalent of potassium hydroxide in an excess of phenol (usually about 10 parts by weight based on the weight of potassium hydroxide); and (2) by warming the chloro compound (1 part by weight) and phenol (3–4 parts) with an excess of powdered ammonium carbonate (1.5–2 parts).   In each case the reaction is usually complete in 1 hour at 95°.   Method (1) is of general value, but method (2) is preferable for the preparation of 6-nitro-4-phenoxycinnolines, as in such cases method (1) is apt to give rise to a good deal of hydroxy compound.[4,9]   As may be seen by comparing Tables V-1 and V-3, almost all known 4-chlorocinnolines have been converted into their 4-phenoxy analogs.

TABLE V-3. 4-Phenoxycinnolines

R1	R2	R3	R4	R5	Prep.[a]	M.p., °C.	Remarks	Ref.
H	H	H	H	H	A	94–95	—	3
H	H	H	H	Cl	A	158–159	—	5
H	H	H	H	NO$_2$	B	166–167	Pale green needles	5,15
H	H	H	H	Me	B	96.5–97	—	5
H	H	H	Cl	H	A	127–128	—	3
H	H	H	NO$_2$	H	B	172–173	Yellow needles	15
H	H	H	Me	H	A	113–114	—	5
H	H	H	Ac	H	B	141–142	—	15
H	H	Cl	H	H	A	128–129	—	3
H	H	Br	H	H	A	151.5–152	—	3
H	H	NO$_2$	H	H	B	190–191	Yellow blades	9
H	H	OMe	H	H	A	108–109	—	3
Me	H	H	H	H	A	78–79	—	4
H	H	H	Cl	Cl	A	213–214	—	2
H	H	H	Me	NO$_2$	C	172–173	—	5
H	H	Cl	Cl	H	A	162–163	—	2
H	H	Cl	Me	H	A	154–155	—	3
H	{NO$_2$ H H / or / H H NO$_2$}			Me	C	160–161	—	5
Me	H	H	H	NO$_2$	B	137.5–138	Yellow blades	4
Me	H	NO$_2$	H	H	B	129–130	Yellow blades	4

[a] A, from the chloro compound, phenol, and potassium hydroxide at 95°. B, from the chloro compound, phenol, and ammonium carbonate at 95°. C, from the chloro compound, phenol, and potassium hydroxide at 150°.

B. Properties. In physical properties these compounds are rather similar to the 4-chloro analogs, being comparatively low melting and soluble in organic solvents. 4-Phenoxycinnoline itself is a weak base, pK_a 2.27 in 50% aqueous alcohol at 21–22°.[11] 4-Phenoxycinnolines are more stable than the chloro compounds, e.g., they do not decompose on keeping, and are not hydrolyzed by boiling water. Nevertheless, they show considerable reactivity. 4-Phenoxycinnoline, for example, gives 4-acetoxycinnoline when refluxed with acetic anhydride, and 4-hydroxycinnoline on prolonged refluxing with alcohol[9]; and, in cases where the experiment has been tried. substituted 4-phenoxycinnolines are readily hydrolyzed to the hydroxy compounds by very dilute acid.[8] When heated in fused ammonium acetate at temperatures of from 140° to about 200°, 4-phenoxycinnolines give 4-aminocinnolines, usually in good yield,[5,9,15] and with primary dialkylaminoalkylamines at temperatures between 130 and 170° (depending on the nature of the amine) 4-dialkylaminoalkylaminocinnolines (as I) are smoothly formed[3]; these compounds are considered in Chapter VI.

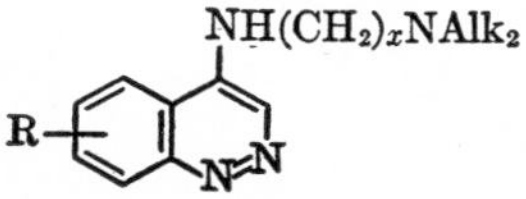

(I)

References

1. Busch and Klett, *Ber.*, **25**, 2847 (1892).
2. Keneford and Simpson, *J. Chem. Soc.*, **1947**, 227.
3. Keneford and Simpson, *J. Chem. Soc.*, **1947**, 917.
4. Keneford and Simpson, *J. Chem. Soc.*, **1948**, 354.
5. Keneford, Morley, and Simpson, *J. Chem. Soc.*, **1948**, 1702.
6. Leonard and Boyd, *J. Org. Chem.*, **11**, 419 (1946).
7. Schofield and Swain, *J. Chem. Soc.*, **1950**, 384.
8. Keneford, Morley, Simpson, and Wright, *J. Chem. Soc.*, **1950**, 1104.
9. Keneford, Schofield, and Simpson, *J. Chem. Soc.*, **1948**, 358.
10. Schofield and Simpson, *J. Chem. Soc.*, **1945**, 512.
11. Keneford, Morley, Simpson, and Wright, *J. Chem. Soc.*, **1949**, 1356.
12. Busch and Rast, *Ber.*, **30**, 521 (1897).
13. Simpson, *J. Chem. Soc.*, **1946**, 480.
14. Simpson, *J. Chem. Soc.*, **1947**, 1653.
15. Schofield and Theobald, *J. Chem. Soc.*, **1949**, 2404.
16. Schofield and Swain, *J. Chem. Soc.*, **1949**, 2393.

CHAPTER VI

4-Aminocinnolines

1. Primary Amino Compounds

A. Preparation. These compounds are prepared from 4-phenoxy-cinnolines by fusion with an excess of ammonium acetate at temperatures up to *ca.* 210–220°, the reaction usually being complete in a few minutes.[1,15] This method is of general application, and works well for a variety of 4-aminocinnolines, as may be seen from Table VI-1. It is in-

TABLE VI-1. Primary 4-Aminocinnolines

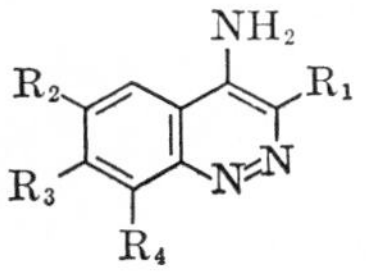

R_1	R_2	R_3	R_4	M.p., °C.	Remarks	Ref.
H	H	H	H	152–154 (hydrate), 209.5–210.5, 212–213	Pale yellow leaflets. Ac deriv., m.p. 272–273°	1,5
H	H	H	NO$_2$	235–236 (dec.), 242–243 (dec.)	Yellow or rust-red needles	4,15
H	H	H	NH$_2$	167–168	Prepared from 8NO$_2$ compd. and Fe-FeSO$_4$-H$_2$O at the b.p. Ac$_2$ deriv., m.p. 299–300°	15
H	H	H	Me	142–152	M.p. varies according to rate of heating	4
H	H	Cl	H	209–210	Pale yellow rods	1
H	H	NO$_2$	H	300–301 (dec.)	Yellow leaflets	15
H	H	NHAc	H	—	Free amine is unknown. 4-Ac deriv., m.p 312° (dec.), is prepared from the 7NO$_2$-4NH$_2$ compd. and Zn dust-Ac$_2$O-AcONa at 95°	15
H	Cl	H	H	277–278	Pale yellow cryst.	1
H	NO$_2$	H	H	288–289	Yellow needles. Ac deriv., m.p. 232–233°	1
H	H	Me	NO$_2$	300 (dec.)	Sandy micro-prisms	4
	5- or 7-NO$_2$		Me	242–243	Orange-red needles	4
Me	H	H	NO$_2$	283–285 (dec.)	Orange needles. Ac deriv., m.p. 177–178°	1
Me	NO$_2$	H	H	Dec. 320	Rust-colored needles	1

teresting to note that treatment of the chloro compound with phenol and ammonium carbonate, which is the standard method for preparing 5-amino compounds in the acridine series,[2] normally yields phenoxy compounds and not 4-amino compounds in the cinnoline series.[3] 4-Aminocinnoline has also been prepared from the chloro compound by direct interaction with ammonia,[5] but the conditions under which this reaction succeeds are evidently critical, because 4-chlorocinnoline and alcoholic ammonia under only slightly different conditions yield no 4-aminocinnoline, but a compound, m.p. 237°, which is possibly a hydrated aminohydroxycinnoline.[1]

B. Properties. Primary 4-aminocinnolines are usually pale or bright yellow solids which may be crystallized from water and frequently form hydrates. They have pronounced basic properties and are easily soluble in aqueous acetic acid, from which, however, they may be reprecipitated by ammonia.[1] The pK_a values of individual compounds are in conformity with this behavior; thus the values (in 50% aqueous alcohol at 25°) for 4-amino- and 6-nitro-4-amino-cinnoline are 6.26 and 5.08,[6] respectively. In cases where the reaction has been tried, primary (and secondary) 4-aminocinnolines do not undergo hydrolysis in acid solution under ordinary conditions.[7] 4-Aminocinnolines are readily acetylated,[1] and they react with methyl iodide in boiling alcohol, forming quaternary salts[3] (see Chapter VII).

2. Secondary Amino Compounds

A. 4-Arylaminocinnolines. These substances are prepared by heating a mixture of a 4-chlorocinnoline and a primary arylamine for a short time (1) without a solvent,[9-11] (2) in benzene,[12] or (3) in acidified aqueous acetone.[2,13] They are yellow or orange compounds (see Table VI-2) which show basic properties; thus Busch and Klett[9] describe hydrochlorides of 4-anilino- and 4-p-toluidino-cinnoline, and 4-anilinocinnoline has pK_a 5.31 (in 50% aqueous alcohol at 21–22°)[6].

B. 4-Dialkylaminoalkylaminocinnolines. As indicated in Table VI-3, a variety of these compounds have been synthesized. The usual method of preparation is to condense the appropriate 4-phenoxycinnoline and aliphatic amine[10] at about 130°, but one or two compounds have also been made from the chlorocinnoline and amine in boiling benzene.[12] These compounds are colorless, or almost colorless, solids with marked basic properties, and in general they crystallize well from neutral organic solvents. Nothing is known of their chemistry except that they are not hydrolyzed by boiling hydrochloric acid.[7] A number of these compounds show antimalarial activity against *Plasmodium gallinaceum* in chicks,[10,14] the

TABLE VI-2. 4-Arylaminocinnolines

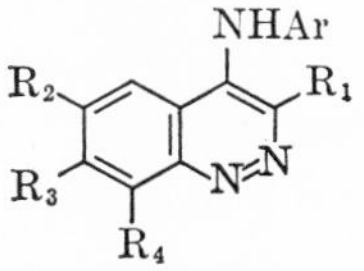

Ar	R_1	R_2	R_3	R_4	Color and cryst. form	M.p., °C.	Ref.
Ph	H	H	H	H	Brown needles	232	9,10
					Yellow needles	229.5–230.5	
Ph	H	NO_2	H	H	Orange needles	228.5–229.5	11
Ph	H	OMe	H	H	Yellow needles	235.5–236	10
Ph	H	H	H	Me	Yellow needles	231–232	4
Ph	H	H	Me	NO_2	Green-yellow needles	262–263 (dec.)	4
Ph	5- or 7-NO_2			Me	Orange-red needles	166–168	4
Ph	Me	H	H	H	Yellow needles	217–218	13
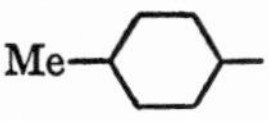 Me—⟨ ⟩—	H	H	H	H	Yellow needles	215	9
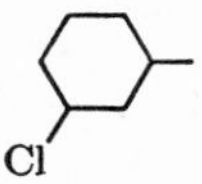 ⟨ ⟩— (Cl)	H	Br	H	H	Yellow plates	246–247	12

TABLE VI-3. 4-Dialkylaminoalkylaminocinnolines

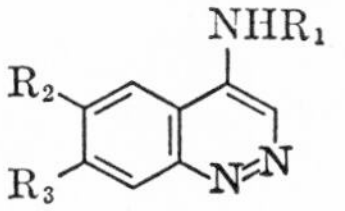

R_1	R_2	R_3	M.p., °C.	Ref.
$CH(Me)(CH_2)_3NEt_2$	H	H	103	14
"	H	Cl	123.5–124.5	10
"	Cl	H	107–108	10
"	Cl	Cl	121.5–123	10
"	Cl	Me	120–121	10
"	Br	H	97.5–98.5	10
"	OMe	H	160	14
$(CH_2)_2NEt_2$	H	H	145	14
"	H	Cl	182.5–183.5	10
"	Cl	Cl	204–204.5	10
$(CH_2)_3NMe_2$	H	Cl	175–176	10
"	Cl	Cl	170–171	10
"	Cl	Me	168–170	10
$(CH_2)_3NEt_2$	H	Cl	162–163, 164–165	10,12
"	Cl	Cl	151.5–152.5	10
"	Br	H	149–150	12
$(CH_2)_3NBu_2^n$	H	Cl	123–124	10
"	Cl	Cl	153.5–154	10
$(CH_2)_3N(CH_2)_5$	H	Cl	180–181	10
"	Cl	Cl	214–215	10

most effective compound being 7-chloro-4,4'-diethylamino-1'-methyl
butylaminocinnoline (I).

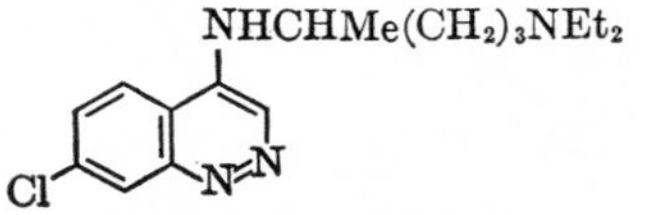

(I) 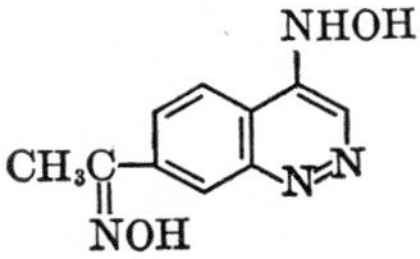   (II)

C. 4-Hydroxylamino-7-acetylcinnolineoxime (II) is produced
by treatment of 4-phenoxy-7-acetylcinnoline with hydroxylamine hydrochloride and sodium acetate in aqueous ethanol.[15] It is a yellow crystalline solid, m.p. 264–265° (dec.), and is converted into 4-hydroxylamino-7-
acetamidocinnoline (pale yellow needles, m.p. 229–230°) by the Beckmann
change.[15]

References

1. Keneford, Schofield, and Simpson, *J. Chem. Soc.*, **1948**, 358.
2. Albert and Gledhill, *J. Soc. Chem. Ind.*, **64**, 169 (1945).
3. Morley and Simpson, *J. Chem. Soc.*, **1948**, 360.
4. Keneford, Morley, and Simpson, *J. Chem. Soc.*, **1948**, 1702.
5. K. Baker, *J. Chem. Soc.*, **1948**, 1713.
6. Keneford, Morley, Simpson, and Wright, *J. Chem. Soc.*, **1949**, 1356.
7. Keneford, Morley, Simpson, and Wright, *J. Chem. Soc.*, **1950**, 1104.
8. Simpson, *J. Chem. Soc.*, **1947**, 1653.
9. Busch and Klett, *Ber.*, **25**, 2847 (1892).
10. Keneford and Simpson, *J. Chem. Soc.*, **1947**, 917.
11. Schofield and Simpson, *J. Chem. Soc.*, **1945**, 512.
12. Leonard and Boyd, *J. Org. Chem.*, **11**, 419 (1946).
13. Keneford and Simpson, *J. Chem. Soc.*, **1948**, 354.
14. Simpson and Schofield, *Nature*, **157**, 439 (1946).
15. Schofield and Theobald, *J. Chem. Soc.*, **1949**, 2404.

CHAPTER VII

Cinnoline Quaternary Salts

A. Preparation. Cinnoline quaternary salts containing a 4-amino, 4-anilino, 4-methyl, or 4-aryl group are readily prepared from the base and alkyl halide by heating under reflux in alcoholic solution,[1-3] provided that the Bz ring does not contain an amino group. Quaternary salts of Bz-aminocinnolines are made either by reduction of the Bz-nitro salts, or alternatively by acetylation of the amino base, followed by conversion into the quaternary salt and hydrolysis, as indicated below; 4,6-diamino-1-methylcinnolinium iodide (I; R = H) and its 3-methyl analog (I; R = Me) are examples of aminoquaternary salts which have been prepared by each of these two methods (Eq. 1).[3] Salts containing a p-dimethylamino-styryl group at C_4 are prepared by heating 4-methylcinnolinium salts with

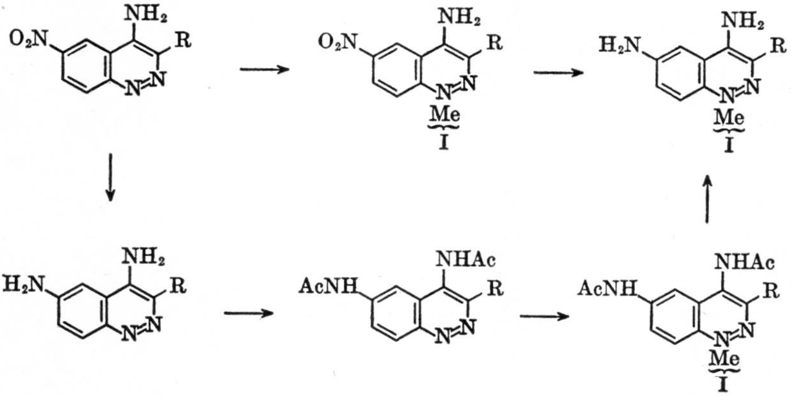

p-dimethylaminobenzaldehyde either in alcohol or in acetic anhydride.[1] The known cinnoline quaternary salts are listed in Table VII-1.

B. Structure. Quaternary cinnolinium salts are represented by the general formula given at the head of Table VII-1, *i.e.*, the site of quaternary salt formation is shown as N_1 and not N_2. This is in accord with evidence obtained from the behavior of the methyl group in 4-methylcinnolines. 4-Styrylcinnoline results when 4-methylcinnoline is refluxed with benzaldehyde and zinc chloride,[4] and p-dimethylaminostyrylcinnolinium salts are formed, as mentioned above, when the 4-methyl quaternary salts and the aldehyde are simply heated in alcohol without a catalyst. These

TABLE VII-1. Cinnoline Quaternary Salts

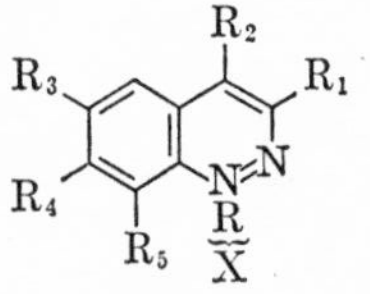

Structure: cinnoline bearing substituents R$_1$, R$_2$, R$_3$, R$_4$, R$_5$ with the N=N ring system and quaternary R/X group.

R$_1$	R$_2$	R$_3$	R$_4$	R$_5$	RX	Prep.[a]	Color and cryst. form	M.p., °C.	Ref.
H	H	H	H	H	MeI	A	Red-brown cryst.	168; 168–170.5 (dec.)	4,7
H	NH$_2$	H	H	H	MeI	A	Green-yellow needles	252–253 (dec.)	3
H	NH$_2$	Cl	H	H	MeI	A	Saffron needles	225–226 (dec.)	2
H	NH$_2$	NO$_2$	H	H	MeI	A	Orange needles	282–283 (dec.)	3
H	NH$_2$	NH$_2$	H	NO$_2$	MeI	A	Orange-red needles	209–210 (dec.)	3
H	NH$_2$	NHAc	H	H	MeI	A	Bronze crystals	237–238 (dec.)	3
H	NHAc	H	H	H	MeI	B,C	Brown needles	273–274	3,11
H	NH$_2$	H	Me	NO$_2$	MeI	A	Yellow needles	265 (dec.)	3
H	NH$_2$	NO$_2$	Me	NH$_2$	MeI	A	Red-orange needles	278 (dec.)	3
H	NH$_2$	NH$_2$	H	H	MeI	B	Red needles	338 (dec.)	3
H	NHPh	NO$_2$	H	H	MeI	F	Scarlet needles	233–234 (dec.)	3
H	NHPh	NH$_2$	H	H	MeI	K	Orange needles	240–241 (dec.)	3
H	NHPh	NHAc	H	H	MeI	A	Yellow needles	267–268 (dec.)	3
H	NHPh	NHAc	H	H	MeCl	G,H	Orange-yellow needles	240–241 (dec.)	3
H	Me	H	H	H	EtI	A	Red needles	152–154	1
H	Me	Cl	H	H	EtI	A	Red needles	204 (dec.)	1
H	Me	H	Cl	H	MeI	A	Red needles	202 (dec.)	1
H	Me	H	Cl	H	EtI	A	Red needles	185	1

R₁	R₂	R₃	R₄	R₆	RX	Prep.[a]	Color and cryst. form	M.p., °C.	Ref.
H	Me CH:CH—⬡—NMe₂	H	CO₂Et	H	EtI	A	Red needles	208 (dec.)	1
H	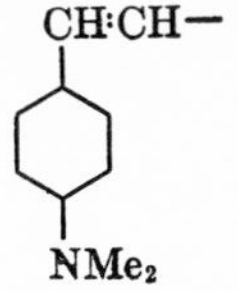 CH:CH—⬡—NMe₂	H	H	H	EtI	J	Blue-green needles	252	1
H	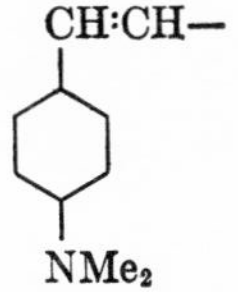 CH:CH—⬡—NMe₂	Cl	H	H	EtI	J	Blue-green needles	248–250 (dec.)	1
H	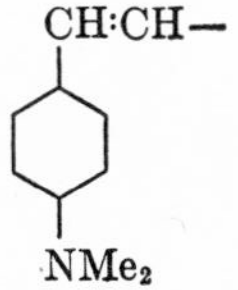 CH:CH—⬡—NMe₂	H	Cl	H	EtI	J	Blue-green needles	246 (dec.)	1
H	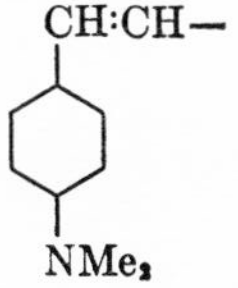 CH:CH—⬡—NMe₃	H	CO₂Et	H	EtI	J	Blue-green needles	250 (dec.)	1

Table continued

TABLE VII-1. Cinnoline Quaternary Salts (continued)

R_1	R_2	R_3	R_4	R_5	RX	Prep.[a]	Color and cryst. form	M.p., °C.	Ref.
H	Ph	H	H	H	MeCl	E	Yellow plates	dec. 215–220	12
H	Ph	H	H	H	MeI	D	Red needles	220 (dec.)	12
H	p-C$_6$H$_4$OH	H	H	H	EtI	A	Scarlet prisms	237–239	2
H	p-C$_6$H$_4$OMe	H	H	H	MeI	D	Red-brown needles	dec. 220	13
Me	NH$_2$	NO$_2$	H	H	MeI	A	Red prisms	280–281 (dec.)	3
Me	NH$_2$	NO$_2$	H	H	p-MeSO$_3$-C$_6$H$_4$Me	I	Yellow blades	283 (dec.)	3
Me	NH$_2$	H	H	NO$_2$	MeI	A	Bronze plates	263–264 (dec.)	3
Me	NH$_2$	NH$_2$	H	H	MeI	B,C	Bronze needles	283–284 (dec.)	3,11
Me	NHAc	NHAc	H	H	MeI	A	Orange-red needles	243–244 (dec.)	3
Me	Ph	H	H	H	EtI	A	Red needles	206–207	2
Ph	p-C$_6$H$_4$OH	H	H	H	EtI	A	Orange leaflets	227–228 (dec.)	2
Ph	p-C$_6$H$_4$OH	H	H	H	2EtI(?)	A	Red blades	216–217	2

[a] A, from the base by heating with the alkyl iodide in methyl or ethyl alcohol under reflux.   B, from the corresponding nitro-4-amino quaternary salt by reduction with iron powder and water.   C, from the diacetamido base by quaternization followed by hydrolysis.   D, from the base, methyl iodide, and methanol at 100°.   E, from the methiodide and silver chloride.   F, from the base by heating with methyl iodide in nitrobenzene at ~80° (reflux condenser).   G, from the corresponding methiodide and dilute hydrochloric acid.   H, from the 6-amino-methiodide by acetylation, followed by treatment as in method G.   I, from the base by fusion with methyl p-toluenesulfonate at 105°.   J, from the corresponding 4-methyl quaternary salt and p-dimethylaminobenzaldehyde in alcohol (reflux).   K, from the corresponding 6-nitro quaternary salt by reduction with iron powder and water.

reactions indicate that the methyl group, already active in the parent base, is made still more active by quaternary salt formation, which therefore clearly occurs at N_1. Furthermore, the synthesis of the compounds (I: R = H and Me) by the two independent methods outlined above indicates that the 4-amino group is not alkylated during quaternary salt formation; the behavior of the 4-aminocinnolines is thus similar to that of 5-amino-acridine[5] and of 4-aminoquinolines,[6] which quaternize on the ring nitrogen, and suggests that the unattacked amino group and the salt-forming nitrogen atom occupy identical relative positions in all three heterocyclic types. Finally, structural proof that the position of quaternary salt formation is N_1 has been obtained[2] in the case of 6-chloro-4-aminocinnoline (II). When the quaternary salt (III) derived from this base is boiled with alkali, ammonia is evolved, and the main product is a compound which is isomeric

(II)   (III)   (IV)   (V)

with 6-chloro-4-methoxycinnoline (IV) (see Chapter V), but identical with the compound obtained from the hydroxycinnoline by methylation with methyl sulfate; it must therefore be 6-chloro-1-methyl-4-cinnolone (V) (Chapter VIII), and the position of alkylation of (II) is thus disclosed.

C. Reactions. Little is known of the chemistry of cinnoline quaternary salts. Apart from the condensation, already described, of p-dimethylaminobenzaldehyde with 4-methyl-1-ethylcinnolinium iodides, the only reaction that has been studied is the alkaline decomposition of some quaternary salts.

Busch and Rast[7] state that when an aqueous solution of cinnoline methiodide is treated with alkali a dark-blue coloration is first produced followed by the separation of amorphous material. The decomposition was not studied by them in detail, but recent work has shown that one of the products of this reaction is cinnoline itself.[8] The alkaline decomposition of 6-chloro-4-amino-1-methylcinnolinium iodide (III), which, as stated above, leads to the formation of the cinnolone (V) as main product, also produces small amounts of a neutral isomer of (V) of unknown constitution.[2]

The alkaline decomposition of certain 4-arylcinnoline quaternary

salts, which can be effected under quite mild conditions (*e.g.*, by cold
aqueous sodium carbonate or hot ammonium hydroxide), follows a different
course, and has been examined in detail in the case of 4-*p*-hydroxyphenyl-
cinnoline ethiodide.[2]   When this salt is heated with aqueous sodium carbonate it is converted into 4-*p*-hydroxyphenylcinnoline and acetaldehyde,
the yield of each product being 70–75 mole per cent;   at room temperature
the reaction proceeds somewhat differently, and an unoriented *x*-iodo-4-*p*-
acetoxyphenylcinnoline, m.p. 158–160°, and 4-*p*-acetoxyphenylcinnoline,
m.p. 127.5–128°,[14] have been isolated from the reaction product after
acetylation.   This type of decomposition is qualitatively similar to that of

(VI)   (VII)

quaternary phenazonium salts (VI), which decompose in accordance with
the equation $2BMe \cdot OH \rightarrow B + BHMe + CH_2O + H_2O$.[9]   It will be
seen, however, that the maximum yield of base and aldehyde obtainable
according to this equation is only 50 mole per cent;   the resemblance between the two decompositions can, therefore, be no more than qualitative.
The isolation of the iodoacetoxyphenylcinnoline, m.p. 158–160°, strength-
ens this qualitative similarity, as the compound presumably arises through
the agency of iodide ion;   a process of anionoid substitution is thus involved, and it is known that such substitution reactions are characteristic
of phenazonium salts also during their alkaline decomposition.[9]   A final
point of resemblance between the two reactions is that alkylphenazonium
salts give rise to free radicals,[9] and there is some evidence that such substances may be present in the oily decomposition products isolated from 4-
p-hydroxyphenylcinnoline ethiodide, which give a brilliant blue solution in
acetone, the color fading on exposure to the air.

3-Phenyl-4-*p*-hydroxyphenylcinnoline ethiodide probably behaves in a
similar manner, as it yields the parent base and acetaldehyde.[2]   It may be
noted here that Ullmann and Dieterle[10] found that 3,4-benzocinnoline
quaternary salts (VII) (Chapter IX) are converted into the unquaternized
base on treatment with alkali, but the reaction has not been further studied.
This type of decomposition is not, however, characteristic of quaternary
salts of all 4-arylcinnolines, as the parent base is not formed when 4-phenyl-
3-methylcinnoline ethiodide is treated with alkali.[2]

References

1. Atkinson and Simpson, *J. Chem. Soc.*, **1947**, 808.
2. Simpson, *J. Chem. Soc.*, **1947**, 1653.
3. Keneford, Morley, and Simpson, unpublished.
4. Jacobs, Winstein, Henderson, and Spaeth, *J. Am. Chem. Soc.*, **68**, 1310 (1946).
5. Albert and Ritchie, *J. Chem. Soc.*, **1943**, 458.
6. Simpson and Wright, *J. Chem. Soc.*, **1948**, 1707.
7. Busch and Rast, *Ber.*, **30**, 521 (1897).
8. Morley and Simpson, *J. Chem. Soc.*, **1949**, 1354.
9. McIlwain, *J. Chem. Soc.*, **1937**, 1704.
10. Ullmann and Dieterle, *Ber.*, **37**, 23 (1904).
11. Keneford *et al.*, *Nature*, **161**, 603 (1948).
12. R. Stoermer and H. Fincke, *Ber.*, **42**, 3115 (1909).
13. R. Stoermer and O. Gaus, *Ber.*, **45**, 3104 (1912).
14. Atkinson and Simpson, *J. Chem. Soc.*, **1947**, 1649.

CHAPTER VIII

Reduced Cinnolines

1. Reduced Cinnolines with Nonoxygenated Rings

A. Dihydrocinnolines. The simplest member of this group is 1,2-dihydrocinnoline (I), which was prepared by Busch and Rast[1] by reduction of 4-chlorocinnoline with iron and 15% sulfuric acid. The compound crystallizes in plates, m.p. 85–87°, and is a weak base of which the salts [hydrochloride, m.p. 149–150° (dec.)] are immediately decomposed by water. It may be distilled without decomposition, and is not reduced by treatment with sodium and alcohol. On oxidation with mercuric oxide it yields cinnoline, and for this reason it is formulated as the 1,2 rather than as the 3,4-dihydro derivative (II).

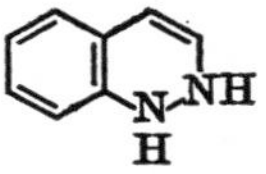

(I) 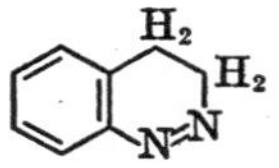   (II) 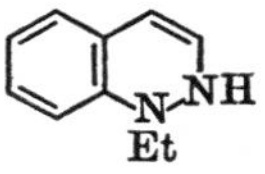   (III) 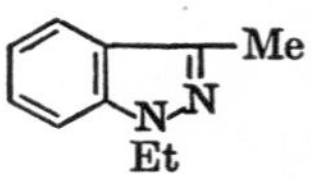   (IV)

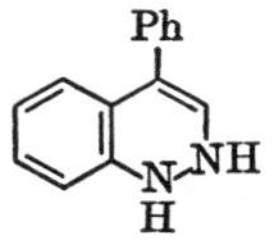

(V) 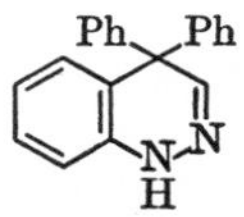   (VI) 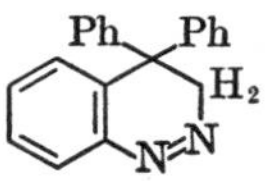   (VII) 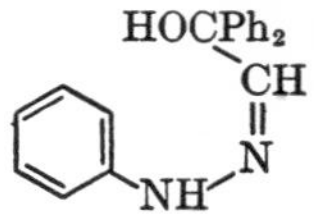   (VIII)

The early literature[2] describes a compound, ethylquinazole, which was represented by (among other formulas) structure (III), but it was subsequently shown[3,4] that this compound is the isoindazole (IV) and not 1-ethyl-1,2-dihydrocinnoline.

4-Phenyl-1,2-dihydrocinnoline (V) is formed in good yield by refluxing a mixture of 4-phenylcinnoline, zinc dust, and ammoniacal alcohol; it crystallizes in colorless needles, m.p. 115–116°.[5] This substance undergoes disproportionation to 4-phenylcinnoline and the hydrochloride of 4-phenyl-1,2,3,4-tetrahydrocinnoline (*vide infra*) when heated in a sealed tube at 100° with alcohol and hydrochloric acid. If it is heated under reflux (1 hour) with alcohol, concentrated hydrochloric acid, and amalgamated zinc, it yields 3-phenylindole (*cf.* Chapter II, Section 1).[5]

A compound regarded as 4,4-diphenyl-1,4-dihydrocinnoline (VI) [or the 3,4-dihydroisomeride (VII)] is obtained when the phenylhydrazone (VIII) of diphenylhydroxyacetaldehyde (from diazoacetic ester and phenylmagnesium bromide) is boiled with N-sulfuric acid; it is a red crystalline solid, m.p. 69–70°, easily soluble in organic solvents, but insoluble in dilute acids. With alcoholic hydrogen chloride it gives a hydrochloride, m.p. 225–230°.[6]

B. Tetrahydrocinnolines. 4-Phenyl-1,2,3,4-tetrahydrocinnoline (IX) is smoothly formed by catalytic reduction (PtO$_2$–AcOH) of the dihydro compound (V); it is a yellow crystalline solid, m.p. 83°, which gives a picrate, m.p. 128°, and a hydrochloride, m.p. 201° (which may be recrystallized from water).[5]

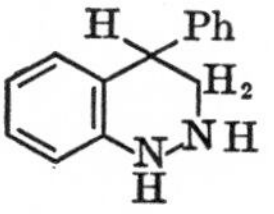

(IX) 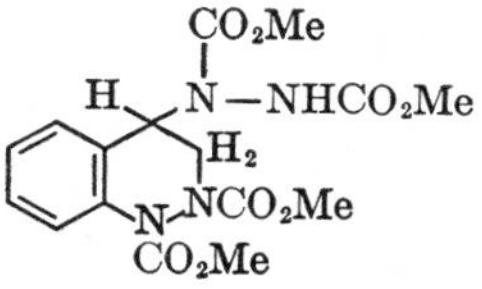 (X) 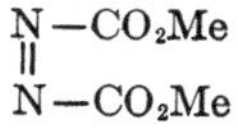 (XI)

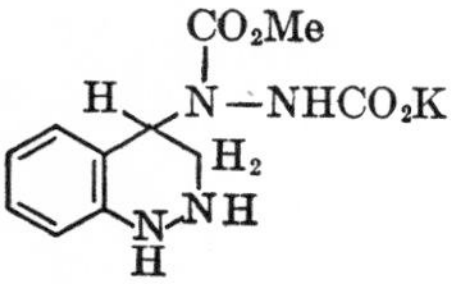

(XII) 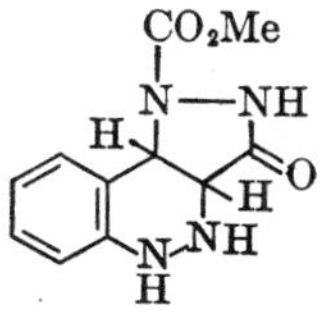 (XIII) 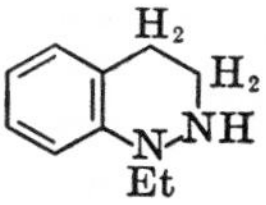 (XIV)

The tetrahydro compound (X) is formed in high yield by addition of 2 moles of dimethyl azodicarboxylate (XI) to styrene.[7] It is a crystalline solid, m.p. 178°, stable to ozone, concentrated aqueous ammonia, and concentrated hydrochloric acid, but degraded by hot 33% potassium hydroxide to the compound (XII), m.p. 146–147° (efferv.), which is readily cyclized to (XIII) (Chapter IX, Section 5).[7]

A compound alleged to be 1-ethyl-1,2,3,4-tetrahydrocinnoline (XIV) is described by Tichwinski[8] as a product of the reaction between diethylzinc and benzenediazonium chloride. N-Ethyl- (XVI) and N,N'-diethylphenylhydrazine (XVII) were also isolated, the whole process being formulated as follows:

$$PhN_2Cl + ZnEt_2 \longrightarrow PhN(Et) \rightleftarrows N \quad (XV)$$
$$ZnEt_2 + H_2O \longrightarrow C_2H_6$$
$$C_2H_6 + (XV) \longrightarrow PhNEtNHEt \quad (XVII)$$
$$(XV) + (XVII) \longrightarrow (XIV) + PhNEtNH_2 \quad (XVI)$$

Tichwinski also obtained (XIV) by reaction between diethylzinc and phenylazoethane.[9] It is a light, yellow, pleasant-smelling oil, b.p. 92–98°/17 mm.; it is insoluble in 2% hydrochloric acid, a fact which does not seem to be in good agreement with the structure proposed for the compound.

C. Hexahydrocinnolines. The only compound of this type which has been described is 1-phenyl-3-methyl-1,4,5,6,7,8-hexahydrocinnoline

(XVIII)

(XVIII). It is produced by treatment of 2-acetonylcyclohexanone with phenylhydrazine,[11] and forms violet-red crystals, m.p. 87°. In view of the color, the structure must be regarded as open to question.

2. Reduced Cinnolines with Oxygenated Rings

A. Reduced 3- and 4-Hydroxycinnolines. A 3-hydroxydihydrocinnoline, m.p. 126°, is mentioned in the literature,[5] but details of its preparation[12] are not accessible. It gives a dibenzoyl derivative, m.p. 167°, and on reduction with phosphorus and hydriodic acid yields oxindole, also obtained by a similar reduction of 3-hydroxycinnoline.[5]

Reduction of 4-hydroxycinnoline with red phosphorus and hydriodic acid (d 1.7, refluxed for 12 hours) yields a compound, m.p. 220° (dec.), which is formulated as the hydriodide of 4-hydroxy-1,2,3,4-tetrahydrocinnoline (I).[5]

(I)   (II)   (III)   (IV)

B. 1-Methyl-4-keto-1,4-dihydrocinnolines. These substances, of general structure (II), are produced by methylation of 4-hydroxycinnolines with methyl sulfate and alkali. Their constitution follows from the fact that they are isomeric and not identical with the corresponding 4-methoxy compounds formed by treatment of the 4-chloro compounds with alcoholic sodium methoxide (see Chapter V, Section 2). Compounds of this type are given in Table VIII-1; 4-hydroxy-6,7-dimethoxycinnoline-3-acetic acid gives both an O- and a N-methyl derivative with methyl sulfate and alkali, but the individual constitutions of these compounds have not been determined (Chapter V, Section 2).

TABLE VIII-1. 1-Methyl-4-keto-1,4-dihydrocinnolines

R_1	R_2	R_3	R_4	R_5	Prep.[a]	M.p., °C.	Remarks	Ref.
H	H	H	H	H	A	165–166.5	—	13
H	H	H	H	NO_2	A,B	243–244	Yellow needles	17,18
*H	H	H	NO_2	H	A	238	Pale orange leaflets	18
H	H	Cl	H	H	A,C	221–222	Pale yellow needles	10
*H	H	NO_2	H	H	A	183–183.5	Yellow needles	13
*H	NO_2	H	H	H	A	188–189	Yellow leaflets	18
*H	$\begin{bmatrix} NO_2 & H & H \\ & \text{or} & \\ H & H & NO_2 \end{bmatrix}$			Me	A	257–258 (dec.)	—	14
*Me	H	NO_2	H	H	A	182–184	Golden-yellow needles	13

* The structures of these compounds are not rigidly proved.
[a] A, from the hydroxycinnoline, aqueous potassium hydroxide, and methyl sulfate at 50°. B, by nitration of 1-methyl-4-cinnolone. C, by alkaline decomposition of 6-chloro-4-aminocinnoline methiodide.

C. Methyl 4-Keto-4,6-dihydrocinnolyl-6-nitronates. If the methylation of 6-nitro-4-hydroxycinnoline is attempted with methyl sulfate and excess alkali, extensive decomposition occurs.[13] By using the minimum amount of alkali, however, a good yield of a crystalline product is obtained, consisting of a mixture of (II; R = H; R' = NO_2) with the isomeric methyl 4-keto-4,6-dihydrocinnolyl-6-nitronate (III; R = H), which forms orange flakes, m.p. 227–229°.[13,14] The 3-methyl analog (III; R = Me) (orange flakes, m.p. 162–163°) is prepared similarly.[14] These substances are unstable to alkali, but stable in acid solution.[14] The formation of these nitronates requires the combination of an o- with a p-quinonoid structure in the two rings of the cinnoline nucleus; 5- (or 7-) nitro-4-hydroxy-8-methylcinnoline (as IV), which cannot give rise to such an arrangement of bonds, gives on methylation the 1-methyl-4-cinnolone (Table VIII-1) as sole product.[14]

D. 3-Acetoxy-2-aryl-6-keto-2,6-dihydrocinnolines. These compounds, of general formula (V), are readily prepared by a simple method of apparently wide applicability in which diazotized arylamines are coupled with m-hydroxyphenylacetic acid in alkaline solution,[15] followed by cyclization of the resulting azo compound with hot acetic anhydride and a trace of sulfuric acid (Eq. 1). The compounds so prepared are listed in Table VIII-2.

The ultraviolet absorption spectra of several of these compounds have been determined; (V; R = Ph) shows maxima at 235, 330, and 413 mμ (log ϵ = 4.65, 3.8, and 3.65); (V; R = p-bromophenyl) at 235, 338, and 415 mμ; and (V; R = p-nitrophenyl) at 239, 311, and 415 mμ.

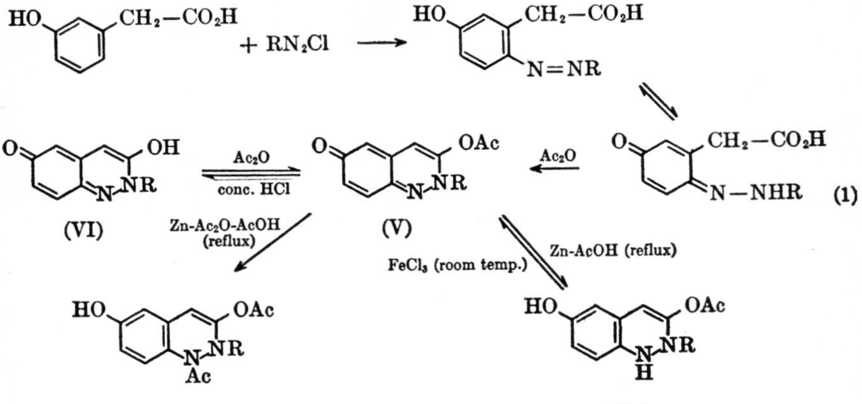

The chemistry of this group of cinnolines has not yet been worked out, but the transformations illustrated above have been carried out in one or two cases, yielding the following products:[15]

> (VI; R = m-acetylphenyl), m.p. 290–300° (dec.).
> (VII; R = β-C$_{10}$H$_7$), colorless plates, m.p. 131–133°.
> (VII; R = m-acetylphenyl), m.p. 164–166°.
> (VII; R = p-acetoxyphenyl), m.p. 164–165°.
> (VIII; R = β-C$_{10}$H$_7$), m.p. 141–143°.

Some of these compounds have been tested for hormonal activity; in particular (V; R = p-acetoxyphenyl), (V; R = m-acetylphenyl), and (VII; R = p-acetoxyphenyl) show one mouse unit of estrogenic activity at levels of 1800, 100, and 500 γ, respectively.[15]

TABLE VIII-2. 3-Acetoxy-2-aryl-6-keto-2,6-dihydrocinnolines[15]

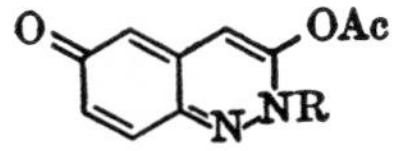

R	M.p., °C.	R	M.p., °C.
Ph	216–218	m-C$_6$H$_4$Ac	237–239
p-C$_6$H$_4$Br	226–228	p-C$_6$H$_4$Ac	220–222
p-C$_6$H$_4$NO$_2$	239–241	p-C$_6$H$_4$COCH$_2$OAc	237–238 (dec.)
p-C$_6$H$_4$NHAc	260–265 (dec.)	β-C$_{10}$H$_7$	188–189
p-C$_6$H$_4$CO$_2$H	>290	3'-pyridyl	213–215
p-C$_6$H$_4$OAc	220–223 (dec.)		

E. 2-Phenyl-3-keto-4-hydroxy-2,3,5,6,7,8-hexahydrocinnoline.

This compound (XI) is one of several products formed when ethyl 2-ketocyclohexylglyoxylate (IX) is condensed with phenylhydrazine in a mixture of ethanol and acetic acid; it is considered to arise from the phenylhydrazone (X). It forms needles, m.p. 189–190°, soluble in sodium carbonate and in concentrated hydrochloric acid. On treatment with fuming hydrochloric acid at 200°, it is converted into 2-phenyl-4,5,6,7-tetrahydroindazole (XII).[16]

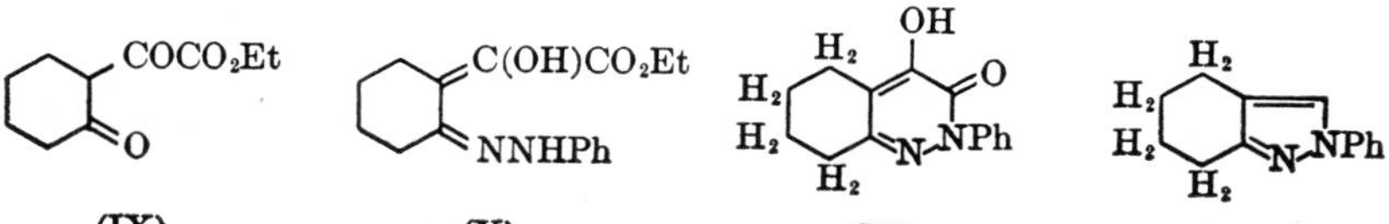

(IX)   (X)   (XI)   (XII)

References

1. M. Busch and A. Rast, *Ber.*, **30**, 521 (1897).
2. E. Fischer and H. Kuzel, *Ber.*, **16**, 652 (1883).
3. E. Fischer and H. Kuzel, *Ann.*, **221**, 261 (1883).
4. E. Fischer and J. Tafel, *Ann.*, **227**, 303 (1885).
5. P. W. Neber, G. Knöller, K. Herbst, and A. Trissler, *Ann.*, **471**, 113 (1929).
6. E. Zerner, *Monatsh.*, **34**, 1609 (1913).
7. O. Diels and K. Alder, *Ann.*, **450**, 237 (1926).
8. M. Tichwinski, *Zentr.*, *I*, 79 (1905) [*J. Russ. Phys. Chem.*, **36**, 1052 (1904)].
9. M. Tichwinski, *Zentr.*, *I*, 80 (1905) [*J. Russ. Phys. Chem.*, **36**, 1056 (1904)].
10. Simpson, *J. Chem. Soc.*, **1947**, 1653.
11. F. Ebel, F. Huber, and A. Brunner, *Helv. Chim. Acta*, **12**, 16 (1929).
12. Reference 5 (G. Bossel, *Inaug.-Diss.*, Tübingen, May, 1925, p. 33).
13. Schofield and Simpson, *J. Chem. Soc.*, **1945**, 512.
14. Keneford, Morley, Simpson, and Wright, *J. Chem. Soc.*, **1950**, 1104.
15. Kornfeld, *J. Am. Chem. Soc.*, **70**, 1373 (1948).
16. K. von Auwers, *Ann.*, **453**, 211 (1927).
17. Schofield and Swain, *J. Chem. Soc.*, **1949**, 1367.
18. Schofield and Theobald, *J. Chem. Soc.*, **1949**, 2404.

CHAPTER IX

Cinnolines Containing Additional
Fused Rings

1. 3,4-Benzocinnolines

A. Preparation. The parent compound (I) of this group, known as phenazone, diphenyleneazone, or, more properly, 3,4-benzocinnoline (*R.I.* 1909), was discovered by Täuber in 1891, who prepared it by reduction of 2,2′-dinitrodiphenyl with 3% sodium amalgam in methanolic solution.[1]

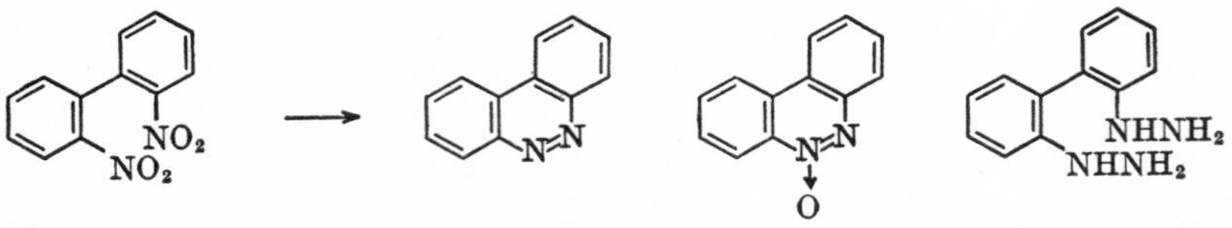

(I) (II) (III)

It may also be prepared from the dinitrodiphenyl by other methods of reduction. Ullmann and Dieterle, for instance, obtained (I) by the action of stannous chloride and fuming hydrochloric acid on the oxide (II), itself prepared from the dinitrodiphenyl by reduction with sodium sulfide in hot aqueous alcohol[2,3]; and Sandin and Cairns prepared (I) by treatment of diazotized 2,2′-diaminodiphenyl with sodium arsenite.[4] Täuber[5] also obtained (I) from 2,2′-dihydrazinodiphenyl (III), both by heating (III) with 20% hydrochloric acid at 150° and also by heating the diacetyl derivative of (III) to 240–260°.

The accessibility of substituted 2,2′-dinitrodiphenyls led Ullmann and Dieterle[2] to investigate the preparation of analogs of (I). These workers found that, in general, reduction with sodium sulfide in hot aqueous alcohol gave the oxide (as II), whereas electrolytic reduction led directly to the benzocinnoline, usually in high yield. Table IX-1 summarizes the known 3,4-benzocinnolines and Table IX-2 their monoxides.

In addition to their preparation from dinitrodiaryls, 3,4-benzocinnolines may also be prepared by dehydrogenation of azo compounds. This transformation can be effected by the action of aluminum chloride on cer-

52

TABLE IX-1. 3,4-Benzocinnolines

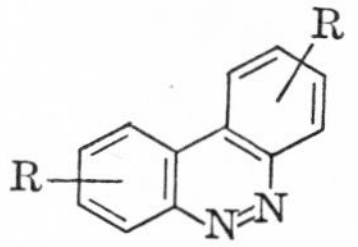

No.	Substituents in 2,2'-dinitro-diphenyl	Prep.[a]	M.p., °C.	Crystalline form	Ref.
1	None	A,C,E, I,J,K	156, 155	Yellow tablets or needles	1,2,4,5, 32,37,38
2	4,4'-di-NH$_2$	C,E	265,267	Dark yellow cryst. Dark red prisms	2,1
3	4,4'-di-NMe$_2$	A,C,D	276	Red needles	2
4	4,4'-di-NEt$_2$	C	184	Red cryst.	2
5	4,4'-di-NH$_2$-5,5'-di-OMe	C	244	Dark yellow crystals	2
6	4,4'-di-OMe	G	197	Dark yellow needles	14
7	4,4'-di-Me	C	188[b]	Yellow cryst.	2
		J	184–185		4
8	5,5'-di-Me[e]	E	187[b]	Yellow prisms	8
9	6,6'-di-Me	C	113–114,	Yellow needles or	11
		E	96–97	prisms	33
10	4,4'-di-F-5,5'-di-Me	E	228	Green-yellow needles	34
11	4,4'-di-NH$_2$-5,5'-di-Me	E	276[d] (dec.)	Dark-red blades	8
12	4,4'-di-CO$_2$H	F	208[c]	—	35

[a] For methods of preparation, see key to Table IX-2.
[b] These two compounds are stated (ref. 2) to be identical.
[c] Compound isolated as acid chloride; the m.p. quoted is that of the acid chloride.
[d] Gives a dibenzylidene derivative, yellow crystals, m.p. 239° (dec.).
[e] Oxidation with chromic acid and aqueous sulfuric acid at 100° gives:

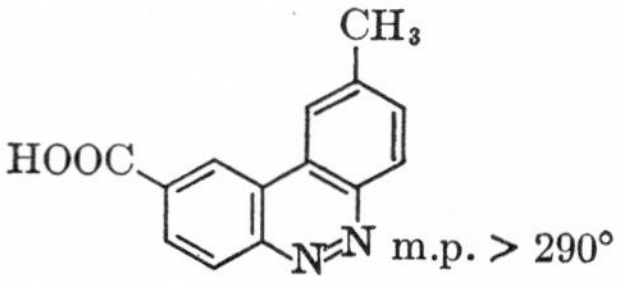

tain azo compounds which have one *o*-position to each nitrogen atom unsubstituted; the reaction is carried out at 60–120° and may be performed in the presence of fluxes or diluents and in the presence or absence of air or other oxidizing agent.[6]

TABLE IX-2. 3,4-Benzocinnoline N-Oxides

Substituents in 2,2'-dinitro-diphenyl	Prep.[a]	M.p., °C.	Crystalline form	Ref.
None	B,E,H	139	Yellow needles	2
		138		3
		152		1
4,4'-di-NMe$_2$	B	242	Red needles	2
4,4'-di-Me	B	209	Brown leaflets	2
6,6'-di-Me	B	153	Yellow needles	13

[a] A, by reduction of monoxide with stannous chloride and hydrochloric acid. B, by reduction of dinitrodiaryl with sodium sulfide in hot aqueous alcohol. C, by electrolytic reduction (sometimes in boiling solution) of dinitrodiaryl (lead anode in sodium carbonate solution; nickel cathode in alcoholic sodium acetate). D, by electrolytic reduction of monoxide. E, by reduction of dinitrodiaryl with sodium amalgam in methanol. F, by reduction of dinitrodiaryl with zinc dust and ammonia, followed by conversion to acid chloride with PCl$_5$ in chlorobenzene. G, by diazotization of diaminodiaryl followed by addition to boiling 50% copper sulfate solution. H, by reduction of dinitrodiphenyl in hot 90% alcohol with zinc dust and 40% aqueous potassium hydroxide (gives mainly the 1,2-dioxide). I, from the dihydrazinodiphenyl by HCl/150° and by pyrolysis of the diacetyl derivative of the dihydrazino compound at 240–260°. J, by diazotization of diaminodiaryl followed by treatment with sodium arsenite. K, from 2,2'-dinitrodiphenyl by treatment with reduced iron or ferrous oxalate dihydrate at 200–250°.

B. Properties.   In general, 3,4-benzocinnolines exhibit basic properties, forming colored salts in acid solution.   Phenazone itself (I), the properties of which have been compared with those of the isomeric phenazine by Täuber,[7] is a weak base, giving pK_a values[36] at 20° of 2.20 ± 0.05 (in water) and 1.6 ± 0.2 (in 50% aqueous alcohol); hence, although soluble in hydrochloric acid, the base and not a hydrochloride is recovered on evaporation.[1]   With some benzocinnolines the color of the solution in acid varies with the amount and strength of the acid, suggesting that several series of salts are being formed; this is particularly characteristic of phenazones containing amino groups.[1,2,8]   In a number of cases crystalline salts have been isolated, as summarized in Table IX-3.   Treatment of quaternary salts of 3,4-benzocinnoline with ammonia regenerates the parent (unquaternized) base.[2]   This decomposition has not been investigated, but it is, at least superficially, reminiscent of the alkaline decomposition of quaternary salts of certain phenazines and cinnolines (see Chapter VII).

3,4-Benzocinnoline N-oxides (see Table IX-2) are usually intermediate stages in the conversion of dinitrodiaryls into benzocinnolines.   Compounds (1) and (8) (Table IX-1), however, give dioxides, m.p. 240° (dec.) and 128° (dec.), respectively.

Oxidation of 3,4-benzocinnoline with aqueous alkaline permanganate on the steam bath gives the dipotassium salt of pyridazine-1,2,3,4-tetracarboxylic acid.[9]

TABLE IX-3. Salts of 3,4-Benzocinnolines

No. of compound in Table IX-1	Salt	M.p., °C.	Ref.
1	Dipicrate	192 (dec.), 191	4,37
1	Methiodide	185–187	32
1	Ethiodide	185–187	32
1	Methochloroplatinate, $[C_{13}H_{11}N_2]_2$, $PtCl_6$	—	32
1	Double salt of methochloride and $ZnCl_2$; $[C_{13}H_{11}N_2Cl]_2$, $ZnCl_2$	235	2
3	Hydrochloride	236	2
3	Nitrate	238	2
5	Dihydrochloride (unstable)	—	2
7	Nitrate	166	2
7	Double salt of methochloride and $ZnCl_2$; $[C_{15}H_{15}N_2Cl]_2$, $ZnCl_2$	231	2
8	Chloroplatinate, $[C_{14}H_{12}N_2]_2$, H_2PtCl_6	—	8

A few observations on the reduction of benzocinnolines have been recorded. Täuber[1] isolated the hydrochloride of a reduction product (presumed to be the 1,2-dihydro derivative) by reducing (I) with zinc dust and hot dilute hydrochloric acid, but the free base was extremely unstable and rapidly reverted to (I); the freshly prepared base reduced cold Fehling solution. Duval[10] found that, contrary to the statement of Täuber,[1] 3,4-benzocinnoline is reducible in alkaline solution (aqueous-alcoholic potassium hydroxide and zinc dust); the reduction product (again presumed to be the 1,2-dihydro derivative) could be isolated as the hydrochloride, but the free base was unstable and showed a strong tendency to regenerate (I). Essentially similar results were obtained by Wittig and Stichnoth[11] with the homolog (IV); reduction with zinc and dilute sulfuric acid yielded a dihydro sulfate, m.p. 134°, which reduced litmus, methylene blue, and

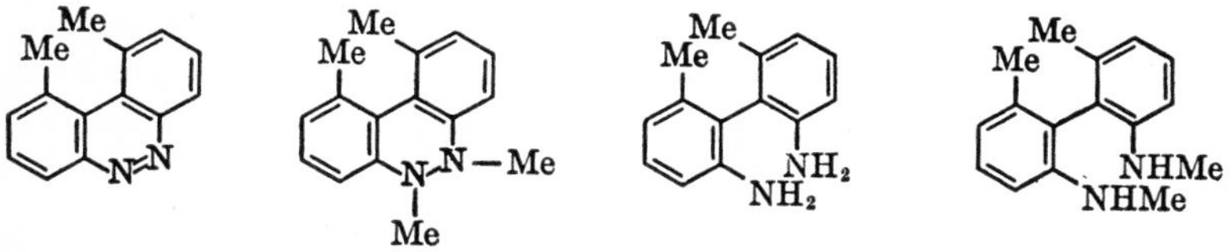

(IV)   (V)   (VI)   (VII)

solutions of silver salts, and basification of this sulfate yielded an oil which rapidly passed into the crystalline base (IV). On treatment with lithium in ether, followed by methyl sulfate, (IV) yields the alkylated reduction product (V), m.p. 84–85°, which is readily dealkylated by oxidizing agents (e.g., hydrogen peroxide in dilute hydrochloric acid) with regeneration of (IV).[11] Treatment of the dihydro sulfate, m.p. 134°, and of (V) with zinc and dilute acid yields the amines (VI) and (VII), respectively.[11]

Very few substitution and replacement reactions have been carried out in the benzocinnoline series. In referring to these reactions, the alternative system of numbering indicated in (VIII) is used (in this paragraph only) for the sake of brevity; individual compounds are thus referred to as derivatives of "phenazone." King and King[3] have shown that phenazone monoxide nitrates chiefly at C_2, yielding 2-nitrophenazone-6-oxide, m.p.

(VIII)   (IX)   (X)   (XI)

269° (dec.), together with a small amount of the 3-nitro isomer, m.p. 226° (dec.). The former compound on reduction with stannous chloride and hydrochloric acid yields 2-aminophenazone, m.p. 243° (dec.), which shows pK_a values[36] at 20° of 6.68 ± 0.05 (in water) and 6.23 ± 0.05 (in 50% aqueous alcohol) [picrate, m.p. 265° (dec.); acetyl derivative, m.p. 233° (dec.)], and the isomer, m.p. 226° (dec.), gives 3-aminophenazone, m.p. 194–195° (dec.) [acetyl derivative, m.p. 171–172° (dec.)]. The orientations of these compounds were established by reductive fission (Raney nickel and hydrogen) of the acetamido compounds, which were thus converted via the corresponding 2,2'-diaminodiphenyl derivatives (IX) into the known 3- and 2-aminocarbazole (X), respectively. 2-p-Toluenesulfonamidophenazone, m.p. 230° (dec.), condenses with the appropriate chloroamine (in presence of sodamide in boiling toluene) to yield, after hydrolysis, 2,2'-diethylaminoethylaminophenazone [dihydrochloride, m.p. 224–225°; dipicrate, m.p. 178–179° (dec.); N-p-toluenesulfonyl derivative, m.p. 122–123°] and 2,3'-diethylaminopropylaminophenazone (dihydrochloride, m.p. 222°; N-p-toluenesulfonyl derivative, m.p. 108–109°).[3]

A patent[12] describes the preparation of "2-hydroxyphenazone," m.p. 275°, of "2-hydroxyphenazone-7-sulfonic acid," and of "2,7-dihydroxyphenazone," m.p. 300°, by alkaline fusion of "phenazone-2-mono- and -2,7-disulfonic acid."*

* This patent was not available to the author, and unfortunately the abstract does not indicate whether the nomenclature is based on (VIII) or on the alternative (XI) which has also been used occasionally (refs. 13, 14).

Ramart-Lucas and Biquard[15] have determined the absorption spectra of phenazone (maxima at ~345 and ~305 mμ, log ϵ = 3.25 and 4.00), its monoxide (~345, 300, and ~290 mμ, log ϵ = 4.00, 4.13, and 4.13), and its dioxide (~385, ~360, and 330 mμ, log ϵ = 3.7, 3.8, and 4.05), and have compared these values with those of azobenzene and azoxybenzene. They comment on the diverse nature of the spectral changes involved in passing from this heterocyclic type on the one hand, and from carbocyclic compounds on the other hand, to the corresponding open-chain compounds.

2. Tetrahydro-3,4-benzocinnolines

The compounds (I; R = H) (yellow prisms, m.p. 98°) and (I; R = Me) (yellow needles, m.p. 111°) are prepared from the monophenylhydrazones of the appropriate cyclohexanediones by treatment with concentrated sulfuric acid[39] (compare Chapter II, Table II-1, method C):

(I)

3. Other Cinnolines with Additional Aromatic Rings

This group comprises compounds (I)–(V).

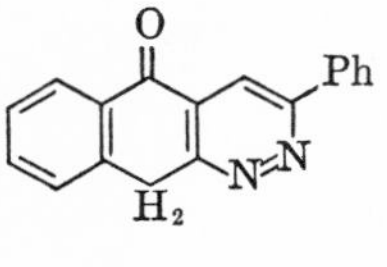

(I) 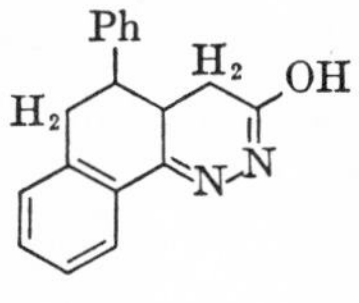   (II) 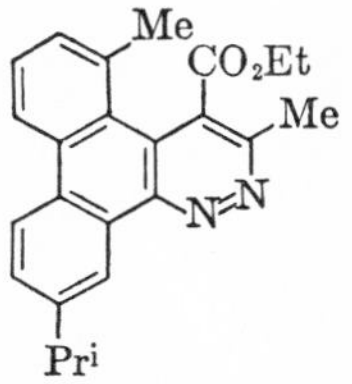   (III)
R.I. 2671

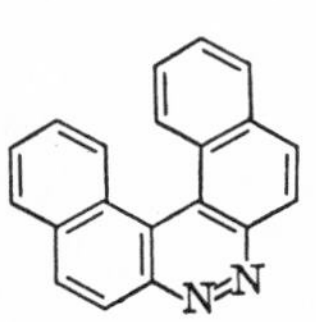

(IV)   (V)
R.I. 3256   R.I. 3775

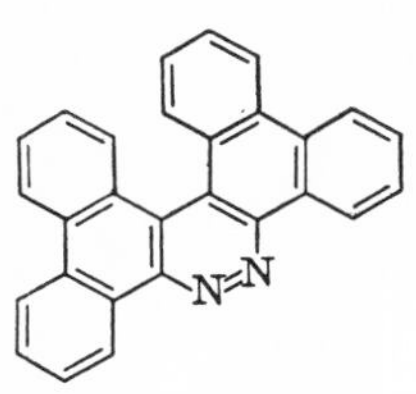

Compound (I) is prepared by cyclization (with aluminum chloride in nitrobenzene at 50–60°) of the chloride of 3-phenyl-6-benzylpyridazine-5-carboxylic acid (Eq. 1). It forms light brown crystals, m.p. 236°, and gives a dinitrophenylhydrazone, m.p. 244°.[16]

Compound (II) is formed by condensing 3-phenyl-1-keto-1,2,3,4-tetrahydronaphthalene-2-acetic acid with hydrazine hydrate in boiling methanol (Eq. 2). It melts at 191° and is insoluble in sodium hydroxide.[17]

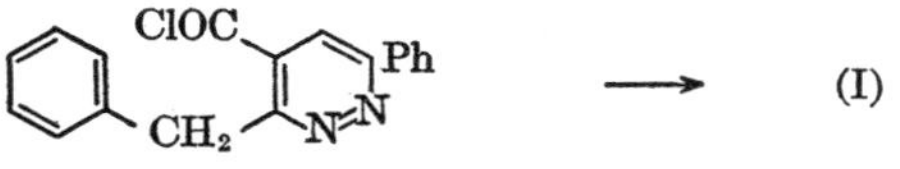

$$\longrightarrow \quad \text{(I)} \tag{1}$$

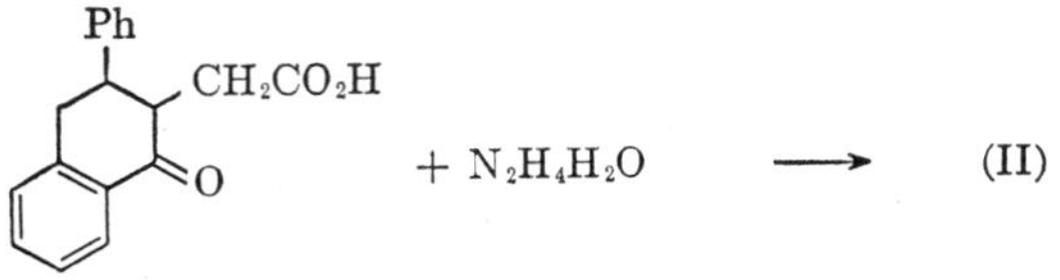

$$+ \ N_2H_4H_2O \quad \longrightarrow \quad \text{(II)} \tag{2}$$

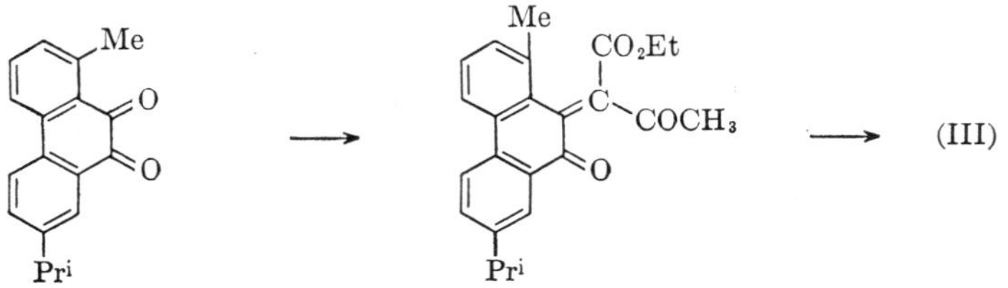

$$\longrightarrow \quad \longrightarrow \quad \text{(III)} \tag{3}$$

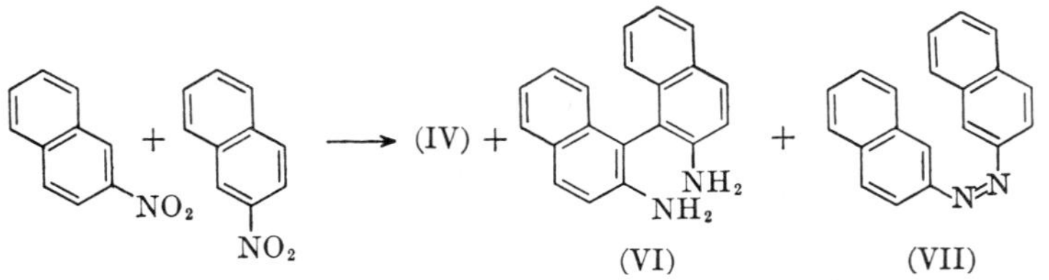

Compound (III) is prepared by the action of hydrazine hydrate (in acetic acid at 100°) on the product formed by condensing retenequinone with acetoacetic ester (Eq. 3). It forms red crystals, m.p. 200–205° (dec.). The structure shown is that given by the authors,[18] but the possibility of condensation at the alternative position of retenequinone, with consequent transposition of the Bz-methyl and -isopropyl groups in the final product, seems not to be excluded.

$$\longrightarrow \quad \text{(IV)} + \quad + \quad \tag{4}$$

5,6-Benzo-3,4,2′,1′-naphthocinnoline (IV) is formed, together with the diamine (VI) and the azo compound (VII), when a boiling alcoholic solution of β-nitronaphthalene is treated with zinc dust followed by 12.5% aqueous sodium hydroxide (Eq. 4).[19] It is obviously closely related to the

3,4-benzocinnolines described in the preceding section, and does in fact show very similar properties. It crystallizes in yellow needles, m.p. 267–268°, giving a red solution in concentrated hydrochloric acid from which the original base is precipitated on dilution. The hydrochloride is unstable, readily losing hydrogen chloride, but the base forms a chloroplatinate. The compound (IV) is unaffected by treatment with zinc and boiling aqueous alcoholic sodium hydroxide, but zinc and acetic acid convert it into (VI), and stannous chloride and hydrochloric acid give what is probably an unstable dihydro derivative which readily regenerates (IV). Reduction of β-nitronaphthalene with alkaline stannous chloride in aqueous ethanol gives the azoxy derivative corresponding to (VII) together with the mono-N-oxide of (IV); this compound forms light yellow needles, m.p. 248° (dec.), and is converted into (IV) by reduction with zinc dust in aqueous alcoholic sodium hydroxide.[19]

5,6,7,8-Dibenzo-3,4,9',10'-phenanthrocinnoline (V) is formed when the epoxide (VIII) is heated at about 380°, sublimation of (V) then occurring (5).[20] It crystallizes in yellow needles, m.p. 290°, moderately soluble in hot chloroform, acetic acid, and pyridine, and soluble in concentrated sulfuric acid to a green solution with strong blue fluorescence; it forms a picrate, m.p. 255–256°. It is stable toward zinc and acetic acid and to-

(VIII)
R.I. 3852

⟶   (V)   (5)

(IX)

ward boiling alcoholic potash. In contrast to 3,4-benzocinnoline (preceding section), it is not oxidized by hot aqueous permanganate; it is attacked by hot chromic anhydride in acetic acid, but, unlike the simpler 3,4-benzocinnoline, which (with permanganate) gives a pyridazine tetracarboxylic acid,[9] the hetero ring of (V) is ruptured, with formation of phenanthraquinone.[20]

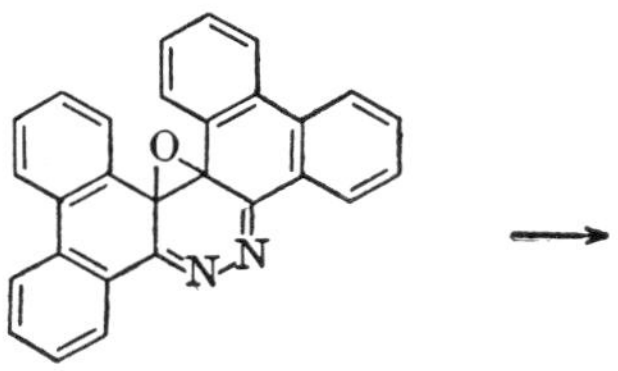

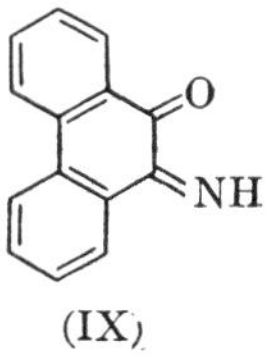

The oxido derivative (VIII) is prepared from phenanthraquinone-imine (IX) by boiling for a short time with acetic anhydride; this reaction was discovered in 1879,[21] but the structure of the product was not elucidated until 1921.[20] It forms yellow needles, m.p. 252°, insoluble in alcohol, but soluble in hot benzene, chloroform, pyridine, and acetic anhydride. It yields a picrate (scarlet needles, m.p. 216–217°), and gives phenanthra-quinone on oxidation with chromic anhydride in acetic acid.[20]

The characteristic reactions of (VIII) are those of an epoxide, and its structure was deduced mainly from these reactions and from the fact that (V) differs from known isomers. When boiled with acetic acid, compound (VIII) yields the acetic acid salt of the glycol monoacetate, which in boiling nitrobenzene is converted into the free monoacetate base (X; R = OAc), m.p. 302–305° (dec.). Oxidation of this compound gives phenanthraqui-none, and alkaline hydrolysis yields the glycol (X; R = OH), which is also

(X)

obtained directly from (VIII) by means of boiling 2% alcoholic sodium ethoxide. This glycol has not been obtained pure, as it is very easily con-verted into (VIII) (e.g., by heating or by attempts to acylate it). The propionic acid salt of the monopropionate, prepared as for the acetate, loses propionic acid at 220°, and the free base (X; R = $EtCO_2$) melts at 306° (dec.). When treated with dry hydrogen chloride in chloroform, compound (VIII) gives the hydrochloride of an unstable chloro compound (X; R = Cl), which regenerates (VIII) when warmed or treated with pyri-dine. Compound (VIII) yields a series of ethers by means of sulfuric acid and the appropriate alcohol. The methyl ether (X; R = OMe) prepared from the initially formed sulfate with methanolic ammonia, has m.p. 202°, is sparingly soluble in organic solvents, insoluble in aqueous alkali, and stable toward reducing agents; it gives a picrate, m.p. 231°. The ethyl analog (X; R = OEt) is prepared similarly (m.p. 180°); it is in-soluble in aqueous alkali but soluble in organic solvents, and forms a series of salts [nitrate, dec. 174°; hydrochloride, m.p. 227–228° (dec.); picrate, m.p. 230°]. The n-propyl ether (X; R = OPr^n) has m.p. 149°.[20]

4. Cinnolines Containing Bridged Rings

The members of this group are compounds (I)–(III).

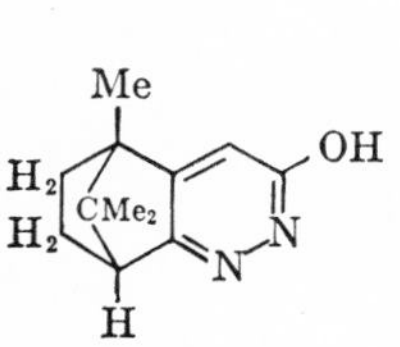

(I)
R.I. 1452

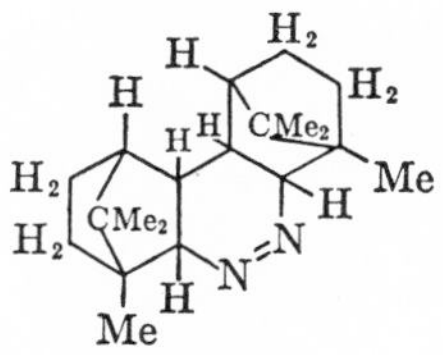

(II)
R.I. 2891

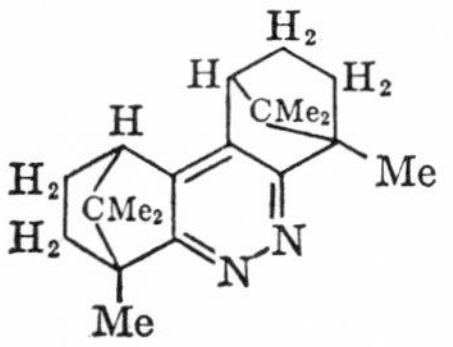

(III)
R.I. 2891

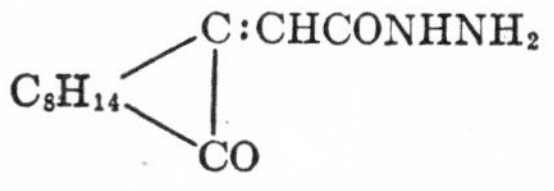

(IV)

Compound (I) is prepared from the hydrazide (IV) by cyclization in boiling dilute mineral acid, or in chloroform by means of dry hydrogen chloride. It forms needles, m.p. 228°, insoluble in aqueous ammonia, but soluble in sodium hydroxide and in dilute hydrochloric acid, and yields a methyl derivative, m.p. 117°, when heated at 100° (sealed tube) with potassium hydroxide, methanol, and methyl iodide.[22] As the structure of (IV) is not established, it is possible that the methyl group of (I) is attached to C_8 instead of to C_5 as shown.

Compound (II), prepared from dicamphor and hydrazine hydrochloride in boiling acetic acid, has m.p. 155–156°, $[\alpha]^{22}$ +118.1°. It is easily soluble in organic solvents, and forms a picrate (m.p. 185–186°), a hydrochloride (m.p. > 265°), a chloroaurate (dec. 200–205°), and a methiodide (m.p. 207–208°).[23]

Compound (III) is prepared similarly from dicamphorquinone; it has m.p. 201–202°, $[\alpha]^{27}$ +52.6°, and forms a number of salts [hydrochloride, m.p. 230–235°; picrate, m.p. 237° (dec.); chloroaurate, m.p. 195–199° (dec.); chloroplatinate, darkens on heating; methiodide, m.p. 201–202°; methochloride, m.p. 170° (dec.); methonitrate, dec. 210°; and methochloroaurate, m.p. 200–202°].[24]

5. Cinnolines Containing Fused Heterocyclic Rings

This section consists of the miscellaneous group of compounds (I)–
(VIIIa).

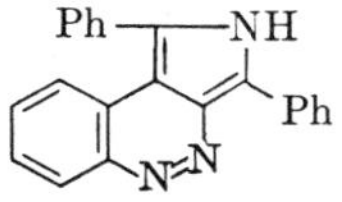

(I)
R.I. 1632

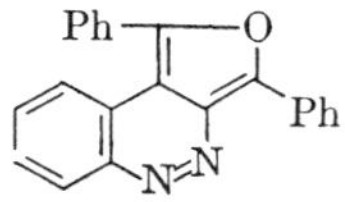

(II)
R.I. 1690

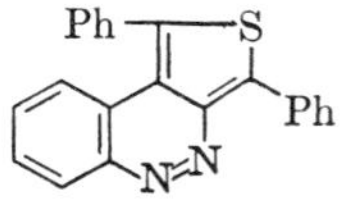

(III)
R.I. 1732

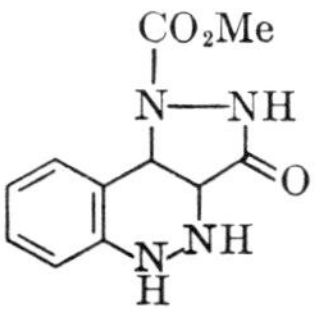

(IV)
R.I. 1566

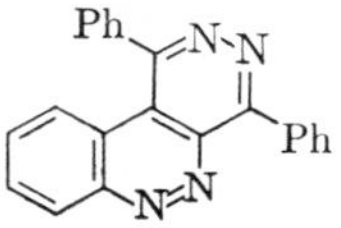

(V)
R.I. 1882

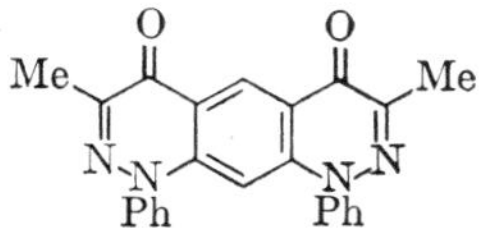

(VI)
R.I. 1873

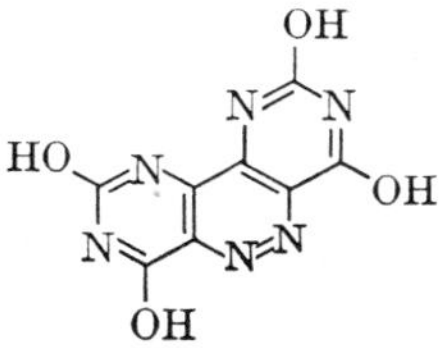

(VII)
R.I. 1869

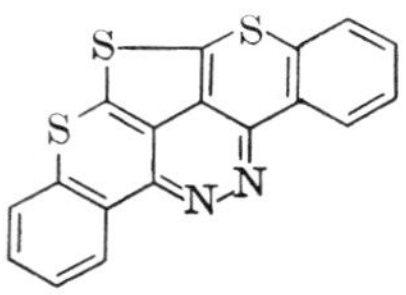

(VIII)
R.I. 3534

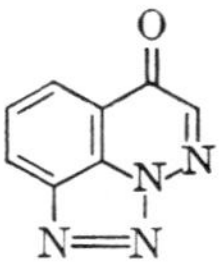

(VIIIa)

2',5'-Diphenyl-3,4-dihydro-3,4,3',4'-pyrrolocinnoline (I) is prepared
from 2,3,5-triphenyl-4-diazopyrrole (IX) by means of boiling 25% sulfuric
acid (6).[25]   It is a red crystalline solid, soluble in alcoholic potash to a violet
solution, and combines with acids to form salts hydrolyzed by water [sul-
fate, light green needles, m.p. 190° (dec.);   nitrate, m.p. 175° (dec.), unstable in light;   picrate, brown needles, m.p. 206° (dec.)].[25,26]   With
alcoholic sodium ethoxide and ethyl iodide it forms an ethyl derivative
(blue needles, m.p. 181°).[25]   Oxidation with a little nitric acid in acetic
acid converts (I) into 3,4-dibenzoylcinnoline (X) (see Chapter II, Section 2).

2',5'-Diphenyl-3,4-dihydro-3,4,3',4'-furanocinnoline (II) is formed
from 3,4-dibenzoylcinnoline (X) by treatment with zinc and acetic acid.[25]
It crystallizes in red needles, m.p. 195°, and gives blue salts with concentrated sulfuric and hydrochloric acids.[25]   When heated with alcoholic ammonia at 180°, or when boiled with acetic acid containing ammonium
acetate, compound (II) is converted into (I).[26]

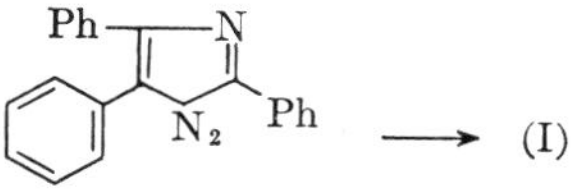

$$\text{(IX)} \longrightarrow \text{(I)} \qquad (6)$$

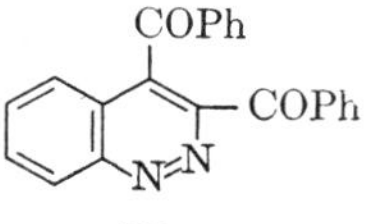

(X) 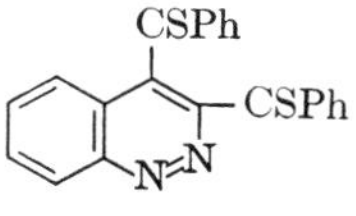   (XI)

2',5'-Diphenyl-3,4-dihydro-3,4,3',4'-thiophenocinnoline (III) is obtained, together with 3,4-di(thiobenzoyl)cinnoline (XI) (see Chapter II, Section 2) by the action of boiling alcoholic ammonium sulfide on 3,4-dibenzoylcinnoline (X).[27] It crystallizes in yellow needles, m.p. 151°, and gives 3,4-dibenzoylcinnoline on oxidation with nitric acid. When heated with hydroxylamine in aqueous solution, compounds (III) and (X) both give the same products, viz., a substance, $C_{44}H_{27}O_3N_9$, m.p. 205–206°, of unknown structure (main product), together with a red pyrrole derivative and a mixture of (probably) the mono- and dioximes of (X).[27]

1'-Carbomethoxy-3'-keto-1,2,3,4-tetrahydro-3,4,4',5'-pyrazolinocinnoline (IV) is prepared from the compound (XII) (Chapter VIII, Section 1B) by treatment with 50% aqueous acetic acid, and melts at 183° (dec.).[28]

3',6'-Diphenyl-3,4,4',5'-pyridazinocinnoline (V) is prepared from (X) by condensation with hydrazine sulfate in aqueous alcoholic alkali. It forms yellow needles, m.p. 240°, and with concentrated sulfuric acid gives a red salt, hydrolyzed by water.[25]

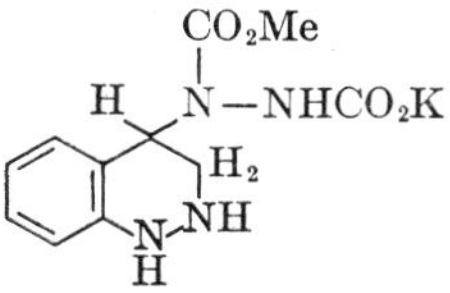

(XII) 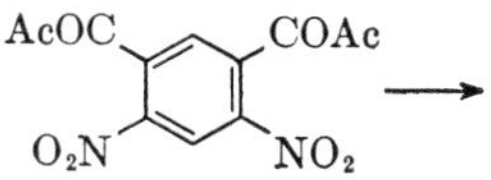   (XIII)

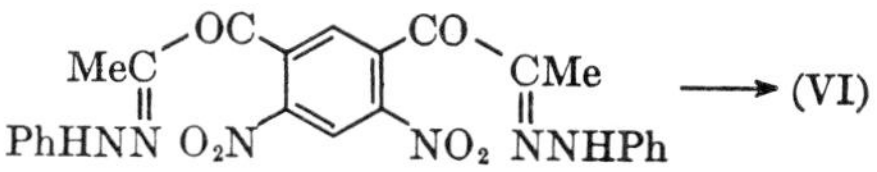

(XIV)

The compound (VI) is prepared from (XIII) via the bisphenylhydrazone (XIV); the latter is prepared in alcoholic solution, and yields (VI) when heated in a mixture of alcohol, pyridine, and aqueous NaOH. The product (VI) forms golden-brown needles, m.p. 353–354° (dec.).[29]

The diazacinnoline (VII) is the product of the action of cold potassium ferricyanide on an alkaline solution of 5-aminouracil (Eq. 7). The compound is obtained by acidification of the potassium salt which separates during the oxidation. It forms orange-yellow plates, m.p. >300°, insoluble in ordinary organic solvents, soluble in concentrated sulfuric acid, and stable to concentrated nitric acid and to bromine water. With sodium hydroxide the compound gives first a red insoluble sodium salt, which dissolves in excess alkali to a yellow solution with orange fluorescence.[30]

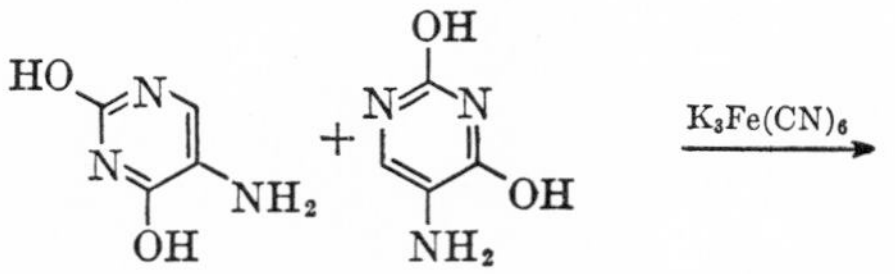

(7)

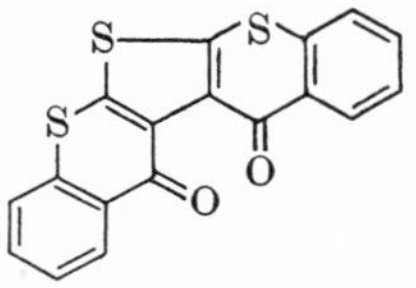

(XV)

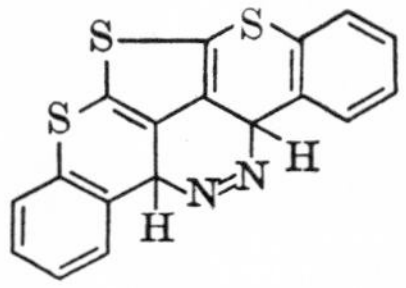

(XVI)
R.I. 3534

The compound (VIII) is formed, along with the dihydro derivative (XVI), when (XV) is condensed with hydrazine hydrate in boiling pyridine. The normal product (VIII) forms blue-violet crystals, m.p. 298–299°, and is unstable in hot aniline or quinoline, an almost colorless product being formed. The dihydro compound (XVI) is a deep red crystalline solid, m.p. 297°, and gives a blue hydrochloride and a blue sulfate.[31]

The compound (VIIIa) is formed by diazotization of 8-amino-4-hydroxycinnoline (Chapter IV, Table 1V-1) in hydrochloric acid.[40] It forms buff-colored leaflets, m.p. 159–160° (dec.).

References

1. Täuber, *Ber.*, **24**, 3081 (1891).
2. Ullmann and Dieterle, *Ber.*, **37**, 23 (1904).
3. F. E. King and T. J. King, *J. Chem. Soc.*, **1945**, 824.
4. Sandin and Cairns, *J. Am. Chem. Soc.*, **58**, 2019 (1936).
5. Täuber, *Ber.*, **29**, 2270 (1896).
6. *Chem. Abs.*, **25**, 1266 (1931) (Germ. Pat. 513,206).
7. Täuber, *Ber.*, **28**, 3883 (1895).
8. Meyer, *Ber.*, **26**, 2238 (1893).
9. Täuber, *Ber.*, **28**, 451 (1895).
10. Duval, *Bull. soc. chim.*, **7**, 485 (1910).

11. Wittig and Stichnoth, *Ber.*, **68**, 928 (1935).
12. *Chem. Abs.*, **28**, 654 (1934) (Germ. Pat. 577,631).
13. Sako, *Bull. Chem. Soc. Japan*, **9**, 393 (1934).
14. Hata, Tatematsu, and Dubota, *Bull. Chem. Soc. Japan*, **10**, 425 (1935).
15. Ramart-Lucas and Biquard, *Bull. soc. chim.*, **3**, 430 (1936).
16. Borsche and Klein, *Ann.*, **548**, 74 (1941).
17. Borsche and Sinn, *Ann.*, **555**, 70 (1944).
18. Heiduschka and Khudadad, *Arch. Pharm.*, **251**, 682 (1913).
19. Meisenheimer and Witte, *Ber.*, **36**, 4153 (1903).
20. Schönberg and Rosenthal, *Ber.*, **54**, 1789 (1921).
21. Zincke, *Ber.*, **12**, 1641 (1879).
22. Rupe and Buxtorf, *Helv. Chim. Acta*, **13**, 444 (1930).
23. Beilstein, 4th ed., XXIII, 197 [Oddo, *Gazz. chim. ital.*, **27**, I, 164 (1897)].
24. Beilstein, 4th ed., XXIII, 206 [Oddo, *Gazz. chim. ital.*, **27**, I, 172 (1897)].
25. Angelico, *Zentr.*, *I*, 445 (1909) [*Atti reale accad. Lincei* (5), **17**, II, 655 (1908)].
26. Angelico and Labisi, *Zentr.*, *I*, 2095 (1910) [*Gazz. chim. ital.*, **40**, I, 411 (1910)].
27. Angelico, *Brit. Chem. Abstr.*, i, 1032 (1911) [*Gazz. chim. ital.*, **41**, 378 (1911)].
28. Diels and Alder, *Ann.*, **450**, 237 (1926).
29. Ruggli and Straub, *Helv. Chim. Acta*, **21**, 1084 (1938).
30. Baudisch and Davidson, *J. Biol. Chem.*, **71**, 497 (1927).
31. Steinkopf, Schmitt, and Fiedler, *Ann.*, **527**, 237 (1937).
32. Wohlfahrt, *J. prakt. Chem.*, **65**, 295 (1902).
33. Kenner and Stubbings, *J. Chem. Soc.*, **1921**, 593.
34. Schiemann and Roselius, *Ber.*, **65**, 737 (1932).
35. *Chem. Abs.*, **26**, 5214 (1932) (Germ. Pat. 555,182).
36. Gore and J. N. Phillips, *Nature*, **163**, 690 (1949).
37. P. Z. Slack and R. Slack, *Nature*, **160**, 437 (1947).
38. Waterman and Vivian, *J. Org. Chem.*, **14**, 289 (1949).
39. B. P. Moore, *Nature*, **163**, 918 (1949).
40. Schofield and Theobald, *J. Chem. Soc.*, **1949**, 2404.

PART II

Phthalazines

CHAPTER X

Phthalazines Unsubstituted in the Hetero Ring

Of the many hundreds of phthalazine derivatives that have been prepared, only two compounds are known in which the hetero ring is devoid of
substituents, *viz.*, phthalazine (*R.I.* 979) itself (I) and 5,6-dihydroxyphthal-
azine (II).

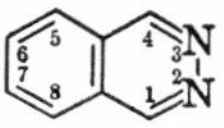

(I) 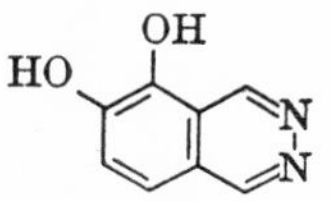   (II)

1. Phthalazine

A. Preparation

(*1*) Phthalazine was first prepared in 1893 by Gabriel and Pinkus[1] from
tetrachloro-*o*-xylene (III) and aqueous hydrazine by heating under pressure at 150° for 2 hours (Eq. 1).   Alternatively, a 1% aqueous suspension

$$\text{(III)} + \text{N}_2\text{H}_4 \longrightarrow 4\,\text{HCl} + \text{(phthalazine)} \tag{1}$$

of (III) could be boiled under reflux for 6–8 hours (hydrolysis to *o*-phthal-
aldehyde), followed by addition of hydrazine sulfate and potassium hydroxide;   the mixture was then evaporated to a small volume.   In either
case, phthalazine hydrochloride crystallized, from which phthalazine was
liberated by basification followed by extraction with benzene.   It was
later found that the preparation was more conveniently accomplished by
using the tetrabromo analog of (III) (88.7% yield of phthalazine hydrochloride).[2]

(*2*) Phthalazine may also be prepared (75% yield) by reduction of 1-(4-) chlorophthalazine with hydriodic acid (b.p. 127°) and red phosphorus under reflux[3,4] (Eq. 2).

$$\text{(Cl-phthalazine)} + 2H \longrightarrow \text{(phthalazine)} + HCl \qquad (2)$$

(*3*) It is formed, together with phthalic or 3-nitrophthalic acid, by oxidation of the compounds (IV; R = H and NO_2) with alkaline permanganate at 2° (Eq. 3).[5]

$$\text{(IV)} \longrightarrow \text{(phthalazine)} + \begin{array}{c} HO_2C \\ HO_2C \end{array} \qquad (3)$$

(IV)

B. Properties. Phthalazine forms pale yellow flat needles, m.p. 90–91°.[1,3] At atmospheric pressure it boils at 315–317° with decomposition, ammonia being evolved,[1,3] but it distils without decomposition at 189°/29 mm. (175°/17 mm.).[3] When warm it has a characteristic quinolinelike odor.[1] It is very easily soluble in water (the solution does not show an alkaline reaction) and in methanol, ethanol, benzene, and ethyl acetate; less soluble in ether; and insoluble in ligroin.[1] It forms well-defined salts, functioning as a monoacid base [hydrochloride, m.p. 231° (efferv.)[1]; hydriodide, m.p. 203°[3]; picrate, m.p. 208–210°[1]; chloroplatinate, m.p. > 260°[1]; chloroaurate, m.p. 200°[3]; ferrocyanide[3]]. With methyl iodide in methanol at room temperature it yields the methiodide, m.p. 235–240°, which crystallizes in yellow needles; the ethiodide also forms yellow needles, m.p. 204–210°.[2] It reacts with benzyl chloride at room temperature to give an adduct, m.p. 97–99°[2]; a hygroscopic adduct is also formed from phthalazine and ethyl chloroacetate, which yields a picrate, m.p. 129–131°, of the expected composition $C_8H_6N_2\cdot CH_2CO_2Et.\ C_6H_2O_7N_3.$[2] Alkaline decompositions of phthalazine methiodide and ethiodide are referred to in Chapter XII (see also Chapters XIII, Section 2A and XXII, Section 1).

On reduction with zinc and concentrated hydrochloric acid, phthalazine yields *o*-aminomethylbenzylamine.[1] On treatment with 7% sodium amalgam in aqueous solution, phthalazine is reduced to tetrahydrophthalazine (90% yield as hydrochloride).[1,5] Oxidation of phthalazine with hot alkaline permanganate gives pyridazine-4,5-dicarboxylic acid (V) in 66% yield (Eq. 4).[4]

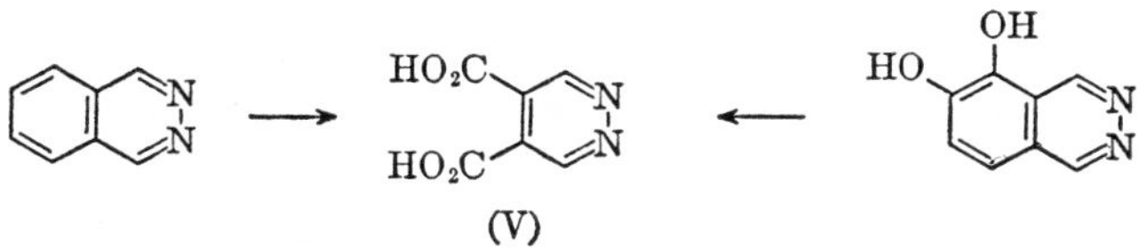

(4)

(V)

2. 5,6-Dihydroxyphthalazine

A. Preparation. This compound is prepared by simultaneous de-methylation and dehalogenation of chloroopiazone [4-chloro-5,6-dimeth-oxyphthalazine (VI)] by means of hydriodic acid and red phosphorus under reflux (Eq. 5).[4]

(5)

(VI)

B. Properties. The free base has not been obtained analytically pure, but its picrate (m.p. 197°), hydrochloride, and chloroplatinate have been described.[4] On oxidation with hot permanganate it yields pyrida-zine-4,5-dicarboxylic acid (V).[4]

References

1. Gabriel and Pinkus, *Ber.*, **26**, 2210 (1893).
2. Gabriel and Müller, *Ber.*, **28**, 1830 (1895).
3. Paul, *Ber.*, **32**, 2014 (1899).
4. Gabriel, *Ber.*, **36**, 3373 (1903).
5. Hatt and E. F. M. Stephenson, *J. Chem. Soc.*, **1943**, 658.

CHAPTER XI

1-Alkyl-, 1-Aryl-, and 1,4-Diarylphthalazines

1. 1-Alkyl- and 1-Arylphthalazines

A. Preparation. 1-Arylphthalazines are prepared by condensing an aromatic aldehyde with an acylhydrazine, followed by cyclization of the product in an acid medium (Eq. 1). They may also be prepared from

$$+ H_2O \tag{1}$$

the corresponding 4-chlorophthalazines by reduction with hydriodic acid (d 1.7) and red phosphorus.

1-Alkylphthalazines are prepared exclusively by the latter method. The products obtained vary, however, with the conditions used. Thus prolonged refluxing (several hours) of 4-chloro-1-methylphthalazine with the reagents gives 1-methylphthalazine, but short refluxing yields 4-iodo-1-methylphthalazine (Chapter XX, Section 1), which on further reduction is converted into 1-methylphthalazine[1]; and 4-chloro-1-ethylphthalazine behaves similarly.[2] The reduction of 4-chloro-1-methylphthalazine also produces small amounts of 4-hydroxy-1-methylphthalazine and 1-methyl-isoindole (I).[1]

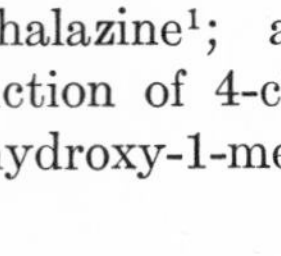

(I)

B. Properties. Table XI-1 lists the known 1-alkyl- and 1-aryl-phthalazines and their physical characteristics. 1-Ethylphthalazine forms a methiodide, m.p. 129° (yellow needles) on treatment with methyl iodide in benzene at room temperature, and a methopicrate, yellow needles,

TABLE XI-1. 1-Alkyl- and 1-Arylphthalazines

Substituent at				Prep.[a]	M.p., °C.	Remarks	Ref.
R_1	R_2	R_3	R_4				
Me	H	H	H	B	—	Hydrochloride, m.p. 222–223°; hydriodide, dec. 287°; nitrate, dec. 159°; picrate, m.p. 205°; chloroplatinate, darkens 240°; chloroaurate, m.p. 175° (dec.); dichromate, dec. 170°; ferrocyanide, m.p. >290°; methiodide, m.p. 142–143°.	1
Et	H	H	H	B	23.5	B.p. 206°/25, 196°/16 mm. Colorless deliquescent cryst., turning brown in air, and dec. on distn. at atm. pressure. Smells of acacia. Neutral reaction. Bitter taste. Hydriodide, m.p. 203°; hydrochloride, m.p. 216°; picrate, m.p. 175° (dec.); chloroplatinate, m.p. 180° (dec.); chloroaurate, m.p. 144°	2
CH₂CHMe₂	H	H	H	B	Oil	Not vol. in steam. Sol. in acids. Chloroplatinate, m.p. 157°; chloroaurate, m.p. 157°; hydriodide, dec. 100°.	4
CH₂Ph	H	H	H	B	81–82	White tablets, very sol. in most solvents. Hydriodide, dec. 100°; picrate, m.p. 146°	3
CH₂Ph[b]	H	H	OMe	A or C	168–169	Picrate, m.p. 208–209°	5

Table continued

TABLE XI-1. 1-Alkyl- and 1-Arylphthalazines (continued)

	Substituent at						
R₁	R₂	R₃	R₄	Prep.[a]	M.p., °C.	Remarks	Ref.
CH₂Ph	H	OMe	OMe	A or C	191–192	Yellow needles	5
CH₂Ph[c]	H	—O—CH₂—O—		A or C	203–204	—	5
[structure: H₂C—ring with OMe, OMe]	H	OMe	OMe	A or C	192–193	Picrate, m.p. 186–187°	5
Ph	H	H	H	B	142–143	White prisms, easily sol. in org. solvents. Hydriodide, dec. 170–180°; picrate, m.p. 180°; chloroplatinate, m.p. 223° (dec.)	3
Ph	H	H	OMe	A or C	174–175	Yellow needles	6
Ph	OMe	H	H	A	167	Yellow needles; picrate, m.p. 208°	6
Ph	H	OMe	OMe	A or C	135	Yellow needles	6
Ph	H	—O—CH₂—O—		A	193–194	Yellow needles	6
Ph	H	—O—CH₂—O—		C	200	Yellow needles	6
[structure: OMe, OMe cyclohexane ring]	H	OMe	OMe	A	193–194	Yellow cryst.	7
[structure: CH₂ methylenedioxy bicyclic]	H	—O—CH₂—O—		A	203–204	Buff cryst.	7

R_1	R_2	R_3	R_4	Prep.[a]	M.p., °C.	Remarks	Ref.
—CH₂CH₂Ph	H	H	H	D	112.5–113.5	Tablets. Hydrochloride, dec. 212–220°; nitrate, dec. 135–136°	1
—CH:CHPh	H	H	H	D	115	Yellow prisms. Hydrochloride, m.p. 220–221°	1
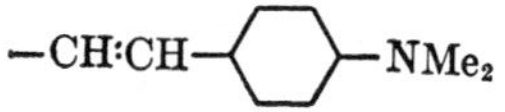 —CH:CH—⬡—NMe₂	H	H	H	E	186–187	Orange needles	14

[a] A, by ring closure of Ar·CH=NNHCOAr′ (from ArCHO and the acylhydrazine) by means of hot amyl alcohol saturated with hydrogen chloride.   B, by reduction of the 4-chloro derivative with hydriodic acid (d 1.7) and red phosphorus (reflux for 4–5 hours).   C, by refluxing ArCH=N·NHCOAr′ (prep. as in method A) with phosphorus oxychloride in chloroform.   D, for preparation, see text.   E, from 1-methylphthalazine, p-dimethylaminobenzaldehyde, and zinc chloride at 160°.

[b] On heating in a sealed tube at 100° with alcohol, HCl, and phthalic acid it gives 1,4-dihydroxyphthalazine and 4,1,2-OMe·C₆H₃(CHO)·COCH₂Ph.

[c] On heating in a sealed tube at 100° with alcohol, HCl, and phthalic acid it gives 1,4-dihydroxyphthalazine and

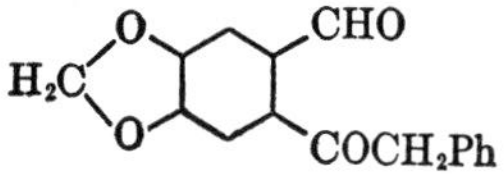

m.p. 171°.[2]   On reduction with zinc and hydrochloric acid, 1-methylphthalazine gives 1-methylisoindole,[1] and on alkaline reduction (sodium amalgam) it and several of its analogs are converted into the corresponding 1,2,3,4-tetrahydro derivatives (Chapter XXII, Section 2).

1-Methylphthalazine contains an active methyl group, as is to be anticipated from its structure.   Thus it yields 1-styrylphthalazine (II) when it is heated with benzaldehyde on the water bath[1];   reduction of the styryl compound with hydriodic acid and red phosphorus gives 1,2′-phenylethylphthalazine (III).[1]   With chloral at 55–60°, 1-methylphthalazine yields the aldol (IV) [white prisms, m.p. 180° (dec.)], which is converted by hot methanolic potassium hydroxide into 2,1′-phthalazylacrylic acid (V) [brown microprisms, m.p. 200° (dec.);   hydrochloride, brownish plates, dec. 218°, hydrolyzed by water;   chloroaurate, yellow needles, dec. 166°;   picrate, m.p. 157–158° (dec.);   chloroplatinate, orange-red crystals, m.p. > 270°].[1]   The phthalone (VI), yellow needles, m.p. 260°, is formed by heating 1-methylphthalazine and phthalic anhydride at 200–210° in an atmosphere of carbon dioxide.[1]

CH:CHPh   CH₂CH₂Ph   CH₂CH(OH)CCl₃

(II)   (III)   (IV)

CH:CHCO₂H   CH:C₈H₄O₂   COPh

(V)   (VI)   (VII)

On oxidation with hot aqueous alkaline permanganate, 1-benzylphthalazine yields 1-benzoylphthalazine (VII) [needles, m.p. 123–124°;   oxime, m.p. 243–244°;   chloroplatinate, m.p. 258° (dec.)].[3]

2. 1,4-Diarylphthalazines

A. Preparation. These compounds are prepared by condensing the appropriate 1,2-diacylbenzene with hydrazine hydrate in the hot (Eq. 2); alcohol, benzene, or acetic acid are used as solvents.   The known examples of this reaction are given in Table XI-2.

B. Properties. 1,4-Diarylphthalazines are colorless crystalline solids which are soluble in dilute mineral acids.

TABLE XI-2. 1,4-Diarylphthalazines

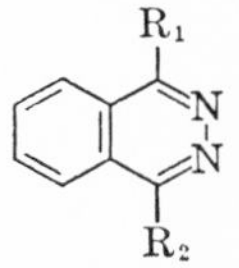

R_1	R_2	M.p., °C.	Ref.
Ph	Ph	192	8
Ph	p-C_6H_4OMe	157–159	9
Ph	p-(?)C_6H_4Me	117	10
p-C_6H_4OMe	p-C_6H_4OMe	205–206	11
p-C_6H_4Me	p-(?)C_6H_4Me	221	10
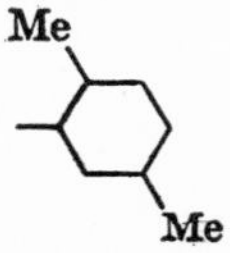	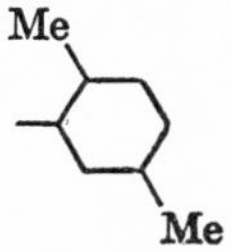	136.5	12
α-$C_{10}H_7$	α-$C_{10}H_7$	176 (sinters 162)	13

References

1. Gabriel and Eschenbach, *Ber.*, **30**, 3022 (1897).
2. Paul, *Ber.*, **32**, 2014 (1899).
3. Lieck, *Ber.*, **38**, 3918 (1905).
4. Wölbling, *Ber.*, **38**, 3925 (1905).
5. Aggarwal, I. das Khera, and Ray, *J. Chem. Soc.*, **1930**, 2354.
6. Aggarwal, Darbari, and Ray, *J. Chem. Soc.*, **1929**, 1941.
7. C. V. Wilson, *J. Am. Chem. Soc.*, **70**, 1901 (1948).
8. Guyot and Catel, *Compt. rend.*, **140**, 1348 (1905).
9. Blicke and Swisher, *J. Am. Chem. Soc.*, **56**, 923 (1934).
10. Guyot and Vallette, *Ann. chim. phys.*, **23**, 363 (1911).
11. Blicke and Weinkauff, *J. Am. Chem. Soc.*, **54**, 1454 (1932).
12. Clar, John, and Hawran, *Ber.*, **62**, 940 (1929).
13. Seer and Dischendorfer, *Sitzungsber. Akad. Wiss. Wien*, **122**, IIb, 749 (1913) [*Monatsh.*, **74**, 1496 (1913)].
14. D. M. Brown and Kon, *J. Chem. Soc.*, **1948**, 2147.

CHAPTER XII

1-Hydroxyphthalazines

A. Preparation. The standard synthesis is the condensation of hydrazine hydrate with an *o*-aldehydo or *o*-keto acid (Eq. 1).

$$\text{(structure)} + N_2H_4 \longrightarrow 2H_2O + \text{(structure)} \tag{1}$$

B. Properties. Physical constants of the known compounds of this group are listed in Table XII-1; the compounds are colorless unless otherwise stated. They show amphoteric properties, but their salts are sometimes unstable owing to hydrolysis. The hetero ring in these compounds is not very stable; 1-hydroxyphthalazine and 1-hydroxy-4-phenylphthalazine, for instance, undergo ring fission in boiling acetic anhydride, and the hetero ring of the latter compound is also attacked by hot alkalis and acids with regeneration of hydrazine and *o*-benzoylbenzoic acid. On reduction with zinc and hydrochloric acid, contraction of the hetero ring occurs, and phthalimidine derivatives (II) are formed; this reaction has been carried out with (I; R = H, Me, Et, Pr^n, Bu^i, CH$_2$Ph, and CO$_2$H) (2).[1-6] On

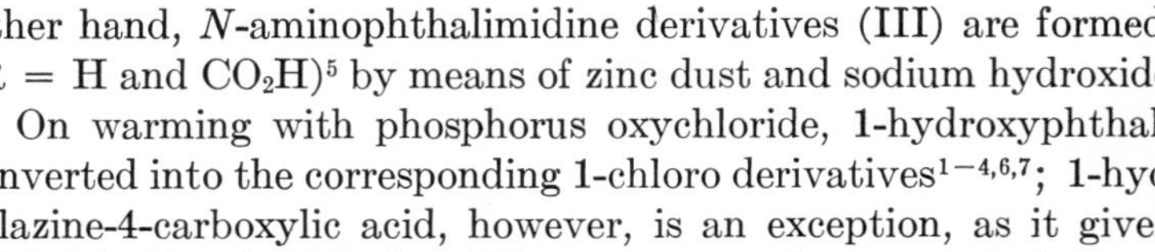

$$\text{(I)} \longrightarrow \text{(II)} \quad \text{(III)} \tag{2}$$

the other hand, *N*-aminophthalimidine derivatives (III) are formed from (I; R = H and CO$_2$H)[5] by means of zinc dust and sodium hydroxide solution. On warming with phosphorus oxychloride, 1-hydroxyphthalazines are converted into the corresponding 1-chloro derivatives[1-4,6,7]; 1-hydroxyphthalazine-4-carboxylic acid, however, is an exception, as it gives only the acid chloride, the 1-hydroxyl being apparently unattacked.[8]

1-Hydroxyphthalazine-4-carboxylic acid is resistant to catalytic hydrogenation (platinum or palladium) in alkaline or in acetic acid solution.[5]

78

TABLE XII-1. 1-Hydroxyphthalazines

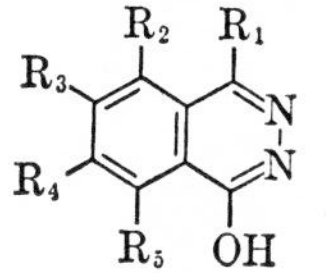

R$_1$	R$_2$	R$_3$	R$_4$	R$_5$	Prep.[b]	M.p., °C.	Remarks	Ref.
H	H	H	H	H	A,K,N	184–185, 183–184, 182	B.p. 337°/755 mm.	1,5,8,10, 11,13,24
H	H	H	Cl	H	A	246.5–246.7 (corr.)	—	14
H	H	H	OMe	H	A,K	221.9–222.2 (corr.)	—	14
H	H	H	OH	OH	B	302–305	Gives intense yellow soln. in alkalis. Pos. FeCl$_3$ reaction	9
H	H	H	OMe	OH	C	226	Pos. FeCl$_3$ reaction. Slowly reduces cold Tollens reagent. Refluxing with Ac$_2$O-AcONa gives mixt. of products which at 195–200° gives 8-OAc deriv., m.p. 209–210° (FeCl$_3$ reaction neg.)	9
H	H	H	OMe	OMe	A	166 (+H$_2$O, 162)	—	9,11
H	H	Cl	H	H	A	272.2–273.5 (corr.)	—	14
H	NO$_2$	H	OMe	OMe	A,D	248 (dec.)	Yellow needles. Gives red K salt	9
Cl	H	H	H	H	E	274	—	15,16
NH$_2$	H	H	H	H	F,G	257–258, 271–272 (corr., dec.)	Diazotization (in HCl or AcOH) gives 1,4-dihydroxyphthalazine. Hydrochloride, m.p. 240°, is readily hydrolyzed. Perchlorate, m.p. 209°	5,17
NHCO$_2$Et	H	H	H	H	M	207		5
NHCH$_2$R^a	H	H	H	H	H	>330	With cold dil. HCl gives 1,4-dihydroxyphthalazine, CH$_2$O, and NH$_4$Cl	18
Me	H	H	H	H	A	222, 224	B.p. 347–348°/755 mm.	2,19,20
Et	H	H	H	H	A	168–169, 170–172	—	3,21
Pr^n	H	H	H	H	I	156	—	6
Bu^i	H	H	H	H	A,I	113	—	4,6

Table continued

TABLE XII-1. 1-Hydroxyphthalazines (continued)

R_1	R_2	R_3	R_4	R_5	Prep.[b]	M.p., °C.	Remarks	Ref.
CH_2Ph	H	H	H	H	A,I	196	—	2,6
Ph	H	H	H	H	A,J	236	—	7,10
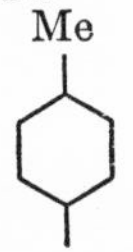 Me	H	H	H	H	A,J	246	—	10
$C_{10}H_7$	H	H	H	H	A	252–253	Not specified if α- or β-$C_{10}H_7$	10,22
					A	>250		
CO_2H	H	H	H	H	A	232	NH_4 salt, m.p. 237°; N_2H_5 salt, m.p. 294–250°. Cu^{2+} and Ag salts. Me ester, m.p. 211°; Et ester, m.p. 169°. Acid chloride, m.p. 186°. Hydrazide, m.p. 234°, gives azide, and thence anilide, m.p. 288°. At the m.p., the acid gives CO_2 and 1-hydroxyphthalazine	5,8,10
CO_2H	H	H	OMe	H	A	230.8–231 (corr.)	Loses CO_2 at the m.p. giving the 1-hydroxy compd.	14
9-Fluorenyl	H	H	H	H	L	275–277	—	23

Table footnotes on next page

a R=

$$\left[\text{NHCH}_2- \right]_2 \quad \text{N}-$$

(phthalazine nucleus with OH)

b A, from the *o*-keto or *o*-aldehydo acid and hydrazine hydrate in hot alcohol or without a solvent, or by means of hydrazine sulfate and sodium acetate or sodium hydroxide in hot water or aqueous alcohol; temperatures employed range from reflux to 120° (sealed tube). B, from the 7-monomethyl or the 7,8-dimethyl ether by heating with hydriodic acid (d 1.76) at 120–130° C, from the 8-methyl ether by heating with amyl bromide (sealed tube), concentrated HCl, or aqueous (25–50%) H_2SO_4. D, from opiazone and concentrated H_2SO_4–HNO_3 (d 1.54). E, from the 1,4-dichloro compound by hydrolysis with dilute mineral acid, or by heating with phthalic acid to 180°. F, from the 4-chloro compound by $(NH_4)_2CO_3$–NH_4OH (d 0.940)/195–210°/21 hrs. G, from the 4-$NHCO_2Et$

compound by boiling with concentrated hydrochloric acid. H, from $\left[o\text{-}C_6H_4 \left\langle \begin{array}{l} CO \\ CO \end{array} \right\rangle NCH_2- \right]_3 N$ and N_2H_4,H_2O–EtOH. I, from

$$o\text{-}C_6H_4 \left\langle \begin{array}{l} COR \\ CO_2\text{alk.} \end{array} \right. \qquad K, \text{ by decarboxyla-}$$

$$o\text{-}C_6H_4 \left\langle \begin{array}{l} COCH_2R \\ CO_2H \end{array} \right. \quad \text{as in method A.} \quad \textbf{J}, \text{ method A, but using}$$

(precursor of $o\text{-}C_6H_4 \left\langle \begin{array}{l} COCH_2R \\ CO_2H \end{array} \right.$)

$$o\text{-}C_6H_4 \left\langle \begin{array}{l} CHR \\ C=O \end{array} \right. \left\langle \begin{array}{l} O \\ CO \end{array} \right.$$

tion of the corresponding 1-hydroxyphthalazine-4-carboxylic acid at the m.p. L, application of method I, but at room temperature,

gives $o\text{-}C_6H_4 \left\langle \begin{array}{l} CO\text{-9-fluorenyl} \\ CONHNH_2 \end{array} \right.$ which is then heated to 220°. M, from the hydrazide ($R_1 = CONHNH_2$) *via* the azide. N,

from hydroxyphthalimidine ($C_6H_4 \left\langle \begin{array}{l} CH(OH) \\ CO \end{array} \right\rangle NH$) and hydrazine in water at 100°.

It is also unaffected by a warm mixture of fuming nitric and concentrated sulfuric acids; in contrast, 1-hydroxyphthalazine reacts exothermally with the cold acid mixture yielding phthalimide and ammonia.[8]

Alkylation of 1-hydroxyphthalazines has been carried out with alkyl halides, usually in alkaline, but sometimes in neutral, media[2,3,9,10]; the products are considered to be N-alkyl derivatives, and their properties are listed in Chapter XIII, Tables XIII-2–4. That N-, and not O-, alkylation occurs has been formally proved only for the methyl and ethyl derivatives of 1-hydroxyphthalazine, which are identical with the compounds obtained by alkaline decomposition of phthalazine methiodide and ethiodide, respectively, and differ from 1-methoxy- and 1-ethoxyphthalazine (Chapter XIII, Table XIII-1). However, in the absence of evidence to the contrary, it is reasonable to assume that other analogs prepared from hydroxy compounds by direct alkylation are, in general, correctly formulated as N-alkyl derivatives; for example, treatment of opiazone (1-hydroxy-7,8-dimethoxyphthalazine) with methyl iodide and with benzyl chloride is considered to result in substitution at N_2, but it is to be noted that demethylation at C_8 also occurs. [The same behavior is observed with 5-nitroopiazone and methyl iodide[9]; on heating with amyl bromide under pressure, however, opiazone is merely demethylated at C_8, and no alkylation of the hetero ring occurs[9].] Nevertheless, N-alkylation of 1-hydroxyphthalazines is not an invariable rule; 1-hydroxy-4-methylphthalazine on treatment with methyl sulfate in nitrobenzene at 130° gives 1-methoxy-4-methylphthalazine, identical with the compound prepared from 1-chloro-4-methylphthalazine by the action of sodium methoxide in boiling methanol (Chapter XIII, Table XIII-1). However, in view of the conditions used, this reaction may justifiably be regarded as an exceptional case.

Acetyl derivatives of 1-hydroxy-, 7,8-dimethoxy-1-hydroxy-, 1-hydroxy-4-phenyl-, and 1,7,8-trihydroxyphthalazine have likewise been formulated[10,11] as N-acetyl derivatives. There is, however, no real evidence to show whether these products are N- or O-derivatives. The fact that 1-hydroxyphthalazines undergo N-alkylation is beside the point; many 4-hydroxycinnolines, hydroxyquinolines, and hydroxyquinazolines give rise to N-methyl derivatives but differ greatly from one another in their susceptibility toward acetylation, and in these groups the acetyl derivatives are regarded as O-acetyl compounds.[12]

References

1. Gabriel and Neumann, *Ber.*, **26**, 521 (1893).
2. Gabriel and Neumann, *Ber.*, **26**, 705 (1893).
3. Daube, *Ber.*, **38**, 206 (1905).
4. Wölbling, *Ber.*, **38**, 3925 (1905).
5. Darapsky and Heinrichs, *J. prakt. Chem.*, **146**, 307 (1936).
6. Bromberg, *Ber.*, **29**, 1434 (1896).
7. Lieck, *Ber.*, **38**, 3918 (1905).
8. Fränkel, *Ber.*, **33**, 2808 (1900).
9. Jacobson, *Ber.*, **27**, 1418 (1894).
10. R. von Rothenburg, *J. prakt. Chem.*, **51**, 140 (1895).
11. Liebermann and Bistrzycki, *Ber.*, **26**, 531 (1893).
12. Keneford, Morley, Simpson, and Wright, *J. Chem. Soc.*, **1950**, 1104.
13. Seekles, *Rec. trav. chim.*, **43**, 329 (1924).
14. Vaughan and Baird, *J. Am. Chem. Soc.*, **68**, 1314 (1946).
15. Drew and Hatt, *J. Chem. Soc.*, **1937**, 16.
16. R. D. Haworth and S. Robinson, *J. Chem. Soc.*, **1948, 777.**
17. E. F. M. Stephenson, *J. Chem. Soc.*, **1944**, 678.
18. F. B. Kipping and F. G. Mann, *J. Chem. Soc.*, **1927**, 528.
19. Rowe and Peters, *J. Chem. Soc.*, **1931**, 1918.
20. Rowe and Peters, *J. Chem. Soc.*, **1933**, 1331.
21. Paul, *Ber.*, **32**, 2014 (1899).
22. Badger, *J. Chem. Soc.*, **1941**, 351.
23. Wislicenus and Neber, *Ann.*, **418**, 274 (1919).
24. Dunet and Willemart, *Bull. soc. chim.*, **15**, 1081 (1948).

CHAPTER XIII

Alkyl, Aryl, and Acyl Derivatives of 4-(1-)Hydroxyphthalazines

1. O-Derivatives

The compounds belonging to this group are 4-alkoxy- and 4-phenoxy-phthalazines (II). They are all prepared by the same reaction, *viz.*, by refluxing, or by warming on the water bath, the appropriate 4-(1-)chloro-phthalazine (I) (Chapter XX, Section 1) with a solution of the sodium alkoxide (phenoxide) in the corresponding alcohol (phenol) (Eq. 1). Table XIII-1 lists the known compounds of this group and their properties.

TABLE XIII-1. 4-(1-)Alkoxy- and 4-(1-)Phenoxyphthalazines

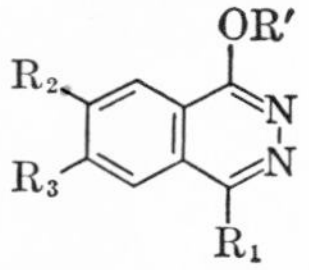

R_1	R_2	R_3	R'	M.p., °C.	Remarks	Ref.
H	H	H	Me	60–61	Yellow needles, faint fruity smell, marked basic properties	1,2
H	H	H	Et	29–31	Easily sol. in common solvents	2
H	H	Cl	Me	116–116.6	Pale green-yellow needles	3
H	Cl	H	Me	134.9–135.9	Pale yellow needles	3
H	OMe	H	Me	125.6–125.9	Pale yellow needles	3
Me	H	H	Me	53–54[a]	Demethylated by cold HBr. Picrate, m.p. 198	4
Me	H	H	Et	56–57	Easily sol. in hot water, acids, and usual solvents	5
Et	H	H	Me	49	—	6
Et	H	H	Et	53	—	6
Et	H	H	Ph	89	—	6
Bu^i	H	H	Et	Oil	Odor of hyacinth: sulfate, m.p. 109	7
Bu^i	H	H	Ph	108		7
CH$_2$Ph	H	H	Et	84–86	Difficultly sol. in HCl	8
CH$_2$Ph	H	H	Ph	155	Sol. in conc. HCl	8

[a] Also prepared from 4-hydroxy-1-methylphthalazine and methyl sulfate in nitrobenzene at 130°.[4]

$$(1)$$

(I)   (II)

2. *N*-Derivatives (3-Substituted-4-keto-3,4-dihydrophthalazines)

A.   Compounds without a 1-Substituent: 3-Aryl-, 3-Alkyl-, and 3-Aralkyl-4-keto-3, 4-dihydrophthalazines

Preparation. Table XIII-2 lists the compounds of this group which have been described in the literature. They have been prepared by a variety of methods, the following being those of most general applicability.

(*1*) Cyclization of the arylhydrazone of an *o*-aldehydo acid (I), or of its lactone isomer (II). The ring closure, which leads to 4-keto-3,4-

(I)   (II)   (III)

dihydrophthalazines (so-called "phthalaz-4-ones") with an aryl substituent at N_3 (III), is most commonly effected with hot or cold concentrated sulfuric acid, or by refluxing in amyl alcohol saturated with hydrogen chloride; but a variety of other reagents (*e.g.*, alcohol, acetic acid, acetic anhydride, acetic anhydride-pyridine, and nitrobenzene at their respective boiling points, or heating the hydrazone slightly below the melting point of the phthalazone) have been used[9] with, however, usually inferior results. The resistance of (I) to cyclization depends on the nature of the substitution in the terminal Ar group, and decreases in the order $2'-NO_2 > 2'$-halogeno-$4'$-NO_2 and $2',6'$-dihalogeno-$4'$-$NO_2 > 4'-NO_2$-$2'$-Me $> 4'-NO_2 > 3'-NO_2$.

(*2*) In many cases the arylhydrazone (I) is too unstable to be isolated, and the phthalazone (III) is obtained simply by heating an *o*-aldehydo acid with an arylhydrazine (or its hydrochloride and sodium acetate) in a suitable solvent (usually alcohol or acetic acid alone or diluted with water).

(*3*) Compounds in which the 3-aryl substituent carries an amino group may be prepared directly from the nitroarylhydrazones (I) by treatment with warm aqueous sodium sulfide, or stannous chloride and a mixture of acetic and hydrochloric acids, these reagents effecting both reduction and cyclization. They may also be prepared from the nitroarylphthalazones

(III) by reduction with sodium sulfide in hot aqueous alcohol; this method fails, however, if the NO_2 group is in the 2'-position, the products from such compounds being ill-characterized materials which are not diazotizable and are possibly the 2'-hydroxylamino compounds.[10]

(4) A method of considerable theoretical interest, as well as of occasional practical utility, is the conversion of 2-aryl-4-ketophthalazines (IV)

(IV)   (IVa)   (IVb)   (III)

into the isomeric compounds (III). Originally this reaction was studied only with compounds containing a nitro group in the 2-aryl substituent,[10] but later work (references in Table XIII-2) has shown that the presence of a nitro group is not necessary. The conversion may be achieved in various acid media, and is generally best performed by heating with approximately 1.2 N hydrochloric acid at 170–200° for periods ranging from 6 to 64 hours; heating with water alone or with aqueous alkalis is ineffective. Substituents in the 2-aryl group affect the rate and extent of the conversion; thus 2'- and 4'-NO_2 give greater conversions than 3'-NO_2; a 2'- or a 4'-methyl group has a strong retarding influence, as also has 2'-halogen, the retarding effect of bromine being more marked than that of chlorine. The presence of a methyl group at C_1 in the phthalazine ring (see Section B) usually facilitates the isomerization. The reaction has been shown to be intramolecular, and it has been suggested[10] that it occurs by the mechanism (IV) → (IVa) → (IVb) → (III).

The transformation (IV) → (III) cannot however be achieved if the substituent aryl residue of (IV) contains an amino group. If the latter is in the 3'- or 4'-position, the compounds (IV) are recovered unchanged; and with compounds containing a 2'-amino group reaction 2 occurs:

(V)   (VI)   (2)

(VIIIa)   (VII)   (VIII)

TABLE XIII-2. 3-Alkyl-, 3-Aryl-, and 3-Aralkyl-4-keto-3,4-dihydrophthalazines

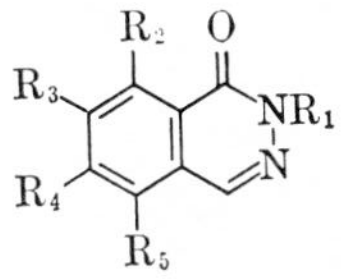

(Structure: phthalazinone ring bearing substituents NR$_1$, O (keto), N, and benzene-ring substituents R$_2$, R$_3$, R$_4$, R$_5$.)

R$_1$	Substituent at				Prep.[b]	M.p., °C.	Remarks	Ref.
	R$_2$	R$_3$	R$_4$	R$_5$				
Me	H	H	H	H	G,N,Y	102–103,[a] 111–112, 113–114, 114	B.p. 301°/755 mm.	1,2,5,17
Me	OH	OH	H	H	L	310	Yellow needles. Gives FeCl$_3$ reaction	18
Me	OH	OMe	H	NO$_2$	J	144	Gives FeCl$_3$ reaction	18
Me	OH	OMe	H	NO$_2$	M	Dec. 286	Red needles	18
Me	OMe	OH	H	H	M	186	Yellow prisms. This and above structure are uncertain in re allocations of OH and OMe groups	18
Me	OMe	OMe	H	H	Z	138	—	19
Et	H	H	H	H	H,I,Y	55, 55–58, 59–60, 67–68	B.p. 295°/760 mm.	2,12,17
CH$_2$Ph	OH	OMe	H	H	K	199–200	—	18
Ph	H	H	H	H	A,C,D,E,O,AA	105, 105–106, 106, 106–107	Gives FeCl$_3$ reaction	13,14,20, 21,22,52
Ph	H	NO$_2$	OMe	H	F	171	—	23
Ph	H	OMe	H	H	X	228	Yellow needles	24
Ph	OMe	OMe	H	NO$_2$	B,C,F	175	—	16,24
Ph	OMe	OMe	H	H	A	173	Yellow needles	16
Ph	H	H	CO$_2$H	H	F	326–327	—	25
Ph	H	H	CH:NNHPh	H	D	264–266	Yellow prisms	25

Table continued

TABLE XIII-2. 3-Alkyl-, 3-Aryl-, and 3-Aralkyl-4-keto-3,4-dihydrophthalazines (*continued*)

Substituent at								
R_1	R_2	R_3	R_4	R_7	Prep.^{b}	M.p., °C.	Remarks	Ref.
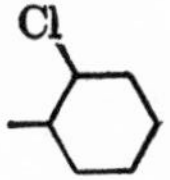 (aryl: Cl, CH₃-substituted ring)	H	H	H	H	A,P	126–127	—	26
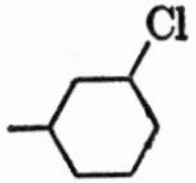 (aryl: Cl, CH₃-substituted ring)	H	H	H	H	D,P	135	—	27
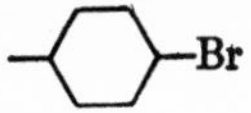 (aryl: Br, CH₃-substituted ring)	H	H	H	H	D	169.5	—	22
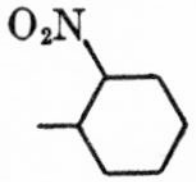 (aryl: O_2N, CH₃-substituted ring)	H	H	H	H	A	201	—	9
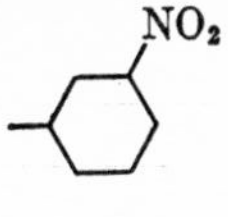 (aryl: NO_2, CH₃-substituted ring)	H	H	H	H	A,P	240	—	9,28
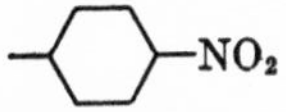 (aryl: NO_2, CH₃-substituted ring)	H	H	H	H	A,P / D	258 / 259	Colorless needles / Orange cryst.	9,15, 22
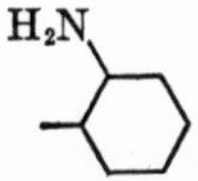 (aryl: H_2N, CH₃-substituted ring)	H	H	H	H	V	184	Ac deriv., m.p. 237°	9,10

Substituent at								
R₁	R₂	R₃	R₄	R₅	Prep.b	M.p., °C	Remarks	Ref.
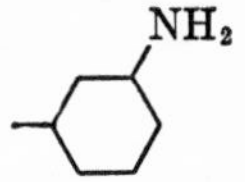 NH₂ (substituted ring)	H	H	H	H	Q	156	Ac deriv., m.p. 225°	9,28
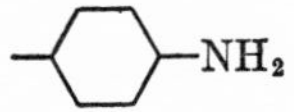 NH₂ (substituted ring)	H	H	H	H	Q,V	184	Ac deriv., m.p. 233°	9,15
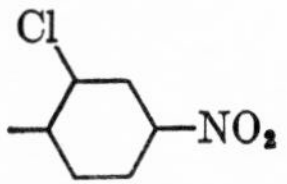 NO₂, Cl (substituted ring)	H	H	H	H	A	171	—	9
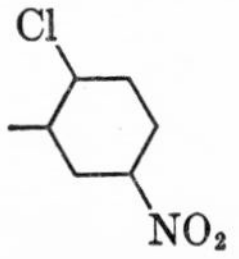 Cl, NO₂ (substituted ring)	H	H	H	H	A	164	—	29
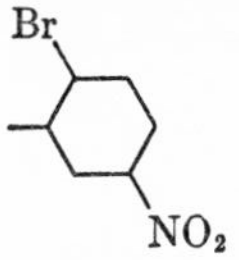 Br, NO₂ (substituted ring)	H	H	H	H	A	154	—	9
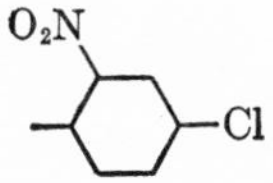 Cl, O₂N (substituted ring)	H	H	H	H	A,P	213–214	—	10

Table continued

TABLE XIII-2. 3-Alkyl-, 3-Aryl-, and 3-Aralkyl-4-keto-3,4-dihydrophthalazines (continued)

R$_1$	Substituent at				Prep.^{b}	M.p., °C.	Remarks	Ref.
	R$_2$	R$_3$	R$_4$	R$_5$				
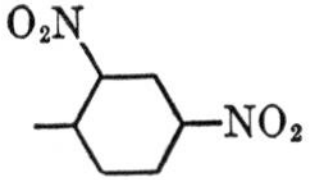 O$_2$N– ring –NO$_2$	H	H	H	H	A,R,S	238	Green prisms	30
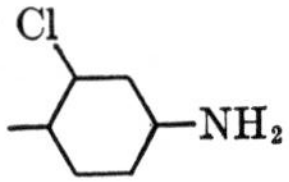 Cl– ring –NH$_2$	H	H	H	H	Q	160	Ac deriv., m.p. 247°	29
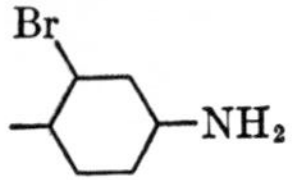 Br– ring –NH$_2$	H	H	H	H	V	203	Ac deriv., m.p. 251°	9
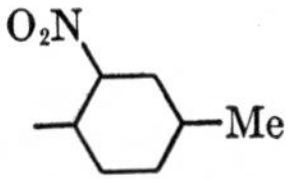 O$_2$N– ring –Me	H	H	H	H	A,P	195	—	10
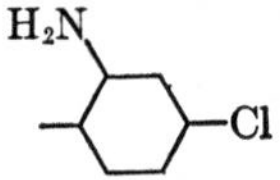 H$_2$N– ring –Cl	H	H	H	H	V	236	Ac deriv., m.p. 289°	10
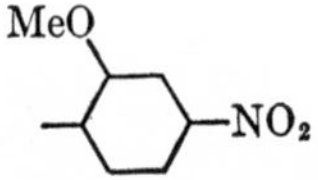 MeO– ring –NO$_2$	H	H	H	H	A,P	175	—	31

R1	Substituent at				Prep.b	M.p., °C.	Remarks	Ref.
	R2	R3	R4	R6				
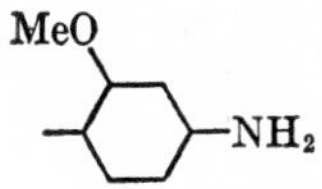 MeO-[ring]-NH_2	H	H	H	H	T,U	215–216	Ac deriv., m.p. 232–233	31
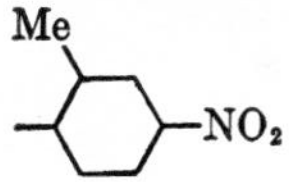 Me-[ring]-NO_2	H	H	H	H	A,P	187–188	—	9,32
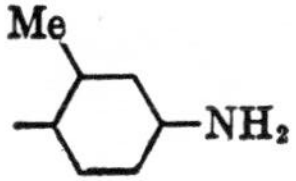 Me-[ring]-NH_2	H	H	H	H	V	187–188	Ac deriv., m.p. 214°	9
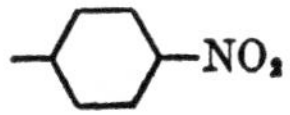 [ring]-NO_2	H	H	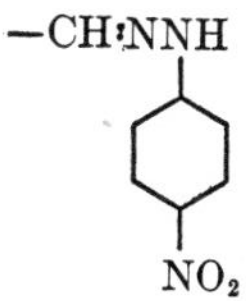 $-CH\!:\!NNH-[ring]-NO_2$	H	W	295 (dec.)	Orange prisms	25
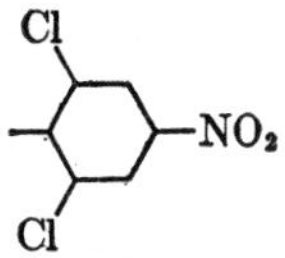 Cl-[ring]-Cl, NO_2	H	H	H	H	A,P	179	—	9
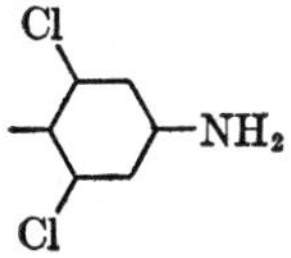 Cl-[ring]-Cl, NH_2	H	H	H	H	V	226	Ac. deriv., m.p. 281°	9

Table continued

TABLE XIII-2. 3-Alkyl-, 3-Aryl-, and 3-Aralkyl-4-keto-3,4-dihydrophthalazines (continued)

| R$_1$ | Substituent at | | | Prep.[b] | M.p., °C. | Remarks | Ref. |
	R$_2$	R$_3$	R$_4$				
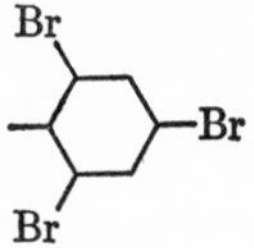 (tribromo-methyl structure)	H	H	H	A,P	182	—	27
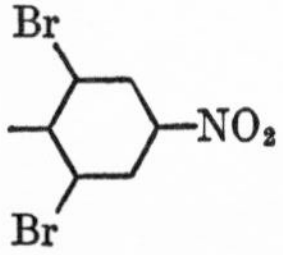 (dibromo-NO$_2$ structure)	H	H	H	A,P	190	—	9
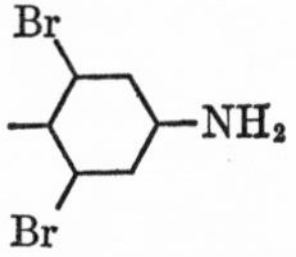 (dibromo-NH$_2$ structure)	H	H	H	V	255	Ac deriv, m.p. 257°	9

[a] According to reference 5, the m.p. 102–103° is observed after distillation, the higher m.p. being that of crystallized but undistilled material.

[b] A, from o-C$_6$H$_4$⟨CO$_2$H / CH:NNHAr⟩ (or the lactone form, o-C$_6$H$_4$⟨CO / O ··· CHNHNHAr⟩) by refluxing with acetic acid or with amyl alcohol saturated with hydrogen chloride, or by treatment with hot or cold concentrated sulfuric acid. B, from (structure: MeO, OMe, CO, CHNHPh)

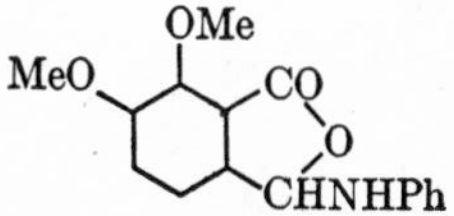

(the ψ-anilide of opianic acid) and phenylhydrazine at 100°. C, from the o-aldehydo acid, phenylhydrazine hydrochloride, and aq. sodium acetate (boil). D, from the o-aldehydo acid and the arylhydrazine in hot or cold aqueous acetic acid or hot alcohol. E, by oxidation of 4-hydroxy-3-phenyl-3,4-dihydrophthalazine with hot alkaline permanganate. F, from the o-aldehydo acid and aqueous phenylhydrazine (or hydrochloride). G, by warming phthalazine methiodide in aqueous solution with freshly prepared silver oxide. H, from phthalazine ethiodide and aqueous potassium hydroxide. I, from the potassium salt of 4-hydroxyphthalazine and ethyl iodide at 100°. J, from 4-hydroxy-5,6-dimethoxyphthalazine, methyl alcohol, and methyl iodide at 120–130° (the hydrogen iodide produced causes the dealkylation). K, from 4-hydroxy-5,6-dimethoxyphthalazine and benzyl chloride at 140–150° (sealed tube). L, from 4-hydroxy-5,6-dimethoxyphthalazine and hydriodic acid at 150° (sealed tube). M, from 8-nitro-4-hydroxy-5,6-dimethoxy-phthalazine, methyl alcohol, and methyl iodide at 150°. N, from 4-hydroxyphthalazine, sodium hydroxide, methyl alcohol, and methyl iodide under reflux. O, by decarboxylation of the -1-carboxylic acid at 250°. P, from the 2-aryl-4-ketophthalazine by heating with aqueous (1:8) hydrochloric acid at 170–200° for 6–64 hours. Q, by reduction of the nitro compound with sodium sulfide in hot aqueous alcohol. R, from 1,4-dihydroxy-3-aryl-3,4-dihydrophthalazine by treatment with concentrated sulfuric acid at 180° or aqueous (1:8) hydrochloric acid at 190°. S, from 1-hydroxy-3-aryl-3,4-dihydrophthalazine-4-acetic acid and concentrated hydrochloric acid. U, from the o-aldehydo acid arylhydrazone and stannous chloride in acetic acid and concentrated hydrochloric acid. V, from the nitroarylhydrazone of the o-aldehydo acid and aqueous sodium sulfide at 50–60°. W, from the o-aldehydo acid and p-nitrophenylhydrazine in hot nitrobenzene. X, from the o-aldehydo-acid phenylhydrazone by heating at 185–190° or by boiling with concentrated hydrochloric acid. Y, from the 4-hydroxy compound, ROH, and RI at 100–120°. Z, from the potassium salt of

opiazone and methyl iodide. AA, from hydroxyphthalimidine

$$C_6H_4 \begin{array}{c} CH(OH) \\ \diagdown \\ CO \end{array} NH$$

and phenylhydrazine in anisole at the b.p.

Reaction 2 has been investigated only in the cases X = H and Cl; the benziminazoles (VII) are the predominant products, accompanied by small amounts of the o-benzylenebenziminazoles (VIII).[10,11] [In the text of the original paper,[10] compounds (VIII) are erroneously represented as (VIIIa).]

(5) 3-Alkyl- and 3-aralkyl-4-keto-3,4-dihydrophthalazines are usually prepared by N-alkylation (see Chapter XII) of 4-hydroxyphthalazines, which may be effected in various ways (see references to individual compounds in Table XIII-2). In cases where the alkylation is brought about by sodium hydroxide and an alkyl iodide in boiling alcoholic solution, fission of the phthalazine ring occurs to some extent with production of compounds of the type (VIIIb; R = H or Me; R' = Me or Et).[5,12]

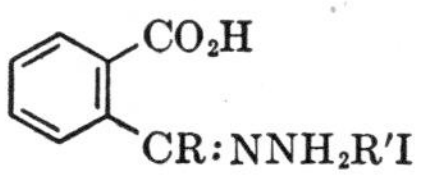

(VIIIb)

(6) An alternative route to the 3-alkyl derivatives is the alkaline decomposition of phthalazine alkiodides. Under appropriate conditions this reaction produces a mixture of (steam volatile) 3-alkyl-3,4-dihydrophthalazine and (non-steam volatile) 3-alkyl-4-keto-3,4-dihydrophthalazine, the former is readily converted into the latter by atmospheric oxidation.

Properties. The 3-substituted phthalaz-4-ones (IX) are stable, mostly colorless, crystalline solids, soluble in organic solvents, but insoluble in alkalis unless phenolic hydroxyl is present. They are usually almost devoid of basic properties; they do not form picrates, and are insoluble in dilute, and but sparingly soluble in concentrated, mineral acids; compound (IX; R = Me) is however described[1] as being soluble in

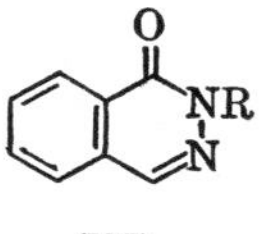

(IX) 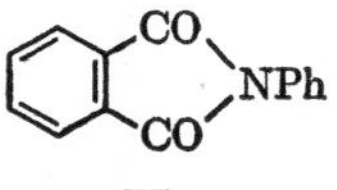   (X) 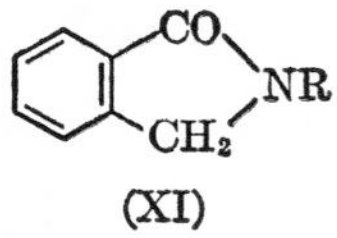   (XI)

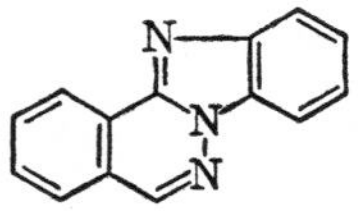

(XII)

hydrochloric acid. Typical compounds are stable to hot reagents such as fuming hydrochloric acid, concentrated sulfuric acid, phosphorus pentachloride, and phosphorus oxychloride.[16] However, compounds in which the 3-substituent is a 2'-aminoaryl group undergo dehydration in the presence of dilute hydrochloric acid at a high temperature and pressure with production of compounds of type (XII) (see Chapter XXIII, Section 1).[10] The compound (IX; R = Ph) distils without appreciable decomposition, but if it is kept at the boiling point for a long time prior to distillation some N-phenylphthalimide (X) is formed.[13] Reduction of (IX; R = phenyl and 4'-nitrophenyl) gives N-phenyl- and N-4'-aminophenyl-phthalimidine (as XI).[14,15]

B. Compounds with a 1-Substituent

These compounds are conveniently divided into (1) 1,3-dialkyl- and 1-alkyl-3-aryl derivatives (Table XIII-3) and (2) miscellaneous 1,3-disubstituted compounds other than the foregoing (Table XIII-4).

Preparation. The compounds of both groups (1) and (2) are, in general, prepared by methods similar to those described in Section A. These are, in brief:

(a) Cyclization of the arylhydrazone of an o-keto acid.

(XIII)

(b) Condensation of an o-keto acid with an arylhydrazine followed by spontaneous ring closure.

(c) Compounds containing an aminoaryl substituent attached to N_3 are best prepared by reduction of the corresponding nitrophthalazones with sodium sulfide in aqueous alcohol.[9] The method fails, however, if the amino group is in the 2'-position of the aryl residue (cf. Section A), and such compounds are prepared by a single-stage reduction and cyclization of the nitroarylhydrazones.[10] Substituents in the Ar group of (XIII) when R is methyl have a similar effect to those observed when R is hydrogen (Section A), but, in general, (XIII; R = Me) are less resistant to cyclization than (XIII; R = H).[9]

(d) Compounds containing a 1-methyl substituent (XV) may be prepared by acid-induced isomerization of 1-methyl-2-aryl-4-ketophthalazines (XIV). The reaction for compounds without a 1-methyl group has already been discussed in Section A; the transformation (XIV) → (XV) is considered to proceed by the same mechanism and is effected under identical conditions, and substituents in the 2-aryl group of (XIV) exert similar influences on the speed and extent of the reaction, except that the isomerization of (XIV) is usually more facile than for compounds without the 1-

(XIV)		(XV)	(XVI)

methyl group.   For (XIV; Ar = 4′-nitrophenyl), the reaction is approxi-mately unimolecular, $k = 48 \times 10^{-4}$.[10]   As with compounds devoid of the 1-methyl group, here also the reaction fails if the 2-aryl residue of (XIV) contains an amino group.   If the latter is in the 3′- or 4′-position, no isom-erization occurs, and the compounds (XIV) are recovered unchanged. With 2′-amino compounds, however, the reaction (XIV) → (XVI) occurs; this transformation has been carried out to give the compounds (XVI; X = H) and (XVI; X = Cl)[10] (Chapter XXIII, Section 1).

   (e) Compounds containing a 3-alkyl group are obtainable by alkylation of 4-hydroxyphthalazines (see Section A).

   Properties.   The physical characteristics of compounds of groups (1) and (2) are given in Tables XIII-3 and 4, respectively.   Unless otherwise stated, they are colorless, or almost colorless, compounds.   Their general chemical properties, and in particular the lack of basicity, are the same as those of the compounds unsubstituted at C_1 (Section A).   Compounds having a 1-methyl group and a 2′-aminoaryl group attached to N_2 are con-verted into the anhydro derivatives (XVI) (Chapter XXIII, Section 1) by treatment with dilute (1:8) hydrochloric acid at 180° for 6 hours.

3. Derivatives of Unknown Structure

   It has already been pointed out (Chapter XII) that, although alkyla-tion of 4- (1-) hydroxyphthalazines can theoretically give either O- or N-alkyl derivatives, the compounds so obtained are usually regarded as N-substitution products.   The same problem of deciding whether O- or N-derivatives are formed arises when the hydroxyphthalazines are acylated. In the earlier literature the products were formulated as N-derivatives,[2,18,19] but Rowe and Peters[4] consider that 4-hydroxy-1-methylphthalazine gives the 4-acetoxy compound.   At present there is no decisive evidence in favor of either structure, and the constitutions of these compounds should therefore be regarded as undetermined.   The compounds in question are summarized in Table XIII-5.

TABLE XIII-3. 1,3-Dialkyl- and 1-Alkyl-3-aryl-4-keto-3,4-dihydrophthalazines

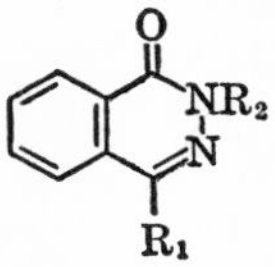

R_1	R_2	Prep.[a]	M.p., °C.	Remarks	Ref.
Me	Me	A,B	109–110, 112	Not demethylated by HBr-AcOH/120° or by HI/140°	4,33
Me	Et	C	75–76	B.p. 309°/735 mm.	5
Me	Ph	D,E	102	—	34,35
Me	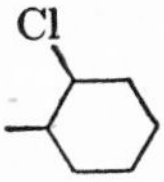 (2-Cl-phenyl)	F,G	147	—	26
Me	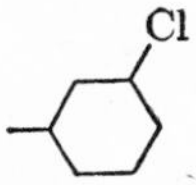 (3-Cl-phenyl)	D,G	140	—	27
Me	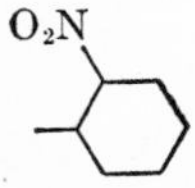 (2-O_2N-phenyl)	F,G	202	—	9,34
Me	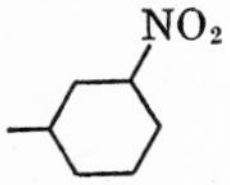 (3-NO_2-phenyl)	D,F,G,H	167	—	9,34
Me	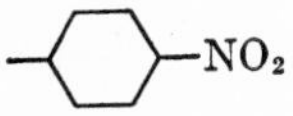 (4-NO_2-phenyl)	F,G,I	214	—	9,34
Me	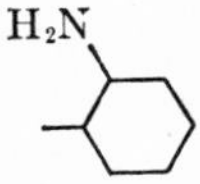 (2-H_2N-phenyl)	J	241	—	10
Me	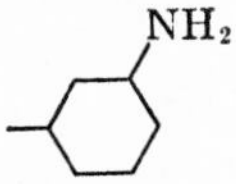 (3-NH_2-phenyl)	K	173	Ac deriv., m.p. 220°	9
Me	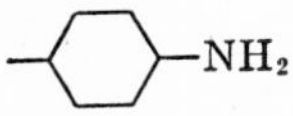 (4-NH_2-phenyl)	K	206–207	Ac deriv., m.p. 252°	9
Me	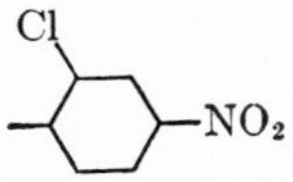 (3-Cl-4-NO_2-phenyl)	F,G	206	—	9

Table continued

TABLE XIII-3. 1,3-Dialkyl- and 1-Alkyl-3-aryl-4-keto-3,4-dihydrophthalazines (*continued*)

R_1	R :	Prep.[a]	M.p., °C.	Remarks	Ref.
Me	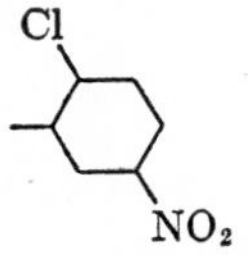 (4-NO_2-2-Cl-phenyl)	F,G,L	163	—	29
Me	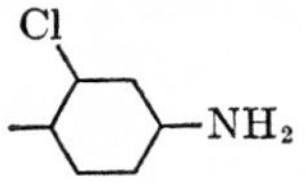 (2-Cl-4-NH_2-phenyl)	K	207	Ac deriv., m.p. 247°	9
Me	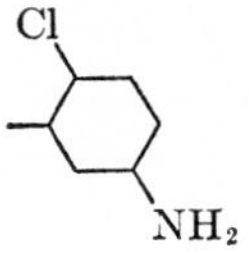 (2-Cl-4-NH_2-phenyl)	K	145	Ac deriv., m.p. 238°	29
Me	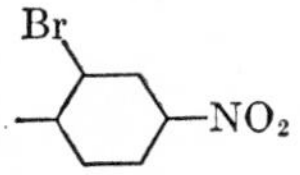 (2-Br-4-NO_2-phenyl)	F,G	200–202	—	9,36
Me	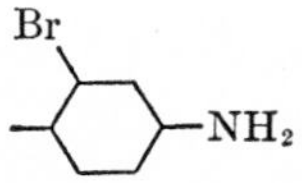 (2-Br-4-NH_2-phenyl)	K	130 (dec.)	Ac deriv., m.p. 255°	9
Me	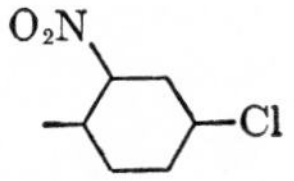 (2-O_2N-4-Cl-phenyl)	F,G	261	—	10
Me	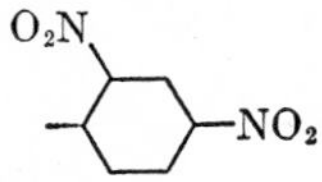 (2-O_2N-4-NO_2-phenyl)	F,L,M,N	248	—	30
Me	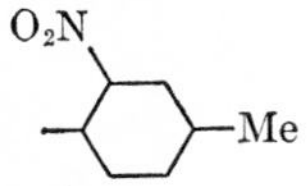 (2-O_2N-4-Me-phenyl)	F,G	258	—	10
Me	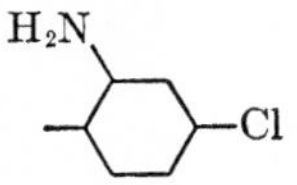 (2-H_2N-4-Cl-phenyl)	J	222–223	Ac deriv., m.p. 304°	10
Me	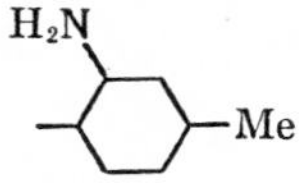 (2-H_2N-4-Me-phenyl)	J	203	Ac deriv., m.p. 263°	10

TABLE XIII-3. 1,3-Dialkyl- and 1-Alkyl-3-aryl-4-keto-3,4-dihydrophthalazines

R_1	R_2	Prep.[a]	M.p., °C.	Remarks	Ref.
Me	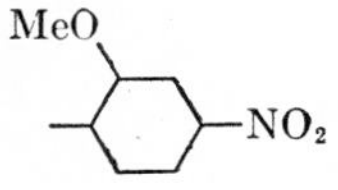 MeO–〈ring〉–NO_2	F,G	237–238	—	31
Me	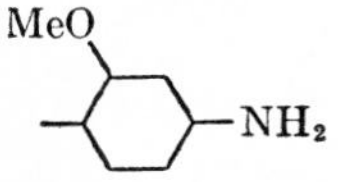 MeO–〈ring〉–NH_2	O,P	258–259	Ac deriv., m.p. 237–238°	31
Me	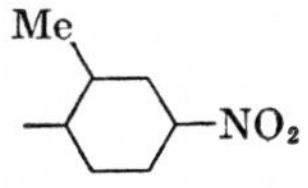 Me–〈ring〉–NO_2	F,G	178	—	9
Me	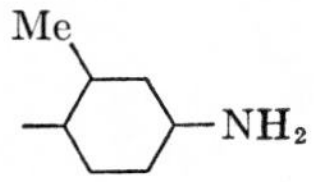 Me–〈ring〉–NH_2	K	191	Ac deriv., m.p. 235°	9
Me	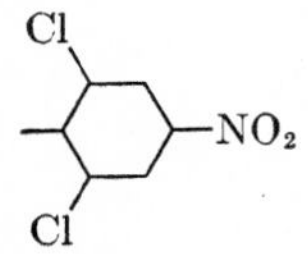 Cl,Cl–〈ring〉–NO_2	F,G	205	—	9
Me	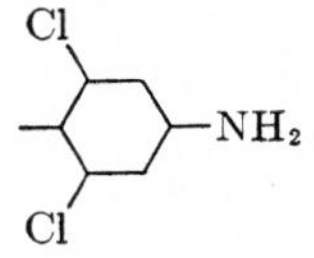 Cl,Cl–〈ring〉–NH_2	K	279	Ac deriv., m.p. 320°	9
Me	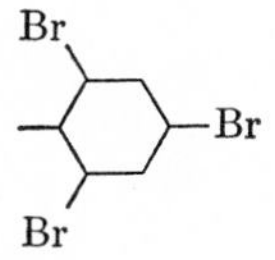 Br,Br–〈ring〉–Br	F,G	195	—	27
Me	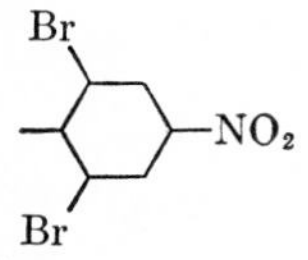 Br,Br–〈ring〉–NO_2	F,G	237	—	9
Me	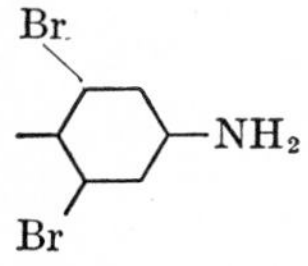 Br,Br–〈ring〉–NH_2	K	274	Ac deriv., m.p. 315°	9

Table continued

TABLE XIII-3. 1,3-Dialkyl- and 1-Alkyl-3-aryl-4-keto-3,4-dihydrophthalazines (*continued*)

R₁	R₂	Prep.[a]	M.p., °C.	Remarks	Ref.
Me	(aryl ring: MeO, —NO₂, OMe)	G	222	Yellow prisms	37
Et	Me	S	78–79	—	12
Et	Et	C	49–50	B.p. 307°	6
Et	Ph	Q,R	111–112, 102	White needles. Yellow prisms	38,39

[a] A, by alkaline decomposition of 1-methyl-1,2,3,4-tetrahydrophthalazine methiodide. B, by methylation of the 4-hydroxy compound with potassium hydroxide and methyl iodide, or with sodium hydroxide, aqueous methanol, and methyl iodide or dimethyl sulfate. C, from the 4-hydroxy compound by refluxing with sodium hydroxide or ethoxide, alcohol, and ethyl iodide. D, from the o-keto acid and the

arylhydrazine in alcohol (warm or reflux). E, from o-C₆H₄ $\begin{smallmatrix}CO_2H\\COCH_2CO_2H\end{smallmatrix}$ and

phenylhydrazine in alcohol-acetic acid (warm). F, from the arylhydrazone of the o-keto acid by refluxing in acetic acid or in pyridine-acetic anhydride, or by treatment with hot or cold concentrated sulfuric acid. G, by isomerization of the 1-methyl-2-aryl-4-ketophthalazine with aqueous (1:8) hydrochloric acid at 170–200° for 6–55 hours. H, from the 3-phenyl analog and fuming nitric acid at 0°. I, from the 4-hydroxy compound, p-chloronitrobenzene, sodium acetate, and aqueous ethanol at 180° for 2 hours. J, from the nitroarylhydrazone of the o-keto acid and aqueous sodium sulfide at 50–60°. K, from the nitro compound and sodium sulfide in boiling aqueous ethanol. L, from the 1,4-dihydroxy-1-methyl-2-aryl-1,2-dihydrophthalazine by treatment with aqueous (1:8) hydrochloric acid at 180° for 3 hours, or by heating with concentrated sulfuric acid. M, from the 1-hydroxy-3-aryl-3,4-dihydrophthalazine-4-acetic acid and fuming hydrochloric acid at 180°.

N, from (structure: indanone with =CH₂ and =NNHAr) and concentrated sulfuric acid at 180–185°. O, from

the nitro compound, stannous chloride, acetic acid, and concentrated hydrochloric acid. P, by reduction as in method O of the o-keto acid arylhydrazone. Q, from

the o-keto acid and phenylhydrazine at 240° (reflux). R, from (structure: bicyclic compound with Et, O₃, Ph, O)

and phenylhydrazine at 235–240° (reflux). S, by alkaline decomposition of 1-ethylphthalazine methiodide.

TABLE XIII-4. 1-Substituted Alkyl-, 1-Aryl-, and 1-Carboxy-3-Substituted-4-keto-3,4-dihydrophthalazines

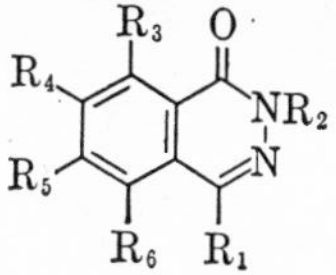

Phthalazinone core structure with positions labeled R_3, O, NR_2, N, R_1, R_4, R_5, R_6.

R_1	R_2	R_3	R_4	R_5	R_6	Prep.[a]	M.p., °C.	Remarks	Ref.
CH$_2$Ph	Me	H	H	H	H	B	148	—	8
CH$_2$Ph	Et	H	H	H	H	C	106	—	8
CH$_2$Ph	Ph	H	H	H	H	T, AI	171–172	—	40
							170		41
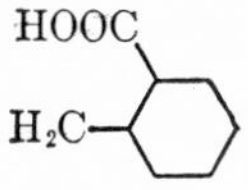 (HOOC–H$_2$C–cyclohexyl structure)	Ph	H	H	H	H	D	206	—	42
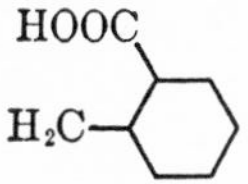 (cyclohexyl structure)	CONH$_2$	H	H	H	H	U	232	Yellow needles	42
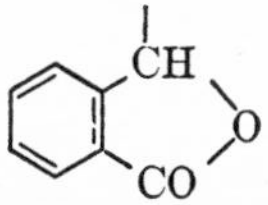 (HOOC–H$_2$C–cyclohexyl structure)	Ph	H	H	H	H	D	207	—	42
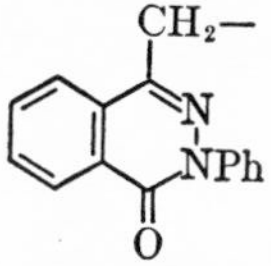 (–CH–O–CO benzo structure)	Ph	H	H	H	H	V	236–237	Unchanged by Zn-AcOH, Sn-conc. HCl, and conc. H$_2$SO$_4$. Nitric acid (d 1.4) at 100° gives NO$_2$-NO deriv., $C_{30}H_{19}O_7N_7$, m.p. 316–318° (ref. 43)	35,43
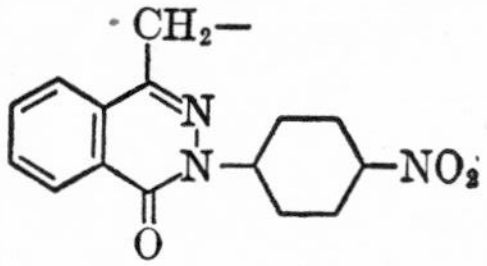 (CH$_2$– phthalazinone with 4-nitrocyclohexyl structure)	 (4-nitrocyclohexyl structure, NO$_2$)	H	H	H	H	V	>350	—	43

Table continued

TABLE XIII-4. 1-Substituted Alkyl-, 1-Aryl-, and 1-Carboxy-3-Substituted-4-keto-3,4-dihydrophthalazines (*continued*)

R₁	R₂	R₃	R₄	R₅	R₆	Prep.[a]	M.p., °C.	Remarks	Ref.
Ph	Me	H	H	H	H	AH	153	—	2
Ph	Et	H	H	H	H	AH	109	—	2
Ph	Ph	H	H	H	H	W	168	—	44
(ring structure: OH, HO, Me)	Ph	H	H	H	H	D	180–182	—	35
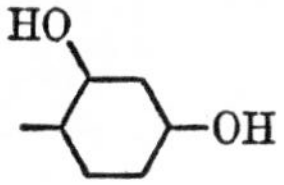 (ring structure: OH, HO, Me)	Ph	H	H	H	H	X	260–261	—	45
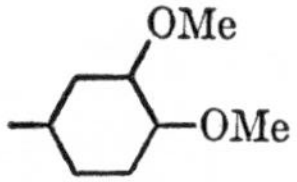 (ring structure: OMe, OMe, Me)	Ph	H	H	H	H	D	189	Yellow needles	46
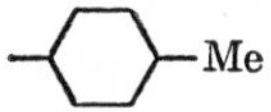 (ring structure: Me)	Me	H	H	H	H	AH	170	—	2
—CO₂H	Ph	H	H	H	H	Y,Z	210 / 214–215	—	13 / 20
—CO₂H	Ph	Cl	H	H	H	AA	215	Both compds. are yellow cryst. It is possible that the m.p.s should be interchanged, as the original text contradicts the formulas	47
—CO₂H	Ph	H	H	H	Cl	AA	155		47
—CO₂H	Ph	H	OMe	OMe	H	AB	244	Yellow cryst. Boiling with PhNO₂ gives a yellow compd., m.p. 218° (not invest.)	48
—CO₂H	CONH₂	H	H	OMe	H	AC	280	—	48
—CO₂Me	Ph	H	H	H	H	AD,AE	114	—	13,49
—CO₂Me	Ph	H	NO₂	H	H	AF	218	Yellow prisms. With dil. NaOH-MeOH gives the acid, m.p. 328° (dec.), whence CH₂-N₂ regenerates the ester	50
—CH₂CO₂H	Ph	H	H	H	H	E	160 (evolves CO₂)	Gives Ca salt, C₁₆H₁₁O₃N₂-0.5Ca·1.5 H₂O	35
—[CH₂]₂CO₂H	Ph	H	H	H	H	AG	210	Gives Ca (0.5) salt + 0.5 H₂O, and Ag salt	35

Table footnote on next page

TABLE XIII-4 (*continued*)

a For methods of preparation quoted in this table and not given below, see key to Table XIII-3. T, by treatment of benzalphthalide or $o\text{-}C_6H_4\!\!\begin{smallmatrix}CO_2H\\COCH_2Ph\end{smallmatrix}$ with phenylhydrazine in boiling alcohol. U, from $o\text{-}C_6H_4\!\!\begin{smallmatrix}CO_2H\\COR\end{smallmatrix}$ and semicarbazide hydrochloride in aqueous alcohol-acetic acid at room temperature. V, from $\left[o\text{-}C_6H_4\!\!\begin{smallmatrix}CO_2H\\COCH_2-\end{smallmatrix}\right]_2$ and the arylhydrazine in boiling alcohol. W, by heating the ψ-anilide of o-benzoylbenzoic acid with phenylhydrazine at 100°. X, by heating $o\text{-}C_6H_4\!\!\begin{smallmatrix}CO_2H\\COR\end{smallmatrix}$ with phenylhydrazine at 140–160°. Y, by warming $o\text{-}C_6H_4\!\!\begin{smallmatrix}CO_2H\\COR\end{smallmatrix}$ with aqueous phenylhydrazine hydrochloride. Z, use of free phenylhydrazine in method Y gives the phenylhydrazone, which is then cyclized by treatment with dilute hydrochloric acid. AA, from $o\text{-}C_6H_3Cl\!\!\begin{smallmatrix}CO_2H\\COR\end{smallmatrix}$ and phenylhydrazine in dilute hydrochloric acid. AB, from the keto acid and phenylhydrazine in water at 100°. AC, from

$$\text{MeO}\!\!-\!\!\square\!\!\begin{smallmatrix}CO_2H\\C(CO_2H){:}NNHCONH_2\end{smallmatrix}\quad(\text{MeO})$$

in boiling acetic acid. AD, from $o\text{-}C_6H_4\!\!\begin{smallmatrix}CO_2H\\COR\end{smallmatrix}$ and phenylhydrazine in methanol. AE, from the acid, methanol, and methyl iodide at 110–120°. AF, by treatment of methyl-5-nitro-2-carbomethoxymethylbenzoate and sodium acetate in methanol with aqueous benzenediazonium chloride at 0°. AG, from the lactone of $o\text{-}C_6H_4\!\!\begin{smallmatrix}CO_2H\\CO[CH_2]_2CO_2H\end{smallmatrix}$ and phenylhydrazine in acetic acid. AH, from the hydroxy compound by heating with the appropriate alkyl iodide and alcohol in a sealed tube. AI,

This salt, freshly prepared, is treated with benzene diazoacetate in acetic acid, giving CO_2 and the intermediate $o\text{-}C_6H_4\!\!\begin{smallmatrix}CO_2H\\C(CH_2Ph){=}NNHPh\end{smallmatrix}$, which cyclizes to the phthalazone.

Table XIII-5. Acyl Derivatives of 4-Hydroxyphthalazines of Unknown Structure

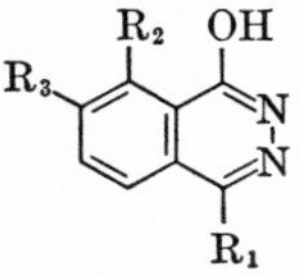

R_1	R_2	R_3	Acyl group intro- duced	M.p., °C.	Remarks	Ref.
H	H	H	1 Ac	135, 132–133	Cryst. from hot water. Prepd. with warm Ac_2O; boiling Ac_2O causes ring fission and elim. of N_2H_4	2,19
H	OH	OH	3 Ac	184–186	Partially hydrolyzed by boiling water	18
H	OMe	OMe	1 Ac	158–159	—	19
NH_2	H	H	2 Bz	252–253 (dec.)	—	51
Me	H	H	1 Ac	130–132	Cryst. from benzene. Is converted into the 4-hydroxy compd. by treatment with alc.	4
Ph	H	H	1 Ac	178–179	Prepd. with warm Ac_2O; boiling Ac_2O causes ring fission and elim. of N_2H_4	2

References

1. Gabriel and Neumann, *Ber.*, **26**, 521 (1893).
2. R. von Rothenburg, *J. prakt. Chem.*, **51**, 140 (1895).
3. Vaughan and Baird, *J. Am. Chem. Soc.*, **68**, 1314 (1946).
4. Rowe and Peters, *J. Chem. Soc.*, **1933**, 1331.
5. Gabriel and Neumann, *Ber.*, **26**, 705 (1893).
6. Daube, *Ber.*, **38**, 206 (1905).
7. Wölbling, *Ber.*, **38**, 3925 (1905).
8. Bromberg, *Ber.*, **29**, 1434 (1896).
9. Rowe, Heath, and Patel, *J. Chem. Soc.*, **1936**, 311.
10. Rowe et al., *J. Chem. Soc.*, **1937**, 90.
11. Rowe, Dovey, Garforth, Levin, Pask, and Peters, *J. Chem. Soc.*, **1935**, 1796.
12. Paul, *Ber.*, **32**, 2014 (1899).
13. Henriques, *Ber.*, **21**, 1607 (1888).
14. Racine, *Ann.*, **239**, 78 (1887).
15. Rowe and Levin, *J. Chem. Soc.*, **1928**, 2550.
16. Liebermann, *Ber.*, **19**, 763 (1886).
17. Gabriel and Müller, *Ber.*, **28**, 1830 (1895).
18. Jacobson, *Ber.*, **27**, 1418 (1894).
19. Liebermann and Bistrzycki, *Ber.*, **26**, 531 (1893).
20. Mitter and Sen, *J. Chem. Soc.*, **1919**, 1145.
21. Thiele and Falk, *Ann.*, **347**, 112 (1906).
22. Seekles, *Rec. trav. chim.*, **43**, 329 (1924).
23. Borsche, Diaconte, and Hanau, *Ber.*, **67**, 675 (1934).

24. Fargher and W. H. Perkin, *J. Chem. Soc.*, **1921,** 1724.
25. W. H. Perkin and Stone, *J. Chem. Soc.*, **1925,** 2275.
26. Brodrick, Peters, and Rowe, *J. Chem. Soc.*, **1948,** 1026.
27. Peters, Pringle, and Rowe, *J. Chem. Soc.*, **1948,** 597.
28. Rowe, Himmat, and Levin, *J. Chem. Soc.*, **1928,** 2556.
29. Rowe, Peters, and Rangwala, *J. Chem. Soc.*, **1948,** 206.
30. Rowe and Osborn, *J. Chem. Soc.*, **1947,** 829.
31. Rowe and Cross, *J. Chem. Soc.*, **1947,** 461.
32. Rowe and Siddle, *J. Chem. Soc.*, **1932,** 473.
33. Gabriel and Eschenbach, *Ber.*, **30,** 3022 (1897).
34. Rowe and Peters, *J. Chem. Soc.*, **1931,** 1918.
35. Roser, *Ber.*, **18,** 802 (1885).
36. Rowe, Jambuserwala, and Partridge, *J. Chem. Soc.*, **1935,** 1134.
37. Rowe, Desai, and Peters, *J. Chem. Soc.*, **1948,** 281.
38. Frank, Eklund, Richter, Vanneman, and Wennerberg, *J. Am. Chem. Soc.*, **66,** 1 (1944).
39. Gottlieb, *Ber.*, **32,** 958 (1899).
40. Ephraim, *Ber.*, **26,** 1376 (1893).
41. Dieckmann, *Ber.*, **47,** 1428 (1914).
42. Ruggli and Meyer, *Helv. Chim. Acta*, **5,** 28 (1922).
43. Reissert and Engel, *Ber.*, **38,** 3281 (1905).
44. Meyer and Turnau, *Monatsh.*, **30,** 481 (1909).
45. Orndorff and Kline, *J. Am. Chem. Soc.*, **46,** 2276 (1924).
46. Lagodzinski, *Ann.*, **342,** 90 (1905).
47. J. von Braun *et al.*, *Ber.*, **56,** 2332 (1923).
48. Kuroda and W. H. Perkin, *J. Chem. Soc.*, **1923,** 2094.
49. Glogau, *Sitzungsber. Akad. Wiss. Wien*, **113,** IIb, 52 (1904) [*Monatsh.*, **25,** 395 (1904)].
50. Borsche and Diacont, *Ann.*, **510,** 287 (1934).
51. E. F. M. Stephenson, *J. Chem. Soc.*, **1944,** 678.
52. Dunet and Willemart, *Bull. soc. chim.*, **15,** 1081 (1948).

CHAPTER XIV

1-Hydroxy-3-aryl-3,4-dihydrophthalazine-4-acetic Acids

These compounds, which have the general formula (I), form the starting point for the preparation of a large number of phthalazine derivatives. The investigation of the reactions leading to the synthesis of (I) and to the subsequent transformations of this class of compound was begun by F. M. Rowe and his associates[1] more than twenty years ago; these studies are of more than passing interest, as they have considerably broadened the scope of phthalazine chemistry, and indeed represent a major contribution to the chemistry of nitrogenous heterocyclic compounds.

A. Preparation. The compounds of this group are all prepared from 2-naphthol-1-sulfonic acid (II) and various primary aromatic amines by reaction 1. The amine is diazotized and coupled with (II)

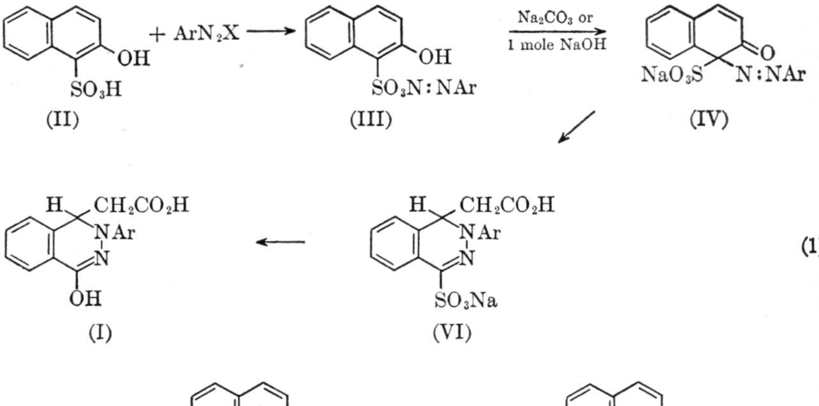

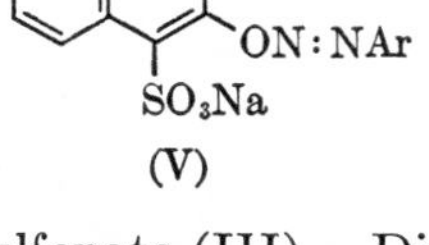

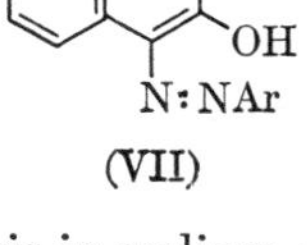

yielding the diazosulfonate (III). Dissolution of this in sodium carbonate or in one equivalent of aqueous sodium hydroxide causes its conversion into the isomeric sodium 1-arylazo-2-naphthaquinone-1-sulfonate (IV) [in the older literature such compounds were formulated as diazo oxides (V)]. If a compound of type (IV) is left in an excess of aqueous sodium hydroxide in the cold for a suitable time, it is converted into the monosodium salt (probably VI) of a 3-aryl-3,4-dihydrophthalazine-1-sulfonic acid-4-acetic acid by a process of hydrolytic ring fission and recyclization, and this sodium salt on acid hydrolysis furnishes the corresponding 3-aryl-1-hydroxy-3,4-dihydrophthalazine-4-acetic acid (I). The yields of (VI) are usually good. Some 1-arylazo-2-naphthol (VII) is formed as the result of incomplete ring fission of (IV), but the amount is generally small; (VII) is, however, the main product when Ar = p-PhN=N—C$_6$H$_4$—, and the yield of (VI) is correspondingly reduced.[2]

Attempts have been made to effect these transformations using other naphthalene derivatives in place of (II), but without result, and the reaction is considered to be specific for this particular compound.[1,3] A wide range of primary aromatic amines has been used in the reaction, as may be seen from Table XIV-1; originally[1] it was considered that the presence of a nitro group or of a p-arylazo group in the aromatic nucleus of the amine was a requisite for the reaction, but later work[4] showed that these groups are unnecessary, and the reactions have recently been carried through with the chloroanilines[4,5] and even with aniline itself.[6]

The conversion of (IV) into (VI) occurs by way of the benzene derivative (VIII). The suggestion[1] that the naphthaquinone derivative (IV) undergoes ring opening in alkaline solution to a substance of this type was first confirmed experimentally[7] by the isolation of (VIII; Ar = 2'-nitro-, 4'-chloro-2'-nitro-, and 5'-chloro-2'-nitrophenyl), and later[8,9] by that of

(VIII; Ar = 2'-nitro-4'-methyl- and 2',4'-dinitrophenyl). These compounds are formed by treatment of (IV) with concentrated sodium hydroxide for a very short time, followed by acidification, and it was believed that this result was due to the conferment of exceptional stability on (VIII) by the 2'-nitroaryl groups. Later work, however,[10] showed that the pres-

ence of a 2'-nitro group is not essential, as by the restricted action of
sodium hydroxide it was possible to isolate crude products consisting of
(VI) mixed with a certain amount of (VIII) from compounds (IV) in which
Ar = 2',6'-dichloro-4'-nitro-, 2',6'-dibromo-4'-nitro-, 2'-chloro- and 2'-
bromo-4'-nitro-, 4'-nitro-2'-methyl-, and 4'-nitrophenyl; the stability of
(VIII) decreases in the order just mentioned. The restricted action of
sodium hydroxide on (IV; Ar = 4'-nitro-2'-methoxyphenyl) also gives
rise to a proportion of (VIII) in addition to (VI).[11] The compounds (VIII)
are converted into (VI) by the prolonged action of sodium hydroxide, but
in hot dilute acid an entirely different reaction is observed; hydrolysis to
(IX) occurs, followed by isomerization of these products to 2-arylaminoiso-
indolinone-3-acetic acids (X).[6−10,12]

Properties. Table XIV-1 gives a list of the known acids of general
formula (I) and their functional derivatives. In a number of cases the
precursors (VI) have also been obtained analytically pure, but they have
no definite melting point. In general, the compounds in Table XIV-1 are
yellow to red in color if the 3-aryl substituent contains a p-arylazo group;
yellow if it contains a nitro group; and colorless if neither chromophore is
present. The hydroxy acids and the N-methyl ethers are soluble in aqueous sodium hydroxide and sodium carbonate, a pronounced deepening of
color often resulting with the hydroxy acids containing a nitro group; the
methyl esters of N-methyl ethers are devoid of acid properties; and hydroxy acids containing a 3-aminoaryl group are amphoteric. The N-
methyl ethers, in agreement with the structure assigned to them, are resistant to the action of hydrobromic acid at 180° and of hydriodic acid at
140°.[13]

1-Hydroxy-3-aryl-3,4-dihydrophthalazine-4-acetic acids (I) undergo
three important general reactions.

(1) On oxidation with hot aqueous potassium permanganate the acetic
acid side chain is lost with production of 1-hydroxy-3-aryl-4-keto-3,4-
dihydrophthalazines (XI) (see Chapter XVIII, Section 2A, Table XVIII-1).

$$(3)$$

(2) Oxidation with cold dichromate in aqueous sulfuric acid converts
the acids into 3-aryl-4-methyl-1-ketophthalazines (XII). This curious
reaction, resulting in the formation of zwitterions, involves the loss from
(I) of the elements of formic acid; for a description of the products (XII)
see Chapter XV, Table XV-2.

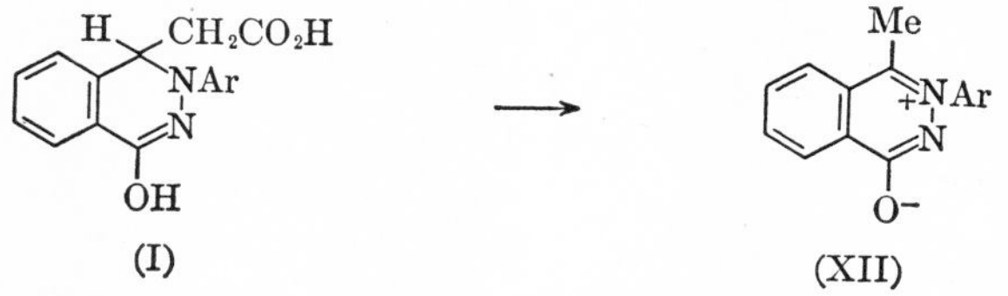

(4)

(I)   (XII)

(*3*) If acids of type (I) are heated under reflux with aqueous sulfuric acid of b.p. 140° (acid:water = 5:6, v/v), loss of the elements of acetic acid occurs, and 3-aryl-1-ketophthalazines (XIII) (Chapter XV, Table 1), the lower homologs of (XII), are produced (Eq. 5). If dilute hydrochloric

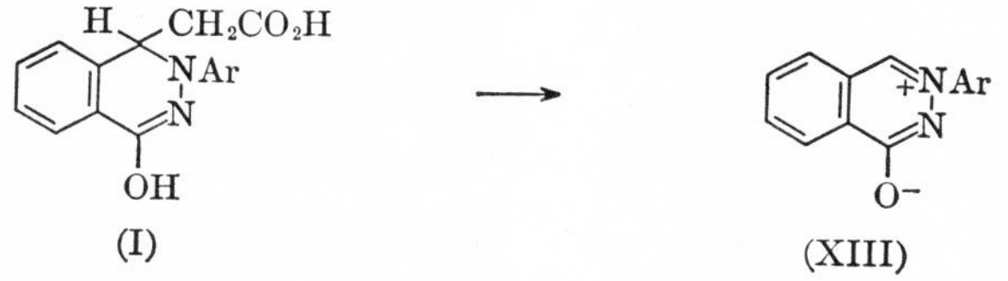

(5)

(I)   (XIII)

acid under pressure is used instead of sulfuric acid, the 3-nitroaryl acids give, according to conditions, (XII), (XIII), or their products of isomerization, *viz.*, 2-aryl-1-keto-1,2-dihydrophthalazines (see Chapter XIII, Section 2).[14]

In addition to these general reactions, certain acids of type (I) undergo the following more specific transformations.

When refluxed for a long time (15–66 hours) with pyridine and acetic anhydride, the five acids in Table XIV-1 which contain a 2′-nitroaryl group attached to N₃ do not yield the expected 1-acetoxy derivatives, but are converted into 2,5-diketo-3-arylisoindolinopyrazolidocolines (XV). This

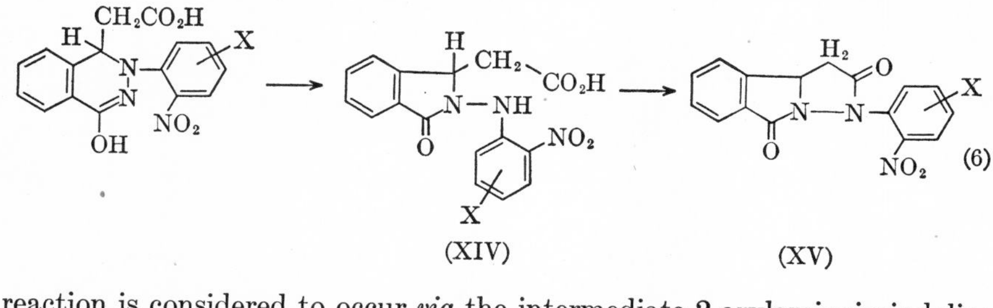

(6)

(XIV)   (XV)

reaction is considered to occur *via* the intermediate 2-arylaminoisoindolin-one-3-acetic acids (XIV); for, as indicated above, a number of these intermediates (XIV) have been prepared in the pure state by acid-induced cyclization of the arylacrylic acids (VIII), and when treated with pyridine-acetic anhydride they readily yield the anhydro derivatives (XV), identical with the compounds prepared by the action of pyridine and acetic anhydride on the nitro acids (I).[7–9]

TABLE XIV-1. 1-Hydroxy-3-aryl-3,4-dihydrophthalazine-4-acetic Acids and Their Functional Derivatives

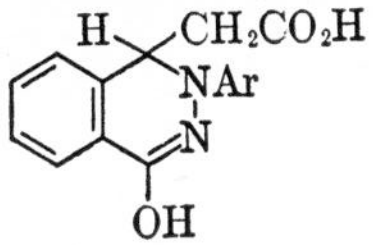

Ar	Prep. of acid[a]	Melting point of:							Ref.
		Acid	Me ester	Et ester	Acetyl acid	Anilide	N-Me ether	N-Me ether, Me ester	
Ph	A	264° (dec.)[b]	—	91–92°	183°	—	184–186°	—	6
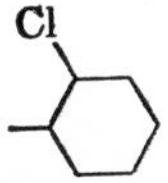 2-Cl	A	224–225°[b]	141–142°	132–133°	—	—	180–181°	—	5
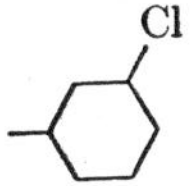 3-Cl	A	200°	123°	—	175–176°	173–175°	197°	—	4
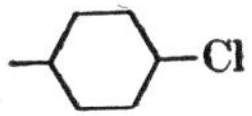 4-Cl	A	236°	—	—	—	—	—	—	4
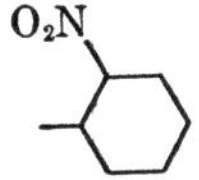 2-NO₂	A	248°	146°	163°	—	128°	207°	133–134°	7
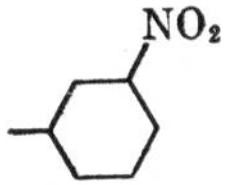 3-NO₂	A	234°	184°	195°	175°	239° (dec.)	235°	180°	10,13,15
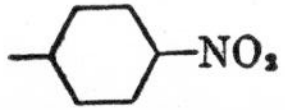 4-NO₂	A	241°	166°	180°	212°	190–192° (dec.)	207°	188°	1,13

Ar	Prep. of acid[a]	Melting point of:							Ref.
		Acid	Me ester	Et ester	Acetyl acid	Anilide	N-Me ether	N-Me ether, Me ester	
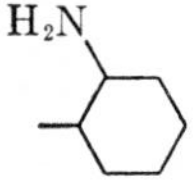 H₂N— ⬡ —NH₂	C	160°; re-solid. at 170°; 293–294°	—	—	—	—	—	—	7
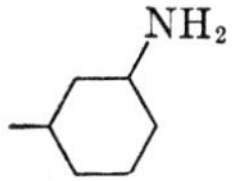 —NH₂	D	252°	Acetyl derivative, m.p. 167°						13,15
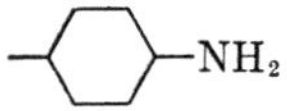 —NH₂	B	239°	—	—	—	—	—	—	1,13
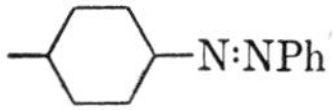 —N:NPh	A	177°	153°	142–143°	229°	250°	189°	Dec. 105° (impure)	2,13
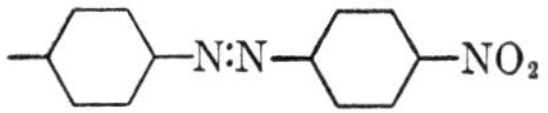 —N:N— ⬡ —NO₂	A	222–223°	—	—	197° (dec.)	281° (dec.)	246°	Impure only	2,13
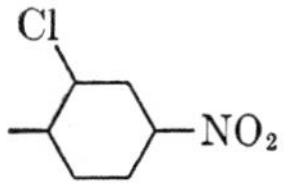 —NO₂	A	204°	166°	169°	153°	195°	218°	210–211°	13,16
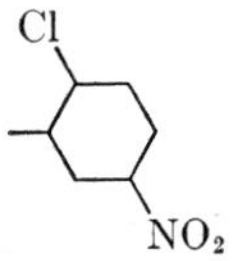 Cl— / —NO₂	A	274°	206°	—	194°	282°	267°	—	17
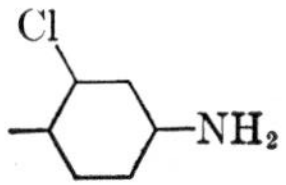 Cl— / —NH₂	B,D	236–237° (dec.)	Acetyl derivative, m.p. 277°						16

Table continued

TABLE XIV-1 (*continued*)

Ar	Prep. of acid a	Melting point of:							Ref.
		Acid	Me ester	Et ester	Acetyl acid	Anilide	N-Me ether	N-Me ether, Me ester	
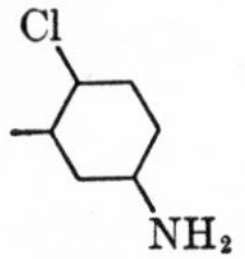 Cl—⬡—NH₂ (methyl)	C	232–233° (dec.)	—	—	—	—	—	—	17
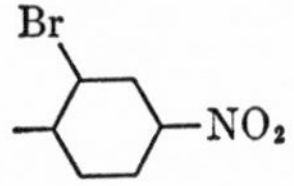 Br—⬡—NO₂ (methyl)	A	235°	179°	178°	121°	207°	229°	212–213°	18
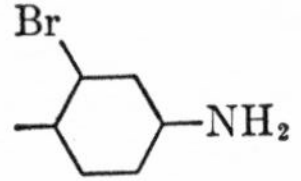 Br—⬡—NH₂ (methyl)	D	233–234°	Acetyl derivative, m.p. 205°						18
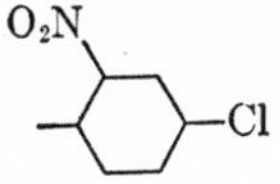 O₂N—⬡—Cl (methyl)	A	229–230°	163–164°	145°	—	130°	207°	129–130°	7
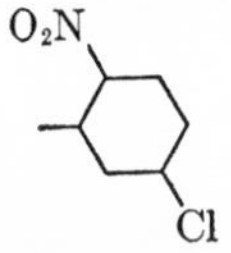 O₂N—⬡—Cl (methyl)	A	241–242°	163°	153°	—	223°	225°	143°	7
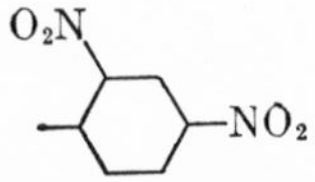 O₂N—⬡—NO₂ (methyl)	A	236°	154°	150°	—	277°	278°	167°	9

Ar	Prep. of acid[a]	Melting point of:							Ref.
		Acid	Me ester	Et ester	Acetyl acid	Anilide	N-Me ether	N-Me ether, Me ester	
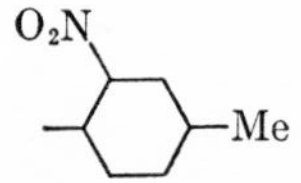 O$_2$N— —Me	A	233°	169°	—	—	—	187–188° (dec.)	—	8
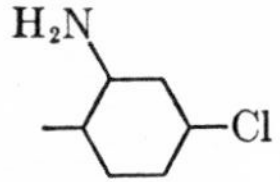 H$_2$N— —Cl	C	214°; re-solid. at 220°; 304°	—	—	—	—	225°c. resolid.; 300° (dec.)	—	7
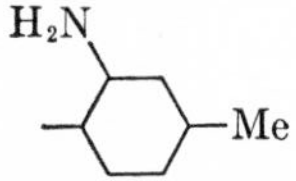 H$_2$N— —Me	C	180–200° (dec.) (crude)	—	—	—	—	—	—	8
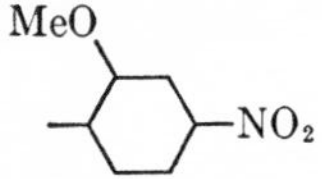 MeO— —NO$_2$	A	231–233°	184–185°	155–156°	186–187°	—	222–223°	152–153°	11
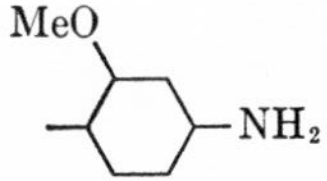 MeO— —NH$_2$	B,D	203–204° (dec.)	—	—	—	—	—	—	11
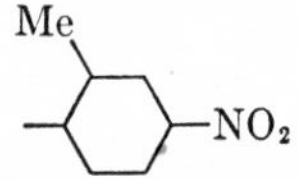 Me— —NO$_2$	A	238°	186°	165°	228°	211–212°	211°	201°	13,19
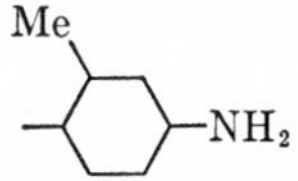 Me— —NH$_2$	B,D	217°	Acetyl derivative (C$_{19}$), m.p. 265°						13,19

Table continued

TABLE XIV-1 (continued)

Ar	Prep. of acid[a]	Melting point of:							Ref.
		Acid	Me ester	Et ester	Acetyl acid	Anilide	N-Me ether	N-Me ether, Me ester	
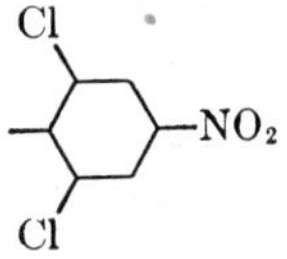 NO_2 (Cl, Cl)	A	245°	169°	160–161°	202–204°	289°	216°	186°	13,20
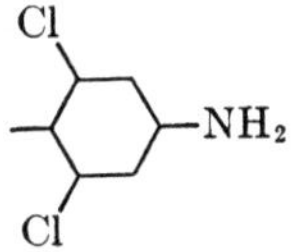 NH_2 (Cl, Cl)	D	242° (dec.)	Acetyl derivative, m.p. 282° (dec.)						20
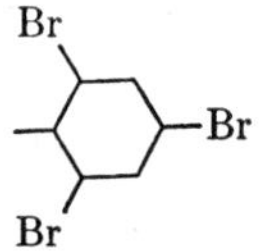 Br, Br	A	227–228°[c]	172°	—	231–232° (dec.)	266°	239–240°	—	4
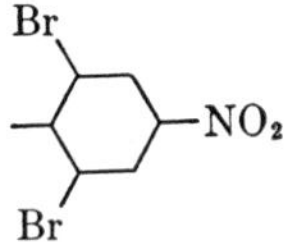 NO_2 (Br, Br)	A	245°	176°	182°	—	280°	240°	215°	13,20
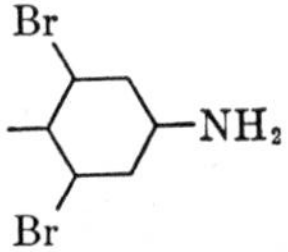 NH_2 (Br, Br)	D	261°	Acetyl derivative, m.p. 270°						20

Ar	Prep. of acid[a]	Melting point of:							Ref.
		Acid	Me ester	Et ester	Acetyl acid	Anilide	N-Me ether	N-Me ether Me ester	
MeO—⟨⟩—NO₂ / OMe	A	212–213°	164°	152°	201–202°	255°	195°	—	12
MeO—⟨⟩—NH₂ / OMe	B	193° (dec.)	—	—	—	—	—	—	12

[a] A, prepared by the reaction scheme shown in text. The alkaline hydrolysis of (IV) is usually exothermic and the temperature requires careful control; temperatures used are 0° to room temperature, and times of reaction are 0.25 hour to 6 days, depending on the nature of Ar. The hydrolysis of (VI) to (I) is usually effected by boiling an aqueous suspension or solution of (VI) and gradually adding concentrated hydrochloric acid until evolution of sulfur dioxide ceases; the reaction generally requires several hours. B, from the corresponding nitro compound by reduction with sodium hydrosulfite and aqueous sodium hydroxide at 70–90°. C, from the corresponding nitro compound by reduction with iron and boiling aqueous acetic acid. D, from the corresponding nitro compound by reduction with stannous chloride and concentrated hydrochloric acid.

[b] On prolonged boiling with pyridine-acetic anhydride (50–70 hours), these acids give the internal anhydrides, C₁₆H₁₂O₂N₂, m.p. > 320° (Ar = Ph), and C₁₆H₁₁O₂N₂Cl, dec. > 340° (Ar = 2'-chlorophenyl).

[c] Prepared from the corresponding nitro compound by reduction with sodium hydrosulfite and aqueous sodium hydroxide at 50°.

Acetyl derivatives are prepared from the hydroxy acids and acetic anhydride, and methyl and ethyl esters by the Fischer-Speier method. The N-methyl ethers are prepared[13] from the hydroxy acids with methyl sulfate (or methyl iodide) and aqueous potassium hydroxide at room temperature; in some cases the reaction is accompanied by formation of the methyl ester of the N-methyl ether, but normally these esters are prepared from the ethers by the Fischer-Speier method.

The acid (I; Ar = 4'-nitro-2'-methoxyphenyl) is converted in poor yield (6%) into the arylaminoisoindolinone-3-acetic acid (X; Ar = 4'-nitro-2'-methoxyphenyl) when it is heated with fuming hydrochloric acid at 180° for 0.5 hour,[11] the main product of the reaction being the corresponding 3-aryl-1-ketophthalazine (XIII).

Acids of type (I) in which the 3-aryl substituent contains a 2'-amino group tend to pass very readily into the lactams (XVI)(see Table XIV-2 for these compounds).

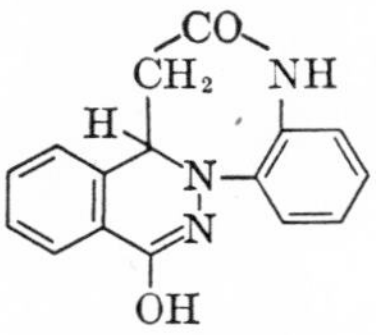

(XVI)
R.I. 2823

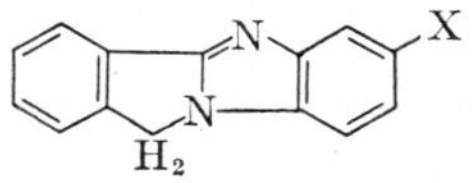

(XVII)

If the acids (I; Ar = 2'-nitrophenyl and 4'-chloro-2'-nitrophenyl) are treated with stannous chloride and boiling concentrated hydrochloric acid, and then reduced further with metallic tin and more acid, they are converted into the benziminazoles (XVII; X = H and Cl, respectively).[7] The same two compounds are also formed from the corresponding 3,2'-aminoaryl acids (I) by refluxing with sulfuric acid and water (5:6, v/v), followed by addition of zinc dust and further refluxing.[7]

TABLE XIV-2. Lactams of 1-Hydroxy-3,2'-aminoaryl-3,4-dihydrophthalazine-4-acetic Acids

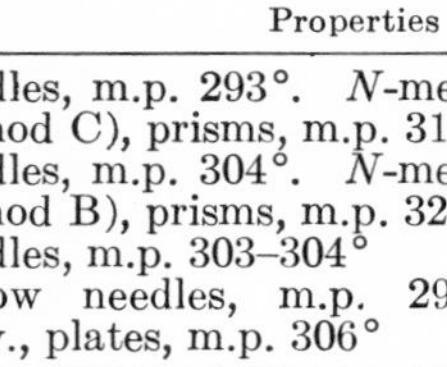

X	Prep.[a]	Properties	Ref.
H	B	Needles, m.p. 293°. N-methyl ether (prep., method C), prisms, m.p. 315–317°	7
4'-Cl	B	Needles, m.p. 304°. N-methyl ether (prep., method B), prisms, m.p. 321°	7
5'-Cl	C	Needles, m.p. 303–304°	7
4'-NH₂	A	Yellow needles, m.p. 290°. Monoacetyl deriv., plates, m.p. 306°	9

[a] A, from the nitroacid, stannous chloride, and boiling concentrated hydrochloric acid. B, from the corresponding amino acid and boiling dilute hydrochloric acid. C, from the corresponding nitro compound, iron, and boiling aqueous acetic acid.

The acid (I; Ar = 2′,4′-dinitrophenyl) shows unexpected properties.[9] If it is refluxed with aqueous sulfuric acid (5:6, v/v) it fails to give
the product (XVIII) which would be expected on the basis of reaction (*3*)
mentioned above, but yields instead the isoindolinone (X; Ar = 2′,4′-
dinitrophenyl), together with a small amount of a compound (XIX) (yellow prisms, m.p. 223°), which may be regarded as a hydration product of
(XVIII). Mixtures of (X) and (XIX) containing higher proportions of
the latter are obtained by using concentrated sulfuric acid (alone or with
acetic acid) instead of aqueous acid. On oxidation with chromic anhydride
in acetic acid at 40°, (XIX) yields the substituted phthalimide (XX). An
analog (XXI) (+ 2H₂O, yellow needles, m.p. 151°) of (XIX) is formed when
the lactam (XXII) is refluxed with aqueous sulfuric acid (5:6, v/v).

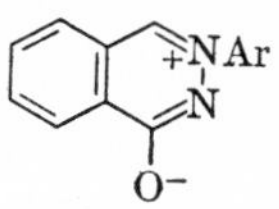

(XVIII) 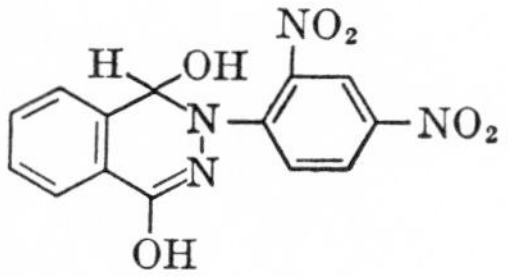   (XIX) 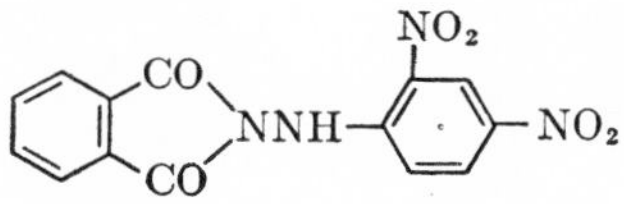   (XX)

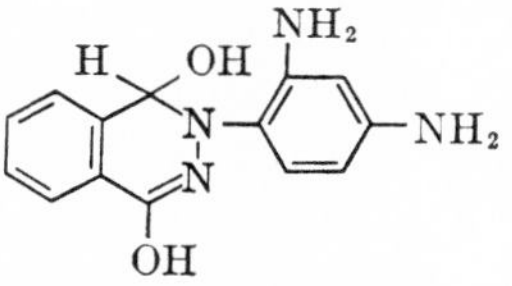

(XXI) 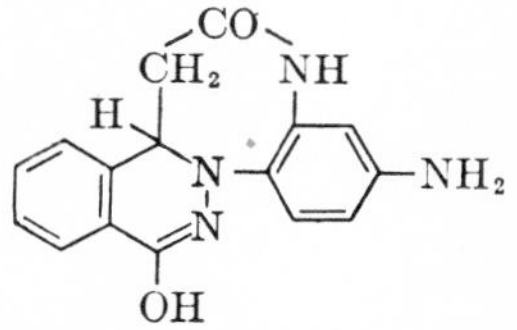   (XXII)
R.I. 2823   (XXIII)

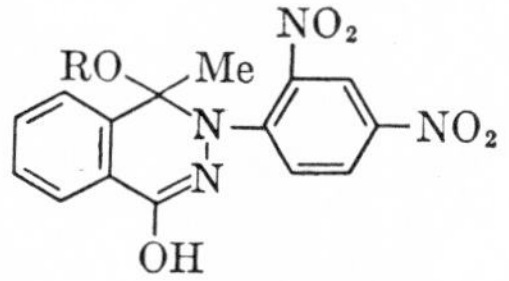

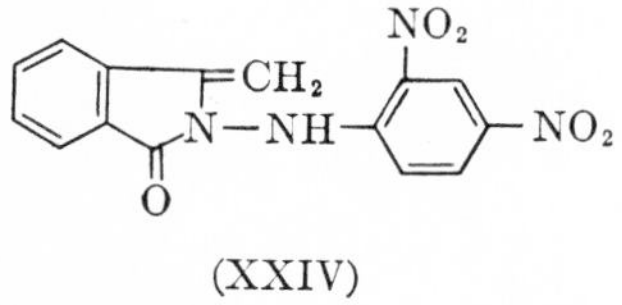

(XXIV) 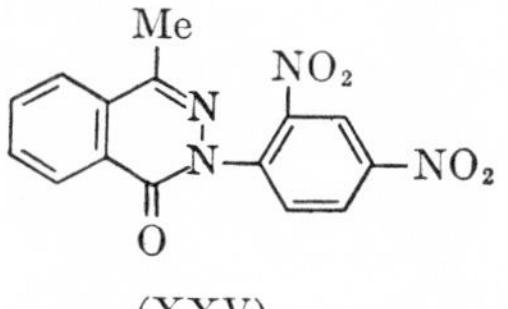   (XXV)

The behavior of (I; Ar = 2′,4′-dinitrophenyl) on oxidation with acid
dichromate is likewise exceptional, the products being the isoindolinone
(XIV; X = 4′-NO₂) and the hydrate (XXIII; R = H) (orange prisms,
m.p. 232°) of the expected product (XII) (*cf.* reaction *2* above); the oxidation can also be brought about with nitric acid. If (XXIII; R = H) is
crystallized from methanol containing a trace of mineral acid it yields the
ether (XXIII; R = Me) (orange needles, m.p. 185°), from which (XXIII;

R = H) is regenerated by boiling for a short time with aqueous ammonia
(d 0.880). That (XXIII; R = H) is not merely the zwitterion (XII)
with a molecule of water of crystallization is shown by its behavior on oxidation with chromic anhydride in acetic acid; the phthalimide derivative
(XX) is thereby formed, whereas the compounds (XII; Ar = 2′-, 3′-, and
4′-nitrophenyl) are unchanged even if the oxidations are attempted at
100°. Treatment of (XXIII; R = H) with aqueous (1:8) hydrochloric
acid at 190° for 6 hours yields the methyleneisoindolinone derivative
(XXIV). With concentrated sulfuric acid at 180°, (XXIII; R = H) is
converted into (XXV)(Chapter XIII, Table 3); this product is likewise
formed by similar treatment of (XXIV), and also, together with the corresponding isoindolinone (X), by the action of fuming hydrochloric acid at
180° on (I; Ar = 2′,4′-dinitrophenyl).

If the acid (I; Ar = 2′,4′-dinitrophenyl) is suspended in water at 80°
and treated with potassium permanganate (added all at once), the normal
oxidation product (as XI) is produced; if, however, the reaction is performed by gradually adding the permanganate at 60°, the product is the
isoindolinone (X; Ar = 2′,4′-dinitrophenyl).

References

1. Rowe, Levin, Burns, Davies, and Tepper, *J. Chem. Soc.*, **1926**, 690.
2. Rowe and Tomlinson, *J. Chem. Soc.*, **1932**, 1118.
3. Rowe and Peters, *J. Chem. Soc.*, **1931**, 1065.
4. Peters, Pringle, and Rowe, *J. Chem. Soc.*, **1948**, 597.
5. Brodrick, Peters, and Rowe, *J. Chem. Soc.*, **1948**, 1026.
6. Peters, Rowe, and Brodrick, *J. Chem. Soc.*, **1948**, 1249.
7. Rowe, Dovey, Garforth, Levin, Pask, and Peters, *J. Chem. Soc.*, **1935**, 1796.
8. Rowe, Haigh, and Peters, *J. Chem. Soc.*, **1936**, 1098.
9. Rowe and Osborn, *J. Chem. Soc.*, **1947**, 829.
10. Rowe, McFadyen, and Peters, *J. Chem. Soc.*, **1947**, 468.
11. Rowe and Cross, *J. Chem. Soc.*, **1947**, 461.
12. Rowe, Desai, and Peters, *J. Chem. Soc.*, **1948**, 281.
13. Rowe and Peters, *J. Chem. Soc.*, **1933**, 1067.
14. Rowe *et al.*, *J. Chem. Soc.*, **1937**, 90.
15. Rowe, Himmat, and Levin, *J. Chem. Soc.*, **1928**, 2556.
16. Rowe and Dunbar, *J. Chem. Soc.*, **1932**, 11.
17. Rowe, Peters, and Rangwala, *J. Chem. Soc.*, **1948**, 206.
18. Rowe, Jambuserwala, and Partridge, *J. Chem. Soc.*, **1935**, 1134.
19. Rowe and Siddle, *J. Chem. Soc.*, **1932**, 473.
20. Rowe, Dunbar, and N. H. Williams, *J. Chem. Soc.*, **1931**, 1073.

CHAPTER XV

3-Aryl-1-ketophthalazines

These substances are dipolar compounds of the general formula (I), where R = H or Me, and Ar = phenyl or substituted phenyl. The compounds in which R = H are listed in Table XV-1, and the 4-methyl homologs in Table XV-2.

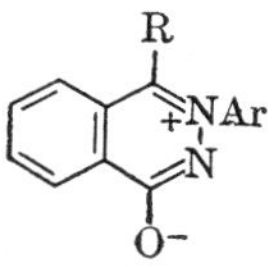

(I)

A. Preparation. These compounds are in general prepared from 1-hydroxy-3-aryl-3,4-dihydrophthalazine-4-acetic acids (II) by removal of the elements of acetic acid to give 3-aryl-1-ketophthalazines (III), or of

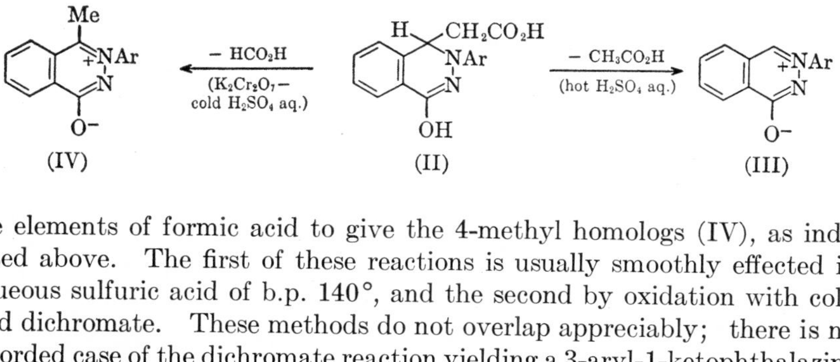

(IV)   (II)   (III)

the elements of formic acid to give the 4-methyl homologs (IV), as indicated above. The first of these reactions is usually smoothly effected in aqueous sulfuric acid of b.p. 140°, and the second by oxidation with cold acid dichromate. These methods do not overlap appreciably; there is no recorded case of the dichromate reaction yielding a 3-aryl-1-ketophthalazine (III) by loss of acetic acid, and there are only two examples of the removal of formic acid to give (IV) *via* the agency of hot dilute sulfuric acid (see Table XV-2). The conversion of (II) into (IV), but not that of (II) into (III), can be effected also in hot alkaline solution. Compounds of either type (III) or type (IV) in which the aryl group contains an amino group may also be prepared by reduction of the corresponding nitro compounds. Other methods of less general application are given in Tables XV-1 and 2.

TABLE XV-1. 3-Aryl-1-ketophthalazines

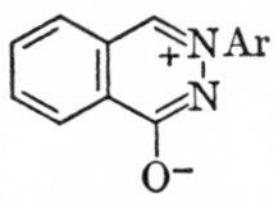

Ar	Prep.[a]	M.p., °C.	Derivatives	Ref.
Ph	A	208	Hydrochloride, m.p. 162–164°; picrate, m.p. 226°; x-sulfonic acid	8
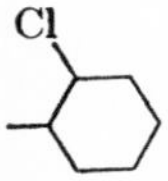 (2-Cl-phenyl)	A,C,D	202–203	Picrate, m.p. 233–234°	7
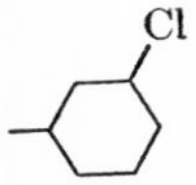 (3-Cl-phenyl)	C	278	Picrate, m.p. 253–254°	6
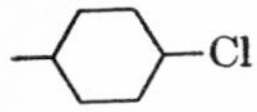 (4-Cl-phenyl)	C	281–283	—	6
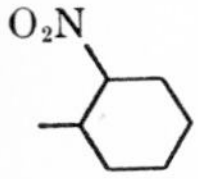 (2-O_2N-phenyl)	C	266	Picrate, m.p. 214–215°	5
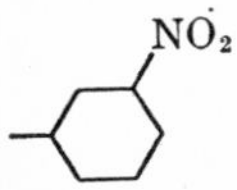 (3-NO_2-phenyl)	C	324	Picrate, m.p. 234°	10
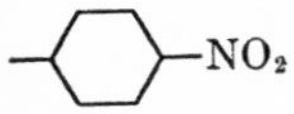 (4-NO_2-phenyl)	C	333	Picrate, m.p. 218°	9
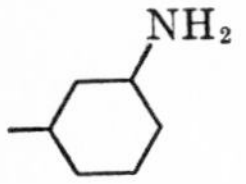 (3-NH_2-phenyl)	C,G	210	Ac deriv., m.p. 204°	10
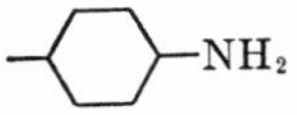 (4-NH_2-phenyl)	G,M	259	Ac deriv., m.p. 348°	9,19
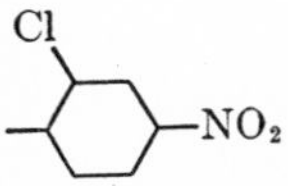 (2-Cl-4-NO_2-phenyl)	C	196	—	2,20
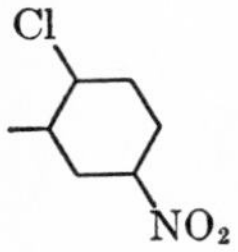 (2-Cl-5-NO_2-phenyl)	D	255	Picrate, m.p. 222°	17
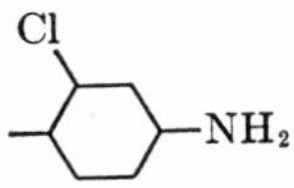 (2-Cl-4-NH_2-phenyl)	C	240 (dec.)	Ac deriv., m.p. 321° (dec.)	2

TABLE XV-1. 3-Aryl-1-ketophthalazines (*continued*)

Ar	Prep.[a]	M.p., °C.	Derivatives	Ref.
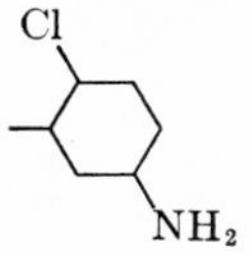 Cl, NH₂ (substituted ring)	D	258 (dec.)	Ac deriv., m.p. 309–310° (dec.)	17
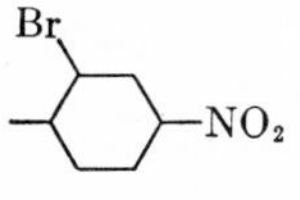 Br, –NO₂	C	209	—	4,20
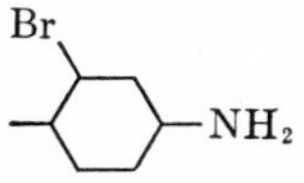 Br, –NH₂	C	242	—	4
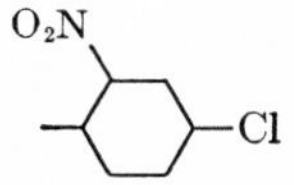 O₂N, –Cl	C	263	Picrate, m.p. 230°	5,20
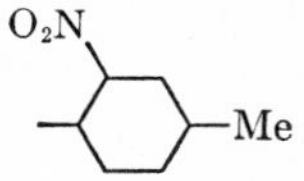 O₂N, –Me	C	256–258	—	16
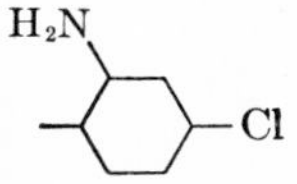 H₂N, –Cl	C,J	Darkens 200, subl. 300–350	Ac deriv., m.p. 130–131°	5
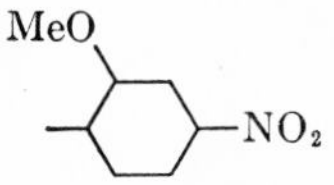 MeO, –NO₂	A,C	228–229	Picrate, m.p. 229–231°	13
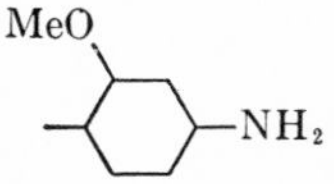 MeO, –NH₂	C,G	267–268 (dec.)	Ac deriv., m.p. 285–286°	13
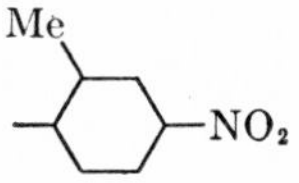 Me, –NO₂	C	279	Picrate, m.p. 208–210	3
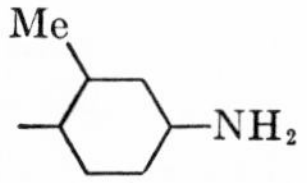 Me, –NH₂	C,G,P	255	Ac deriv., m.p. 300–302°	
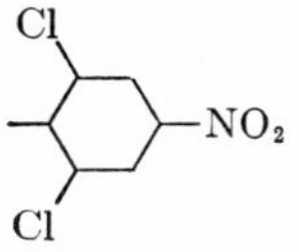 Cl, –NO₂, Cl	C	315 (dec.)	Picrate, m.p. 233°	12

Table continued

TABLE XVI-1. 3-Aryl-1-ketophthalazines (*continued*)

Ar	Prep.[a]	M.p., °C.	Derivatives	Ref.
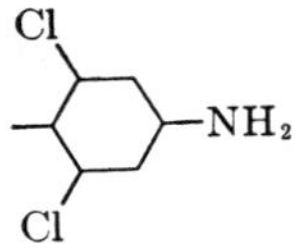 Cl, Cl —NH₂ (dichlorophenyl)	C,G	302	Ac deriv., m.p. 334°	12
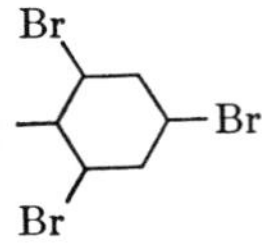 Br, Br —Br (tribromophenyl)	C,D	305 (dec.)	Picrate, m.p. 266° (dec.)	6
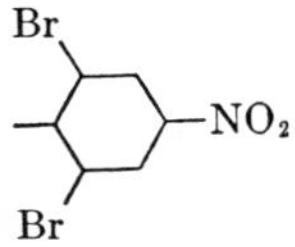 Br, Br —NO₂	C	306	Picrate, m.p. 252°	12
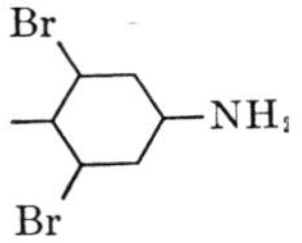 Br, Br —NH₂	C,G	304	Ac deriv., m.p. 338	12

[a] For methods of preparation, see key to Table XV-2.

TABLE XV-2. 3-Aryl-4-methyl-1-ketophthalazines

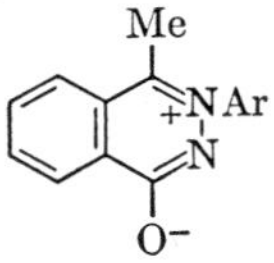

Ar	Prep.[a]	M.p., °C.	Derivatives	Ref.
Ph	B	235	Picrate, m.p. 197°; x-sulfonic acid	8
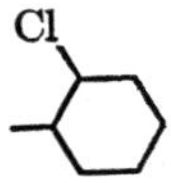 Cl (2-chlorophenyl)	E,F	253–255	Picrate, m.p. 199–200° (dec.)	7
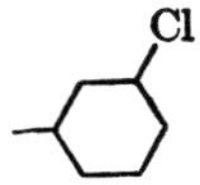 Cl (3-chlorophenyl)	E	—	Picrate, m.p. 219°; sulfate, m.p. 320°	6
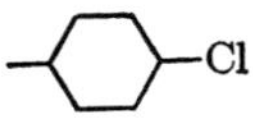 —Cl (4-chlorophenyl)	E	238	Picrate, m.p. 200°	6
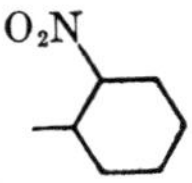 O₂N (nitrophenyl)	E	226 (dec.)	Picrate, m.p. 217°	5

Table continued

TABLE XV-2. 3-Aryl-4-methyl-1-ketophthalazines (*continued*)

Ar	Prep.[a]	M.p., °C.	Derivatives	Ref.
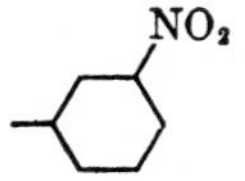 (NO₂-substituted aryl)	B,E	260 (dec.)	Picrate, m.p. 197°	1,16
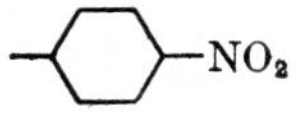 (—NO₂ aryl)	E,F,R	251	Picrate, m. p. 208°; nitrate, m.p. 169°; sulfate, m.p. 246°	8,11, 15,20
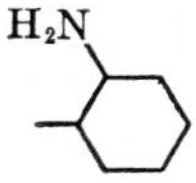 (H₂N aryl)	G,K	218	Ac deriv., m.p. 274°	5
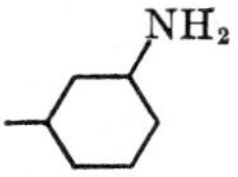 (NH₂ aryl)	E,G,H	271	Ac deriv., m.p. 274°	1
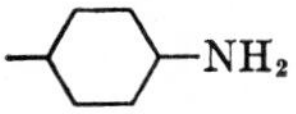 (—NH₂ aryl)	E,G,H,L,Q	277	Ac deriv., m.p. 316–317°	11,12, 21
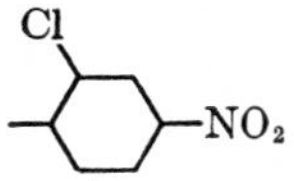 (Cl, —NO₂ aryl)	E	201	Picrate, m.p. 204–205°	2
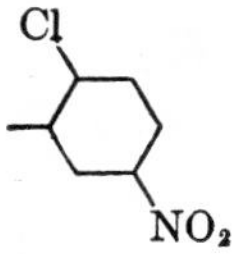 (Cl, NO₂ aryl)	E,F	244	Picrate, m.p. 234°	17
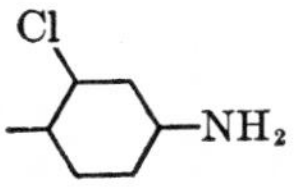 (Cl, —NH₂ aryl)	E,G,H,P	285	Ac deriv., m.p. 308° (dec.)	2
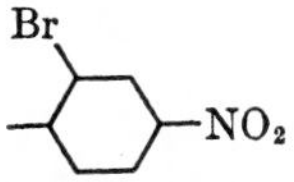 (Br, —NO₂ aryl)	E	225	—	4
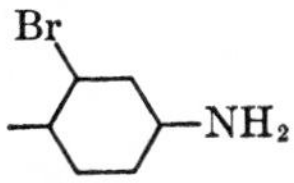 (Br, —NH₂ aryl)	E,G,H	279–280	—	4
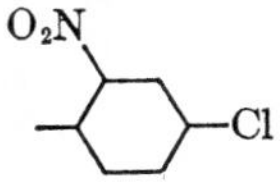 (O₂N, —Cl aryl)	E	237	Picrate, m.p. 223°	5
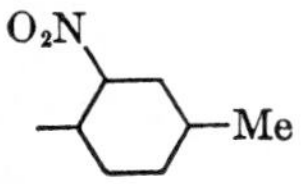 (O₂N, —Me aryl)	E	236	—	16

Table continued

TABLE XV-2. 3-Aryl-4-methyl-1-ketophthalazines *(continued)*

Ar	Prep.[a]	M.p., °C.	Derivatives	Ref.
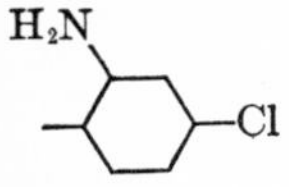 H$_2$N— (ring) —Cl	G,K	257	Ac deriv., m.p. 296°	5
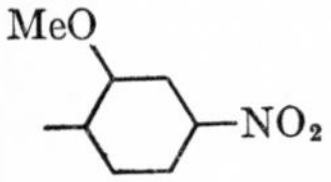 MeO— (ring) —NO$_2$	E	223–224 (dec.)	Picrate, m.p. 216–217° (dec.)	13
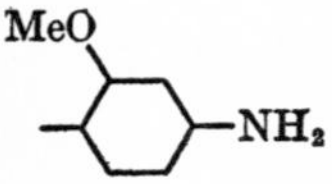 MeO— (ring) —NH$_2$	C,G,H,I	287–288 (dec.)	Ac deriv., m.p. 296–297° (dec.)	13
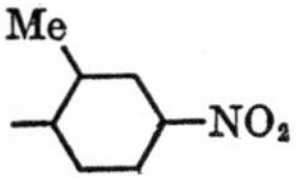 Me— (ring) —NO$_2$	E	209–210	Picrate, m.p. 229–230°	3
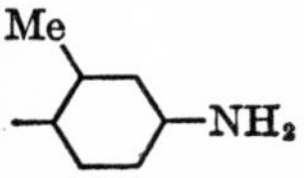 Me— (ring) —NH$_2$	E,G,H,P	287–288	Ac deriv., m.p. 304–305°	3
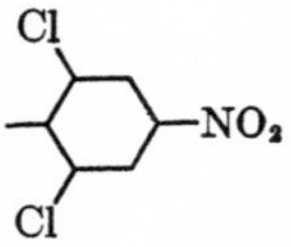 Cl, Cl— (ring) —NO$_2$	E	240 (dec.)	Picrate, m.p. 225°	12
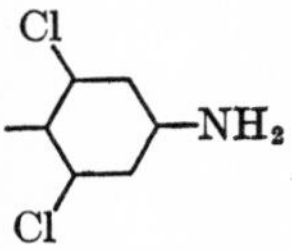 Cl, Cl— (ring) —NH$_2$	E,G,H	325	Ac deriv., m.p. 311°	12
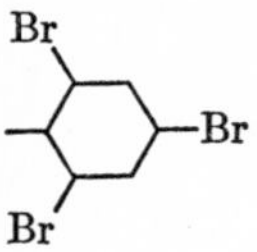 Br, Br— (ring) —Br	E,F	252	—	6
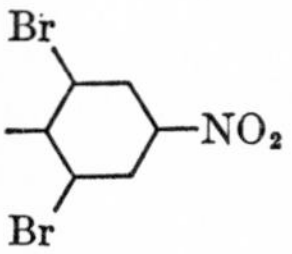 Br, Br— (ring) —NO$_2$	E	254	Picrate, m.p. 215°	12
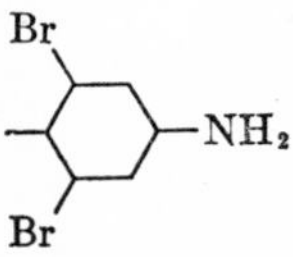 Br, Br— (ring) —NH$_2$	E,G,H	315	Ac deriv., m.p. 315°	12

TABLE XV-2. 3-Aryl-4-methyl-1-ketophthalazines *(continued)*

Ar	Prep.[a]	M.p., °C.	Derivatives	Ref.
MeO—⬡—NO₂ (OMe)	A,C,D,E,F	254	Picrate, m.p. 229°	14
MeO—⬡—NH₂ (OMe)	G	260	—	14
	E,N,O	302	—	5,20
	E,O	314	—	5

---

[a] A, from the 1-hydroxy-3-aryl-3,4-dihydrophthalazine-4-acetic acid (a) and fuming hydrochloric acid at 160–180°. B, from (a) and chromic anhydride in aqueous acetic acid at 20°. C, from (a) and dilute sulfuric acid (usually 5:6, v/v) under reflux. D, from (a) and concentrated sulfuric acid-acetic acid (1:1, v/v) under reflux. E, from (a), sodium or potassium dichromate, and aqueous sulfuric acid, usually in the cold. F, from (a) and nitric acid (*d* 1.5) at 0–50°. G, from the corresponding nitro compound and boiling aqueous sodium sulfide. H, from (a) and aqueous sodium hydroxide (under reflux or at 95°), or alcoholic potassium hydroxide under reflux. I, from (a) and hydrogen peroxide-aqueous sodium hydroxide at 50°. J, from the lactam of the 1-hydroxy-3,2′-aminoaryl-3,4-dihydrophthalazine-4-acetic acid (b) by refluxing with aqueous sulfuric acid (5:6, v/v). K, from the lactam of the 1-keto-3,2′-aminoarylphthalazine-4-acetic acid (see last two compounds in Table XV-2 for type formula) by boiling with aqueous sodium sulfide.

L, by method C, using the compounds (a; Ar = —⬡—N=NPh) and (a;

Ar = —⬡—N=N—⬡—NO₂). M, from (a) and concentrated hydro-

chloric acid under reflux. N, from (b) and nitric acid (*d* 1.5) at room temperature. O, from (b), sodium dichromate, and aqueous sulfuric acid at 50°. P, from the corresponding 1-hydroxy-3-aryl-3,4-dihydrophthalazine (or its 4-methyl homolog) by prolonged boiling with nitrobenzene or with concentrated hydrochloric acid. Q, from the 2′,6′-dibromo analog (in poor yield) by reduction with sodium hydrosulfite in boiling aqueous-alcoholic sodium hydroxide. R, by nitration of 1-hydroxy-3-phenyl-3,4-dihydrophthalazine-4-acetic acid [nitric acid (*d* 1.5) at ≯10°].

B. Properties and Reactions.   The 3-aryl-1-ketophthalazines are yellow crystalline solids except in those cases in which the 3-aryl substituent contains neither a nitro nor an amino group; such compounds are colorless.   The solubility characteristics of this group reflect well their zwitterion structure.   Thus typical compounds are soluble in polar solvents (pyridine, nitrobenzene, acetic acid), but insoluble or sparingly soluble in nonpolar solvents.   Furthermore, the compounds are amphoteric; with dilute or moderately concentrated mineral acids they form salts (which are easily hydrolyzed), and, although insoluble in sodium carbonate, they dissolve in warm dilute sodium hydroxide; the acidic character of the zwitterions is, however, much reduced if the 3-substituent is aminoaryl.   The N-acetyl derivatives of 3-aminoaryl-1-ketophthalazines are usually colorless compounds which frequently turn blue on exposure to light and air.   As indicated in Tables XV-1 and 2, 3-aryl-1-ketophthalazines form well-defined picrates.

On reduction, 3-aryl-1-ketophthalazines yield, according to conditions, either 1-hydroxy-3-aryl-3,4-dihydrophthalazines (V)[1-8] or N-arylphthalimidines (VI).[2-4,6-14]   This behavior is characteristic of the group; it holds good for the two types R = H and R = Me, and applies to compounds in

(VI)   (V)

which Ar contains NO_2, NH_2, or neither of these groups.   [If Ar contains NO_2, this is reduced to NH_2 in the resultant compounds (V) or (VI).]   The reduction to (V) may be carried out either in alkaline (sodium hydrosulfite and sodium hydroxide) or acid (zinc dust or amalgamated zinc and dilute hydrochloric or sulfuric acid) media, but the conversion into the phthalimidines (VI) is invariably carried out in acid solution (zinc dust or amalgamated zinc and dilute hydrochloric acid).   It is frequently possible to prepare at will either the dihydrophthalazine (V) or the phthalimidine (VI) from a given 3-aryl-1-ketophthalazine according to conditions, those for the reduction to (VI) being the more drastic.   However, 3-polyhalogenoaryl- and 3-methoxyaryl-1-ketophthalazines tend to give (VI) rather than (V); and if the 3-aryl substituent contains bromine, this is sometimes wholly or partially replaced by hydrogen during the reduction.[4,6,12]

On treatment with warm methyl sulfate either alone or in nitrobenzene, 3-aryl-1-ketophthalazines are converted into methylated products con-

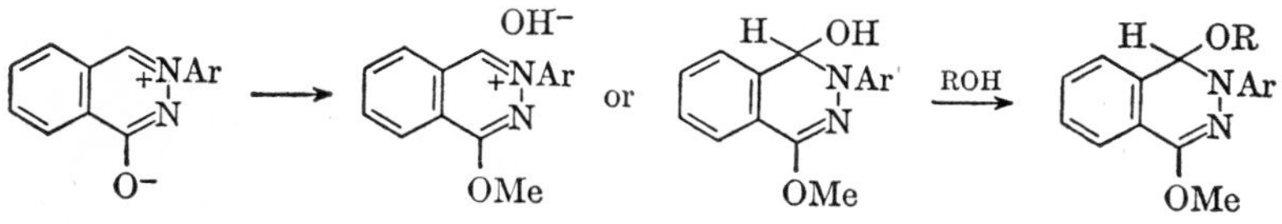

(VII)   (VIII)   (IX)

taining a methoxyl group at C_1. If the original zwitterion contains a hydrogen atom at C_4, the initial reaction product (after basification) is the
quaternary or pseudo base (VII or VIII). Such compounds, however,
are usually ill-defined, and, although one or two quaternary perchlorates
derived from (VII) have been prepared (Chapter XVI, Section 1B),[13,15]
the usual procedure has been to characterize the initial products, by crystallization from methyl or ethyl alcohol, as the 1,4-dialkoxy derivatives
(IX).[3,5−10,12,13,15,16] 3-Aryl-4-methyl-1-ketophthalazines, on the other
hand, yield (after basification) 4-methylene derivatives (X), giving salts
of the type (XI) with acids.[2,3,6,7,11−15,17]

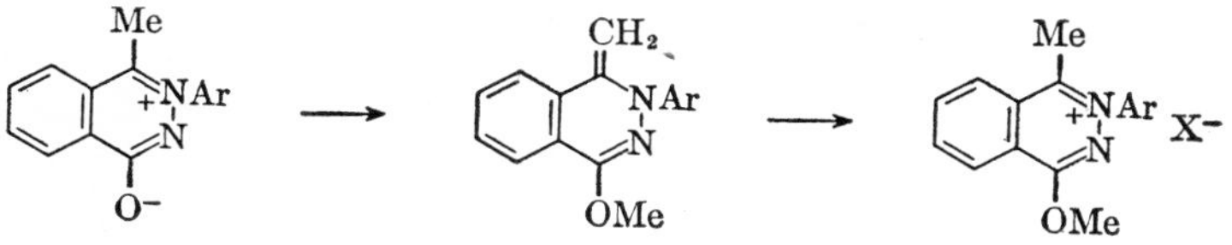

(X)   (XI)

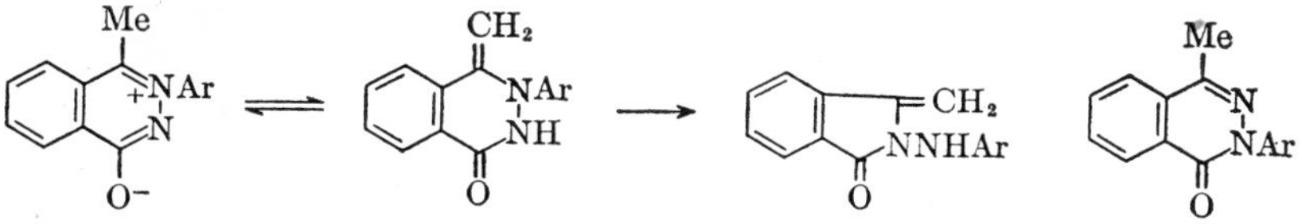

(XII)   (XIII)

An interesting reaction, but of more restricted scope than the foregoing,
is the conversion of certain 3-aryl-4-methyl-1-ketophthalazines into the
isomeric 2-arylamino-3-methyleneisoindolinones (XII). The reaction,
which takes place in an acid medium, is considered to proceed *via* the tautomeric form of the zwitterion, as shown above.[18] It occurs only with compounds in which the 3-aryl substituent contains a 2'- or a 4'-NO_2 group.
The conditions of reaction are considerably milder than those necessary to
effect the isomerization of 3-aryl-1-ketophthalazines into 2-aryl-1-keto-1,2-
dihydrophthalazines (Chapter XIII, Section 2); thus the formation of
(XII) occurs to a small extent even on heating the 3-aryl-1-ketophthalazine
in water. Optimum conversion is sometimes achieved by refluxing the
zwitterion in dilute hydrochloric acid, but the maximum yield of (XII) is
usually attained by using 0.1–0.2 N hydrochloric acid at 150° for 6 hours.

The reaction rates are influenced by substituents, and are in the order 4'-Cl-2'-NO$_2$ > 2'-NO$_2$ > 2'-NO$_2$-4'-Me > 2'-Cl-4'-NO$_2$ > 2'-Br-4'-NO$_2$ > 2',6'-Cl$_2$-4'-NO$_2$; for the 4'-nitro compounds more drastic conditions are required.   When 3,2'-nitrophenyl-4-methyl-1-ketophthalazine is refluxed with 0.8 N hydrochloric acid, the reaction is approximately unimolecular, $k = 41 \times 10^{-3}$.   The compounds (XII) formed from this reaction are converted into the isomeric 2-aryl-4-methyl-1-keto-1,2-dihydrophthalazines (XIII) with dilute (1:8) hydrochloric acid at 180–190° for 6 hours (or with concentrated sulfuric acid at 180° for 1–2 minutes).   Despite this observation, the authors[18] consider that the conversion of 3-aryl-1-ketophthalazines in general into the isomeric 2-aryl-1-keto-1,2-dihydrophthalazines does not proceed *via* the intermediate formation of compounds analogous to (XII) owing to the failure to isolate such compounds other than in the few cases referred to above.

The compounds (XIV; R = H and Me) show exceptional properties in that they undergo hydration when heated with aqueous (1:8) hydrochloric acid for some hours at 135–145°, giving the compounds (XV; R = H) (yellow needles, m.p. 225–227°) and (XV; R = Me) (yellow needles, m.p. 238°), respectively.[17]

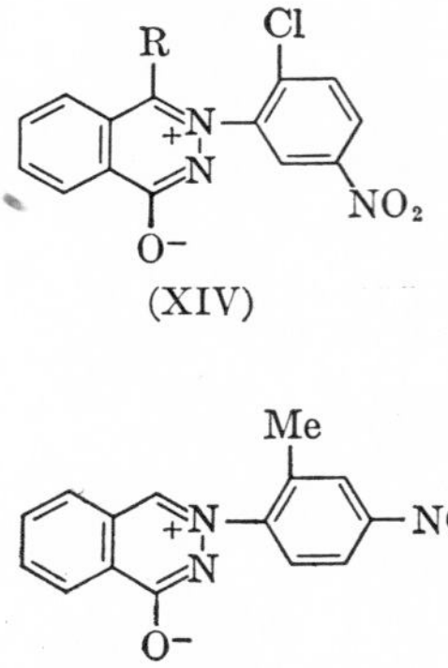

(XIV) 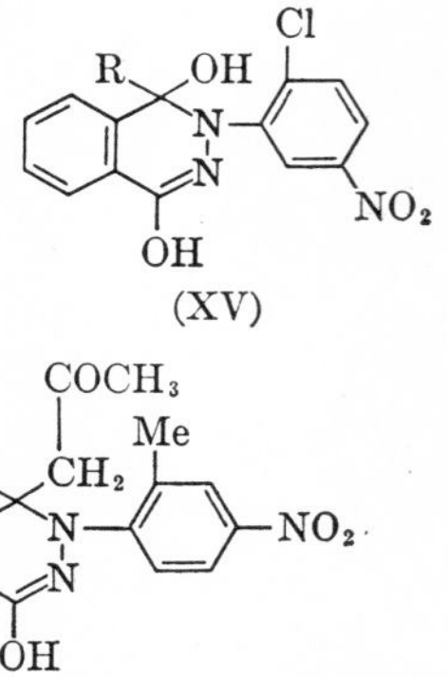   (XV)

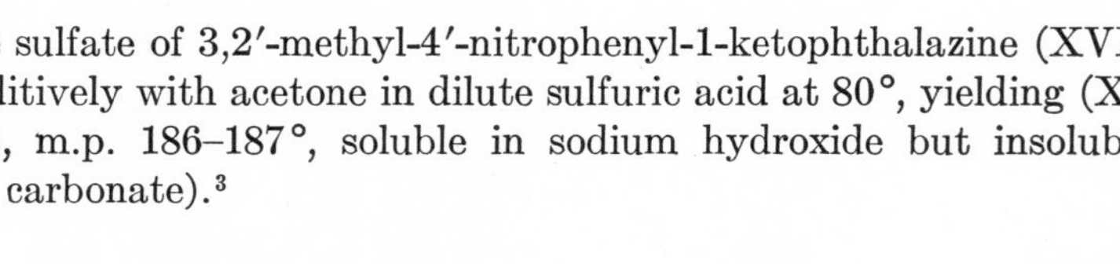

(XVI)   ⟶   (XVII)

The sulfate of 3,2'-methyl-4'-nitrophenyl-1-ketophthalazine (XVI) reacts additively with acetone in dilute sulfuric acid at 80°, yielding (XVII) (needles, m.p. 186–187°, soluble in sodium hydroxide but insoluble in sodium carbonate).[3]

References

1. Rowe and Peters, *J. Chem. Soc.*, **1931**, 1918.
2. Rowe and Dunbar, *J. Chem. Soc.*, **1932**, 11.
3. Rowe and Siddle, *J. Chem. Soc.*, **1932**, 473.
4. Rowe, Jambuserwala, and Partridge, *J. Chem. Soc.*, **1935**, 1134.
5. Rowe, Dovey, Garforth, Levin, Pask, and Peters, *J. Chem. Soc.*, **1935**, 1796.
6. Peters, Pringle, and Rowe, *J. Chem. Soc.*, **1948**, 597.
7. Brodrick, Peters, and Rowe, *J. Chem. Soc.*, **1948**, 1026.
8. Peters, Rowe, and Brodrick, *J. Chem. Soc.*, **1948**, 1249.
9. Rowe and Levin, *J. Chem. Soc.*, **1928**, 2550.
10. Rowe, Himmat, and Levin, *J. Chem. Soc.*, **1928**, 2556.
11. Rowe, Levin, and Peters, *J. Chem. Soc.*, **1931**, 1067.
12. Rowe, Dunbar, and N. H. Williams, *J. Chem. Soc.*, **1931**, 1073.
13. Rowe and Cross, *J. Chem. Soc.*, **1947**, 461.
14. Rowe, Desai, and Peters, *J. Chem. Soc.*, **1948**, 281.
15. Rowe and Twitchett, *J. Chem. Soc.*, **1936**, 1704.
16. Rowe, Haigh, and Peters, *J. Chem. Soc.*, **1936**, 1098.
17. Rowe, Peters, and Rangwala, *J. Chem. Soc.*, **1948**, 206.
18. Rowe, *et al.*, *J. Chem. Soc.*, **1937**, 90.
19. Rowe, Levin, Burns, Davies, and Tepper, *J. Chem. Soc.*, **1926**, 690.
20. Rowe and Osborn, *J. Chem. Soc.*, **1947**, 829.
21. Rowe and Tomlinson, *J. Chem. Soc.*, **1932**, 1118.

CHAPTER XVI

Methylated Derivatives of 3-Aryl-1-ketophthalazines

1. Derivatives of Compounds Containing a Hydrogen Atom at C$_4$

A. 1-Methoxy-4-alkoxy-3-aryl-3,4-dihydrophthalazines

Preparation. These compounds have the general formula (II; R = Me or Et), and are prepared by treatment of 3-aryl-1-ketophthalazines with methyl sulfate. Temperatures of 70–150° are employed; the reactions at the higher temperatures have usually been carried out using nitrobenzene as solvent, but it has been stated[1] that better results may be obtained by omitting the nitrobenzene and working at a lower temperature. If nitrobenzene is used, it is removed in steam; the mixture is then made alkaline with sodium carbonate and the product recrystallized from methanol or ethanol. A pseudo base (Ia) is probably first formed, which then gives the O-ether (II) (Eq. 1).

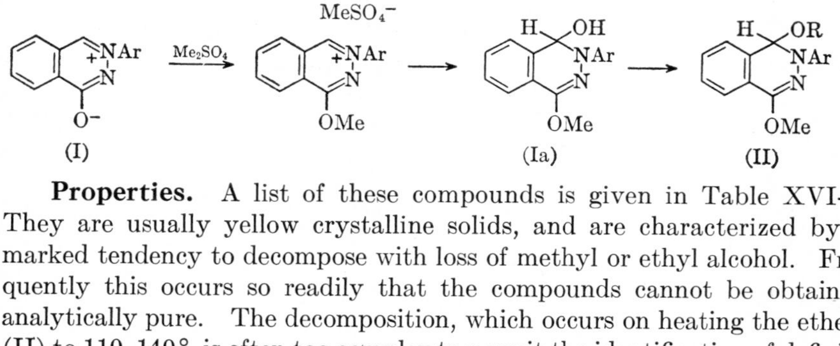

Properties. A list of these compounds is given in Table XVI-1. They are usually yellow crystalline solids, and are characterized by a marked tendency to decompose with loss of methyl or ethyl alcohol. Frequently this occurs so readily that the compounds cannot be obtained analytically pure. The decomposition, which occurs on heating the ethers (II) to 110–140°, is often too complex to permit the identification of definite products.[2-6] However, the compounds (II; Ar = Ph) and (II; Ar = 2'-chlorophenyl) decompose comparatively smoothly according to equation 2, giving fair yields of the products (III; Ar = Ph) [yellow needles, m.p. 234° (dec.)] and (III; Ar = 2'-chlorophenyl) [yellow cubes, m.p. 239° (dec.)].[7,8] Compounds of unknown structure, but which may possibly be impure specimens of (III), have been isolated in one or two other instances. Thus if the crude methylation product of (I; Ar = 4'-nitro-2'-

TABLE XVI-1. 1-Methoxy-4-alkoxy-3-aryl-3,4-dihydrophthalazines

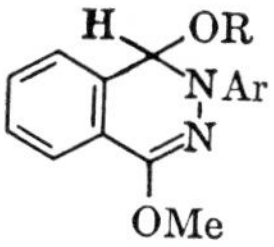

Ar	M.p., °C.		Ref.
	R = Me	R = Et	
Ph	—	86–87	7
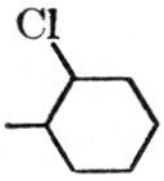 2-Cl-C6H4	78	86	8
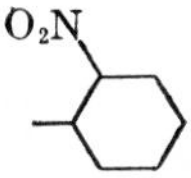 2-O2N-C6H4	135	150	2
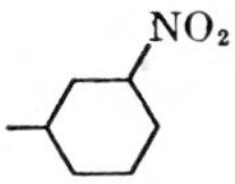 3-NO2-C6H4	114–117	116–120	11
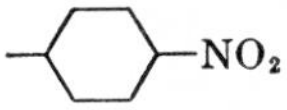 4-NO2-C6H4	138–141	173–175	10
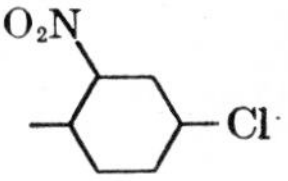 2-O2N-4-Cl-C6H3	138	110	2
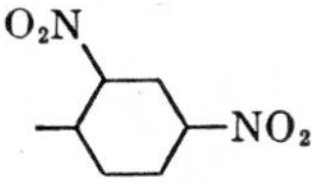 2-O2N-4-NO2-C6H3 a	196	197	6
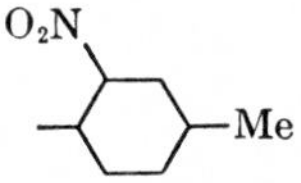 2-O2N-4-Me-C6H3	119–121	115–117	4
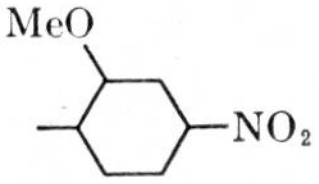 2-MeO-4-NO2-C6H3	161–163	116–117	5
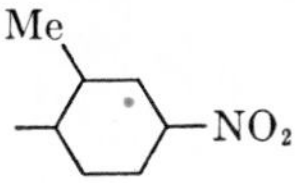 2-Me-4-NO2-C6H3	149–150	93	12
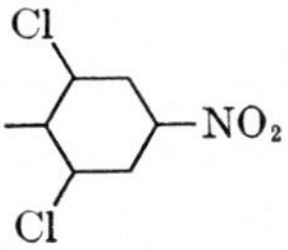 2,5-Cl2-4-NO2-C6H2	157	111	9

Table continued

TABLE XVI-I. 1-Methoxy-4-alkoxy-3-aryl-3,4-dihydrophthalazines (*contd.*)

Ar	M.p., °C.		Ref.
	R = Me	R = Et	
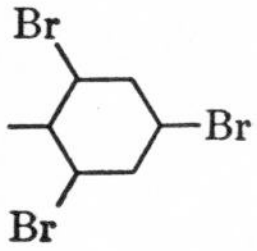 Br / Br / Br-substituted aryl (—Br)	138–139	135–136	14
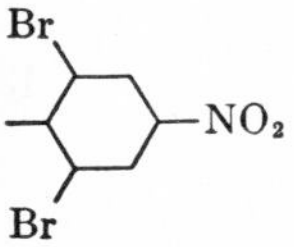 Br / Br-substituted aryl (—NO₂)	138	110–112	9

[a] Prepared by methylation of the 1,4-dihydroxy-3-aryl-3,4-dihydrophthalazine, followed by crystallization from ROH.

$$2\ (\text{II}) \longrightarrow 2\text{ROH} + \left[\begin{array}{c} \text{NAr} \\ \text{N} \\ \text{OMe} \end{array} \right]_2 \tag{2}$$

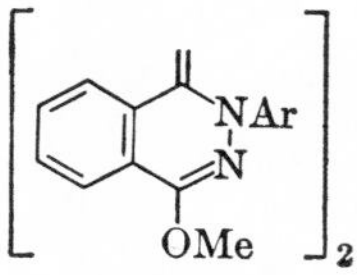

(III)

methoxyphenyl) is crystallized from ethyl acetate instead of from methanol or ethanol, a product, m.p. 261–264°, is obtained, analysis of which suggests that partial dehydration of the pseudo base (Ia) has occurred[5]; and if the ethers (II; Ar = 2',6'-dichloro- and 2',6'-dibromo-4'-nitrophenyl) are heated to 110–140°, products are formed (m.p. 235 and 228°, respectively) which from analysis are likewise anhydro derivatives of (Ia).[9]

In three other cases (II; Ar = 3'- and 4'-nitrophenyl and 4'-nitro-2'-methylphenyl) a fairly smooth thermal decomposition of a different kind occurs; it is accompanied by oxidation, and the products are the 4-keto derivatives (IV).[10−12]

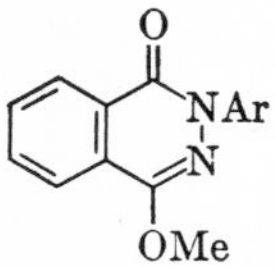

(IV)

4-Hydroxy-3-phenyl-3,4-dihydrophthalazine (V), although unrelated in origin to the compounds (II) described in Table XVI-1, shows properties similar to those of their precursors (Ia), and is conveniently considered here. It is prepared from *o*-phthalaldehyde and phenylhydrazine hydrochloride in boiling aqueous solution, or by refluxing the diphenylhydrazone

(3)

(V)

in dilute hydrochloric acid.[13]   The reaction clearly involves hydrolysis of the latter compound (Eq. 3).   The compound (V) melts at 128–129°, and is soluble in acids and in most organic solvents.   When dissolved in methanol or ethanol, it is converted into the ethers (VI; R = Me), m.p. 59–60°, and (VI; R = Et), m.p. 96–97°, respectively, which in presence of sodium carbonate regenerate (V).   If (V) or (VI; R = Me or Et) is dissolved in benzene and treated with dry hydrogen chloride, the quaternary salt (VII) is formed; this salt forms needles, m.p. 106–107°, and gives a chloroaurate, m.p. 181°, and a chloroplatinate, m.p. 224–225°.[13]

The compound (VIII), which is similar in structure and properties to (V), is described in Chapter XIV.

(VI)   (VII)   (VIII)   (IX)

B. 1-Methoxy-3-arylphthalazinium Perchlorates

The methylated bases (Ia or the isomeric quaternary bases) derived from 3-aryl-1-ketophthalazines (I) are ill-defined compounds which are difficult to purify.   They are therefore usually characterized as the 4-alkoxy derivatives (II) described above.   An alternative method of characterization, however, is to treat the crude base (or its precursor, the methosulfate) with perchloric acid, whereby well-defined, colorless, crystalline perchlorates (IX) are formed.   In this way (IX; Ar = 3'-nitrophenyl) (m.p. 215°) and (IX; Ar = 4'-nitrophenyl) (m.p. 249°) have been prepared.[1]

2. Derivatives of Compounds Containing a Methyl Group at C_4: 1-Methoxy-3-aryl-4-methylene-3,4-dihydrophthalazines

Preparation.   These compounds (see Table XVI-2) are invariably prepared from 3-aryl-4-methyl-1-ketophthalazines by the action of methyl sulfate.   Nitrobenzene (subsequently removed in steam) has been used as a solvent, but it has been stated that in a number of cases the reaction proceeds more advantageously without its use.[1]   The reaction temperature varies for individual cases, but is usually within the range 60–

130°. On treatment of the reaction product with sodium carbonate, the quaternary or pseudo base is first formed and then undergoes dehydration with formation of the methylene compound (I) (Eq. 4).

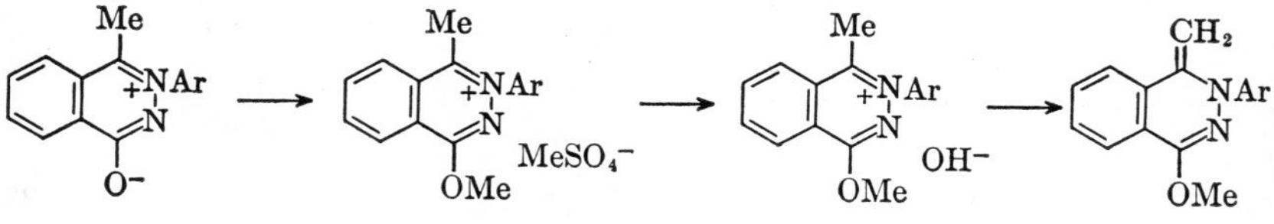

TABLE XVI-2. 1-Methoxy-3-aryl-4-methylene-3,4-dihydrophthalazines

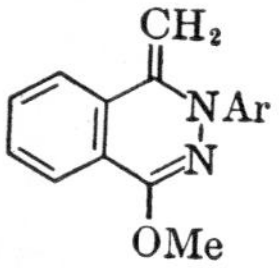

Com-pound No.	Ar	M.p., °C.	Remarks	Ref.
1	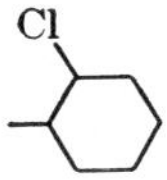 Cl (aryl)	119	Forms perchlorate, m.p. 202°	8
2	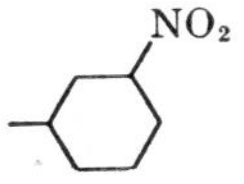 NO₂ (aryl)	—	Noncryst. Forms perchlorate, m.p. 223–224°	1
3	 —NO₂ (aryl)	134	Forms perchlorate, m.p. 199° (dec.). Gives the 3-aryl-4-methyl-1-ketophthalazine zwitterion with HBr-AcOH/110°	1,15
4	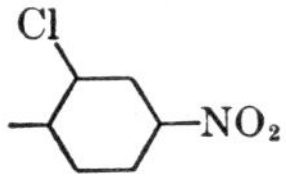 Cl, —NO₂ (aryl)	133	—	16
5	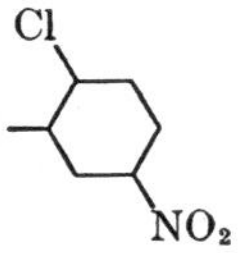 Cl, NO₂ (aryl)	142	Forms perchlorate, m.p. 224°	17
6	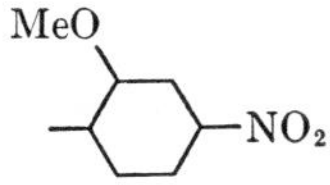 MeO, —NO₂ (aryl)	146–147	Forms perchlorate, m.p. 199–200°. Unchanged by HBr-AcOH/150°/0.5 hour	5
7	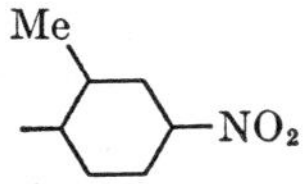 Me, —NO₂ (aryl)	118	—	12

TABLE XVI-2. 1-Methoxy-3-aryl-4-methylene-3,4-dihydrophthalazines (*contd.*)

Compound No.	Ar	M.p., °C.	Remarks	Ref.
8	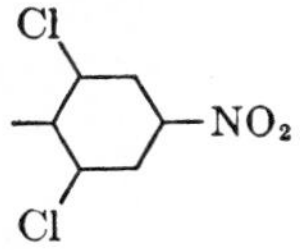 Cl / —NO₂ / Cl (with NO_2)	136	Forms perchlorate, m.p. 228°	1,9
9	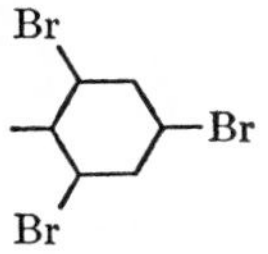 Br / —Br / Br	153	Forms perchlorate, m.p. 230°	14
10	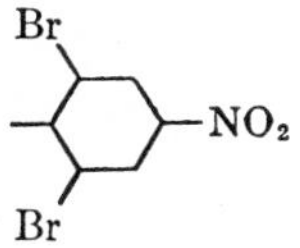 Br / —NO₂ / Br	129	—	9
11	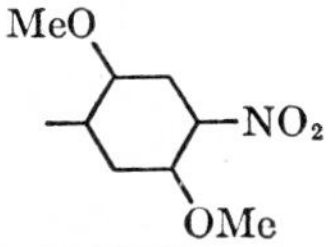 MeO / —NO₂ / OMe	131–132	Forms perchlorate, m.p. 240°	18

Properties. Compounds 1 and 9 in Table XVI-2, which do not contain a nitro group, are yellow, and the others are reddish-brown crystalline solids. They are nonacidic, but have well-marked basic properties; in particular, they yield well-defined perchlorates (I → II), which are colorless crystalline solids.

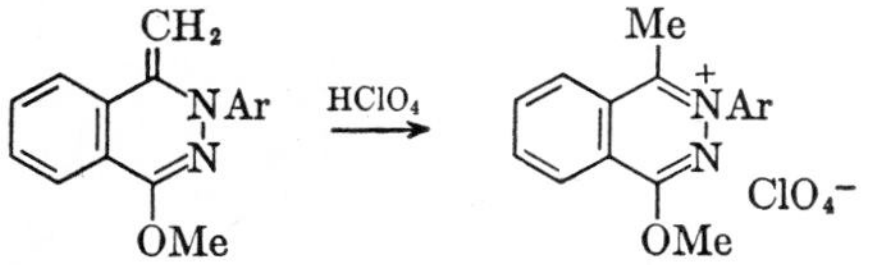

(I)   (II) 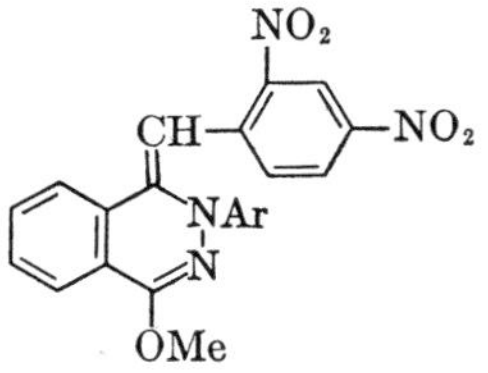   (III)

The characteristic reactions of the bases (I) involve the 4-methylene group, which displays considerable reactivity, as is shown by the following transformations.

(*1*) The methylene bases readily condense with 2,4-dinitrochlorobenzene in boiling alcohol containing potassium acetate, giving, by elimination of hydrogen chloride, compounds of type (III), as listed in Table XVI-3.

TABLE XVI-3. Compounds of Type (III)

Substituents in Ar	M.p., °C.	Remarks	Ref.
2'-Cl	186	Black needles	8
3'-NO$_2$	210	Black prisms	1
4'-NO$_2$	255	Black prisms	1
2'-Cl, 5'-NO$_2$	285	Red needles, sol. in dil. HCl	17
4'-NO$_2$, 2'-OMe	226–227	Orange-red prisms	5
2',4',6'-Br$_3$	138–140	Dark red needles	14
4'-NO$_2$, 2',5'-(OMe)$_2$	230	Blue-red prisms	18

(*2*) The methylene bases condense with 1-phenyl-3-methyl-4-anilino-methylene-5-keto-4,5-dihydropyrazole, yielding products (IV) (Table XVI-4) as indicated in equation 5.

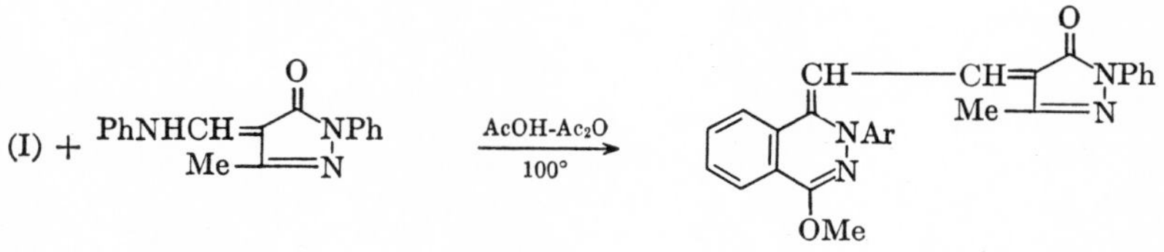

TABLE XVI-4. Compounds of Type (IV)

Substituents in Ar	M.p., °C.	Remarks	Ref.
4'-NO$_2$	258	Green-black prisms	1
2',4',6'-Br$_3$	224	Green-black prisms	14
4'-NO$_2$, 2',5'-(OMe)$_2$	258	Brown-red prisms	18

(*3*) On addition of aqueous sodium nitrite to an acetic acid solution of (I; Ar = 4'-nitrophenyl) at 0°, the corresponding nitroso derivative (V) is formed, which decomposes *in situ* to the compound (VI); the latter is also formed by refluxing (I) and *p*-nitrosodimethylaniline in alcoholic solution (Eq. 6). See Table XVI-5.

Table XVI-5. Compounds of Type (VI)

Substituents in Ar	Prep.[a]	M.p., °C.	Remarks	Ref.
2'-Cl	B	136–137	Colorless prisms	8
4'-NO$_2$	A,B	199	HBr gives the corresponding 1-hydroxy compd.	1
2'-Cl, 5'-NO$_2$	B	170	Sandy prisms. HBr gives corresponding 1-hydroxy compd.	17

[a] A, from the methylene compound (I), acetic acid, and aqueous sodium nitrite at 0°. B, from the methylene compound (I) and *p*-nitrosodimethylaniline in boiling alcohol. For alternative methods of preparing these compounds see Chapter XIX Section 2, Table 1.

$$(I) + HNO_2 \longrightarrow (V) \longrightarrow (VI) + HCN \qquad (6)$$

(4) A number of miscellaneous compounds of types (VII) and (VIII) have been prepared[1] by various condensation reactions involving the methylene compounds (I). The substances belonging to each type, and

their methods of preparation, are given in Tables XVI-6 and 7, respectively. Compounds (VII) are quaternary salts with the basic center situated at N_3 of the phthalazine nucleus. Compounds (VIII), on the other hand, are more complex. They are, in fact, related to the cyanine dyes, and their representation as (VIII) is thus a matter of formal convenience only, and does not imply that the charge on the cation is localized as indicated.

TABLE XVI-6. Compounds of Type (VII)[a]

R	X' Prep.[b]		Ar =—⟨⟩—NO₂	Ar =—⟨⟩—NO₂	Ar =—⟨Cl,Cl⟩—NO₂
CH_2Ph	I	A	Yellow needles, m.p. 174°	Yellow needles, m.p. 185°	—
N=NPh	ClO_4	B	Red powder, indef. m.p.	Red-brown needles, m.p. 224°	—
N=N—⟨⟩—NO₂	ClO_4	B	Red powder, m.p. 235°	Red-blue prisms, m.p. 268°	Orange-yellow prisms, m.p. 254°

[a] Reference 1 for all compounds.
[b] A, from (I) and benzyl iodide in alcohol (reflux). B, from (I) and ArN_2Cl-AcONa-AcOH aq. and then $HClO_4$ (HCl omitted for Ar = —⟨Cl,Cl⟩—NO₂)

Table XVI-7 follows on page 138.

TABLE XVI-7. Compounds of Type (VIII)^a

R	X	Prep.^{b}	Ar 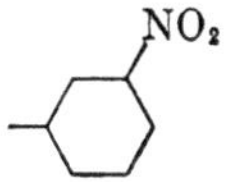 = (nitrocyclohexyl)	Ar = (p-nitrocyclohexyl) 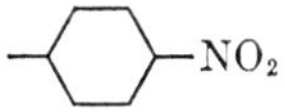	Ar = (dichloronitro) 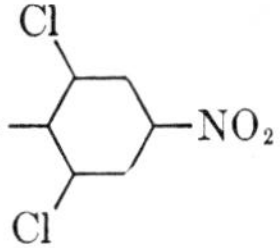
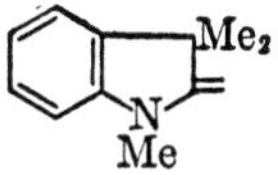 [1,3,3-trimethylindoline =CH structure]	ClO$_4$	A	—	Red plates, m.p. 182°	—
 [=CH–C$_6$H$_4$–NMe$_2$ structure]	ClO$_4$	B	Black amorph. powder, m.p. 198°	Dark green needles, m.p. 238°	Dark green needles, m.p. 254° (dec.)
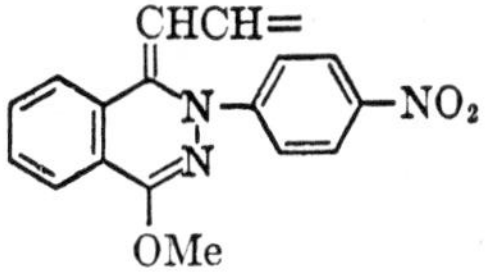 [CHCH= N–N(p-NO$_2$C$_6$H$_4$)(OMe) phthalazinone structure]	ClO$_4$	C	Dark bronze prisms, m.p. 244° (dec.)	Dark coppery prisms, m.p. 258–260° (dec.)	—
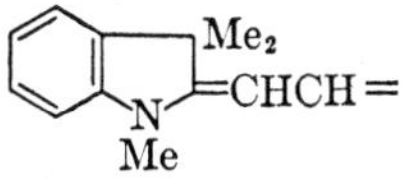 [indoline Me$_2$/Me –CHCH= structure]	ClO$_4$	D	—	Green prisms, m.p. 265° (dec.)	Green prisms, m.p. 246°
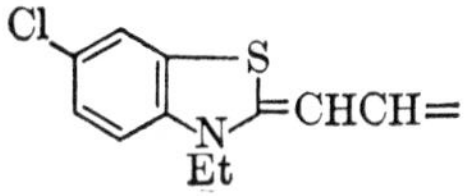 [5-chloro-benzothiazoline Et –CHCH= structure]	I	E	—	—	Green-brown plates, m.p. 254°

^{a} Reference 1 for all compounds.

^{b} A, from (I) and the perchlorate of 1,3,3-trimethyl-2-oximinomethylindolenine in Ac$_2$O/100°. B, from (II) and p-dimethylaminobenzaldehyde in AcOH-Ac$_2$O/100°/5 hrs. C, from (I), (II), and either ethyl orthoformate or diphenylformamidine in acetic anhydride. D, from (I) and [1,3,3-trimethylindolenine] CH:CHNPhAc in boiling Ac$_2$O. E, from (I) and [5-chloro-3-ethylbenzothiazolium] CH:CHNPhAc in Ac$_2$O.

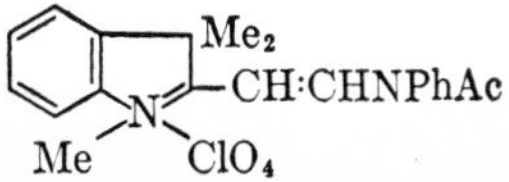

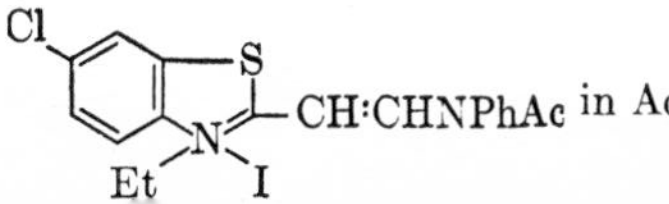

References

1. Rowe and Twitchett, *J. Chem. Soc.*, **1936**, 1704.
2. Rowe, Dovey, Garforth, Levin, Pask, and Peters, *J. Chem. Soc.*, **1935**, 1796.
3. Rowe, Gillan, and Peters, *J. Chem. Soc.*, **1935**, 1808.
4. Rowe, Haigh, and Peters, *J. Chem. Soc.*, **1936**, 1098.
5. Rowe and Cross, *J. Chem. Soc.*, **1947**, 461.
6. Rowe and Osborn, *J. Chem. Soc.*, **1947**, 829.
7. Peters, Rowe, and Brodrick, *J. Chem. Soc.*, **1948**, 1249.
8. Brodrick, Peters, and Rowe, *J. Chem. Soc.*, **1948**, 1026.
9. Rowe, Dunbar, and N. H. Williams, *J. Chem. Soc.*, **1931**, 1073.
10. Rowe and Levin, *J. Chem. Soc.*, **1928**, 2550.
11. Rowe, Himmat, and Levin, *J. Chem. Soc.*, **1928**, 2556.
12. Rowe and Siddle, *J. Chem. Soc.*, **1932**, 473.
13. Thiele and Falk, *Ann.*, **347**, 112 (1906).
14. Peters, Pringle, and Rowe, *J. Chem. Soc.*, **1948**, 597.
15. Rowe, Levin, and Peters, *J. Chem. Soc.*, **1931**, 1067.
16. Rowe and Dunbar, *J. Chem. Soc.*, **1932**, 11.
17. Rowe, Peters, and Rangwala, *J. Chem. Soc.*, **1948**, 206.
18. Rowe, Desai, and Peters, *J. Chem. Soc.*, **1948**, 281.

CHAPTER XVII

1,4-Dihydroxyphthalazines

A. Preparation

(*1*) The usual procedure for the preparation of a 1,4-dihydroxyphthal-azine (I) is to condense a derivative of the appropriately substituted phthalic acid with hydrazine. The key to Table XVII-1 (pp. 147–151) shows that the free acid (II), acid ester (III), neutral ester (IV), acid hydrazide (V), anhydride (VI), imide (VII), or *N*-arylimide (VIII) may all be used for this purpose; the condensations involve the elimination of $2H_2O$, $H_2O + R'OH$, $2R'OH$, H_2O, H_2O, NH_3, and $ArNH_2$, respectively.

(*2*) *N*-Aminophthalimides (IX) undergo isomerization into (I) in acid or alkaline media, or by heating alone to a high temperature. A variant

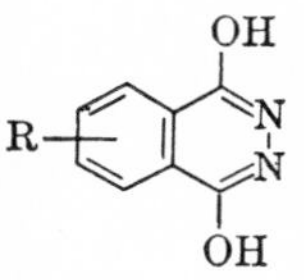

(I) 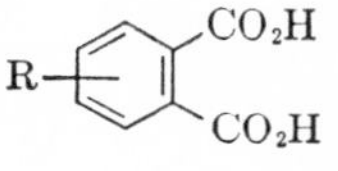　　　　(II) 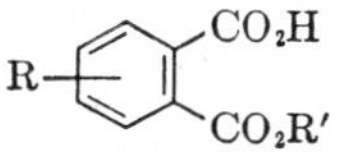　　　　(III) 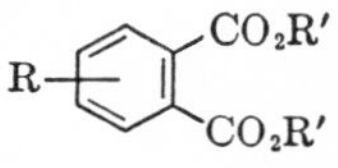　　　　(IV)

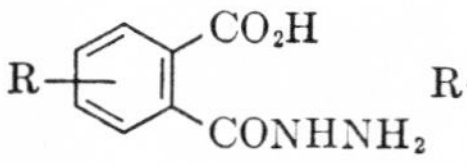

(V) 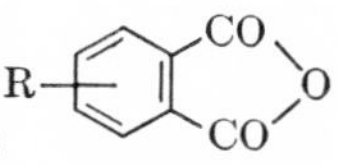　　　　(VI) 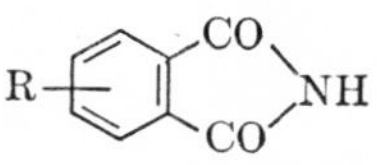　　　　(VII) 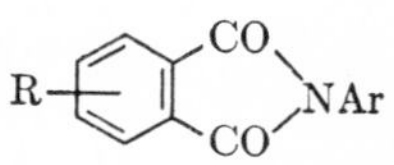　　　　(VIII)

of this reaction consists in the use of *N*-dimethylaminophthalimide (X), which on treatment with hydrazine undergoes, in effect, displacement of the dimethylhydrazine residue by an unsubstituted hydrazine residue, with formation of 1,4-dihydroxyphthalazine. A somewhat comparable success-ful competition of hydrazine with a substituted hydrazine already com-bined in the molecule is the production of 1,4-dihydroxyphthalazine from the 2,3-dimethyl derivative (XI) by boiling with hydrazine hydrate (see Table XVII-1). The greater reactivity of hydrazine as compared with substituted hydrazines is also illustrated by the observation[1] that phenyl-hydrazine and *p*-nitrophenylhydrazine, in contrast to hydrazine itself, do not condense with the arylphthalimides (VIII).

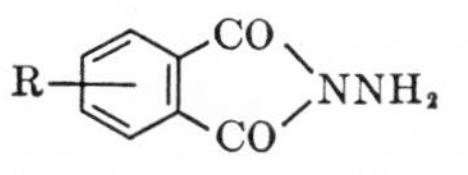

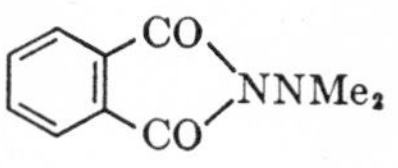

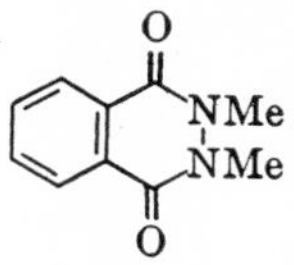

(IX)   (X)   (XI)

(*3*) Interesting reactions leading to 1,4-dihydroxyphthalazine are those in which the compounds (XII)–(XV) are treated with hydrazine hydrate in alcoholic solution, with elimination of acetylacetone, fluorene, and glycine ester, respectively. These reactions should be contrasted with that in which 1-hydroxy-4-alkyl- or -aralkyl-phthalazines (XVII) are formed from (XVI) by condensation with hydrazine hydrate, where no fission of the ethylenic linkage occurs (Chapter XII).

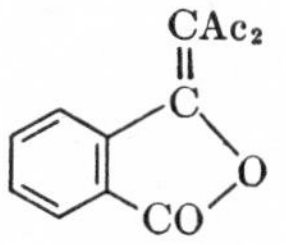

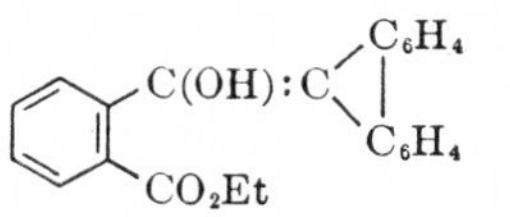

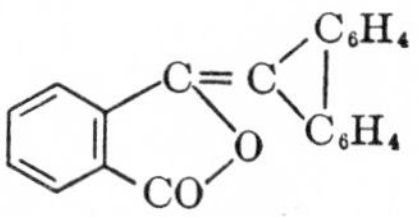

(XII)   (XIII)   (XIV)

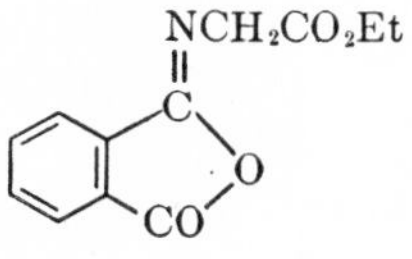

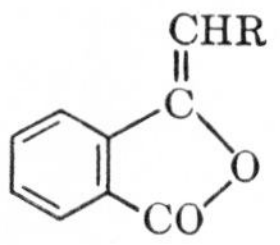

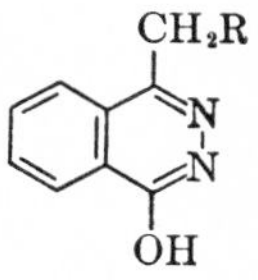

(XV)   (XVI)   (XVII)

(*4*) 5-Amino- and 5-methylamino-1,4-dihydroxyphthalazine may be prepared by, *inter alia*, the novel reaction 1. The isooxazole ring of (XVIII; R = H or Me) is opened when the compound is refluxed with hydrazine hydrate; (XIX) and (XX) are hypothetical isomeric intermediates, the latter of which yields (XXI) by reduction (through the agency of

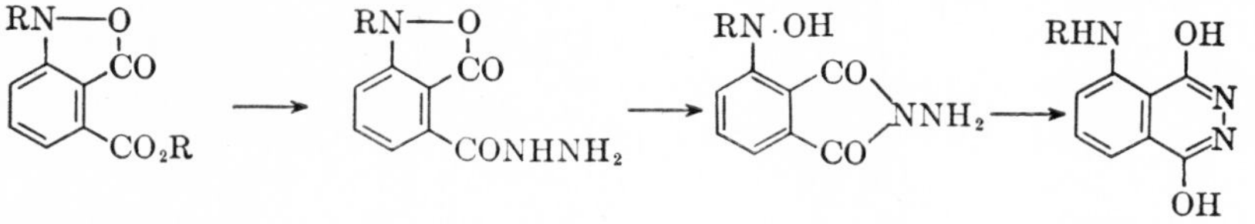

(XVIII)   (XIX)   (XX)   (XXI)

excess hydrazine) and ring enlargement. One may note at this point that 5- and 6-amino-1,4-dihydroxyphthalazines are obtainable from the nitro-phthalic esters by using excess of hydrazine hydrate in order to achieve reduction of the nitro group.[2,3]

In many of the reactions outlined above and listed in Table XVII-1 the nature and purity of the products are somewhat sensitive to changes in the reaction conditions. The desired 1,4-dihydroxyphthalazines are sometimes isolated as the hydrazine salts formed by virtue of the acidic nature of these compounds.[2-4] Furthermore, the N-aminophthalimide (IX) is sometimes an isolable intermediate in the formation of the dihydroxyphthalazine (I); these compounds are isomeric, and as the action of hydrazine on the phthalic anhydride could conceivably give rise also to a third isomer (XXII), it is not surprising that discordant views are to be found in the early literature.[5,6]

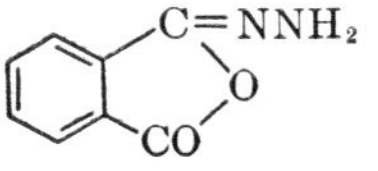

$$\text{(XXII)} \qquad \text{(XXV)}$$

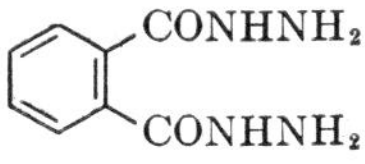

Valuable clarification was later achieved by Radulescu and Georgescu,[7] who found that pure 1,4-dihydroxyphthalazine could be isolated from the products of the action of hydrazine hydrate on both phthalimide and phthalic anhydride in alcohol and of hydrazine acetate on phthalic anhydride in acetic acid; the possible alternative structures (IX; R = H) and (XXII) are excluded by the properties of 1,4-dihydroxyphthalazine (see below).

In a more recent study of the preparation of 1,4-dihydroxyphthalazine from phthalic anhydride and hydrazine in acetic acid, Drew and Hatt[8] have concluded that the transformations of equation 2 are involved. The reaction would thus appear to be considerably more complex than the stoichio-

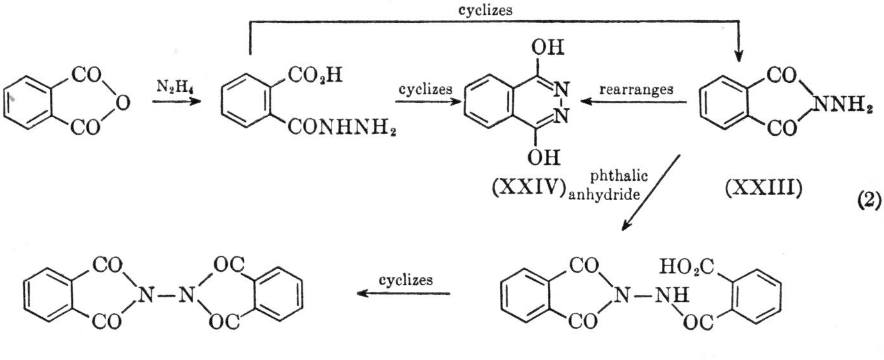

$$(2)$$

metric relationships outlined in method (1) above would indicate. The rearrangement of the N-aminophthalimide (XXIII) in presence of hydrazine to the dihydroxyphthalazine (XXIV) is considered by Drew and Pearman[9] to occur by addition and loss of hydrazine, the dihydrazide (XXV) thus functioning as an intermediate. Other substituents being the same, the presence of two hydrazide groups in o-positions is thus held to favor the formation of the 6-membered ring (XXIV), but if one of the hydrazide groups is replaced by CO_2H, $CONH_2$, or $CONHNHPh$, the 5-membered ring (XXIII) is formed in preference to (XXIV). The same authors[9] also conclude that, if the two o-substituents are kept constant, the formation of N-aminophthalimides (as XXIII) is favored by 3-Cl, 3-NH$_2$, 3,6-Cl$_2$, and 3,4,5,6-Cl$_4$; but 3-OH, 4-NH$_2$, 4,5-Cl$_2$, and probably also 3-NO$_2$ and 4-NO$_2$ influence the direction of ring closure in favor of the 1,4-dihydroxyphthalazine (as XXIV). They explain their results in terms of bond fixa-

R—⟨ring⟩—COX / COX (XXVI)   R′—⟨ring⟩—COX / COX (XXVII)

tion by the various substituents, (XXVI) giving rise to the N-aminophthalimide, and (XXVII) to the dihydroxyphthalazine. The course of the reaction is also somewhat dependent upon temperature.[10]

B.   Properties

(a) *General.*   1,4-Dihydroxyphthalazines are mostly colorless or faintly colored solids characterized by extremely high melting or decomposition points and sparing solubility in organic solvents. Occasionally they are virtually insoluble in all solvents except solutions of alkalis. They have pronounced acidic character, reacting as monobasic acids; the alkali metal, ammonium, and calcium salts are well-defined and often rather sparingly soluble,[3,9-12] and salts with hydrazine are sometimes formed during the preparation of the compounds (see above).

(b) *Special*

(i) *1,4-Dihydroxyphthalazine.*   According to reliable sources, this compound melts at 332–334°,[7] 333–337°,[13] 341–344° (corr.).[8]   It reacts as a monobasic acid which is weaker than carbon dioxide and gives a series of well-characterized salts,[6,7] the silver salt being stable to heat and light.   It does not reduce Fehling solution, and is not hydrolyzed in boiling acid or alkaline solution.[7]   Although it does not react with aldehydes in boiling acetic acid,[7] it does so when refluxed for some time with benzaldehyde or anisaldehyde, yielding compounds of the type (XXVIII), identical with those prepared from N-aminophthalimide.[8]   On short boiling with cinnamaldehyde, the compound (XXIX) (yellow crystals, m.p. 224–228°, turning green in bright light) is formed.[8]   1,4-Dihydroxyphthalazine con-

(XXVIII)   (XXIX)   (XXX)
                    R.I. 1564

denses with *o*-carbomethoxybenzoyl chloride, giving (XXX) (see Chapter XVIII, Section 2A, Table XVIII-1), and with phthaloyl chloride (in nitrobenzene at 160–210°) giving (XXXI) (yellow needles, m.p. 350–360°)[8] (see also Chapter XXIII, Section 3).   When heated under reflux at 215–220° with *o*-bromomethylbenzyl bromide, 1,4-dihydroxyphthalazine is converted into (XXXII) (yellow leaflets, m.p. 196.5–197.5°)[14] (see also Chapter XXIII, Section 3).   On attempted nitration, it is either oxidized or unattacked.[3]   It yields 1,4-dimercaptophthalazine (yellow crystals, m.p. 262–265°) when heated at 200° with phosphorus pentasulfide.[7]

(XXXI)   (XXXII)
R.I. 2644   R.I. 2644

The course of the alkylation of 1,4-dihydroxyphthalazine depends greatly on the conditions used, and hinges on the fact that the silver salt is evidently different in structure from the sodium and ammonium salts. Thus, treatment of the sodium salt with methanol and methyl iodide at 125° gives the *N*-methyl derivative[13] (Chapter XVIII, Section 2A, Table XVIII-1), but if either the sodium salt or the ammonium salt is converted into the silver salt, and this is treated with methanol and methyl iodide at 125°, or under reflux, the product is the *O*-ether[13] (Chapter XVIII, Section 1).   [The sodium salt of this *O*-ether behaves similarly, as it yields the 1,3- (*i.e.*, the *O*-*N*-) dimethyl derivative[13] (Chapter XIX, Section 2, Table XIX-1)].   On the other hand, Curtius and Foersterling, working with the silver salt and methyl iodide at 150°, obtained what is undoubtedly the *N*-methyl derivative.[6]   With methyl sulfate and alkali, 1,4-dihydroxyphthalazine yields the *N*-monomethyl derivative and the 1,3-dimethyl compound.[13]

Statements in the literature regarding the acetylation of 1,4-dihydroxyphthalazine were originally misleading, but have now been satisfactorily clarified.[8]   When refluxed with acetic anhydride it yields a diacetyl deriva-

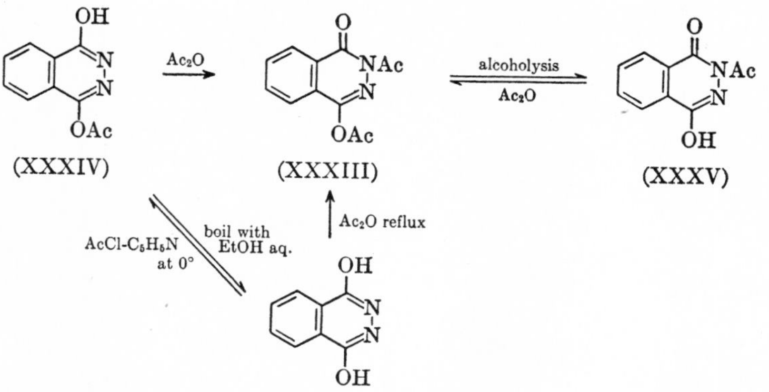

OH

N

N

OAc

(XXXIV)

Ac₂O →

O

NAc

N

OAc

(XXXIII)

alcoholysis ⇌ Ac₂O

O

NAc

N

OH

(XXXV)

(3)

AcCl-C₅H₅N at 0°   boil with EtOH aq.   Ac₂O reflux

OH

N

N

OH

tive, m.p. 139–140° after shrinking at 133°, which has the structure (XXXIII). The proof of this structure depends on the formation of the diacetyl compound, as indicated in scheme 3, from each of two isomeric monoacetyl derivatives, (XXXIV) and (XXXV), m.p. 175–176° (dec.) and 172–173° (dec.), respectively. The compound (XXXIV) is formed by selective acetylation of 1,4-dihydroxyphthalazine, and (XXXV) is produced from (XXXIII) by alcoholysis in absolute alcohol or benzene-alcohol. Hydrolysis of (XXXIV) with aqueous alcohol regenerates 1,4-dihydroxyphthalazine. It is possible that the formulas of (XXXIV) and (XXXV) should be reversed, but the above representation, involving preferential formation and removal of O-Ac rather than of N-Ac, would seem to be the more reasonable choice. Earlier references to these compounds[6,7,13,15] seem to indicate that either the existence of two different isomers (XXXIV) and (XXXV) was not recognized or the authors worked with impure materials, particularly in the case of the diacetyl derivative (XXXIII).

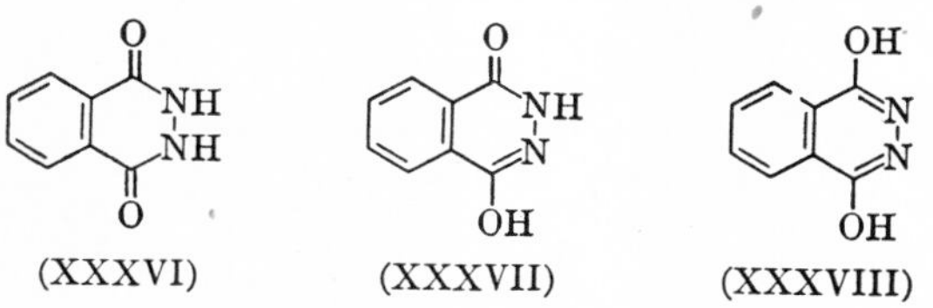

O

NH

NH

O

(XXXVI)

O

NH

N

OH

(XXXVII)

OH

N

N

OH

(XXXVIII)

The question of the fine structure of 1,4-dihydroxyphthalazine has received some consideration, the three tautomeric forms (XXXVI), (XXXVII), and (XXXVIII) being a priori possibilities. Drew and Hatt[8] consider that the compound is best represented as (XXXVI) [particularly in view of its condensation with cinnamaldehyde to give (XXIX)], but they do not exclude the possibility of tautomerism. Rowe and Peters,[13] on the other hand, conclude that (XXXVIII) represents the structure of the compound in neutral or acid solution, and (XXXVII) that in alkali hydroxide solution.   Data derived from chemical reactions, however, do not disclose the structure of the resting molecule in such a case as this, and a decision on this point, as well as on the nature of the species present in alkaline and acid media, would be most likely reached by spectrographic examination.

For halogen derivatives of 1,4 dihydroxyphthalazine, see Chapter XX.

(ii) *5-Nitro-1,4-dihydroxyphthalazine.*   The method of choice for the preparation of this compound is to evaporate to dryness an aqueous solution of 3-nitrophthalic acid, hydrazine sulfate, and sodium acetate, after which the residue is heated at $160 \pm 10°$;[16] the yield is almost theoretical.   It forms yellow or buff needles, m.p. 297–300° (uncorr.)[16] [314° (dec.)[9]], very sparingly soluble in water and acetic acid, but more soluble in pyridine and nitrobenzene.[9]   It is decomposed by caustic alkalis.[17] With acetic anhydride it yields two isomeric monoacetyl derivatives (see Chapter XVIII, Section 3).

(iii) *6-Nitro-1,4-dihydroxyphthalazine.*   This compound forms yellow plates, moderately soluble in water, alcohol, and pyridine,[9] and, unlike 1,4-dihydroxyphthalazine, soluble in alkali carbonates.[3]   At 150° it is hydrolyzed by concentrated hydrochloric acid into 4-nitrophthalic acid and hydrazine.[3]   It is also converted into 4-nitrophthalic acid by oxidation with permanganate or acid dichromate.[3]

(iv) *5-Amino-1,4-dihydroxyphthalazine.*   This compound is prepared by the methods shown in Table XVII-1; method W is recommended for the preparation of absolutely pure material.[18]   It is familiarly known as luminol on account of its chemiluminescent properties (*vide infra*), and is very sparingly soluble in ordinary solvents.   It is amphoteric, but the salts with alkalis are decomposed by carbon dioxide; those with acids are hydrolyzed by water,[9] but there appears to be some confusion in the literature on this point.[2,4]   After diazotization it may be coupled with alkaline β-naphthol to form an azo derivative, $C_{18}H_{12}O_3N_4$.[2,9]   It shows a blue fluorescence (very similar in color to the chemiluminescence mentioned above) in neutral or weak acid solutions, but not in alkali.[2,4,18,19]   It shows ultraviolet absorption maxima at ~320 mμ (log ϵ = ~3.9) in alkaline solution, and at 290 and 350 mμ (log ϵ = ~3.75 and ~3.65, respectively) in acid solution.[20]   When heated under pressure with concentrated hydrochloric acid (145–150°), it yields the hydrochloride of *m*-aminobenzoic acid.[4]

(v) *6-Amino-1,4-dihydroxyphthalazine.*   This compound crystallizes in yellow needles; its aqueous solution shows an acid reaction, but, like the 5-isomer, it is precipitated from alkaline solution by passage of carbon dioxide.[3]   It is soluble in hot dilute mineral acids, but the free base is precipitated when the solutions are cooled,[3] and the compound is less basic than luminol.[9]   Hydrolysis with concentrated hydrochloric acid at 150° gives the hydrochloride of *m*-aminobenzoic acid.[3]

TABLE XVII-1. 1,4-Dihydroxyphthalazines

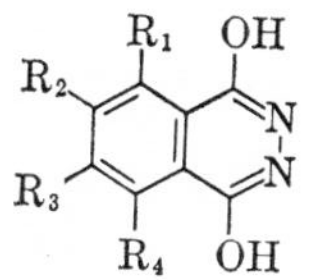

R_1, OH — N=N — R_4, OH ; R_2, R_3

R_1	R_2	R_3	R_4	Prep.[a]	M.p., °C.	Remarks	Ref.
H	H	H	H	O,Q,R,S,AC, AD,AE,AF, AO	341–344 (corr.), 332–334	See text	7,8, 31,38, 39,40
Cl	H	H	H	D,L	338 (dec.)	—	41
Br	H	H	H	D	322	—	9
NO_2	H	H	H	B,C,D,E,M	297–300, ~320 (dec.), 314 (dec.)	See text	11, 9,16, 17
NH_2	H	H	H	AA,P,D,F, H,V,W	319–320, 332–333	See text	2,4,9, 16,18
NHAc	H	H	H	B,D,G	325–326 (dec.)	—	9
NHBz	H	H	H	D	319 (dec.)	—	9
NHCO	H	H	H	B	320 (dec.)	—	32
NHAc|NHCO|—NHR	H	H	H	U	>300	R = 5,1,4-dihydroxy-phthalazyl. With conc. HCl at 140–150° it gives m-aminobenzoic acid	4
$NHCO_2Et$	H	H	H	AN	>300	—	4
$NHCOCH_2Cl$	H	H	H	AP	263 (dec.)	—	43
$NHCOCH_2NH_2$	H	H	H	AQ	244–245 (dec.)	ω-Acetyl deriv., m.p. 270° (dec.)	43
$NHCOCH_2NHNH_2$	H	H	H	AR	dec 310	Reduces cold Fehling soln.	43

Table continued

TABLE XVII-1. 1,4-Dihydroxyphthalazines (*continued*)

R_1	R_2	R_3	R_4	Prep.[a]	M.p., °C.	Remarks	Ref.
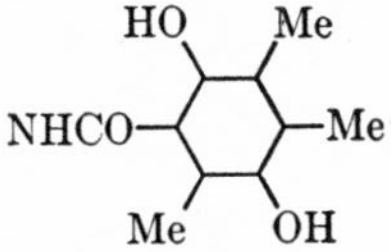 (HO, Me, Me, OH, NHCO cyclohexane)	H	H	H	D	dec. 215	—	43
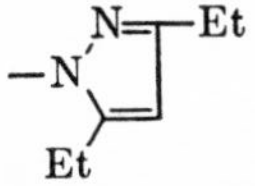 (Et, Et pyrazole)	H	H	H	D	232–234	—	43
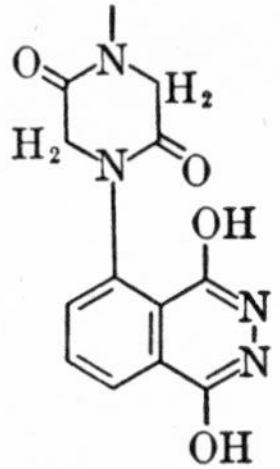 (OH, N–N, OH structure)	H	H	H	AS	>325	—	43
$NHNH_2$	H	H	H	D,L,X	312 (dec.), 280–300 (dec.)	Nonfluorescent Stable hydrochloride	10,34
$NHNHSO_3Na$	H	H	H	D	—	Easily sol. in water	10
$NHN:CHPh$	H	H	H	Y	310–312	—	34
$NHMe$	H	H	H	W,D	310–325 (dec.), 331 (dec.)	Fluoresces in alk. but not acid	10,18
$NAcMe$	H	H	H	D	329 (dec.)	—	10
$NHPh$	H	H	H	A	325 (dec.)	—	1
 NH—Me (cyclohexane)	H	H	H	A	~320 (dec.)	—	1

R_1	R_2	R_3	R_4	Prep.[a]	M.p., °C	Remarks	Ref.
NH-C₁₀H₇-β	H	H	H	A	325 (dec.)	Yellow needles	1
OH	H	H	H	Z,D	~300 (dec.),	$FeCl_3$ gives deep brown color	9,34
CONHNH₂	H	H	H	S	330 (dec.)	Hydrochloride, m.p. >300°, is hydrolyzed to base by hot water, and gives the *azide* with HNO_2	4
CONHPh	H	H	H	AM	>300	—	4
CONHN:CHPh	H	H	H	T	>300	—	4
Me	H	H	H	B,M	340	Insol. except in alk.	11
H	Cl	H	H	D	348–350	—	14
H	Br	H	H	D	343	—	11
H	I	H	H	D	345	—	11
H	NO₂	H	H	B,M,AG,C,D	>300, 298, 299–300 (dec.)	See text	3,9,17
H	NH₂	H	H	AH,AI,D,F	>305, 339° (dec.)	See text	3,9
H	NHAc	H	H	D	341 (dec.)	—	9
H	OH	H	H	AJ	>300	—	3
H	N:NNHPh	H	H	AL	dec. 185–187	Orange-yellow solid	3
H	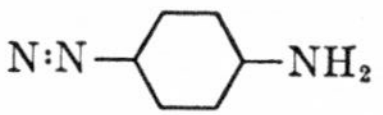 N:N—C₆H₄—NH₂ (structure)	H	H	AM	>300	Red amorph. solid. Hydrochloride, red micro-prisms. M.p. ~240°	3
H	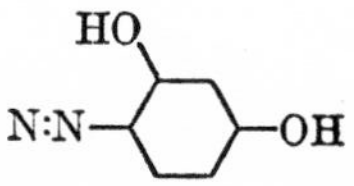 N:N—C₆H₃(HO)(OH) (structure)	H	H	AK	—	Dark red powder	3
NO₂	H	NO₂	H	M	306–307	Sol. in hot water	34
Cl	H	H	Cl	B,H,J	>350	—	9

Table continued

TABLE XVII-1. 1,4-Dihydroxyphthalazines (continued)

R_1	R_2	R_3	R_4	Prep.ᵃ	M.p., °C.	Remarks	Ref.
NH_2	H	H	NH_2	D,H	329 (dec.)	Yellow needles. Aq. soln. is acid to litmus and has very strong green fluorescence. Diazotizable. Oxidized by air in NaOH. Hydrochloride is hydrolyzed by H_2O	10
$NHAc$	H	H	$NHAc$	D,H	279 (dec.)	Not fluorescent	10
$NHPh$	H	H	$NHPh$	A	276	Red or yellow needles	1
NH–cyclohexyl–Me	H	H	NH–cyclohexyl–Me	A	~285	Red needles	1
OH	H	H	OH	M	>340	Insol. in ordinary solvents	34
H	Cl	Cl	H	B,D	>350	—	9
H	NH_2	NH_2	H	K	>340	With phenanthraquinone gives a phenazine deriv., orange cryst., m.p. >340°	10
Cl	Cl	Cl	Cl	Z	286–287	Yellow cryst.	12

ᵃ A, from $ArNH \cdot C_6H_3 (CO)_2 NAr$ by boiling with pyridine and hydrazine hydrate. B, from the appropriately substituted phthalic anhydride and hydrazine hydrate in boiling acetic acid, aqueous ethanol, or water, or at 120–130° without solvent. C, from the acid hydrazine salt of the appropriate nitrophthalic acid by heating at 150° for 24 hours. D, from the imide of the appropriately substituted phthalic acid and hydrazine hydrate in water or alcohol (reflux). E, from $1,2,3\text{-}NO_2 \cdot (CO_2H)C_6H_3 \cdot CONHNH_2$ by boiling in water for 2 hours, or by heating dry at 160° for 12 hours. F, from the nitro compound, stannous chloride, and concentrated hydrochloric acid at 50–60°. G, from the amino compound by acetylation, followed by selective hydrolysis of the product with boiling dilute ammonia. H, from the appropriately substituted N-aminophthalimide by treatment with boiling sodium hydroxide, hydrazine hydrate, or concentrated hydrochloric acid; or by heating with hydrazine hydrate under pressure; or by heating alone at the m.p. I, from the 5-amino compound by diazotization in concentrated sulfuric acid and addition of phosphoric acid, followed by a Sandmeyer reaction. J, from the hydrazine salt of 3,6-dichlorophthalic acid by heating at 160° for 6 hours. K, from the 6,7-dichloro compound, cuprous iodide, and ammonia (d 0.880) at 160–170° for 16 hours. L, from the 5-$NHNHSO_3Na$ compound and concentrated hydrochloric acid. M, from the appropriately substituted phthalic acid or anhydride by evaporation with hydrazine hydrate, followed by dry heating at 165–250°. N, the corresponding acetamido compound is prepared (crude) by method B, and then hydrolyzed with aqueous sodium hydroxide. O, from o-

C₆H₄$<$ (C:CAc₂, O, CO) and hydrazine hydrate in alcohol at room temperature. P, from 1,2-NO₂·(CO₂H)C₆H₃·CO₂Et by refluxing with excess hydrazine hydrate. Q, the compound o-C₆H₄$<$(C(OH):C$<$CO₂Et, C₆H₄) ... C:C$<$C₆H₄, O, CO$>$C₆H₄ (from diethyl phthalate and the sodium derivative of fluorene) is refluxed with hydrazine hydrate in alcohol. R, from o-C₆H₄ and hydrazine hydrate in alcohol (reflux). S, from the appropriately substituted dimethyl or diethyl phthalate and hydrazine hydrate in hot alcohol. T, from the corresponding —CONHNH₂ compound, benzaldehyde, and dilute hydrochloric acid. U, by treatment of the azide with boiling water. V, from the urethan (RNHCO₂Et) or the urea (RNHCONHR) and concentrated hydrochloric acid at 100° (sealed tube).

W, from [RN$<$O, CO ... CO₂R] (R = H or Me) and hydrazine hydrate (reflux). X, from the amino compound by diazotization and reduction with stannous chloride and hydrochloric acid. Y, from the —NHNH₂ compound and benzaldehyde in alcoholic sodium hydroxide. Z, from the appropriately substituted phthalic acid and hydrazine sulfate, or by refluxing with hydrazine hydrate. AA, from the corresponding nitro compound, hydrogen sulfide, and aqueous ammonium sulfide (reflux). AB, from the dinitro compound, tin, and hydrochloric acid. AC, from ethereal phthalyl chloride and alcoholic hydrazine hydrate (3 moles). AD, from

[o-C₆H₄$<$C:NCH₂CO₂Et, O, CO] and hydrazine hydrate in warm alcohol. AE, from the 2,3-dimethyl derivative by boiling with hydrazine hydrate. AF, from N-dimethylaminophthalimide and hydrazine. AG, from diethyl 3-nitrophthalate and hydrazine hydrate in alcohol (reflux). AH, from the nitro compound, ammonium hydroxide, and hydrazine hydrate at 130–140°. AI, from diethyl 4-nitrophthalate and hydrazine hydrate at 60°. AJ, from the 6-amino compound by diazotization and warming in aqueous sulfuric acid. AK, from the 6-amino compound by diazotization in aqueous sulfuric acid and coupling with resorcinol. AL, from the 6-amino compound by diazotization in aqueous hydrochloric acid, followed by addition of aniline hydrochloride and aqueous sodium acetate. AM, from the corresponding azide and aniline. AN, from the corresponding azide by treatment with alcohol. AO, from N,N′-bis-o-carbomethoxybenzoylhydrazine by heating with 0.1 N-sulfuric acid. AP, from the amino compound and chloroacetyl chloride. AQ, from the chloroacetamido compound and cold aqueous ammonia. AR, from the chloroacetamido compound and cold hydrazine hydrate. AS, from 5-chloroacetamido-1,4-dihydroxyphthalazine monoacetate and aqueous potassium carbonate at 100°.

TABLE XVII-2. 1,4-Dihydroxyphthalazines Containing Modified or Additional Rings

Compound	Prep.[a]	M.p., °C.	Remarks	Ref.
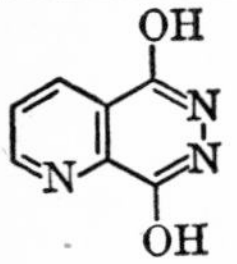	M	309	Sol. in dil. HCl and NH₄OH	34
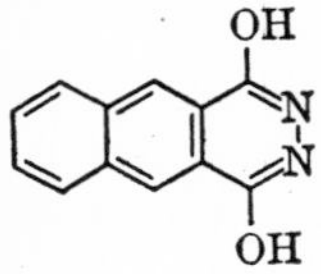	B	345	Gives yellow mono-sodium salt	11
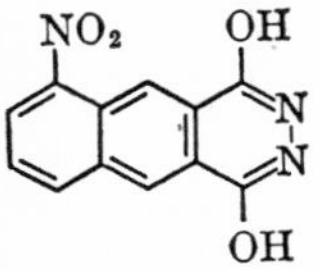	B	>350	Yellow powder. Gives sparingly sol. red monosodium salt	11
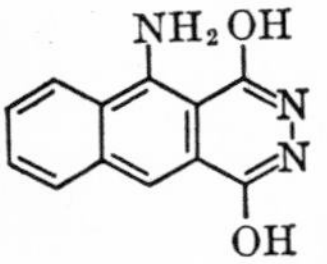	D	342–344 (dec.)	Soluble in ammonia	44
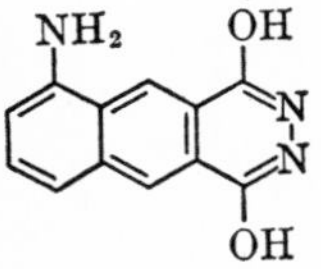	N	320 (dec.)	Brown powder, sol. in alk.	11
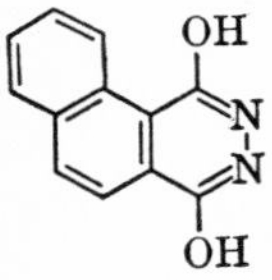	B	>360	Sol. in alk.	11
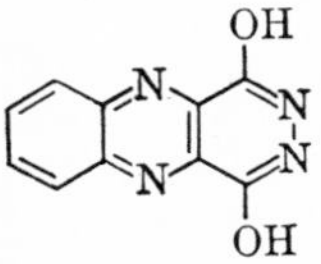	M	>330	Impure	34
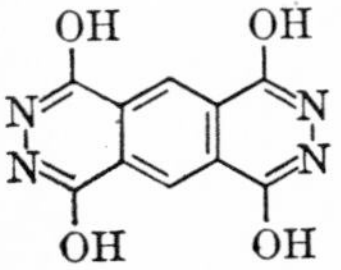	B	dec. 450	Insol. in ordinary solvents. Gives disodium salt. Boiling with Ac₂O gives Ac₄ deriv., m.p. 235–238°	10,42

TABLE XVII-2. 1,4-Dihydroxyphthalazines Containing Modified or Additional Rings (*continued*)

Compound	Prep.[a]	M.p., °C.	Remarks	Ref.
OH NO₂ OH structure	M	>260	Yellow powder, sol. in water. Gives violet color with NaOH	34
OH NH₂ OH structure	AB	42; solidifies at 68–69; not molten at 250	Not analyzed	34

[a] For methods of preparation see key to Table XVII-1.

C. Chemiluminescence of Phthalazine Derivatives.

When 5-amino-1,4-dihydroxyphthalazine is oxidized in alkaline solution under certain conditions, the reaction is accompanied by a characteristic blue luminescence; for this reason the compound is known by the trivial name *luminol*. The nature of this process (chemiluminescence), and the conditions on which it depends, have aroused considerable interest. A detailed discussion of the phenomenon is beyond the scope of this book, but the main features of the problem are outlined below; the papers referred to form only a small proportion of those dealing with the subject.

Albrecht[21] showed that the luminescence produced by treatment of an alkaline solution of luminol with hypochlorite or ferricyanide is intensified in presence of hydrogen peroxide. It was subsequently stated[18] that no light is emitted with luminol and peroxide alone in alkaline solution (this statement conflicts with later publications and has not been confirmed), but that the effect is produced by adding to the reactants catalysts such as manganese dioxide, colloidal platinum, or blood, and it was shown that the catalytic effect of blood is greatly surpassed by that of crystalline hemin.[18, 22] In sodium carbonate solution, light emission occurs if ozone is used instead of hydrogen peroxide, but the intensity produced under these conditions is not appreciably increased by adding hemin.[23]

The peroxide-induced luminescence (which occurs only in alkaline solution) has been studied by numerous workers, mainly from the point of view of the effect produced by adding various catalysts. The effect of different concentrations of ferricyanide has been examined by Stross and Branch,[19] who conclude that oxidizing agents which produce the chemiluminescence are of three types, namely, those producing: (*1*) a dull glow of short duration (ferricyanide); (*2*) a dull glow of long duration (hydrogen peroxide); (*3*) a bright glow of short duration (ferricyanide and peroxide mixed). The reaction is catalyzed by various iron complexes[24] and also by a number of metallic derivatives of phthiocol (2-hydroxy-3-methyl-1,4-naphthaquinone), the order of effectiveness[25] of the latter being $Co^{II} > Cu^{II} > Fe^{II} > Fe^{III} > Ni^{II} > Mn^{II}$; other catalysts are copper salts[26] and iron phthalocyanine[27] (other phthalocyanines have little or no catalytic action).

Various compounds have the property of inhibiting the chemiluminescence of luminol. For example, when ferricyanide is used as catalyst, ferrocyanide has inhibitory properties.[19] With hemin as catalyst, cysteine hydrochloride, quinol, metol, adrenaline, and ascorbic acid act as inhibitors.[28] Salicylaldoxime inhibits the catalytic effect of copper salts, but does not affect catalysis by hemin[26]; similarly, the catalytic effect of iron phthalocyanines is much diminished by concentrations of hydrogen cyanide which are without effect on the hemin-catalyzed reaction.[27]

Flosdorf *et al.*[29] state that the sodium derivative of luminol "and sonically produced peroxide may be energised to produce chemiluminescence in the absence of the usual secondary oxidants, the reaction giving visual confirmation that chemical activation occurs during sonic cavitation."

Steigmann[26] describes experimental conditions designed to produce maximum chemiluminescence, and discusses[30] the use of the reaction in analysis for the detection of peroxide, copper and ferrous salts, cyanides, etc., by methods depending on the catalytic or inhibitory effect of these compounds. Gleu and Pfannstiel[18] state that luminol containing small amounts of impurities gives a greenish chemiluminescence, but that the color is blue throughout its duration when absolutely pure luminol is used; they recommend that luminol for chemiluminescent experiments should be prepared from the benzisooxazolone derivative (XVIII) (*vide supra*) and stored as the hydrochloride which, in contrast to the free base, keeps indefinitely without decomposition.

In the search for an explanation of these facts and also of their bearing on other examples of chemiluminescence, many phthalazine compounds have been examined. Light emission is much reduced by the introduction of methyl groups into the hetero ring of luminol,[31-33] and Drew and his co-workers, who have made a detailed study of the phenomenon, conclude that both hydrogen atoms in the hetero ring are essential[32]; the weak chemiluminescence which has been attributed to luminol derivatives alkylated in the hetero ring is probably due to traces of unalkylated material. The effect of changing the nature and position of the substituent in the Bz ring has also been examined extensively.[10,33,34,43,44] Wegler[34] states that 5-hydrazino-1,4-dihydroxyphthalazine gives a more powerful luminescence than does luminol, but Drew and Pearman[10] do not confirm this result. 1,4-Dihydroxyphthalazine shows some degree of chemiluminescence,[34,35] as also do a few of its 6-substituted derivatives.[10,35] In general, the substituents which confer a high degree of chemiluminescence are those which render a compound easily oxidizable (hydroxyl, amino, methylamino, acetamido, etc.), but there is no quantitative correspondence between oxidizability and intensity of chemiluminescence.[33,34] Drew and his associates[10,11] conclude that the substitution of electron-donating groups (e.g., NH_2, OH, Cl) in the Bz ring of 1,4-dihydroxyphthalazine, particularly at C_5 and C_8, increases the luminescent power, whereas the introduction of electron-attracting groups (e.g., NO_2) has an opposite or at least a much weaker effect; they also observe that the order of brightness is changed with increase of temperature.

The mechanism of the reaction (with luminol) has been discussed by various workers.[19,21,32,36,37] Stross and Branch[19] consider that the luminescence is terminated by the formation, by oxidation of luminol, of the (hypothetical) product (XXXIX), and that the light may be emitted during some other transformation undergone by luminol. The most convincing mechanism so far suggested is that of Drew and Garwood,[32,36] according to which the ion (XL) is an essential intermediate, combining with peroxide

(XXXIX)   (XL)

(XL) + O–O   (XLII) R.I. 1800 + 2H₂O   (XLI) R.I. 1800

to yield (XLI). Reaction of more peroxide with (XLI) gives the ion-radical (XLII), which then breaks up into oxygen and (XL), this being the stage at which the luminescence is considered most likely to occur. The luminol thus functions as a vehicle for the oxidation of hydrogen peroxide by itself or by another oxidizing agent, this oxidation being assisted by catalysts (hemoglobin, copper salts, etc.). In support of their claims, Drew and Garwood[36] have isolated a crystalline sodium salt of (XLI), a solution of which in water gives a bright luminescence on addition of hemoglobin or a copper salt as catalyst.

References

1. Marriott and R. Robinson, *J. Chem. Soc.*, **1939**, 134.
2. Curtius and Semper, *Ber.*, **46**, 1162 (1913).
3. Curtius and Hoesch, *J. prakt. Chem.*, **76**, 301 (1907).
4. Curtius, *J. prakt. Chem.*, **91**, 39 (1915).
5. R. von Rothenburg, *Ber.*, **27**, 691 (1894).
6. Curtius and Foersterling, *J. prakt. Chem.*, **51**, 371 (1895).
7. Radulescu and Georgescu, *Bull. soc. chim.*, **37**, 881 (1925).
8. Drew and Hatt, *J. Chem. Soc.*, **1937**, 16.
9. Drew and Pearman, *J. Chem. Soc.*, **1937**, 26.
10. Drew and Pearman, *J. Chem. Soc.*, **1937**, 586.
11. Drew and Garwood, *J. Chem. Soc.*, **1939**, 836.
12. Phelps, *Am. Chem. J.*, **33**, 586 (1905).
13. Rowe and Peters, *J. Chem. Soc.*, **1933**, 1331.
14. Hatt and E. F. M. Stephenson, *J. Chem. Soc.*, **1943**, 658.
15. Blanksma and Bakels, *Rec. trav. chim.*, **58**, 497 (1939).
16. Huntress, Stanley, and Parker, *J. Am. Chem. Soc.*, **56**, 241 (1934).
17. Bogert and Boroschek, *J. Am. Chem. Soc.*, **23**, 740 (1901).
18. Gleu and Pfannstiel, *J. prakt. Chem.*, **146**, 137 (1936).
19. Stross and Branch, *J. Org. Chem.*, **3**, 385 (1938).
20. Briner and Perrotet, *Helv. Chim. Acta*, **23**, 1253 (1940).
21. Albrecht, *Z. physik. Chem.*, **A136**, 321 (1928).
22. Schales, *Ber.*, **72**, 167 (1939).
23. Briner, *Helv. Chim. Acta*, **23**, 320 (1940).
24. Thielert and Pfeiffer, *Ber.*, **71**, 1399 (1938).
25. Geyer, Haendler, and G. McP. Smith, *J. Am. Chem. Soc.*, **63**, 3071 (1941).
26. Steigmann, *J. Soc. Chem. Ind.*, **1941**, 889.
27. A. H. Cook, *J. Chem. Soc.*, **1938**, 1845.
28. Baur, *Helv. Chim. Acta*, **23**, 449 (1940).
29. Flosdorf, Chambers, and Malisoff, *J. Am. Chem. Soc.*, **58**, 1069 (1936).
30. Steigmann, *J. Soc. Chem. Ind.*, **1942**, 36.
31. Drew, Hatt, and Hobart, *J. Chem. Soc.*, **1937**, 33.
32. Drew and Garwood, *J. Chem. Soc.*, **1937**, 1841.
33. C. N. Zellner and Dougherty, *J. Am. Chem. Soc.*, **59**, 2580 (1937).
34. Wegler, *J. prakt. Chem.*, **148**, 135 (1937).
35. Witte, *Rec. trav. chim.*, **54**, 471 (1935).
36. Drew and Garwood, *J. Chem. Soc.*, **1938**, 791.
37. L. Harris and A. S. Parker, *J. Am. Chem. Soc.*, **57**, 1939 (1935).
38. Bülow and Deseniss, *Ber.*, **39**, 2275 (1906).
39. Wislicenus and Neber, *Ann.*, **418**, 274 (1919).
40. Curtius and Radenhausen, *J. prakt. Chem.*, **52**, 433 (1895).
41. Curtius and Davidis, *J. prakt. Chem.*, **54**, 66 (1896).
42. Seka, Sedlatschek, and Preissecker, *Monatsh.*, **57**, 86 (1931).
43. Cross and Drew, *J. Chem. Soc.*, **1949**, 638.
44. Cross and Drew, *J. Chem. Soc.*, **1949**, 1532.

CHAPTER XVIII

Monoalkyl and Monoacyl Derivatives of 1,4-Dihydroxyphthalazines

1. O-Derivatives

Only three compounds can be assigned with certainty to this group. Of these, the simplest is 1-hydroxy-4-methoxyphthalazine (I; R = H), which is prepared from the silver salt of 1,4-dihydroxyphthalazine (*via* the

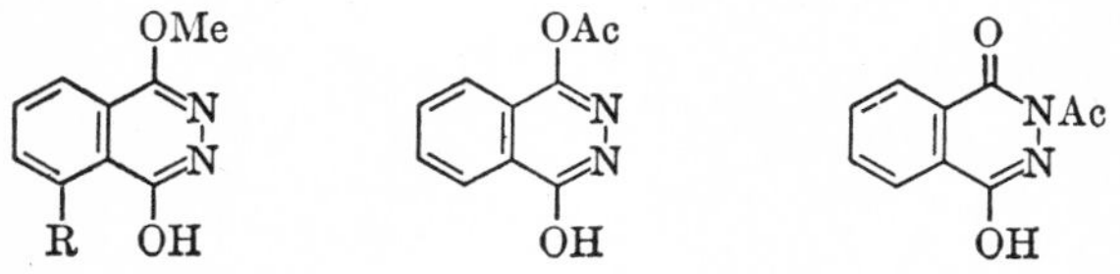

(I)   (II)   (III)

intermediate ammonium or sodium salt) by treatment with methanol and methyl iodide at 125° or under reflux. It melts at 188°[1] (Heller[2] gives 187°), is insoluble in cold but soluble in hot mineral acids and alkalis, and gives 1,4-dihydroxyphthalazine on treatment with hydrobromic acid at 100°.[1] Its structure derives from the fact that it is different from the *N*-methyl isomer of established constitution (this chapter, Section 2).

8-Nitro-1-hydroxy-4-methoxyphthalazine [5-nitro-4-hydroxy-1-methoxyphthalazine] (I; R = NO₂) melts at 269°, and gives an acetyl derivative, m.p. 188–190°[5]; for its preparation and proof of structure see Chapter XIX, Section 2. On reduction with tin and hydrochloric acid it gives the amino compound (I; R = NH₂), m.p. 234°.[5]

On acetylation with acetyl chloride in pyridine at 0°, 1,4-dihydroxyphthalazine gives a monoacetyl derivative, m.p. 175–176° (dec.),[3] which is probably 1-hydroxy-4-acetoxyphthalazine (II), although the alternative structure (III) cannot be excluded with certainty. The argument for regarding the compound as (II) rather than as (III) is given in Chapter XVII (pages 140–156).

2. *N*-Derivatives (1-Hydroxy-3-substituted-4-keto-3,4-dihydro-phthalazines)

A. *Compounds Containing No Substituent in the Benzene Ring*

Preparation. These compounds have the general formula (I). In most cases R is an aryl group, and four general methods are available for the preparation of such compounds.

(1) Isomerization of the appropriate *N*-arylaminophthalimide (R = Ar) is induced by heating with alcoholic sodium ethoxide (Eq. 1).

$$(1)$$

(2) The corresponding 1-hydroxy-3-aryl-3,4-dihydrophthalazine-4-acetic acid (II) (Chapter XIV) is oxidized with potassium permanganate (Eq. 2). In a number of instances a comparison of this with the foregoing

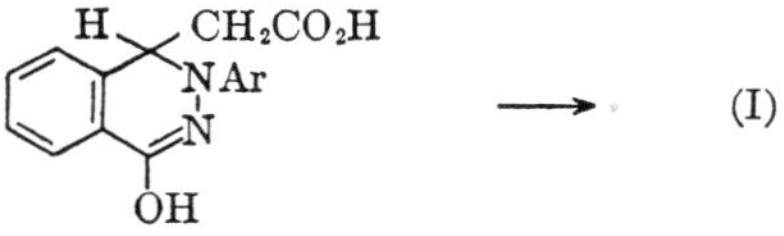

$$(I) \qquad (2)$$

method has been made, and it is clear (see Table XVIII-1) that the oxidation of (II) is usually to be preferred to the isomerization of the *N*-arylamino-phthalimide.

(3) The *O*-methyl ethers of (I) are demethylated by treatment with hydrobromic acid.

(4) Compounds in which the 3-aryl substituent contains an amino group may be prepared by reduction of the corresponding nitro compounds.

Properties. These compounds are usually colorless, but occasionally yellow, crystalline solids. Typical members are soluble in aqueous sodium carbonate but insoluble in dilute mineral acids. It is considered[4] that these compounds react in the form (I) rather than as the tautomeric 1-keto-1,2-dihydro compounds, because they give (in the few cases where the point has been investigated) readily hydrolyzable acetyl derivatives which are therefore presumed to be *O*-acetyl compounds, and also because they undergo *O*- and not *N*-methylation. The formation of *O*-methyl

TABLE XVIII-1. 1-Hydroxy-3-substituted-4-keto-3,4-dihydrophthalazines

R	Prep.[a]	M.p., °C.	Remarks	Ref.
Me	M,N,P,Q	232, 235, 238, 239	Not demethylated by HBr or HI/140°	1,6, 8–10
CH₂Ph	L	204	—	11
Ph	A,C,D,I	210, 212–213	—	4,12, 13
	B	247–248	—	14
	B	226–230	—	15
	A	252	—	12
	A(0.7%), B(46%)	293–294	—	4
	A(90%), B(67%), F	280	—	4,16
	A(30.5%), B(72%), F	307	—	4,17
	K	247	Brown-red plates	18
	H	~430 (dec.)	Ac₂ deriv., m.p. 224–225°	19
	E,F,G	233–234	3′-NHAc deriv., m.p. 153–154°	19
	E,F	247–248	4′-NHAc deriv., m.p. 299–300°	19

Table continued

TABLE XVIII-1. 1-Hydroxy-3-substituted-4-keto-3,4-dihydrophthalazines (*continued*)

R	Prep.[a]	M.p., °C.	Remarks	Ref.
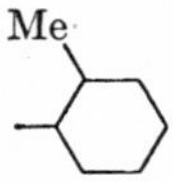 (2-Me-phenyl)	A	207	—	12
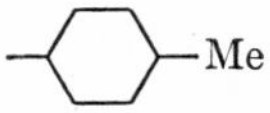 (4-Me-phenyl)	A	225	—	12
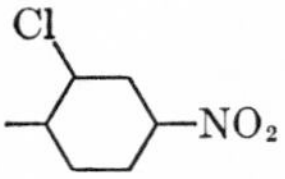 (2-Cl-4-NO₂-phenyl) Cl ... NO₂	A(nil), B(24%)	271–272	—	4
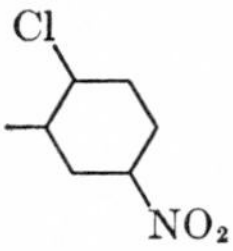 (2-Cl-phenyl, NO₂) Cl ... NO₂	F	282	—	20
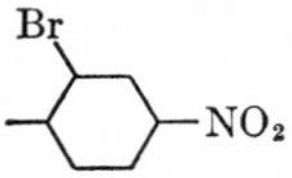 (2-Br-4-NO₂-phenyl) Br ... NO₂	A(nil), B(59%)	273–274	—	4
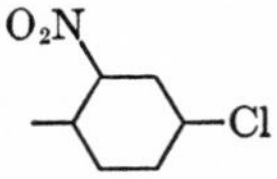 (2-O₂N-4-Cl-phenyl) O₂N ... Cl	B	286–287	—	19
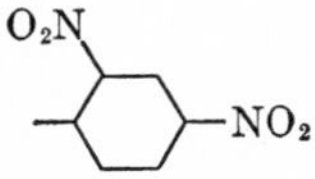 (2-O₂N-4-NO₂-phenyl) O₂N ... NO₂	B	271	—	21
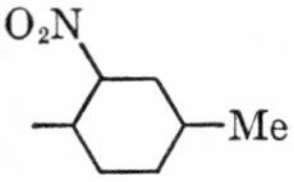 (2-O₂N-4-Me-phenyl) O₂N ... Me	B	286–288	—	22
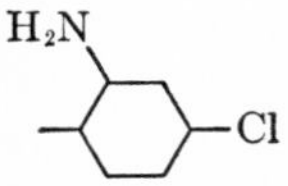 (2-H₂N-4-Cl-phenyl) H₂N ... Cl	H	>440	Ac₂ deriv., m.p. 245–246°	19
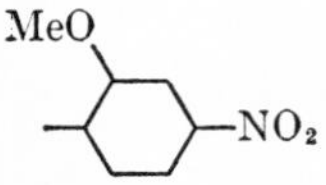 (2-MeO-4-NO₂-phenyl) MeO ... NO₂	B	256–257	—	23
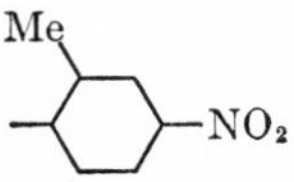 (2-Me-4-NO₂-phenyl) Me ... NO₂	A(27%), B(63%), F	271	—	4,24

TABLE XVIII-1. 1-Hydroxy-3-substituted-4-keto-3,4-dihydrophthalazines
(*continued*)

R	Prep.[a]	M.p., °C.	Remarks	Ref.
(2,4-dichlorophenyl, —NO₂)	A(nil), B(51%)	308–310	—	4
(tribromophenyl, —Br)	B	333–334	—	15
(dibromophenyl, —NO₂)	A(nil), B(v. poor)	327–329	—	4
—CO— (phenyl-CO₂Me)	O	165–170° (dec.); resolidifies and remelts 270–290	Gives phthalic acid and 1,4-dihydroxyphthalazine with boiling AcOH or aq. alkali	3
—CONH₂	J,K	249 ~262 (dec.)	— —	18 13

[a] A, from o-C₆H₄$\begin{smallmatrix}\diagup\text{CONHNHAr}\\\diagdown\text{CO}_2\text{H}\end{smallmatrix}$ by cyclization to the N-arylaminophthalimide, which is then heated with alcoholic sodium ethoxide (either under reflux or in a sealed tube at 100°). B, from the 1-hydroxy-3-aryl-3,4-dihydrophthalazine-4-acetic acid and aqueous permanganate at 70–100°. C, from o-C₆H₄$\begin{smallmatrix}\diagup\text{CONHNHAr}\\\diagdown\text{CO}_2\text{H}\end{smallmatrix}$ and nitrobenzene (reflux). D, from the N-arylaminophthalimide in glycerol (10 hours at 240°). E, from the nitro compound, sodium hydrosulfite, and aqueous sodium hydroxide (reflux). F, from the 1-methoxy compound and hydrobromic acid (d 1.7), with or without acetic acid, at 100–170°. G, from the nitro compound, iron, and aqueous acetic acid (reflux). H, from the nitro compound, stannous chloride, and concentrated hydrochloric acid (reflux). I, by heating phthalic anhydride with phenyl semicarbazide or phenylhydrazine. J, from phthalic anhydride and semicarbazide hydrochloride. K, from o-C₆H₄$\begin{smallmatrix}\diagup\text{C}\cdot\text{Ac}_2\\\diagdown\text{CO}\end{smallmatrix}$O and RNHNH₂ ($R$ = CONH₂, or p-NO₂·C₆H₄—) in alcohol or acetic acid at room temperature (CH₂Ac₂ is the other product of reaction). L, from phthalic anhydride and benzylhydrazine by evaporation of an alcoholic solution, followed by heating at 215°. M, from phthalimide and methylhydrazine in boiling aqueous acetic acid. N, from 1,4-dihydroxyphthalazine by refluxing with methyl sulfate and aqueous-methanolic potassium hydroxide. O, from 1,4-dihydroxyphthalazine and o-carbomethoxybenzoyl chloride in pyridine at room temperature. P, from the silver salt of 1,4-dihydroxyphthalazine and methyl iodide at 150°. Q, from the sodium salt of 1,4-dihydroxyphthalazine, methyl alcohol, and methyl iodide at 125°.

derivatives from compounds of type (I) is considered in detail in Chapter XIX; particular interest attaches to this reaction by virtue of the fact that heterocyclic compounds containing the group N:C(OH) or N:C·C:C-(OH) commonly yield N-methyl derivatives.

B. Compounds Containing a Substituent in the Benzene Ring

Preparation. These compounds may be prepared by interaction of a 3- or 4-substituted phthalic anhydride with the appropriately substituted hydrazine; phthalazine derivatives containing a N-alkyl group may also be made from the substituted 1,4-dihydroxyphthalazine by alkylation. The position is complicated by the fact that, owing to the Bz substitution, a single anhydride or a single dihydroxyphthalazine can give rise to two isomeric N-substitution products as indicated in scheme (3).

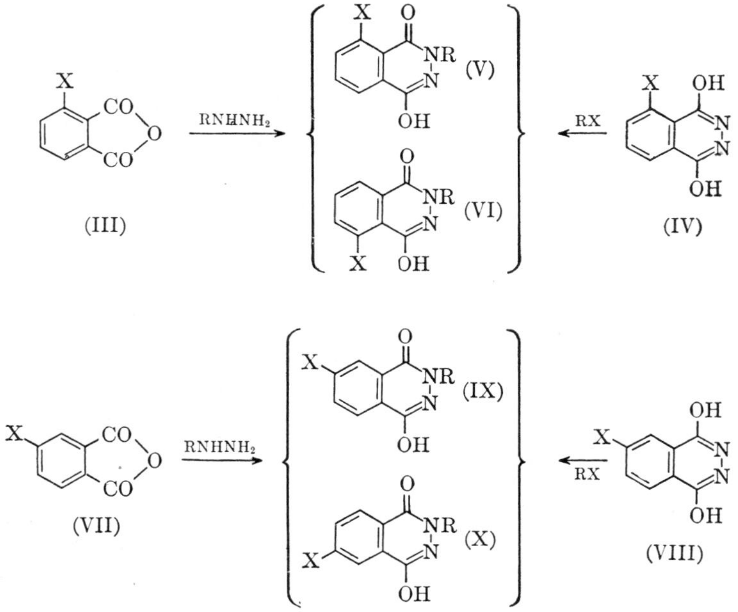

(3)

An interesting illustration of these principles is provided by the N-methylated compounds arising from 3-nitrophthalic anhydride and 5-nitro-1,4-dihydroxyphthalazine (III and IV; X = NO$_2$). The 5-nitro- and 5-amino-1-hydroxy-3-methyl-4-keto-3,4-dihydrophthalazines (V) are described in the literature as the "β-series" and the 8-substituted isomers (VI) as the "α-series." The compounds of these two series and their methods of preparation are summarized in Table XVIII-2. The configurations assigned to them have been deduced[5] from the behavior of the isomeric azo compounds (XI) [m.p. 326° (dec.)] and (XII) [m.p. 334° (dec.)] which are formed when diazotized 5- and 8-amino-1-hydroxy-3-methyl-4-keto-3,4-dihydrophthalazine, respectively, are coupled with β-naphthol. On treatment with cupric chloride and ammonia, (XI) and (XII) are converted into the corresponding copper derivatives, $C_{19}H_{17}O_4N_5Cu$ (XIII) and $C_{19}H_{15}O_3N_5Cu$ (XIV). When these are further boiled with aqueous cupric chloride, the O_4 compound takes up an additional half atom of copper per

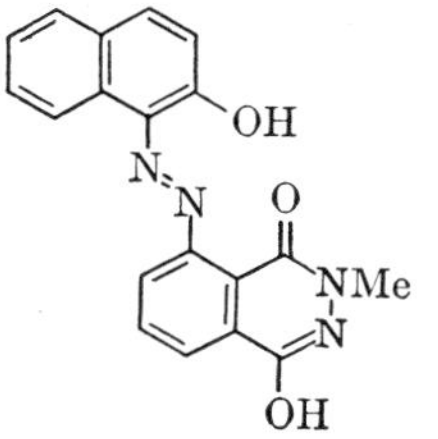

(XI)

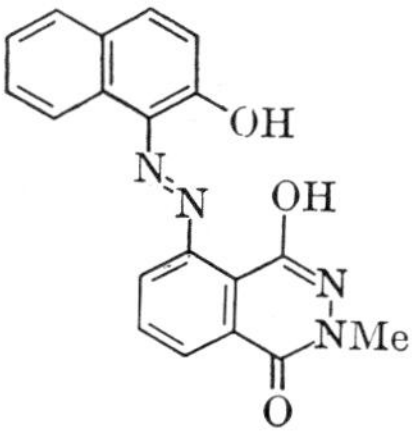

(XII)

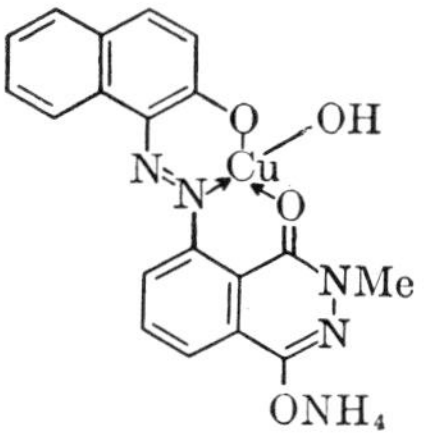

(XIII)

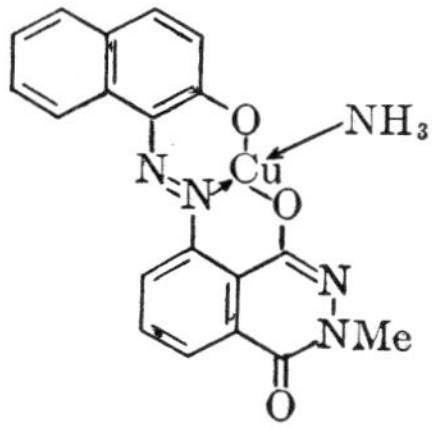

(XIV)

molecule, giving a compound $C_{38}H_{26}O_8N_8Cu_3 \cdot 2H_2O$; on the other hand, no such further absorption of copper occurs with the O_3 copper compound. The reaction of the O_4 salt involves the replacement of the NH_4 groups of two molecules by an atom of copper, and is clearly feasible only with (XIII); this compound is derived from the "β-series" (vide supra), which are therefore the 5-substituted compounds.

The azo compound (XII) also forms a pyridino-cupric salt analogous to (XIV) in which the NH_3 residue is replaced by C_5H_5N.

Similar isomeric possibilities also hold good for the 6- and 7-substituted compounds (IX) and (X), both of which are theoretically derivable from a single precursor (VII) or (VIII). Here also compounds belonging to an "α-series" and a "β-series" have been described,[6,7] but no proof of configuration exists at present. These compounds, together with others of unknown structure, are listed in Table XVIII-3.

TABLE XVIII-2. 5- and 8-Nitro- and -Amino-1-hydroxy-3-methyl-4-keto-3,4-
dihydrophthalazines

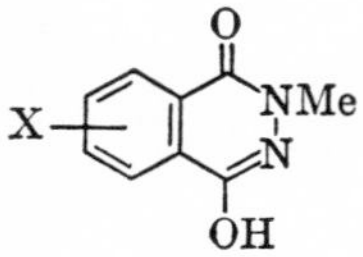

X	M.p., °C.	Prep.[a]	M.p. of acetyl deriv. (Ac in hetero ring), °C.	Ref.
5-NO₂	273[b]	A	144[b]	7
	272 (dec.)	A	158	6
	275	C	—	5
8-NO₂	305[b]	A	211[b]	7
	292 (dec.)	A	204–205	6
5-NH₂	299 (dec.)	B	—	6
8-NH₂	308 (dec.)	A,B,D	—	5,6
8-NHAc	291	A	—	5

[a] A, from the anhydride and methylhydrazine (or its sulfate and sodium acetate or sodium hydroxide) in water or acetic acid. B, from the corresponding nitro compound by reduction with tin and concentrated hydrochloric acid. C, from 5-nitro-1,4-dihydroxyphthalazine and methyl sulfate at 120–130°. D, by hydrolysis of the 8-acetamido compound.
[b] M.p. is corrected.

TABLE XVIII-3. 3-Substituted-1-hydroxy-4-keto-3,4-dihydrophthalazines of Undetermined Structure

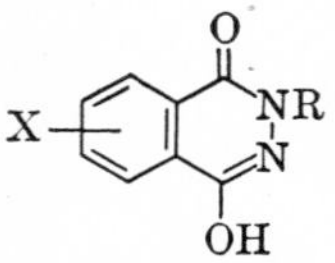

Nature and position of X	R	Prep.[a]	M.p., °C.	Remarks	Ref.
6- or 7-NO₂	Me	A	310–311[b]	Ac deriv., m.p.[b] 213–214°	7
	Me	A	307 (dec.)	Ac deriv., m.p. 210°	6
	Me	A	271–272[b]	Ac deriv., m.p.[b] 170–171°	7
	Me	A	293 (dec.)	Ac deriv., m.p. 195° (dec.)	6
	Me	C	295	Formulated by authors, without proof, as 7-NO₂	25
	CH₂Ph	I	212–213	—	11
	Ph	D	253	Ac deriv., m.p. 186°	7
	CO₂Et	E	115	Formulated by authors, without proof, as 7-NO₂. On boiling with water gives 6-nitro - 1,4 - dihydroxy-phthalazine	25

TABLE XVIII-3. 2-Substituted-1-hydroxyl-4-keto-3,4-dihydrophthalazines of Undetermined Structure (*continued*)

Nature and position of X	R	Prep.[a]	M.p., °C.	Remarks	Ref.
6- or 7-NH₂	Me	B	320 (dec.)	From the NO₂-compd., m.p. 307°	6
	Me	B	>360 (dec.)	From the NO₂-compd., m.p. 293°	6
	Et	F	~155	Formulated by authors, without proof, as 7-NH₂	25
	CH₂Ph	J	~216	Probably a mixt.	11
	Ph	H	222	The possibility that it is the isomeric *N*-anilinophthalimide is not excluded. Monoacetyl deriv., m.p. 178°	26
6- or 7-NHCO₂Et	CO₂Et	G	148–150	Formulated by authors, without proof, as the 3,7-di-CO₂Et compd.	25
5- or 8-NHMe	Me	K	230	Gives blue fluorescence in alk. and AcOHsoln. but not in mineral acids	26

[a] A,B see key to Table XVIII-2. C, from the potassium salt of 6-nitro-1,4-dihydroxyphthalazine and methyl iodide at 150°. D, from 4-nitrophthalic anhydride and phenylhydrazine in acetic acid (reflux). E, from the potassium salt of 6-nitro-1,4-dihydroxyphthalazine and ethyl chloroformate (reflux). F, from the sodium salt of 6-amino-1,4-dihydroxyphthalazine and ethyl iodide at 130–140°. G, from the sodium salt of 6-amino-1,4-dihydroxyphthalazine and ethyl chloroformate at 150°. H, from

$$\text{HN—O}\quad\text{CO}$$
$$\text{(benzene ring)}$$
$$\text{CO}_2\text{Me}$$

and phenylhydrazine (short boiling).

I, from 3-nitrophthalic anhydride and benzylhydrazine at 165–200°. J, from the nitro compound, m.p. 212–213°, by reduction with tin and hydrochloric acid or catalytically (H₂-Pd-C). K, from 5-methylamino-1,4-dihydroxyphthalazine, methyl sulfate, and aqueous sodium carbonate.

[b] M.p. corrected.

3. Derivatives of Unknown Structure

A number of compounds are known—mostly derived from Bz-substituted 1,4-dihydroxyphthalazines—to which it is impossible on the available evidence to assign definite constitutions. These compounds are listed in Table XVIII-4. In several cases definite structures have been allocated to the substances by the authors concerned, but reference to other sections of this book (this Chapter, Section 2A; Chapter IV, Section 2A; Chapter

VIII, Sections 2B and C;   Chapters XII and XVII;   Chapter XIX, Section 2) indicates that arbitrary decisions as to whether N- or O-substitution
is involved are not justified in the absence of independent evidence.

TABLE XVIII-4. Monoalkyl and Monoacyl Derivatives of 1,4-Dihydroxyphthal-
azines of Unknown Structure

R	Substituent alkyl or acyl radical	Prep.[a]	M.p., °C.	Remarks	Ref.
H	CH$_2$Ph	D	156	Insol. in NaOH, sol. in moderately conc. HCl. Heating with conc. HCl gives PhCH$_2$Cl. Formulated as O-CH$_2$Ph	11
H	CH$_2$CO$_2$H	C	>300	—	10
H	CH$_2$CO$_2$Et	B	>300	Formulated as N-deriv.	10
H	Bz	G	221–222	Easily hydrolyzed; formulated as O-Bz	2
H	CO$_2$Et	H	145; then solidifies and remelts ~180	Easily hydrolyzed; formulated as O-CO$_2$Et	2
5-NO$_2$	Pr	E	207–210	Somewhat sol. in NaOH	11
5-NO$_2$	Ac	A	221	Does not reduce Fehling solution. Hydrolyzed by cold 5% NaOH	27
5-NO$_2$	Ac	A	205	Reduces Fehling solution. Hydrolyzed by hot, but not by cold, 5% NaOH	27
5-NO$_2$	Bz	A	228	Yellow needles, hydrolyzed by cold 5% NaOH	27
5,8-di-NHAc	Ac	A	306 (dec.)	—	28
5,6,7,8-Cl$_4$	CO$_2$Et	F	244–245	Formulated as N-CO$_2$-Et	29

[a] A, from the 1,4-dihydroxy derivative by acylation.   B, from the potassium salt
of 1,4-dihydroxyphthalazine and ethyl chloroacetate at 160°.   C, from the ethyl
ester by acid hydrolysis.   D, from the silver salt (*ex* potassium salt) of 1,4-di-
hydroxyphthalazine and benzyl chloride at 130°.   E, from the silver salt of 5-nitro-1,4-
di-hydroxyphthalazine and propyl iodide in benzene.   F, from the silver salt of the
1,4-dihydroxy compound and ethyl chloroformate (reflux).   G, from the potassium
salt of 1,4-dihydroxyphthalazine and benzoyl chloride in benzene at 60–70°.   H,
from the silver salt of 1,4-dihydroxyphthalazine and ethyl chloroformate in benzene
at room temperature.

References

1. Rowe and Peters, *J. Chem. Soc.*, **1933**, 1331.
2. Heller, *J. prakt. Chem.*, **111**, 1 (1925).
3. Drew and Hatt, *J. Chem. Soc.*, **1937**, 16.
4. Rowe, Gillan, and Peters, *J. Chem. Soc.*, **1935**, 1808.
5. Drew and Garwood, *J. Chem. Soc.*, **1937**, 1841.
6. Drew, Hatt, and Hobart, *J. Chem. Soc.*, **1937**, 33.
7. C. N. Zellner and Dougherty, *J. Am. Chem. Soc.*, **58**, 1811 (1936).
8. Radulescu and Georgescu, *Bull. soc. chim.*, **37**, 881 (1925).
9. Blanksma and Bakels, *Rec. trav. chim.*, **58**, 497 (1939).
10. Curtius and Foersterling, *J. prakt. Chem.*, **51**, 371 (1895).
11. Wegler, *J. prakt. Chem.*, **148**, 135 (1937).
12. Chattaway and Tesh, *J. Chem. Soc.*, **1920**, 711.
13. Dunlap, *J. Am. Chem. Soc.*, **27**, 1091 (1905).
14. Brodrick, Peters, and Rowe, *J. Chem. Soc.*, **1948**, 1026.
15. Peters, Pringle, and Rowe, *J. Chem. Soc.*, **1948**, 597.
16. Rowe, Himmat, and Levin, *J. Chem. Soc.*, **1928**, 2556.
17. Rowe and Levin, *J. Chem. Soc.*, **1928**, 2550.
18. Bülow and Deseniss, *Ber.*, **39**, 2275 (1906).
19. Rowe, Lécutier, and Peters, *J. Chem. Soc.*, **1938**, 1079.
20. Rowe, Peters, and Rangwala, *J. Chem. Soc.*, **1948**, 206.
21. Rowe and Osborn, *J. Chem. Soc.*, **1947**, 829.
22. Rowe, Haigh, and Peters, *J. Chem. Soc.*, **1936**, 1098.
23. Rowe and Cross, *J. Chem. Soc.*, **1947**, 461.
24. Rowe and Siddle, *J. Chem. Soc.*, **1932**, 473.
25. Curtius and Hoesch, *J. prakt. Chem.*, **76**, 301 (1907).
26. Gleu and Pfannstiel, *J. prakt. Chem.*, **146**, 137 (1936).
27. Drew and Pearman, *J. Chem. Soc.*, **1937**, 26.
28. Drew and Pearman, *J. Chem. Soc.*, **1937**, 586.
29. Phelps, *Am. Chem. J.*, **33**, 586 (1905).

CHAPTER XIX

Dialkyl and Diacyl Derivatives of 1,4-Dihydroxyphthalazines

Three types of compound are theoretically derivable from 1,4-dihydroxyphthalazines by introducing two substituents into the hetero ring, namely, the 1,4- (I), 1,3- (II), and 2,3-derivatives (III).

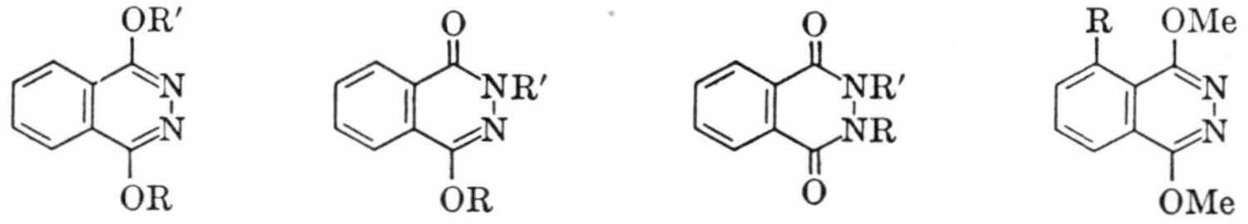

(I) (II) (III) (IV)

1. 1,4-Derivatives

1,4-Dimethoxyphthalazine (I; R = R′ = Me) is prepared by refluxing the silver salt of 1-hydroxy-4-methoxyphthalazine (Chapter XVIII, Section 1) with methanol and methyl iodide. It has m.p. 121° (sinters at 100°), and gives 1,4-dihydroxyphthalazine on evaporation with 48% hydrobromic acid.[1] Its structure follows from its nonidentity with (II and III; R = R′ = Me), the constitution of each of which is established (this Chapter, Tables XIX-1 and 3).

5-Nitro-1,4-dimethoxyphthalazine (IV; R = NO_2), prepared similarly from the silver salt of 5-nitro-4-hydroxy-1-methoxyphthalazine (Chapter XVIII, Section 1), melts at 212–214°.[1] It is one of the four compounds theoretically derivable from 5-nitro-1,4-dihydroxyphthalazine by dimethylation of the hetero ring, and its constitution follows from the fact that those of the remaining isomers are established (Tables XIX-2 and 3).

5-Amino-1,4-dimethoxyphthalazine (IV; R = NH_2) is obtained from the above nitro compound by reduction with tin and hydrochloric acid at 60°; it forms yellow prisms, m.p. 172–174°, and is soluble in acids but not in alkalis.[1]

2. 1,3-Derivatives (1-Alkoxy- and 1-Acetoxy-3-substituted-4-keto-3,4-dihydrophthalazines)

A. Preparation

(1) The few 1-acetoxy compounds that are known are prepared from the corresponding 1-hydroxy derivatives, either by direct acetylation with acetic anhydride or by treatment of the silver salt with acetyl chloride in hot benzene.

(2) 1-Alkoxy compounds are generally prepared from the 1-hydroxy derivatives (III), either by alkylation in alkaline solution with an alkyl halide or *via* the silver salt (see Table XIX-1 for conditions).

(3) In certain cases (see Table XIX-1) 1-methoxy compounds (II) have been prepared by heating the 4-alkoxydihydro derivatives (I; $R'' =$ Me or Et) at 110–140°. The mechanism of this reaction is not, however, established, and it fails with the majority of compounds of type (I).

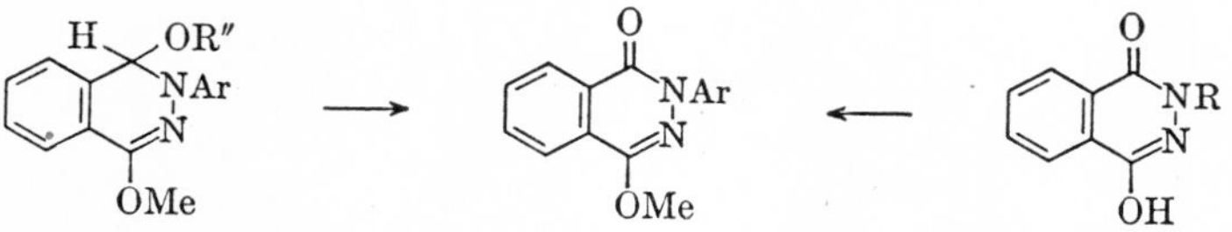

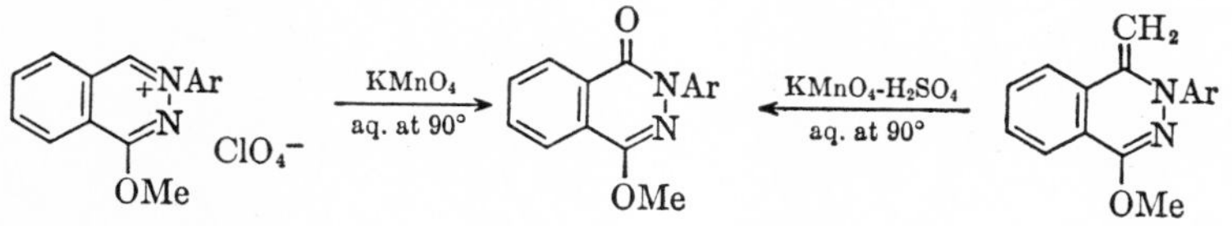

(4) In one or two cases oxidative methods [(IV) and (V) → (II)] have been employed.

(5) If N-arylaminophthalimides (VI) are heated with an alkyl iodide and alcoholic sodium ethoxide under pressure, rearrangement and alkylation occur:

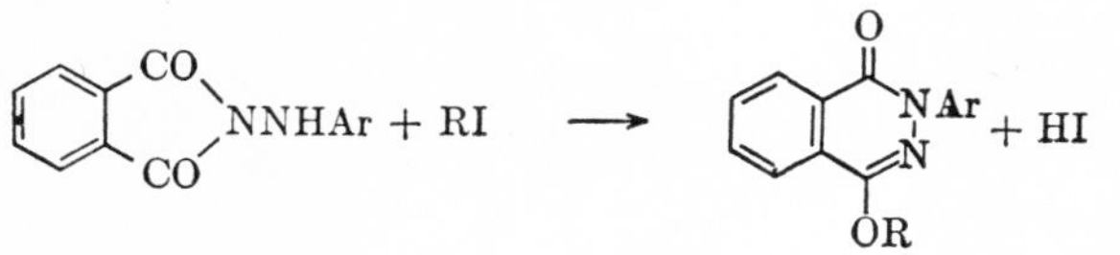

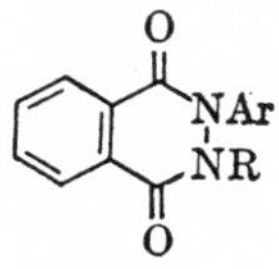

A number of compounds prepared by this method are formulated in the literature as N,N'-dialkylated derivatives (VII). While it is true that O-methylation is believed to be the exception rather than the rule with hydroxy heterocyclics containing the grouping $N:C(OH)$ or $N:C\cdot C:C-$ (OH), there is no real evidence in favor of (VII) as a representation of the structure of the products obtained by alkylation of (VI); and for reasons discussed below these products are here treated as 1,3-derivatives and are included in Table XIX-1 (marked with an asterisk).

(6) Compounds in which the 3-aryl substituent contains an amino group are prepared by reduction of the corresponding nitro compounds.

B. Properties. The known compounds of this group are listed in Tables XIX-1 and 2. They are colorless or pale yellow crystalline solids of normal solubility. The 1-acetoxy derivatives are easily hydrolyzed and the 1-methoxy compounds are readily demethylated to the 1-hydroxy compounds.[2]

TABLE XIX-1. 1-Alkoxy- and 1-Acetoxy-3-substituted-4-keto-3,4-dihydrophthalazines Containing No Substituent in the Benzene Ring

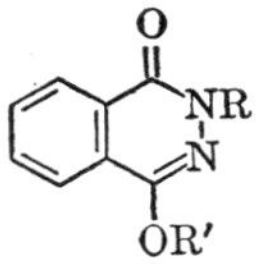

R	R'	Prep.[a]	M.p., °C.	Remarks	Ref.
Me	Me	Q,R	93	Sol. in dil. HCl, insol. in alk. For proof of structure see footnote[b]	4
Me	Ac	B	140 141 142	Sol. in dil. mineral acids. Gives the 1-OH compd. with hot aq. EtOH	4–6
CH₂Ph	CH₂Ph	P	96–97	—	3
Ph	Me	C,F,L	109–111	—	2,7
	Et	E,F,G	108–109 109* 105–106*	—	2,8
	Prⁿ	G	75*	—	8
	Prⁱ	G	103*	—	8
	Allyl	G	90*	—	8
	[—CH₂]₃OR''	G	187ᶜ	—	8
	Ac	B	127*	—	8
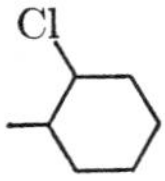 (Cl-cyclohexyl structure)	Me	D	136–137ᵈ	—	9
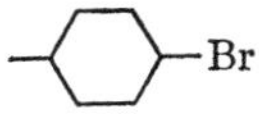 (Br-cyclohexyl structure)	Allyl	H	129*	—	8

Table continued

TABLE XIX-1 (*continued*)

R	R'	Prep.[a]	M.p., °C.	Remarks	Ref.
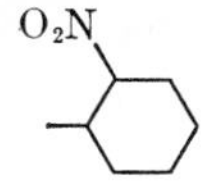 O₂N— (2-nitrophenyl)	Me	D	176–177	—	2
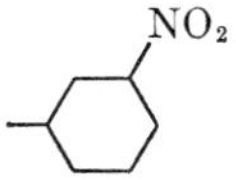 NO₂ (3-nitrophenyl)	Me Ac	D,I,O A,B	182 164	— —	2,10 2
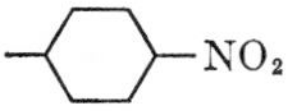 —NO₂ (4-nitrophenyl)	Me Ac	C,I,J,O A,B	199[d] 222	— —	2,11 2
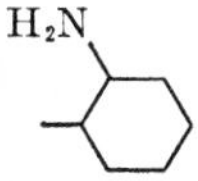 H₂N— (2-aminophenyl)	Me	M	234–235	NHAc deriv., m.p. 219–220°	7
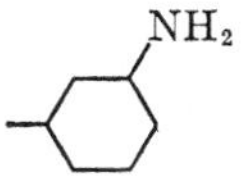 NH₂ (3-aminophenyl)	Me	M	181	NHAc deriv., m.p. 246–247°	7
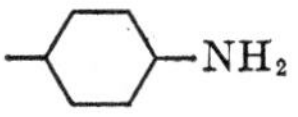 —NH₂ (4-aminophenyl)	Me	K	197	NHAc deriv., m.p. 216°	7
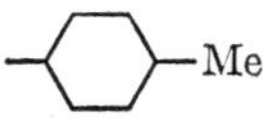 —Me (4-methylphenyl)	Allyl	G	102*	—	8
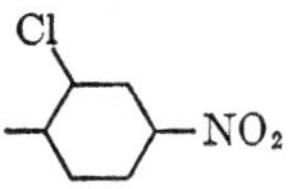 Cl, —NO₂ (2-chloro-4-nitrophenyl)	Me	D	193–194	—	2
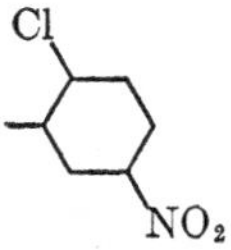 Cl, NO₂ (2-chloro-5-nitrophenyl)	Me	—	170[d]	—	12
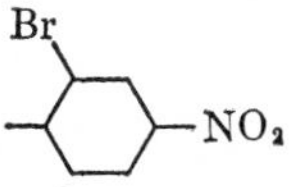 Br, —NO₂ (2-bromo-4-nitrophenyl)	Me	D	167–168	—	2
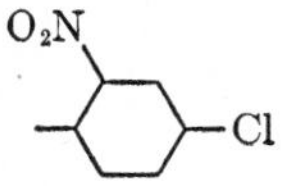 O₂N—, —Cl (2-nitro-4-chlorophenyl)	Me	D	225–228	—	7
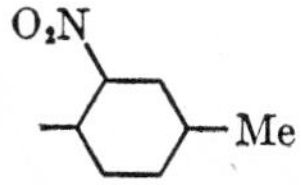 O₂N—, —Me (2-nitro-4-methylphenyl)	Et	D	185	—	13

Table continued

TABLE XIX-1 (*continued*)

R	R'	Prep.[a]	M.p., °C.	Remarks	Ref.
H₂N–⟨ring⟩–Cl	Me	N	217–219	NHAc deriv., m.p. 272–274°	7
Me–⟨ring⟩–NO₂	Me	D,O	184–185	—	2,14
Cl, Cl–⟨ring⟩–NO₂	Me	D	178–179	—	2

* These compounds are given in the literature[8] as *N*-substituted derivatives.

[a] A, from the silver salt of the 1-hydroxy compound and acetyl chloride in benzene (reflux).   B, from the 1-hydroxy compound and acetic anhydride (reflux).   C, from the silver salt of the 1-hydroxy compound, methanol, and methyl iodide (reflux).   D, from the silver salt of the 1-hydroxy compound, benzene (or toluene), and alkyl iodide (reflux).   E, from the silver salt of the 1-hydroxy compound, ethanol, and ethyl iodide (reflux).   F, from the 1-hydroxy compound, ethyl iodide, and alcoholic potassium hydroxide (reflux).   G, from the *N*-arylaminophthalimide, alcoholic sodium ethoxide, and alkyl iodide at 120–130° for ~12 hours.   H, from the 1-hydroxy compound, alcoholic sodium ethoxide, and allyl iodide (reflux for 7–8 hours).   I, from the 1-methoxy-3-arylphthalazinium perchlorate and aqueous permanganate at 90°.   J, from the 1-methoxy-3-aryl-4-methylene-3,4-dihydrophthalazine and permanganate in aqueous sulfuric acid at 90°.   K, from the nitro compound by boiling with sodium hydrosulfite and sodium hydroxide in aqueous alcohol.   L, from the 4'-amino compound by diazotization and treating with alkaline stannite.   M, from the nitro compound, stannous chloride, and concentrated hydrochloric acid (reflux).   N, from the nitro compound, iron, and aqueous acetic acid (reflux).   O, from the 1-methoxy-4-alkoxy-3-aryl-3,4-dihydrophthalazine by heating at 110–140°.   P, from the silver salt of the 1-hydroxy compound, by heating with benzyl chloride.   Q, from 1,4-dihydroxyphthalazine by refluxing with methyl sulfate and aqueous potassium hydroxide.   R, from 4-hydroxy-1-methoxyphthalazine by refluxing with methyl iodide, methyl alcohol, and aqueous potassium hydroxide; or from the sodium salt thereof, methyl iodide, and methyl alcohol at 125°.

[b] The structure of this compound follows from the facts (*1*) that it differs from the *N*,*N*'-isomer (Section 3), and (*2*) that it gives 1-hydroxy-3-methyl-4-keto-3,4-dihydrophthalazine on treatment with HBr at 100°.[4]

[c]

R''=⟨structure: O, NPh, N⟩

[d] For an alternative preparation of these compounds see Chapter XVI, Section 2.

TABLE XIX-2. 1-Alkoxy-3-substituted-4-keto-3,4-dihydrophthalazines Containing a Substituent in the Benzene Ring

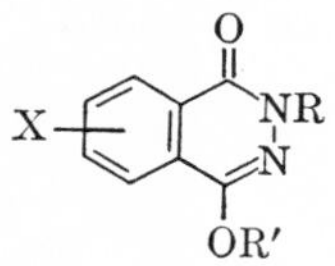

X	R	R′	Prep.[a]	M.p., °C.	Remarks	Ref.
5-NO$_2$	Me	Me	B,C,D	139	—	1
			E	138–139[b]	—	15
8-NO$_2$	Me	Me	D	199–200	—	1
			E	207[b]	—	15
5-NH$_2$	Me	Me	A	222	NHAc deriv., m.p. 220°	1
8-NH$_2$	Me	Me	A	136	NHAc deriv., m.p. 187°	1

[a] A, from the corresponding nitro compound by reduction with tin and hydrochloric acid. B, from 5-nitro-1,4-dihydroxyphthalazine and methyl sulfate at 120–30°. C, from the silver salt of 5-nitro-1,4-dihydroxyphthalazine, methyl alcohol, and methyl iodide (reflux); this gives the 1-methoxy derivative, which is then treated with methyl sulfate and sodium hydroxide. D, from the silver salt of the appropriate N-methyl compound, methyl alcohol, and methyl iodide (reflux). E, from the appropriate N-methyl compound, methyl sulfate, and alkali.
[b] M.p. is corrected.

C. Structure of Alkoxy Compounds.

Among the general methods of preparation described above, methods (2) and (5) do not enable one to differentiate between the two alternative structures (VIII) and (IX) which are theoretically possible for the products. The observed ready demethylation of certain compounds in which R′ = Me is, of course, evi-

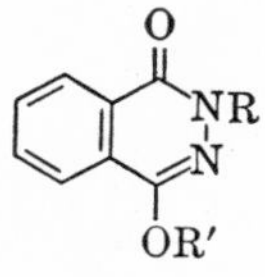

(VIII) 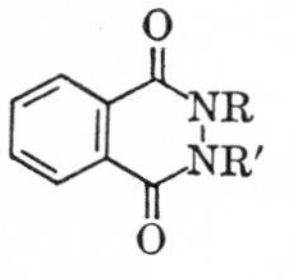   (IX) 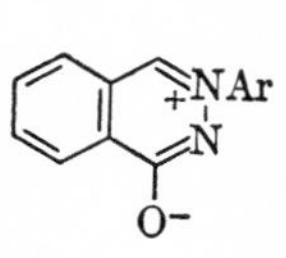   (X)

dence in favor of structure (VIII),[2] but the behavior of many compounds of the group in this respect has not been investigated. It is therefore of great importance from the structural aspect that in a number of cases complementary evidence exists which provides formal proof of the correctness of structure (VIII).

In the first place, method (3) enables compounds to be prepared from starting materials (I) which already contain the 1-methoxyl group. [The compounds (I) are themselves prepared by the action of methyl sulfate on 1-keto-3-arylphthalazines (X), and the dipolar nature of the latter virtually rules out any structure alternative to (I).] Examination of Table XIX-1 shows that identical compounds (VIII) have been obtained both by method (2) and also by method (3) for the three cases R' = Me; R = 3'-nitrophenyl, 4'-nitrophenyl, and 4'-nitro-2'-methylphenyl.

Second, the compound (VIII; R = R' = CH₂Ph), prepared by method (2), is different from an isomer, m.p. 153–154°, which must be the N,N'-derivative (IX; R = R' = CH₂Ph) by reason of its formation from N,N'-dibenzylhydrazine and phthalic anhydride[3] (Eq. 1).

$$\text{(phthalic anhydride)} + \begin{array}{c}\text{NHCH}_2\text{Ph}\\ |\\ \text{NHCH}_2\text{Ph}\end{array} \longrightarrow \text{(IX; R = R' = CH}_2\text{Ph)} \tag{1}$$

(XI)   (XV)   (XII)

MeI on Ag salt   MeI on Ag salt

(XVI)   (XIII)   (XIV)

Me₂SO₄ / NaOH

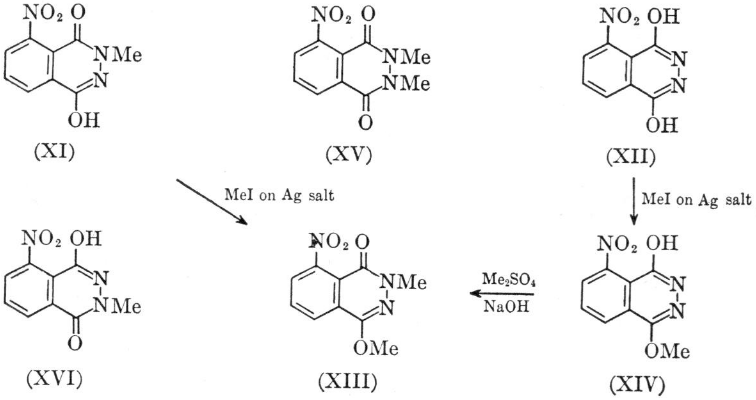

Third, reference to Table XIX-2 shows that the compound (XIII), m.p. 139°, may be prepared from (XI) by method (2).   Now (XIII) is different from the N,N'-dimethyl isomer (XV), m.p. 194–195° (this Chapter, Section 3), of established structure; and, as the constitution of (XI) is likewise certain (Chapter XVIII, Section 2B), that of (XIII) immediately follows.

The constitution of (XIII) being thus established, that of (XIV) (Chapter XVIII, Section 1) also follows.   This compound, m.p. 269°, is an intermediate in the preparation of (XIII) from (XII),[1] as indicated above, and as it is not identical with either of the N-methyl isomers (XI) and (XVI) (Table XIX-1), the structures of both of which are certain (Chapter XVIII, Section 2B), it must clearly have the constitution shown above.

It is thus seen that method (2) results in O-alkylation of compounds of type (III) in five cases at least, and it is thus reasonable to assume that the same reaction occurs in other cases also where method (2) is employed.

Hence the compound (VIII; $R' = $ Et; $R = $ Ph) is in all probability correctly formulated; it is, however, also prepared by method (5) (see Table XIX-1), and there is thus good evidence for the view that the latter reaction gives the O-ethers (VIII) and not, as assumed in the literature, the N-isomers (IX). Nevertheless, one must recall that there are cases, cited elsewhere in this volume, which show that mere *prediction* of O or N-alkylation may be extremely hazardous, and nothing short of formal proof is sufficient to place the issue entirely beyond doubt in any given case.

3. 2,3-Derivatives

The compounds of this group are listed in Table XIX-3. They are all prepared, directly or indirectly, by condensing phthalic anhydride or its analogs with N,N'-disubstituted hydrazines, and, as there is no reason to believe that migration of substituents occurs during the reaction, this method of synthesis is considered to be unambiguous.

TABLE XIX-3. N,N-Dialkyl Derivatives of 1,4-Dihydroxyphthalazines

R	R'	Prep.[a]	M.p., °C.	Remarks	Ref.
H	Me	A	175 175–176	Hydrolyzed to components by hot 2 N HCl. Boiling with aq. hydrazine gives N,N'-dimethylhydrazine and 1,4-dihydroxyphthalazine	5,16
H	CH$_2$Ph	B	153–154	—	3
5-NO$_2$	Me	A	194–195 203[b]	Hydrolyzed to components by hot 2 N HCl/16 hours	15,16
6-NO$_2$	Me	A	198–199 203.5[b]	Slowly hydrolyzed to components by hot HCl	15,16
5-NH$_2$	Me	C	192	Diazotization and coupling with β-naphthol gives azo compd., C$_{20}$H$_{16}$O$_3$N$_4$, m.p. 312–316° (dec.). Gives Ac deriv., m.p. 221–222°	16
6-NH$_2$	Me	C	262–263	Diazotization and coupling with β-naphthol gives azo compd., C$_{20}$H$_{16}$O$_3$N$_4$, m.p. 270–272°. Gives Ac deriv., m.p. 269–270°	16

[a] A, from the appropriately substituted phthalic anhydride, N,N'-dimethylhydrazine, and boiling aqueous acetic acid. B, from phthalic anhydride and N,N'-dibenzylhydrazine at 165° (open vessel). C, from the corresponding nitro compound, stannous chloride, and concentrated hydrochloric acid at 50°.
[b] M.p. is corrected.

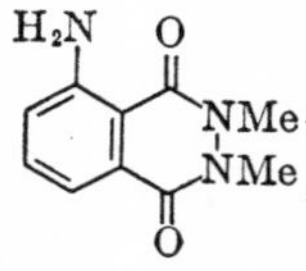

(I) 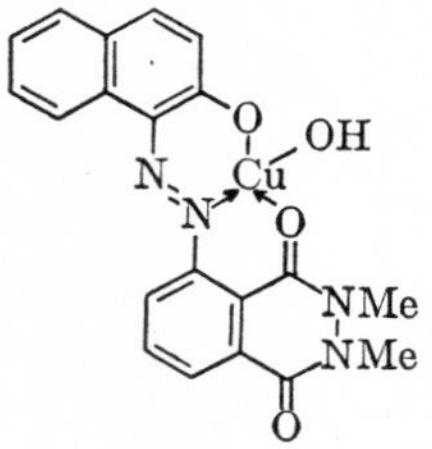   (II)

The properties of these compounds are given in Table XIX-3. The azo compound, m.p. 312–316° (see Table XIX-3), from 5-amino-2,3-dimethyl-1,4-diketo-1,2,3,4-tetrahydrophthalazine (I) yields a copper derivative (II) on treatment with cupric chloride in pyridine (*cf.* Chapter XVIII, Section 2B).[1]

4. Derivatives of Unknown Structure

The compounds in this group, in contrast to those in the preceding section, are prepared by alkylation or acylation of 1,4-dihydroxyphthalazines, and it is therefore impossible to assign structures to them with any degree of certainty. The compounds are given in Table XIX-4.

TABLE XIX-4. Dialkyl and Diacyl Derivatives of 1,4-Dihydroxyphthalazines of Unknown Structure

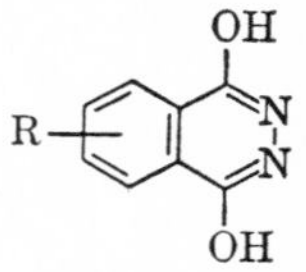

R	Substituent alkyl or acyl radicals	Prep.[a]	M.p., °C.	Remarks	Ref.
H	$2CO_2Et$	E	136	Formulated as 2,3-$(CO_2Et)_2$	20
5-NO$_2$	2Pr	C	119	Insol. in NaOH	3
6-NO$_2$	2Ac	A	165	Hydrolyzed by boiling water	17
5-NH$_2$	2Pr	D	142	—	9
5-NH$_2$	2Ac	A	262	—	18
5-NH$_2$	2Bz	B	263	—	18
6-NH$_2$	2Ac	A	212	Yellow tablets; some hydrolysis of the Ac groups occurs in boiling water. Formulated as 2,6-Ac$_2$	17
5,6,7,8-Cl$_4$	2Ac	A	203–204	Formulated as 2,3-Ac$_2$	19

[a] A, from the 1,4-dihydroxy derivative by acetylation. B, from the sodium salt of luminol, benzoyl chloride, and pyridine. C, from the silver salt of the 1,4-dihydroxy compound and propyl iodide in benzene. D, from the corresponding nitro compound (m.p. 119°) by reduction. E, from the silver salt of 1,4-dihydroxyphthalazine and ethyl chloroformate in benzene at room temperature.

References

1. Drew and Garwood, *J. Chem. Soc.*, **1937**, 1841.
2. Rowe, Gillan, and Peters, *J. Chem. Soc.*, **1935**, 1808.
3. Wegler, *J. prakt. Chem.*, **148**, 135 (1937).
4. Rowe and Peters, *J. Chem. Soc.*, **1933**, 1331.
5. Blanksma and Bakels, *Rec. trav. chim.*, **58**, 497 (1939).
6. Radulescu and Georgescu, *Bull. soc. chim.*, **37**, 881 (1925).
7. Rowe, Lécutier, and Peters, *J. Chem. Soc.*, **1938**, 1079.
8. Chattaway and Tesh, *J. Chem. Soc.*, **1920**, 711.
9. Brodrick, Peters, and Rowe, *J. Chem. Soc.*, **1948**, 1026.
10. Rowe, Himmat, and Levin, *J. Chem. Soc.*, **1928**, 2556.
11. Rowe and Levin, *J. Chem. Soc.*, **1928**, 2550.
12. Rowe, Peters, and Rangwala, *J. Chem. Soc.*, **1948**, 206.
13. Rowe, Haigh, and Peters, *J. Chem. Soc.*, **1936**, 1098.
14. Rowe and Siddle, *J. Chem. Soc.*, **1932**, 473.
15. C. N. Zellner and Dougherty, *J. Am. Chem. Soc.*, **58**, 1811 (1936).
16. Drew, Hatt, and Hobart, *J. Chem. Soc.*, **1937**, 33.
17. Curtius and Hoesch, *J. prakt. Chem.*, **76**, 301 (1907).
18. Drew and Pearman, *J. Chem. Soc.*, **1937**, 26.
19. Phelps, *Am. Chem. J.*, **33**, 586 (1905).
20. Heller, *J. prakt. Chem.*, **111**, 1 (1925).

CHAPTER XX

1-Halogeno- and 1,4-Dihalogenophthalazines

1. 1-Halogenophthalazines

A. Preparation. Chloro compounds are prepared from the corresponding hydroxy compounds by heating (usually for a short time) with phosphorus oxychloride on the steam bath; the mixture is then poured into water and neutralized with sodium hydroxide or ammonia. Iodo compounds are made from the corresponding chloro compounds by warming for a short time or refluxing with constant-boiling hydriodic acid, either with or without the addition of red phosphorus.

B. Properties. 1-Halogenophthalazines are usually colorless crystalline solids. They are unstable, but the precise nature of, and conditions producing, this instability have not been closely investigated. In many cases well-defined salts of the compounds have been prepared (see Table XX-1), but these also are unstable and tend to resinify on recrystallization.

C. Reactions

(*1*) 1-Chlorophthalazines exhibit the reactivity characteristic of chloro heterocyclic compounds containing the group —N=C—Cl or its vinyl analog. When warmed with a solution of a sodium alkoxide in the corresponding alcohol (or with sodium phenoxide in phenol) they are converted into 1-alkoxy- (or 1-phenoxy-) phthalazines (Chapter XIII, Section 1) (Eq. 1).

$$\text{(structure)} + \text{R'ONa} \longrightarrow \text{(structure)} + \text{NaCl} \tag{1}$$

(*2*) 1-Chlorophthalazines react with amines in the manner characteristic of compounds containing reactive halogen. With aniline, *p*-chloroaniline, and dialkylaminoalkylamines under appropriate conditions, 1-*sec*-aminophthalazines (Chapter XXI) may be prepared (Eq. 2).

178

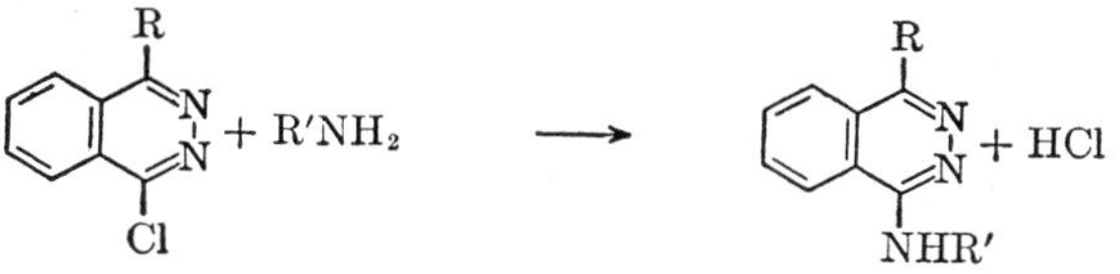

$$+ R'NH_2 \longrightarrow + HCl \qquad (2)$$

(*3*) Reduction of 1-chlorophthalazines occurs readily, with formation of one or the other of two products according to conditions.

(*a*) When refluxed with hydriodic acid (*d* 1.7) and red phosphorus, usually for about 5 hours, the corresponding phthalazine is produced (Eq. 3). This reaction has been carried out with 1-chlorophthalazine itself[1-3]

$$\longrightarrow \qquad (3)$$

and with 1-chloro-4-methyl-,[1] -4-ethyl-,[2] -4-isobutyl-,[4] -4-benzyl-,[5] and -4-phenylphthalazine.[5]   1-Chloro-7,8-dimethoxyphthalazine (chloroopia-zone) undergoes demethylation as well as reduction, yielding 7,8-dihy-droxyphthalazine (Chapter X, Section 2).[3]   It should be noted that, if the reduction is stopped after a short time, 1-iodophthalazines can be isolated (see Table XX-1).

(*b*) On reduction with zinc and hydrochloric acid, 1-chlorophthal-azines are converted with loss of ammonia into dihydroisoindoles (Eq. 4).

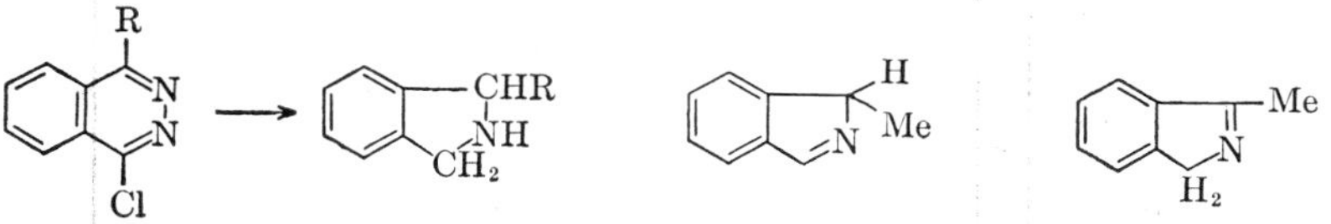

(I)   (II)   (4)

Examples of this are R = H,[6] Et (tin and fuming acid are used here),[7] Pr[n,8] and Bu[i,8]. 1-Chloro-4-methylphthalazine is exceptional in giving the isoindole (I or II) and not the dihydro derivative when treated in this way or with hydriodic acid and red phosphorus at 200°.[1,9]

2. 1,4-Dihalogenophthalazines

A. Preparation.   The only known compounds of this group, 1,4-dichloro- and 1,4-dibromophthalazine (I; R = Cl and Br), are both pre-pared from 1,4-dihydroxyphthalazine and the corresponding phosphorus pentahalide.[13-15]   The recommended procedure for 1,4-dichlorophthala-zine[14,15] is to heat the reactants at 150° for 8 hours; if the dihydroxy com-pound is treated with a mixture of phosphorus pentachloride and oxychlo-

TABLE XX-1. 1-Halogenophthalazines

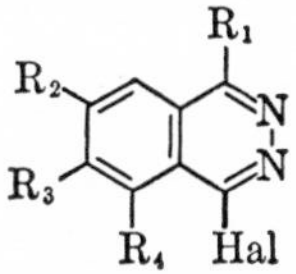

Hal.	R1	R2	R3	R4	Prep.[a]	M.p., °C.	Derivatives	Ref.
Cl	H	H	H	H	A	113	Yellow needles, easily sol. in mineral acids. Chloroplatinate, m.p. 205°; ferrocyanide, dec. on heating; picrate, m.p. 135°. Salts resinify on attempted recrystn.	2,6
Cl	H	H	Cl	H	A	161–162	—	10
Cl	H	H	OMe	H	A	144.9–145.5 (dec.)	—	10
Cl	H	H	OMe	OMe	A	152	Easily resinified. M.p. depends on rate of heating. Hydrochloride, m.p. 260° (dec.), is hydrolyzed by cold water	3,11,12
Cl	H	Cl	H	H	A	150–151 (dec.)	—	10
Cl	NHPh	H	H	H	G	200	Hydrochloride, m.p. 270°	14
Cl	 NH-C₆H₁₀-Cl (4-chlorocyclohexylamino)	H	H	H	G	241	Hydrochloride, m.p. 256°	14
Cl	OH	H	H	H	B,C,D	274	Cryst. from hot water, sol. in acids. Chloroplatinate, m.p. >280°; chloroaurate, m.p. 149–150°; picrate, m.p. 154°; ferrocyanide	14–16
Cl	Me	H	H	H	A	130	—	1,9

Hal.	R₁	R₂	R₃	R₄	Prep.ᵃ	M.p., °C.	Derivatives	Ref.
Cl	Et	H	H	H	A	93	Hydrochloride, m.p. 183–184°; chloroaurate, m.p. 116°; picrate; chloroplatinate; ferrocyanide; dichromate	2,7
Cl	Prⁿ	H	H	H	A	67	Sol. in warm dil. HCl	8
Cl	Buⁱ	H	H	H	A	38	Sol. in acids. Chloroplatinate, m.p. 216°; picrate, m.p. 122°	4,8
Cl	CH₂Ph	H	H	H	A	152	—	9
Cl	Ph	H	H	H	A	160–161	—	5
Br	OH	H	H	H	E	273	—	13
I	H	H	H	H	F	78	—	3
I	Me	H	H	H	F	116 (dec.)	Further reduction gives 1-methylphthalazine	1
I	Et	H	H	H	F	78	Hydriodide, m.p. 178°. Picrate, m.p. 141°. Hydrochloride, m.p. 173°	2
I	Buⁱ	H	H	H	F	—	Hydriodide, orange-yellow needles, m.p. 127°. Free base is unstable	4
I	CH₂Ph	H	H	H	F	146 (dec.)	—	5
I	Ph	H	H	H	F	188–189 (dec.)	—	5

ᵃ A, from the corresponding hydroxy compound by heating with phosphorus oxychloride on the steam bath. B, from 1,4-dihydroxyphthalazine by heating with phosphorus pentachloride and phosphorus oxychloride on the steam bath. C, by heating 1,4-dichlorophthalazine with phthalic acid at 180°, either alone or in nitrobenzene. D, by hydrolysis of 1,4-dichlorophthalazine with warm dilute mineral acid. E, from 1,4-dihydroxyphthalazine and phosphorus pentabromide. F, from the corresponding 4-chloro compound by boiling for a short time with hydriodic acid (d 1.7) either alone or with red phosphorus. G, from 1,4-dichlorophthalazine and ArNH₂ (1 mole) in alcohol (reflux).

(I)   (II)

ride at water-bath temperature, the product is mainly 1-chloro-4-hydroxy-phthalazine.[16] The formation of the 1,4-dibromo compound is accompanied by that of 1-bromo-4-hydroxyphthalazine.[13]

B. Properties.   1,4-Dichlorophthalazine forms colorless needles, m.p. 164°[15] (163°,[13] 161–162°[14]); 1,4-dibromophthalazine has m.p. 162°, and also crystallizes in colorless needles.[13]

1,4-Dichlorophthalazine is very readily converted into 1-chloro-4-hydroxyphthalazine; the transformation may be effected by heating it with phthalic acid at 180° (alone or in nitrobenzene),[15] or by hydrolysis in weakly acid solution.[14] It is stable toward water and alkalis (conditions unspecified), but is less stable than 2,3-dichloroquinoxaline.[14] When refluxed with aniline (2 moles) in alcohol, it yields 1,4-dianilinophthalazine (Chapter XXI); with 1 mole of the base in boiling alcohol, the product is 1-chloro-4-anilinophthalazine, which, however, does not react further with aniline under these conditions.[14] Both 1,4-dichloro- and 1,4-dibromo-phthalazine yield the compound (II) (Chapter XXIII, Section 3) when refluxed with sodium azide in alcohol.

References

1. Gabriel and Eschenbach, *Ber.*, **30**, 3022 (1897).
2. Paul, *Ber.*, **32**, 2014 (1899).
3. Gabriel, *Ber.*, **36**, 3373 (1903).
4. Wölbling, *Ber.*, **38**, 3925 (1905).
5. Lieck, *Ber.*, **38**, 3918 (1905).
6. Gabriel and Neumann, *Ber.*, **26**, 521 (1893).
7. Daube, *Ber.*, **38**, 206 (1905).
8. Bromberg, *Ber.*, **29**, 1434 (1896).
9. Gabriel and Neumann, *Ber.*, **26**, 705 (1893).
10. Vaughan and Baird, *J. Am. Chem. Soc.*, **68**, 1314 (1946).
11. Liebermann and Bistrzycki, *Ber.*, **26**, 531 (1893).
12. Jacobson, *Ber.*, **27**, 1418 (1894).
13. Stollé and Storch, *J. prakt. Chem.*, **135**, 128 (1932).
14. R. D. Haworth and S. Robinson, *J. Chem. Soc.*, **1948**, 777.
15. Drew and Hatt, *J. Chem. Soc.*, **1937**, 16.
16. Radulescu and Georgescu, *Bull. soc. chim.*, **37**, 881 (1925).

CHAPTER XXI

1-Aminophthalazines

The number of compounds belonging to this group is small, and nothing is known of their chemistry.   They are prepared from 1-chlorophthalazines by interaction with the appropriate amines (see Table XXI-1), and are mostly colorless crystalline solids.

References

1. Drake and Peck, *J. Am. Chem. Soc.*, **68**, 1313 (1946).
2. R. D. Haworth and S. Robinson, *J. Chem. Soc.*, **1948**, 777.
3. E. F. M. Stephenson, *J. Chem. Soc.*, **1944**, 678.
4. Darapsky and Heinrichs, *J. prakt. Chem.*, **146**, 307 (1936).
5. F. B. Kipping and F. G. Mann, *J. Chem. Soc.*, **1927**, 528.
6. Lieck, *Ber.*, **38**, 3918 (1905).
7. Albert, Goldacre, and J. Phillips, *J. Chem. Soc.*, **1948**, 2240.

Table XXI-1 follows on page 184.

TABLE XXI-1. 1-Aminophthalazines

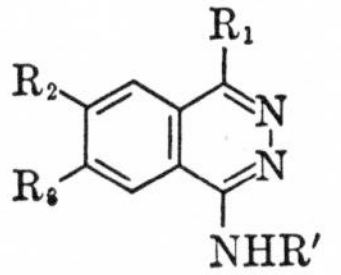

R₁	R₂	R₃	R'	Prep.ᵃ	M.P., °C.	Remarks	Ref.
H	H	H	H	—	210–211	—	7
H	H	H	CHMe[CH₂]₃NEt₂	H	Oil	Triphosphate, m.p. 179–180°	1
H	H	Cl	CHMe[CH₂]₃NEt₂	H	Oil	Dihydriodide, m.p. 164.6–165.8°	1
H	Cl	H	CHMe[CH₂]₃NEt₂	H	Oil	Diphosphate, m.p. 235° (dec.)	1
NHPh	H	H	[CH₂]₂NEt₂	E	148–149	Picrate, m.p. 197–199°	2
NHPh	H	H	[CH₂]₃NEt₂	E	174	—	2
NHPh	H	H	Ph	B,C,D	223	Yellow plates	2
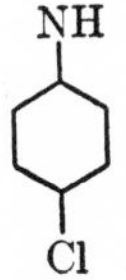 NH–C₆H₁₀–Cl	H	H	[CH₂]₂NEt₂	E	145	—	2
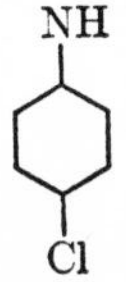 NH–C₆H₁₀–Cl	H	H	[CH₂]₃NEt₂	F	181–182	—	2

R₁	R₂	R₃	R'	Prep.[a]	M.p., °C.	Remarks	Ref.
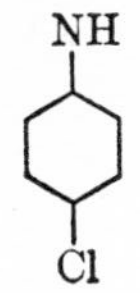 (NH—C₆H₁₀—Cl structure)	H	H	CHMe[CH₂]₃NEt₂	G	Oil	B.p. 215–230°/0.002 mm. Dipicrate, m.p. 203–204°	2
OH	H	H	H	See Table XII-1	257–258, 271–272 (corr., dec.)	See Table XII-1	3,4
OH	H	H	CO₂Et	See Table XII-1	207	—	4
OH	H	H	CH₂X[b]	See Table XII-1	>330	See Table XII-1	5
CH₂Ph	H	H	Ph	A	231	—	6
Ph	H	H	Ph	A	180	—	6

[a] A, from the corresponding chloro compound and excess aniline (warm). B, from 1-chloro-4-anilinophthalazine and aniline (reflux). C, from 1-chloro-4-anilinophthalazine and aniline hydrochloride in alcohol (reflux). D, from 1,4-dichlorophthalazine and aniline (2 moles) in alcohol (reflux). E, from the 1-chloro-4-arylaminophthalazine and R'NH₂ at 150–160°. F, from the 1-chloro-4-arylaminophthalazine and R'NH₂ at 100° for 36 hours. G, from the 1-chloro-4-arylaminophthalazine and R'NH₂ at 140°. H, from the corresponding chloro compound and R'NH₂ at 87–100°.

[b] X= (structure: NHCH₂— attached to phthalazine with N—N, bracketed ₂)

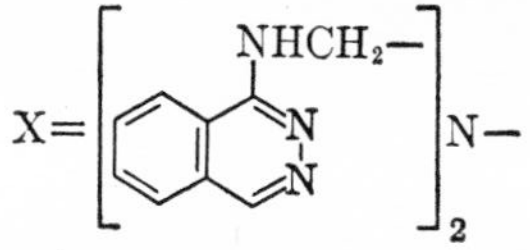

CHAPTER XXII

Reduced Phthalazines

1. 3,4-Dihydrophthalazines

Many 3,4-dihydrophthalazines have already been described in the preceding chapters. 1,3-Disubstituted-4-keto-dihydrophthalazines (I) of various types are discussed in Chapters XIII, XVIII, and XIX; 4-alkoxy- and 4-methylene-3-aryl-3,4-dihydrophthalazines (II and III) in Chapter XVI; and 1-hydroxy-3-aryl-3,4-dihydrophthalazine-4-acetic acids (IV)

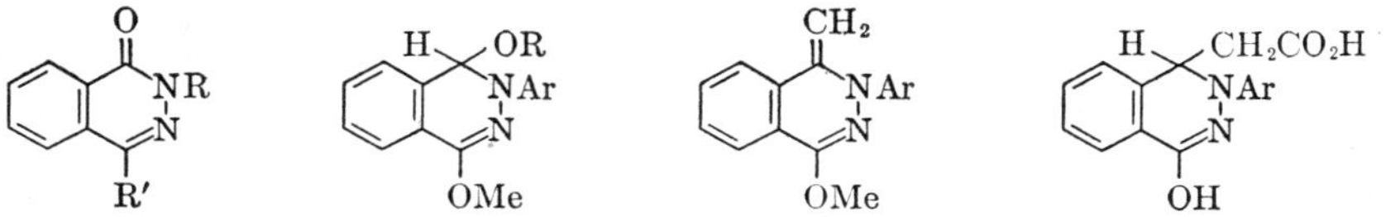

(I)   (II)   (III)   (IV)

in Chapter XIV. There remain for description a number of miscellaneous 3,4-dihydrophthalazines of the general formula (V) in which, unlike types

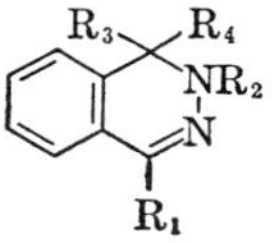

(V)

(I)–(IV), the substituents at C_4 (R_3 and R_4) are hydrogen or unreactive hydrocarbon radicals; these compounds are summarized in Table XXII-1.

Preparation of Compounds in Table XXII-1. The two main methods of preparation are:

(1) Alkaline decomposition of a 3-methylphthalazinium iodide; this

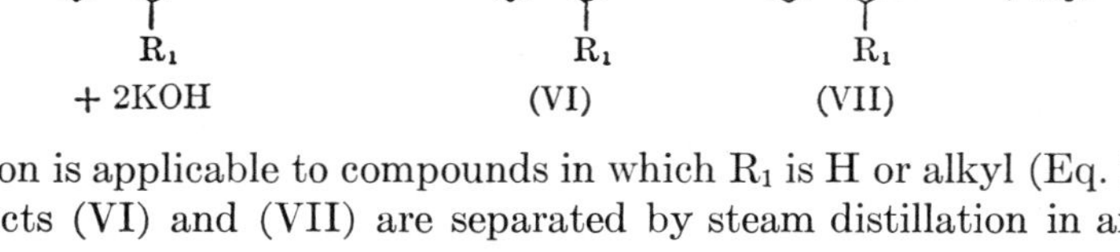

$$+ 2\text{KOH}$$

(VI)   (VII)   (1)

reaction is applicable to compounds in which R_1 is H or alkyl (Eq. 1). The products (VI) and (VII) are separated by steam distillation in an atmos-

TABLE XXII-1. 3,4-Dihydrophthalazines

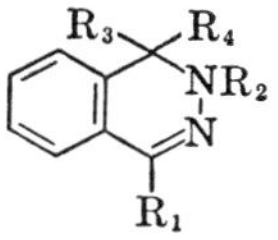

R_1	R_2	R_3	R_4	Prep.[a]	M.p., °C.	Remarks	Ref.
H	Me	H	H	A	—	Unstable; gives 3-methyl-4-keto-3,4-dihydrophthalazine on atm. oxidation. Vol. in steam. Hydrochloride, m.p. 140–141° (dec.); picrate, m.p. 93–95° (dec.); methiodide, m.p. 153–154	3
OH	Ph	H	Me	B	171	—	4
OH	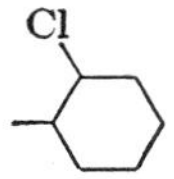	H	H	C	216–218	—	5
OH	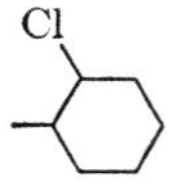	H	Me	B,C	199–200	—	5
OH	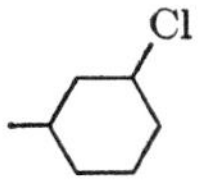	H	Me	D	178	—	6
OH	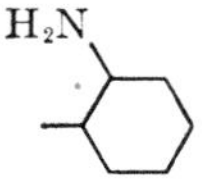	H	Me	E	221	Yellow prisms, insol. in alk., sol. in dil. mineral acids	7
OH	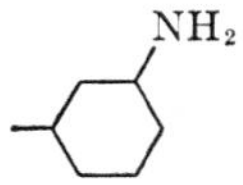	H	H	B,F	225	Further reduction with Zn dust and dil. H_2SO_4 gives the phthalimidine	8
OH	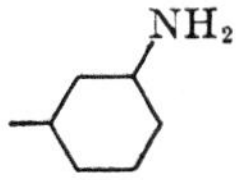	H	Me	F	188	Further reduction with Zn dust and dil. H_2SO_4 gives the phthalimidine	8
OH	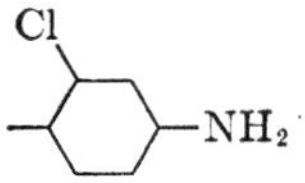	H	H	B	220–223	Acetyl deriv., m.p. 217–219°	9
OH	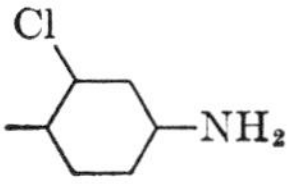	H	Me	B,F	220–223	Acetyl deriv., m.p. 218–220°	9

Table continued

TABLE XXII-1. 3,4-Dihydrophthalazines (*continued*)

R_1	R_2	R_3	R_4	Prep.[a]	M.p., °C.	Remarks	Ref.
OH	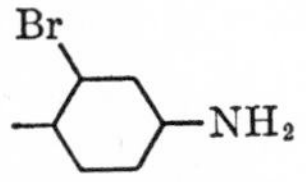 Br-substituted ring —NH₂	H	Me	F	211–212	Not obtained pure	10
OH	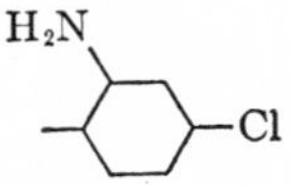 H₂N-substituted ring —Cl	H	Me	E	200	—	7
OH	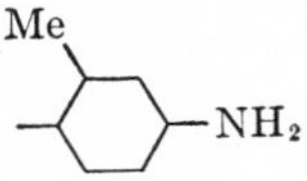 Me-substituted ring —NH₂	H	H	B	203–205	Yellow needles. Acetyl deriv., yellow prisms, m.p. 212–214°	11
OH	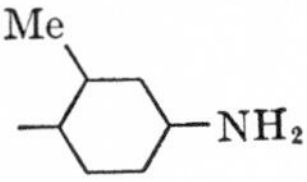 Me-substituted ring —NH₂	H	Me	B	204–205	Yellow needles	11
Me	Me	H	H	A	—	Vol. in steam. Picrate, dec. 120°; chloroplatinate, dec. ~230°; hydrochloride, m.p. 245°	12
Et	Me	H	H	A	—	Vol. in steam. Picrate, red needles, m.p. 108°; chloroplatinate; ferrocyanide	13
Ph	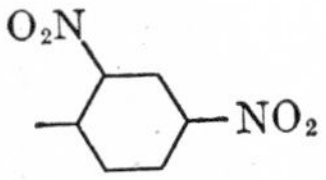 O₂N-substituted ring —NO₂	Ph	Ph	G	245–247	Red needles, easily sol. in most solvents	14

[a] A, from the corresponding 3-methylphthalazinium iodide by decomposition with aqueous potassium hydroxide, followed by steam distillation in hydrogen. B, from the corresponding 3-aryl-1-ketophthalazine by reduction with sodium hydrosulfite in boiling aqueous sodium hydroxide. C, from the corresponding 3-aryl-1-ketophthalazine by reduction with amalgamated zinc and aqueous hydrochloric acid at 70–80°. D, from the corresponding 3-aryl-1-ketophthalazine sulfate by reduction with amalgamated zinc and hydrochloric acid in aqueous alcohol and acetic acid at 90°. E, from the corresponding 3-amino- or 3-nitro-aryl-1-ketophthalazine by reduction with zinc dust in boiling aqueous sulfuric acid. F, from the corresponding 3-aryl-1-ketophthalazine by reduction with zinc dust in boiling dilute hydrochloric acid. G, from $o\text{-}C_6H_4$ with $\begin{smallmatrix}CPh_2\\O\\C(OH)Ph\end{smallmatrix}$ and 2,4-dinitrophenylhydrazine in boiling alcoholic hydrochloric acid; the reaction probably occurs via the ketocarbinol, $o\text{-}C_6H_4$ $\begin{smallmatrix}C(OH)Ph_2\\COPh\end{smallmatrix}$.

phere of hydrogen in order to prevent conversion of (VI) into (VII) by atmospheric oxidation; only (VI) is volatile.

(2) 3-Aryl-1-ketophthalazines (VIII; R_4 = H or Me) are reduced under appropriate conditions; compounds (V; R_1 = OH; R_3 = H; R_4 = H or Me) are thus obtained (Eq. 2).

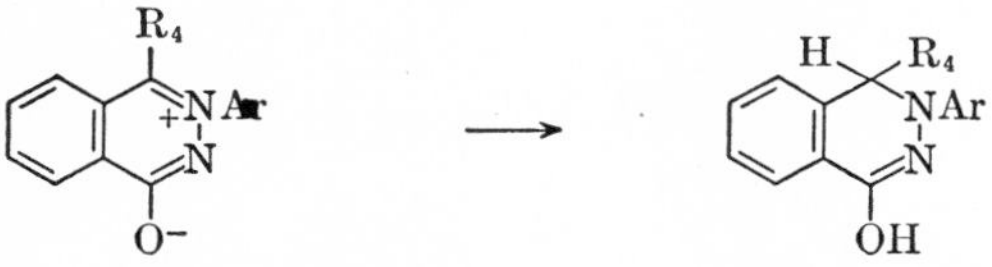

(2)

(VIII)

2. 1,2,3,4-Tetrahydrophthalazines

Compounds of this type are few in number. 2,3-Dialkyl-1,4-diketo-1,2,3,4-tetrahydrophthalazines (I) have already been described (Chapter XIX); the remaining members of the group are 1,2,3,4-tetrahydrophthala-

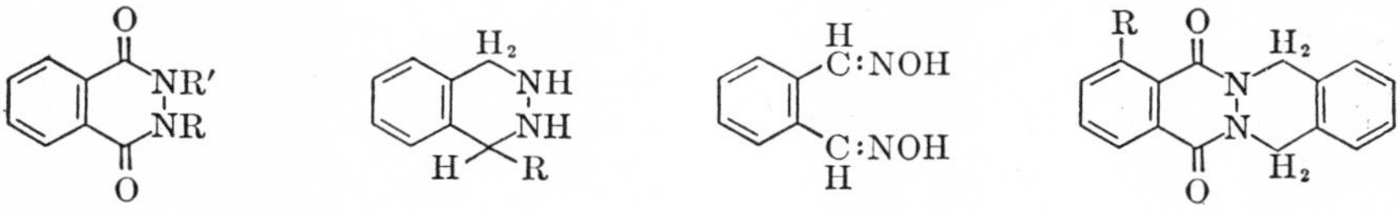

(I)   (II)   (III)   (IV)

zines of the general formula (II). These compounds are prepared from the corresponding phthalazines by reduction with sodium amalgam in aqueous medium. Their properties and derivatives are given in Table XXII-2. The formation of dibenzoyl derivatives shows that they are 1,2,3,4- and not Bz-tetrahydrophthalazines; the hydrochlorides reduce

TABLE XXII-2. 1,2,3,4-Tetrahydrophthalazines

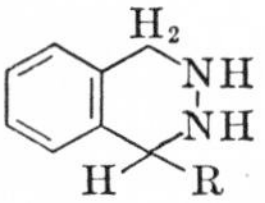

R	Base	Melting point, °C.				Ref.
		Dibenzoyl derivative	Hydrochloride	Picrate	Chloro-platinate	
H	Unstable and darkens	207–208	231 (efferv.)	159–160 (efferv.)	—	1,2
Me	Alkaline reaction in water	185	190	146 (dec.)	—	12
Et	Oil	159	168	—	—	13
CH₂Ph	Oil	135–136	Dec. 190–200	—	Dec. 180°	15
Ph	—	158–159	Dec. 220–250	—	Dec. 140°	15

Fehling solution.   On diazotization in sulfuric acid, 1,2,3,4-tetrahydro-
phthalazine gives an unstable solid, which in ethyl acetate yields a compound of formula $C_8H_8O_2N_2$, possibly *o*-phthalaldehyde dioxime (III).[1]
1,2,3,4-Tetrahydrophthalazine condenses with phthaloyl and 3-nitro-
phthaloyl chloride, giving the compounds (IV; R = H and NO_2) (Chapters XVII and XXIII, Section 3).[2]

References

1. Gabriel and Pinkus, *Ber.*, **26**, 2210 (1893).
2. Hatt and E. F. M. Stephenson, *J. Chem. Soc.*, **1943**, 658.
3. Gabriel and Müller, *Ber.*, **28**, 1830 (1895).
4. Peters, Rowe, and Brodrick, *J. Chem. Soc.*, **1948**, 1249.
5. Brodrick, Peters, and Rowe, *J. Chem. Soc.*, **1948**, 1026.
6. Peters, Pringle, and Rowe, *J. Chem. Soc.*, **1948**, 597.
7. Rowe, Dovey, Garforth, Levin, Pask, and Peters, *J. Chem. Soc.*, **1935**, 1796.
8. Rowe and Peters, *J. Chem. Soc.*, **1931**, 1918.
9. Rowe and Dunbar, *J. Chem. Soc.*, **1932**, 11.
10. Rowe, Jambuserwala, and Partridge, *J. Chem. Soc.*, **1935**, 1134.
11. Rowe and Siddle, *J. Chem. Soc.*, **1932**, 473.
12. Gabriel and Eschenbach, *Ber.*, **30**, 3022 (1897).
13. Paul, *Ber.*, **32**, 2014 (1899).
14. Seidel and Bezner, *Ber.*, **65**, 1566 (1932).
15. Lieck, *Ber.*, **38**, 3918 (1905).

CHAPTER XXIII

Condensed Phthalazines and Azaphthalazines

1. 1',2',3,4-Benziminazolo-3,4-dihydrophthalazines

Preparation. A few compounds of this group are known; they have the general formula (I) and are listed in Table XXIII-1. They may

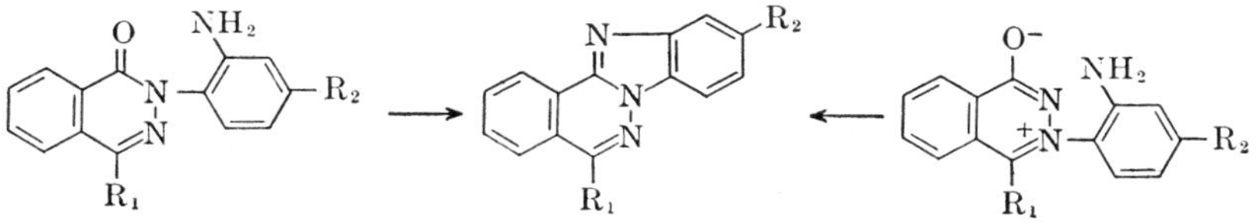

(II)   (I)   (III)
R.I. 2384

TABLE XXIII-1. 1',2',3,4-Benziminazolo-3,4-dihydrophthalazines

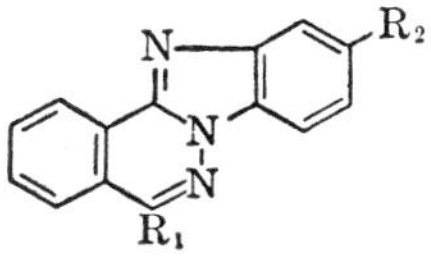

R₁	R₂	Prep.ᵃ	M.p., °C.	Derivatives	Ref.
H	H	A	178	—	33
H	Cl	A	230	—	33
OH	H	E	>430	Acetyl, m.p. 222–223°	34
OH	Cl	E	>440	Acetyl, m.p. > 440°	34
Me	H	A,B,C,D	163	—	33
Me	Cl	A,B,C	193	—	33
Me	Me	A,B	186	—	33

ᵃ A, from corresponding 3,2'-aminoaryl-4-keto-3,4-dihydrophthalazine and 1.2 *N*

hydrochloric acid at 180° for 6 hours. B, from [structure] R₂ (Table

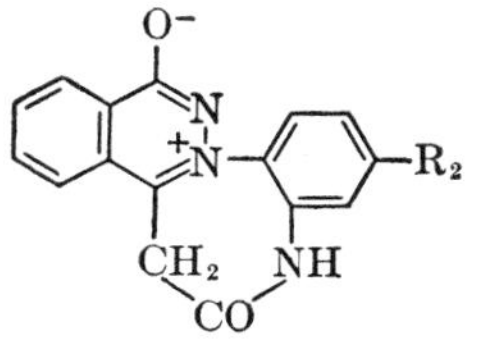

XV-2), by treatment as in A. C, from the corresponding 1-methyl-2,2'-aminoaryl-4-ketophthalazine by treatment as in A. D, from 1-methylene-2,2'-aminoanilino-isoindolin-3-one by treatment as in A. E, from the corresponding 1-hydroxy- or 1-methoxy-3,2'-aminoaryl-4-keto-3,4-dihydrophthalazine and 1.2 *N* hydrochloric acid at 170–180° for 6 hours.

be regarded as dehydration products of 3,2'-aminoaryl-4-keto-3,4-dihydro-
phthalazines (II), and are in fact prepared from these compounds (Chapter
XIII, Section 2), or from their isomeric precursors (III), by treatment with
dilute hydrochloric acid at a high temperature.

2. Compounds Prepared from 1,4-Diketones

This section contains a number of miscellaneous compounds containing
three or more rings, nearly all of which are prepared from the corresponding
1,4-diketones, 1,4-keto acids, or 1,4-keto esters by condensation with hydrazine hydrate or phenylhydrazine.

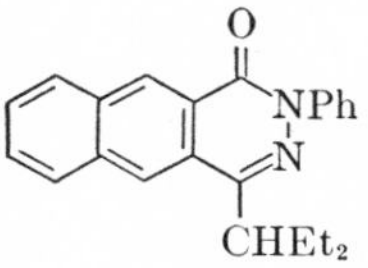

(I)
R.I. 1904

(II)
R.I. 1880

(III)
R.I. 1880

Prepared from the o-keto
acid and phenylhydrazine
at 240°. M.p. 175°.[1]

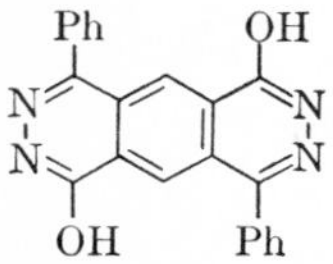

Prepared in alc. at 120°.
Dec. 445°; sol. in hot aniline, pyridine, and acetic
acid;   sparingly sol. in
other common solvents.[2]

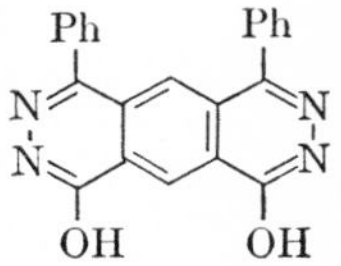

Prepared as compd. (II).
Dec. 430°. Solubilities as
for compd. (II).[2]

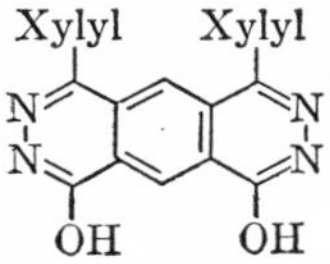

(IV)
R.I. 1884

(V)
R.I. 1910

(VI)
R.I. 1910

Prepared as compd. (II).
Dec. on strong heating.[2]

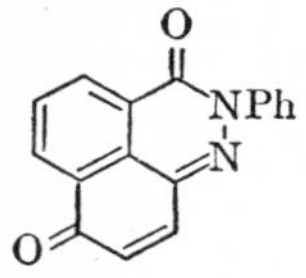

Yellow needles from ben-
zene, m.p. 238–240°. Sol.
in hot strong alkali, pptd.
by acid.[3]

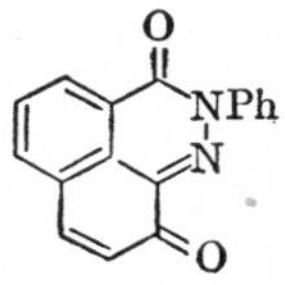

Red needles from benzene,
m.p. 201–202°.   Sol. in
caustic alkali;   pptd. by
acid.[3]

V.   Prepared from 4-hydroxynaphthalic acid by coupling with benzenediazonium chloride in aqueous sodium acetate (Eq. 1).

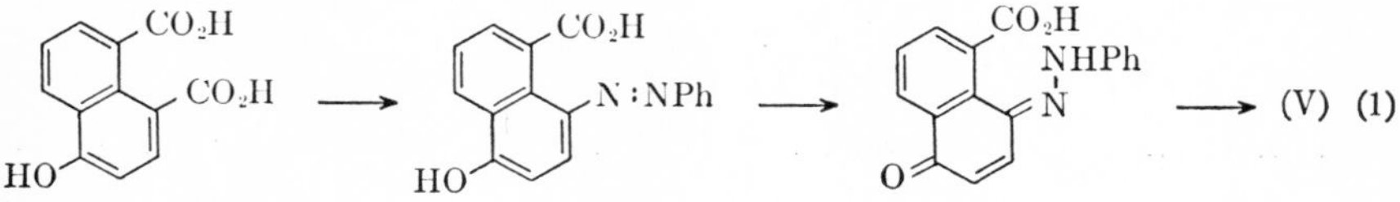

VI.   Prepared as above from 2-hydroxynaphthalic acid.

XII.   Prepared from the chloride of anthraquinone-1-carboxylic acid.

XIII.   Prepared from the phenylhydrazone of fluorenone-1,5-dicar-
boxylic acid by heating in acetic acid, or alone at 240°.

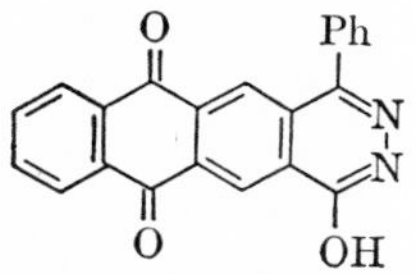

(VII)
R.I. 2665

Prepared as compd. (II).
Light yellow powder, dec.
374°; sol. in hot nitro-
benzene, aniline, pyridine
quinoline, and acetic an-
hydride.

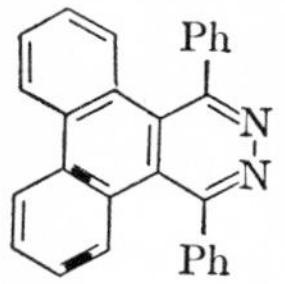

(VIII)
R.I. 2673

Prepared in aq. pyridine.
M.p. 340°, sol. in ben-
zene.[4]

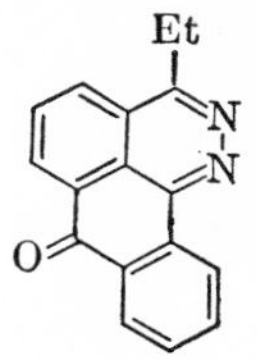

(IX)
R.I. 2674

Prepared in boiling tolu-
ene. Yellow needles from
benzene, m.p. 204°.[5]

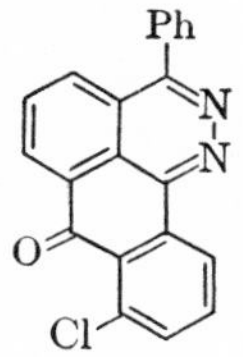

(X)
R.I. 2674

M.p. >300°.[6]

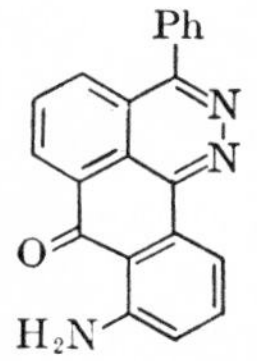

(XI)
R.I. 2674

M.p. 257–259°.[7]

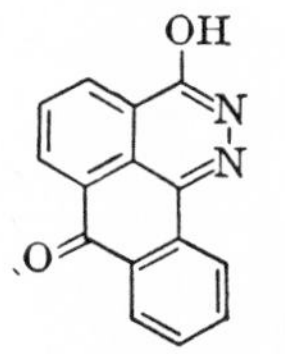

(XII)
R.I. 2674

Yellow needles sparingly
sol. in ordinary solvents.
Sol. in dil. NaOH.[8]

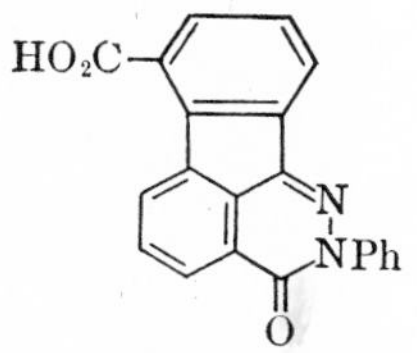

(XIII)
R.I. 2521

M.p. 294–295°.[9]

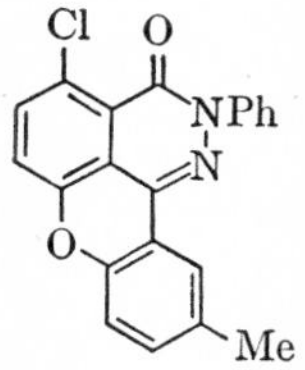

(XIV)
R.I. 2662

Yellow needles, from ace-
tic acid, m.p. 264–266°
(corr.).   Conc. H_2SO_4
gives   yellow - brown
color.[10]

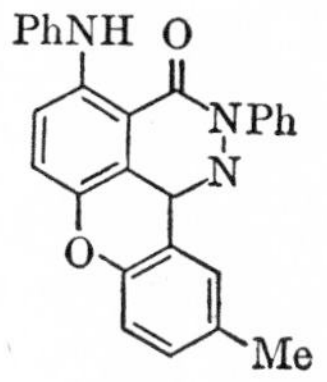

(XV)
R.I. 2662

Yellow-green cryst., m.p.
257–258° (corr.). Conc.
H_2SO_4 gives dark green
color.[10]

XIV.   Prepared from the keto acid by boiling for a short time with
phenylhydrazine.

XV.   Prepared from compound XIV by boiling with aniline, potassium acetate, and a trace of copper acetate.

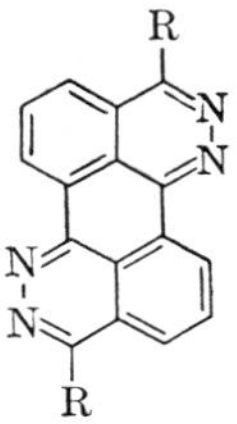

(XVI)
R.I. 3237

R = *m*-xylyl. Prepared in boiling toluene. Brown-yellow needles, m.p. 330°. Conc. H₂SO₄ gives orange color.[11]

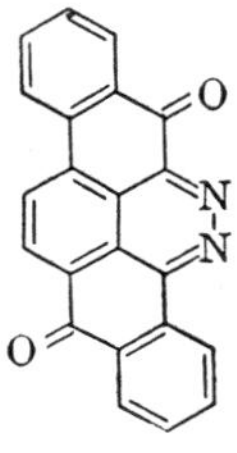

(XVII)
R.I. 3601

Prepared in boiling pyridine and crystd. from nitrobenzene. Light brown needles, m.p. >375°. Conc. H₂SO₄ gives red-violet color. Alk. Na₂S₂O₄ gives dark green product turning violet in air.[12]

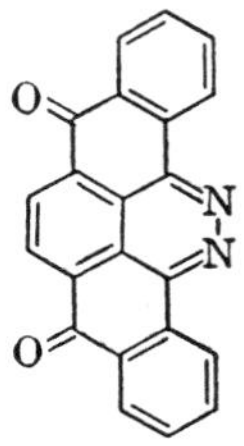

(XVIII)
R.I. 3602

Prepared as (XVII). Orange-red needles, dec. 440° (under H₂). Conc. H₂SO₄ gives orange-red color. Alk. Na₂S₂O₄ gives cherry-red vat.[13]

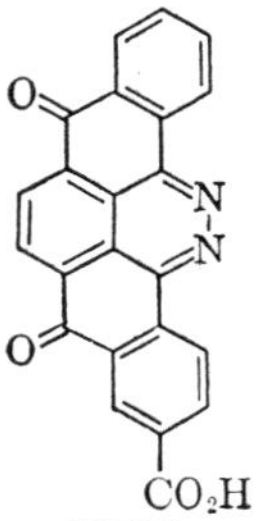

(XIX)
R.I. 3602

Prepared in boiling *m*-cresol. Brown-yellow solid, very sparingly sol. in org. solvents and insol. in NaOH. Conc. H₂SO₄ gives orange-red color. Alk. Na₂S₂O₄ gives cherry-red color.[14]

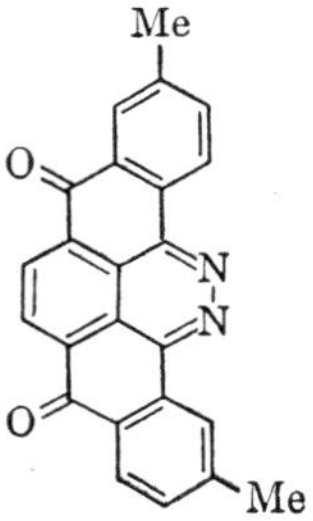

(XX)
R.I. 3602

Prepared as (XVII). Red-brown needles, m.p. >380°. Conc. H₂SO₄ gives orange-red color. Alk. Na₂S₂O₄ gives cherry-red vat.[15]

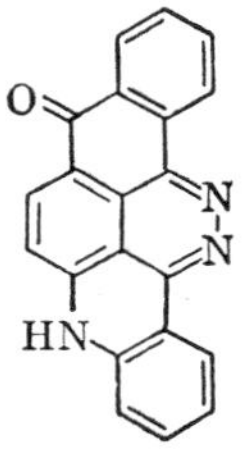

(XXI)
R.I. 3588

Prepared in boiling pyridine. Orange-red needles, very sparingly sol. in org. solvents. Conc. H₂SO₄ gives red color.[16]

XXIV. On treatment with moderately concentrated hydrochloric and sulfuric acids, this base forms a hydrochloride (B·HCl) (blue-black needles) and a sulfate (B·H₂SO₄) (wine-red crystals) which are believed to be of type (A):

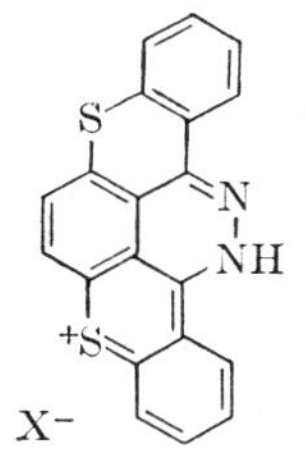

(A)

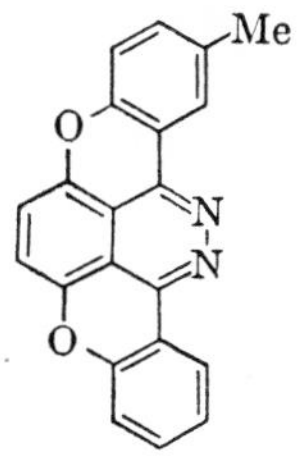

(XXII)

Prepared in warm pyri-
dine. Yellow cryst., m.p.
265°, sol. in alc., benzene,
and pyridine.   Hydro-
chloride, red needles from
acetic acid, m.p. 274°
(dec.).[10]

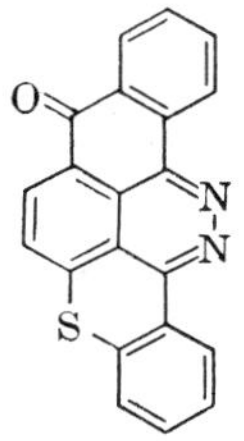

(XXIII)
R.I. 3592

Yellow solid, m.p. >330°,
weakly basic properties.[17]

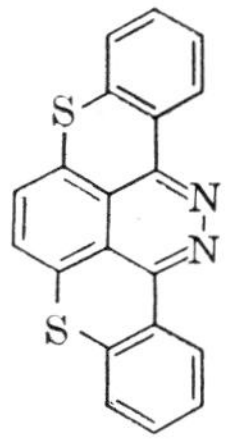

(XXIV)
R.I. 3591

Prepared in boiling pyri-
dine. Orange-red needles,
m.p. 348–349°, from ben-
zoic acid.[18]

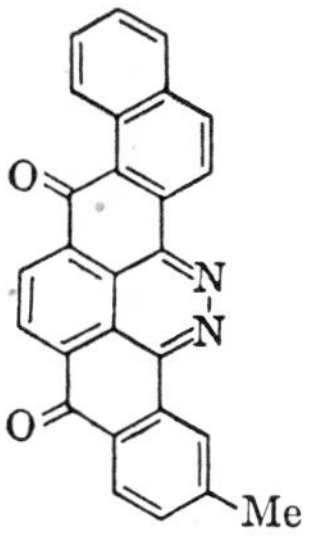

(XXV)

Prepared as (XXVII).
Red-brown plates. Conc.
H₂SO₄ gives red color.[19]

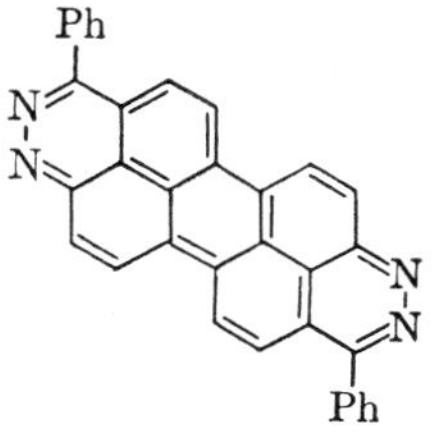

(XXVI)
R.I. 3758

Prepared in boiling tolu-
ene.   Brown-red cryst.
(not analytically pure).
Conc. H₂SO₄ gives violet-
red color.[20]

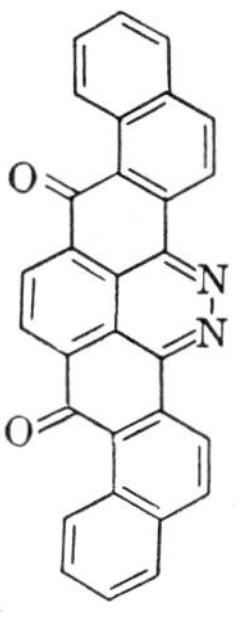

(XXVII)

Prepared in boiling pyri-
dine, followed by aeration
and crystn. from nitro-
benzene.   Brown leaflets.
Conc. H₂SO₄ gives red-
violet color. Alk. Na₂S₂O₄
gives violet vat.[19]

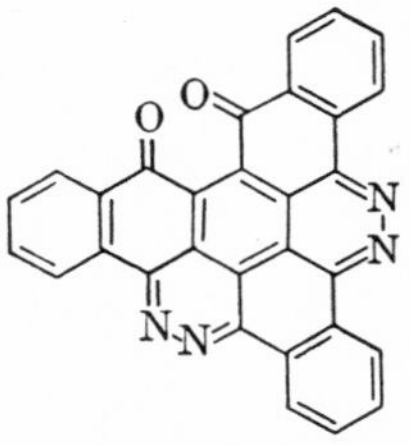

(XXVIII)

Prepared in boiling nitrobenzene-pyri-
dine. Dec. >420°; sub. 330°/0.07 mm.
in brown micro-needles. Does not yield
a vat dye.[21]

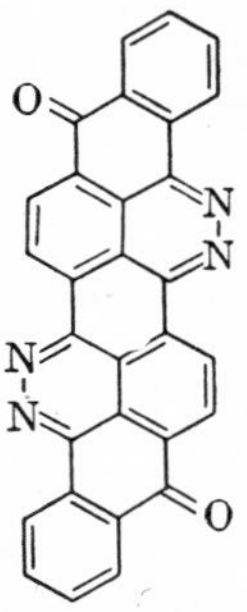

(XXIX)

Prepared in boiling quinoline, with subsequent oxidation of initial dihydro
compd. (best by warming with conc.
H_2SO_4). Red needles, almost insol. in
org. solvents. Conc. H_2SO_4 gives yellow-
red color. Alk. $Na_2S_2O_4$ gives dark blue
product.[22]

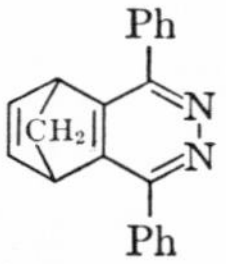

(XXX)

From the 1,4-diketone and hydrazine.[35]

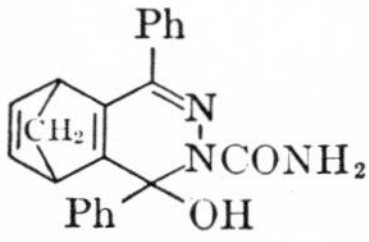

(XXXI)

From the 1,4-diketone and semicarbazide.[35]

3. Miscellaneous Compounds

A number of phthalazine derivatives containing additional fused rings
have already been described. Thus, 1,4-dihydroxyphthalazines containing

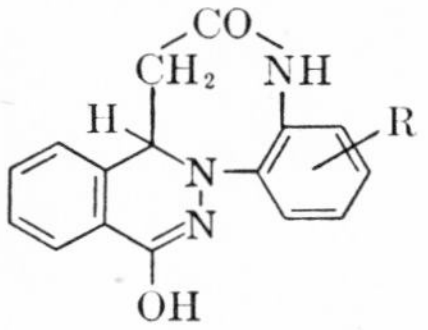

(I)

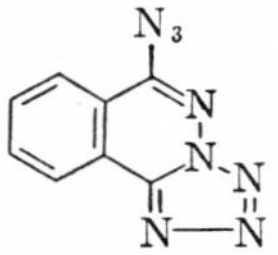

(II)
R.I. 1473

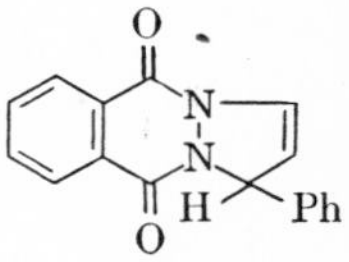

(III)

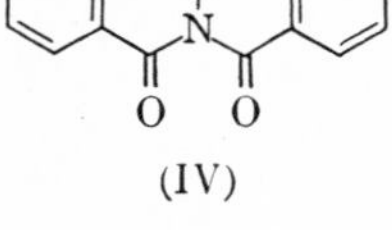

(IV)

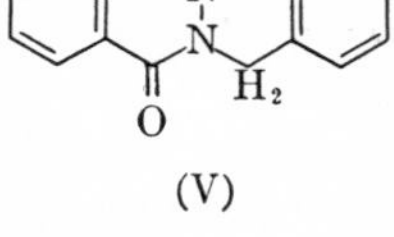

(V)

additional nuclei are listed in Table XVII-2; compounds of type (I) are given in Table XIV-2; the preparation of (II) is described in Chapter XX; and compounds (III), (IV), and (V; R = H) are mentioned in Chapter XVII.

The compound (II) crystallizes in needles, m.p. 152°, soluble in alcohol, sparingly so in ether, and very slightly soluble in hot water. When re-fluxed with excess of sodium ethoxide in ethanol it is converted into (VI; R = OH); this compound forms leaflets, m.p. 258° (dec.), and yields an acetyl derivative, m.p. 165°, which is very easily hydrolyzed. On treat-ment with one equivalent of sodium methoxide in boiling methanol, (II)

(VI)
R.I 1473

yields (VI; R = OMe) (tablets, m.p. 211°), which is easily hydrolyzed to (VI; R = OH) with aqueous-alcoholic sodium hydroxide; the ethyl ether (VI; R = OEt)(prisms, m.p. 187°) is prepared similarly, and is likewise easily hydrolyzed. With phosphorus pentachloride at 140°, (VI; R = OH) yields the chloro derivative (VI; R = Cl), which forms needles, m.p. 195° (dec.), and gives (II) when boiled with sodium azide in alcohol. The amino compound (VI; R = NH$_2$), which crystallizes in needles, m.p. 305°, may be prepared from (II) by heating in tetralin at 200°, and also from (VI; R = Cl) and aqueous-alcoholic ammonia at 150°; treatment of (II) under the latter conditions gives a mixture of the amine and (VI; R = OH).   The amine gives mainly a diacetyl derivative (VI; R = NAc$_2$) [m.p. 191° (dec.)], together with a little monoacetyl derivative (VI; R = NHAc) [m.p. 200° (dec.)], when it is refluxed with acetic anhydride.[23] Treatment of (VI; R = Cl) with hydrazine at 130° yields (VI; R = NHNH$_2$), m.p. 287°, thence, by the action of nitrous acid, the azide (II).[36]

Compound (III) yields 5-(3-)phenylpyrazoline when refluxed with sodium ethoxide in ethanol.[24]

Compound (IV), in addition to its synthesis from 1,4-dihydroxyphthal-azine and phthaloyl chloride (Chapter XVII), is also formed, along with unidentified material, when (a) 6-nitro-1,4-dihydroxyphthalazine and phthaloyl chloride, (b) 5-nitro-1,4-dihydroxyphthalazine and phthaloyl chloride, and (c) 1,4-dihydroxyphthalazine and 3-nitrophthaloyl chloride are allowed to interact in hot nitrobenzene; its production by reactions (a)–(c) is considered to be due to disproportionation of the tetracyclic condensation products initially formed. It is readily converted into 1,4-

dihydroxyphthalazine by treatment with hydrazine in aqueous or acetic acid solution, with boiling aqueous sodium hydroxide, and with boiling 0.1 N sulfuric acid in acetic acid; with ammonium acetate in acetic acid it gives 1,4-dihydroxyphthalazine and phthalimide.[24]

Compound (V; R = H) has been synthesized by the method described in Chapter XVII, and also by condensation of phthaloyl chloride with 1,2,3,4-tetrahydrophthalazine hydrochloride in boiling pyridine (Eq. 2). It dissolves in concentrated sulfuric acid to a colorless solution, and is

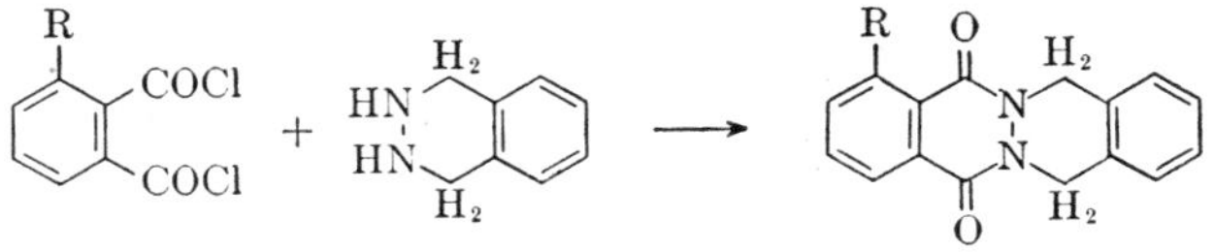

$$(2)$$

(VII)   (V)
                                                          R.I. 2644

precipitated unchanged on dilution. It is hydrolyzed by alcoholic sodium ethoxide to (VIII; R = H), an unstable substance which readily regenerates the parent compound by cyclization (Eq. 3)[25].

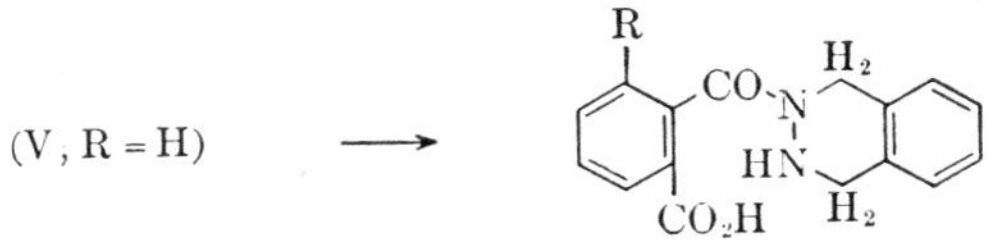

$$(3)$$

(V, R = H)

(VIII)

The analog (V; R = NO$_2$) is prepared from 3-nitrophthaloyl chloride (VII; R = NO$_2$) and 1,2,3,4-tetrahydrophthalazine as indicated above, and forms yellow parallelepipeds, m.p. 249–250° (slight dec.). Like (V; R = H), it is hydrolyzable to (VIII; R = NO$_2$), oxidation of which yields phthalazine and 3-nitrophthalic acid (Chapter X). On reduction with stannous chloride and hydrochloric acid at 50–70°, (V; R = NO$_2$) is converted into the amine (V; R = NH$_2$), which crystallizes in yellow rhombs, m.p. 185–187° (dec.), and yields a benzoyl derivative, m.p. 260–261° (slight dec.).[25]

4. Azaphthalazines

3-Phenyl-1-methyl-4-keto-1,2,3,4-tetrahydro-8-azaphthalazine (I) is prepared from 2-acetylpyridine-3-carboxylic acid and phenylhydrazine hydrochloride in hot aqueous solution; it crystallizes from hot water, in which it is rather sparingly soluble, in needles, m.p. 121°.[26]

The N-phenyl derivative of 1,4-dihydroxy-7-azaphthalazine (II or III) is formed when the diphenylhydrazide (IV) of pyridine-3,4-dicarboxylic

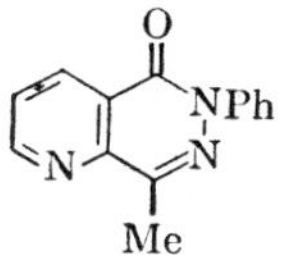

(I)
R.I. 971

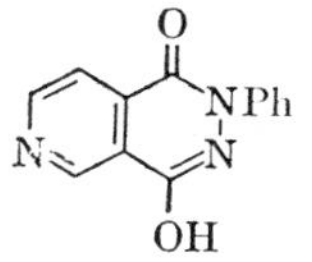

(II)
R.I. 971

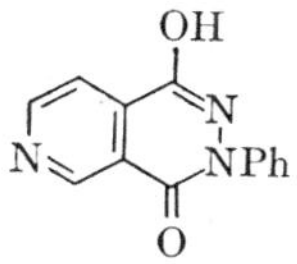

(III)
R.I. 971

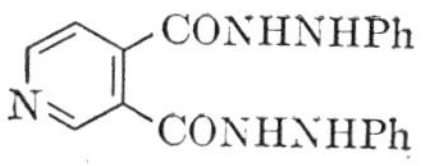

(IV)

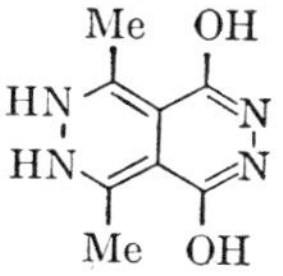

(V)
R.I. 961

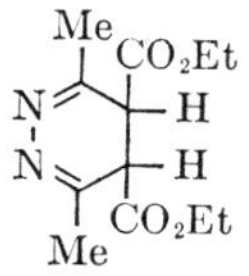

(VI)

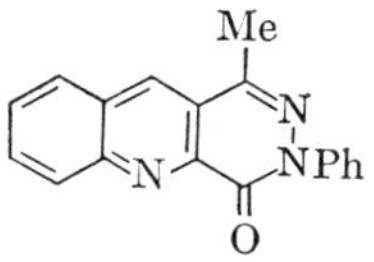

(VII)
R.I. 1889

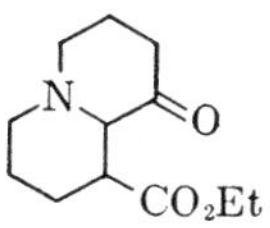

(IX)

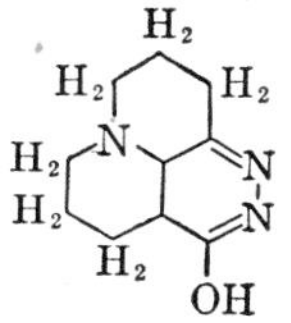

(VIII)
R.I. 1885

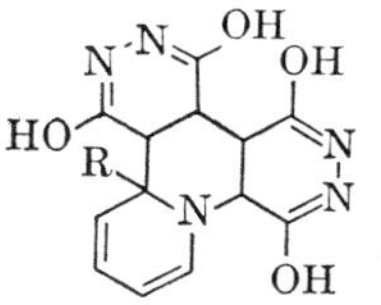

(X)
R.I. 2639

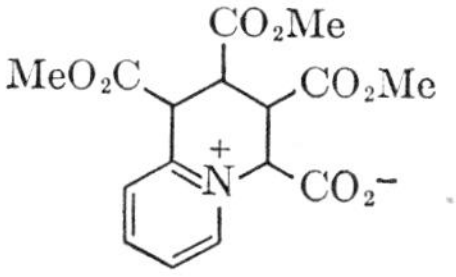

(XI)

acid is heated to 100–110°. It is a yellow powder, m.p. > 260°, easily soluble in dilute hydrochloric acid and sodium hydroxide.[27]

1,4-Dihydroxy-5,8-dimethyl-6,7-dihydro-6,7-diazaphthalazine (V) is the product of the action of hot alcoholic hydrazine hydrate on the dihydropyridazine derivative (VI),[28] and is also formed from hydrazine hydrate and 2,5-dimethyl-3,4-dicarbethoxyfuran in alcohol at 100–120°.[37] It is unchanged at 275°, is soluble in alkali carbonates and dilute mineral acids, gives a violet coloration with ferric chloride, and reduces Tollens reagent. It forms a hydrochloride and a dibenzoyl derivative (m.p. 190–191°), and yields hydrazine when boiled with dilute acids. The compound was originally prepared and described by Curtius,[29] who, however, failed to recognize its true structure.

4 - Methyl - 2 - phenyl - 1 - keto - 6,7 - benzo - 1,2 - dihydro - 8 - azaphthalazine (VII) is formed when the phenylhydrazone of ethyl 3-acetylquinoline-2-carboxylate is heated at 180–200° in an atmosphere of carbon dioxide; it crystallizes in yellow needles, m.p. 244°.[30]

1 - Hydroxy - 4,5 - trimethylene - 5,6,7,8,9,10 - hexahydro - 5 - azaphthalazine (VIII) is produced exothermally when hydrazine hydrate is allowed to interact with the keto ester (IX); it crystallizes from water and melts at 137°.[31]

The compound (X; R = $NHNH_2$) is produced by boiling the betaine (XI) with an excess of hydrazine hydrate. It forms golden plates, m.p. > 350°, from hot water, and is converted into (X; R = OH) by the action of boiling dilute hydrochloric acid; the latter compound crystallizes from boiling water, and slowly turns red on standing.[32]

References

1. Freund and Fleischer, *Ann.*, **402**, 51 (1914).
2. Seka, Sedlatschek, and Preiszecker, *Monatsh.*, **57**, 86 (1931).
3. Dziewonski and Stolyhwo, *Ber.*, **57**, 1540 (1924).
4. Dilthey, Henkels, and Leonhard, *J. prakt. Chem.*, **151**, 97 (1938).
5. Waldmann and Oblath, *Ber.*, **71**, 366 (1938).
6. *Chem. Abs.*, **31**, 6898 (1937) (Swiss Pat. 189,407).
7. *Chem. Abs.*, **32**, 7284 (1938) (Swiss Pat. 194,341).
8. Ullmann and Schalk, *Ber.*, **44**, 128 (1911).
9. Charrier and Ghigi, *Zentr.*, **I**, 1323 (1934) [*Gazz.*, **63**, 685 (1933)].
10. Knesebeck and Ullmann, *Ber.*, **55**, 306 (1922).
11. Scholl, Meyer, and Winkler, *Ann.*, **494**, 201 (1932)
12. Clar, *Ber.*, **62**, 1574 (1929).
13. Scholl and Neumann, *Ber.*, **55**, 118 (1922).
14. Scholl, G. von Hornuff, and Meyer, *Ber.*, **69**, 706 (1936).
15. Clar, John, and Hawran, *Ber.*, **62**, 940 (1929).
16. Ullmann and Sone, *Ann.*, **380**, 336 (1911).
17. Ullmann, *Ber.*, **43**, 536 (1910).
18. Steinkopf, H. F. Schmitt, and Fiedler, *Ann.*, **527**, 237 (1937).
19. Clar, John, and Avenarius, *Ber.*, **72**, 2139 (1939).
20. Benndorf and Sorns, *Sitzber. Akad. Wiss. Wien*, IIb, **143**, 81 (1934) [*Monatsh.*, **64**, 167 (1934)].
21. Pummerer, Pfaff, Riegelbauer, and Rosenhauer, *Ber.*, **72**, 1623 (1939).
22. Scholl and Meyer, *Ber.*, **61**, 2550 (1928).
23. Stollé and Storch, *J. prakt. Chem.*, **135**, 128 (1932).
24. Drew and Hatt, *J. Chem. Soc.*, **1937**, 16.
25. Hatt and E. F. M. Stephenson, *J. Chem. Soc.*, **1943**, 658.
26. Rosenheim and Tafel, *Ber.*, **26**, 1501 (1893).
27. Strache, *Sitzber. Akad. Wiss. Wien*, IIb, **99**, 153 (1891) [*Monatsh.*, **11**, 147 (1890)].
28. Bülow, *Ber.*, **37**, 91 (1904).
29. Beilstein, 4th Ed., XXVI, 488.
30. Koller and Ruppersberg, *Monatsh.*, **58**, 238 (1931).
31. Clemo, W. Mc. G. Morgan, and Raper, *J. Chem. Soc.*, **1937**, 965.
32. Diels and Alder, *Ann.*, **505**, 103 (1933).
33. Rowe *et al.*, *J. Chem. Soc.*, **1937**, 90.
34. Rowe, Lécutier, and Peters, *J. Chem. Soc.*, **1938**, 1079.
35. Dupont and Germain, *Compt. rend.*, **223**, 743 (1946).
36. Stollé and Hanusch, *J. prakt. Chem.*, **136**, 9 (1933).
37. Seka and Preiszecker, *Monatsh.*, **57**, 81 (1931).

PART III
Quinoxalines

CHAPTER XXIV

Preparation of Quinoxalines from Primary Aromatic *o*-Diamines and 1,2-Dicarbonyl Compounds

The condensation of primary aromatic *o*-diamines with 1,2-diketones or 1,2-ketoaldehydes yields quinoxalines according to equation 1. This

$$R_1 \underset{NH_2}{\overset{NH_2}{\diamond}} + \underset{OCR_2}{\overset{OCR_3}{|}} \longrightarrow 2H_2O + R_1 \underset{N}{\overset{N}{\diamond}} \underset{R_2}{\overset{R_3}{<}} \tag{1}$$

R.I. 978

reaction has long been recognized as a simple and convenient means of identifying *o*-diamines and 1,2-dicarbonyl compounds, and in consequence it has been widely used. The reaction almost invariably proceeds smoothly in alcohol or acetic acid, but in a few refractory instances dimethylaniline has been found to be a solvent of choice.[1] Generally speaking, the individual reactions of the quinoxalines prepared by this method have not been studied, as the interest attaching to these compounds has been mainly their usefulness for identification purposes.

The new quinoxalines obtained by this method of synthesis which have appeared in the literature since 1917 are given in Tables XXIV-1 and 2. It will be observed that these compounds frequently exhibit halochromy in concentrated sulfuric acid, and in a few cases this phenomenon has been studied in some degree of detail (see Chapter XXXIII, Section 2).

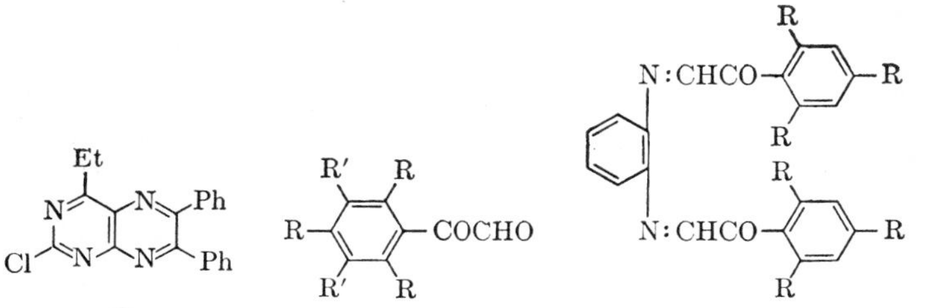

(I)   (II)   (III)

The synthesis is also applicable to heterocyclic *o*-diamines, the condensation of benzil with 2-chloro-4,5-diamino-6-ethylpyrimidine, for example, yielding[2] the substance (I) m.p. 179–181°; this compound, 2-chloro-8,9-diphenyl-6-ethylpteridine (for numbering see *Annual Reports*, 1946, 43, 251), belongs to the important group of pterins (*cf.* Chapter XXXIX).

Despite the very large range of compounds (Tables XXIV-1–3, and Chapter XXXVIII) which have been prepared by this synthesis, several cases are on record in which the reaction has either failed completely or has taken an abnormal course. Thus the arylglyoxals (II; R = Me, Et

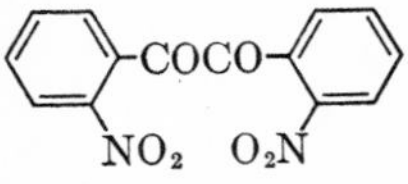

(IV)

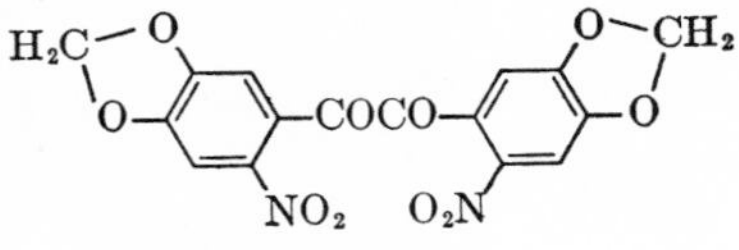

(V)

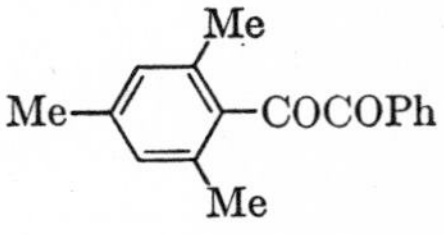

(VI)

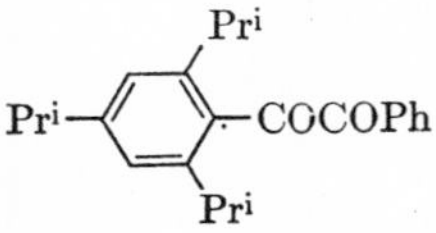

(VII)

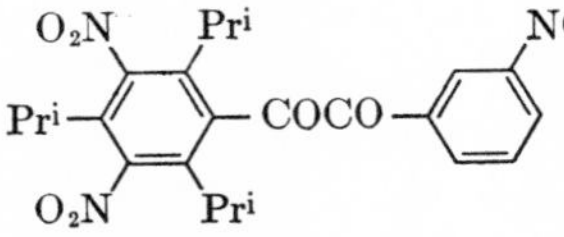

(VIII)

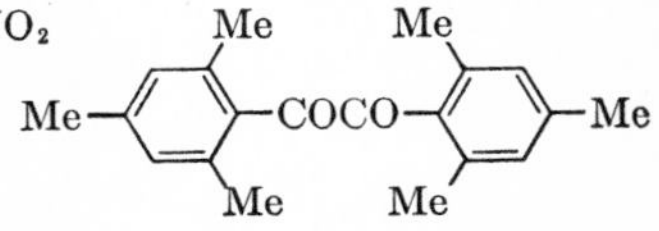

(IX)

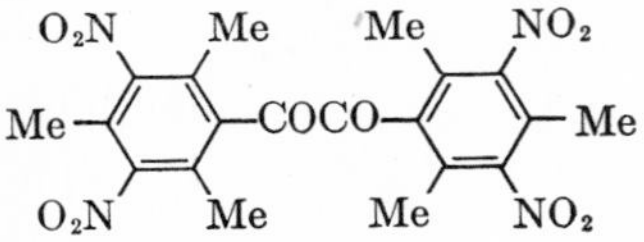

(X)

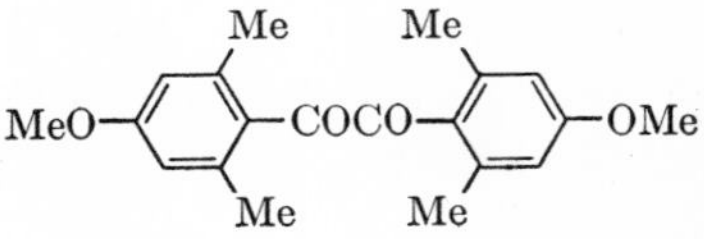

(XI)

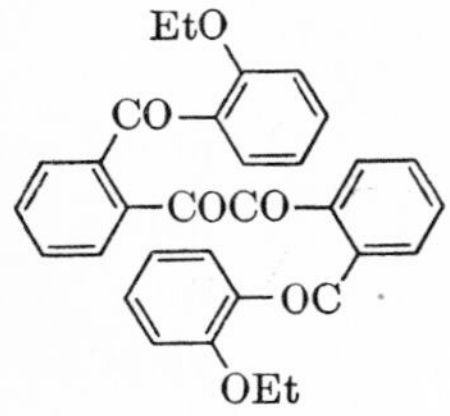

(XII)

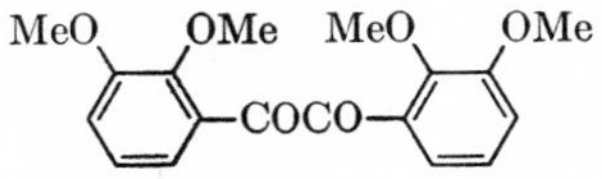

(XIII)

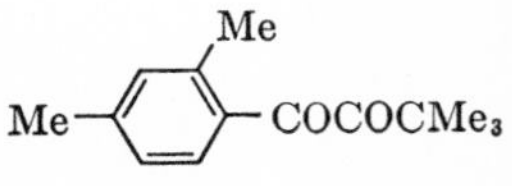

(XIV)

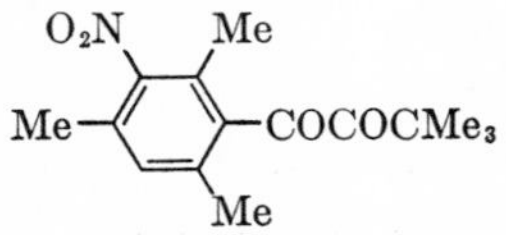

(XV)

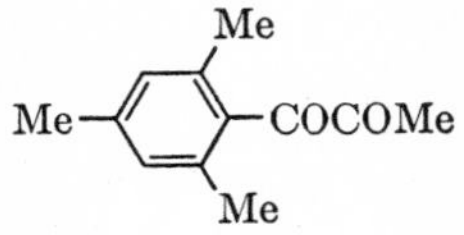

(XVI)

or Pr^i; R′ = H) give only the corresponding double Schiff bases (III)[3-5]; this result is particularly striking when compared with the normal quinoxaline formation which occurs with (II; R = Me, R′ = NO$_2$).[4] The following diketones do not react with o-phenylenediamine: 2,2′-dinitrodiphenyl- (IV),[6] 2,2′-dinitro-4,4′,5,5′-bismethylenedioxydiphenyl- (V),[7] mesitylphenyl- (VI),[5] 2,4,6-triisopropylphenylphenyl- (VII),[5] 3,5-dinitro-2,4,6-triisopropylphenyl-3′-nitrophenyl- (VIII),[5] dimesityl- (IX),[5] and its tetranitro derivative (X),[5] 4,4′-dimethoxy-2,2′,6,6′-tetramethyldiphenyl- (XI),[5] 2,2′-bis-o-ethoxybenzoyldiphenyl- (XII),[8] and 2,2′,3,3′-tetramethoxydiphenyl-glyoxal (XIII).[9] The mixed ketones (XIV)–(XVI) also fail to react with o-phenylenediamine.[5,10]

In considering these results, it should first be noted, as pointed out by Fuson and Soper,[5] that benzils (diarylglyoxals) either react normally or do not react at all, whereas monoarylglyoxals either react normally or yield double Schiff bases. With regard to the anomalies shown by diarylglyoxals, it is clear that the phenomenon falls into the broad category of steric effects, but the results are complicated by the operation of other (electronic) factors and cannot be explained in terms of the obvious deductions to be made from considerations of steric hindrance. Thus, Fuson et al.[4] suggest that the difference in behavior (see above) between (II; R = Me; R′ = H) and (II; R = Me; R′ = NO$_2$) could be explained by assuming that hydrogen bonding between the NO$_2$ groups and the pair of o-Me groups lessens the steric hindrance exerted by the latter, and thus facilitates the normal reaction of the second compound; but later work[5] has demonstrated that an unreactive benzil can be induced to undergo the normal reaction by the insertion of a nitro group or bromine atom into the other phenyl residue also [i.e, the one not containing the o-methyl groups; e.g., (VI) is unreactive, but its 3′- and 4′-nitro, and 4′-bromo derivatives react normally (Table XXIV-1)], and the inadequacy of the earlier[4] conception is thus disclosed. Attempts have been made to correlate the failure of certain benzils to give quinoxalines with their color and with the reactivity of the corresponding benzaldehydes, but no clear-cut results have emerged.[1,11-13]

The failure of (XII) to react is of interest in view of the comparative reactivity of the corresponding di-o-methoxy analog.[14] One may note, however, that with none of these refractory benzils does the reaction seem to have been tried in dimethylaniline, a solvent which has been conspicuously successful in inducing quinoxaline formation with certain benzils previously considered to be unreactive.[1,11]

Two variations of the diketone-diamine (or ketoaldehyde-diamine) quinoxaline synthesis may conveniently be considered here. In the first variation, the ketoaldehyde (XVII) is replaced by the corresponding α-

$$
\begin{array}{cc}
\text{CHO} & \text{CH}_2\text{Cl} \\
| & | \\
\text{COR} & \text{COR} \\
(\text{XVII}) & (\text{XVIII})
\end{array}
$$

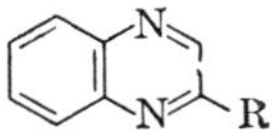

(XIX) 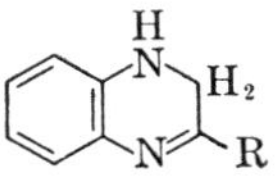   (XX)

halogeno ketone (XVIII) in the formation of a 2-substituted quinoxaline (XIX)[15,16]; 2-phenylquinoxaline, m.p. 78°, 2-phenyl-6- (or 7-) methyl-quinoxaline, m.p. 135°, and 2,6- (or 2, 7-) dimethylquinoxaline, m.p. 54° (b.p. 267–268°), may thus be obtained. The reactions, which proceed in hot water or boiling alcohol, are slow, and involve the *in situ* oxidation of the 3,4-dihydro derivatives (XX) which are the unstable primary products (*cf.* Chapter XXXVII, Section IB).

The second variation consists in the condensation, in alcoholic solution, of an *o*-diamine with a nitroso ketone (XXI) (monoxime of diketone or ketoaldehyde)[17-19] (2). For the preparation of 2-phenylquinoxaline, this

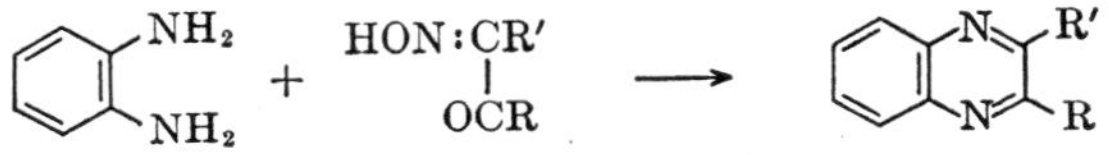

$$
\begin{array}{ccc}
\begin{array}{l}
\nearrow\text{NH}_2 \\
\diagdown\text{NH}_2
\end{array}
& + &
\begin{array}{l}
\text{HON:CR'} \\
| \\
\text{OCR}
\end{array}
\end{array}
\longrightarrow
$$

(XXI)

(2)

$$
\begin{array}{l}
\text{HON:CR'} \\
| \\
\text{HON:CR}
\end{array}
$$

(XXII)   (XXIII)

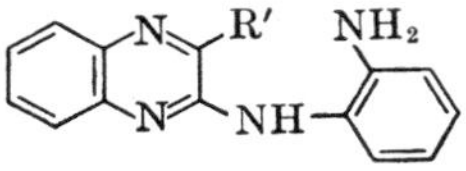

method [*i.e.*, using (XXI; R = Ph, R' = H)] is greatly superior to the use of phenacyl bromide.[18] Dioximes (XXII; R and R' = alkyl or aryl) do not normally yield quinoxalines under these conditions[20]; but reaction occurs with (XXII; R = Cl, R' = alkyl or aryl) in the presence of excess of *o*-diamine, the product being the corresponding 2-*o*-aminoanilinoquinoxaline (XXIII)[20] (see Chapter XXXI, Section 1B).

TABLE XXIV-1. Quinoxaline Derivatives, [structure], Prepared from o-Diamines and 1,2-Dicarbonyl Compounds, Containing Alkyl, Aryl, Aralkyl, Alkenyl, or Acyl Substituents at C_2 and/or C_3, but No Substituent in the Bz Ring

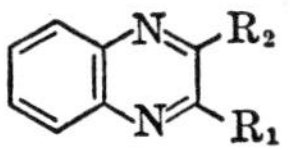

R_1	R_2	M.p., °C.	Remarks	Ref.
H H	—CH$_2$OH CH$_2$Ph	165,250–251 Oil	Yellow solid Picrate, m.p. 117°	21,22 23
H	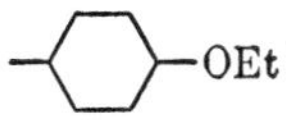 [cyclohexyl-OEt structure]	128	—	24
H	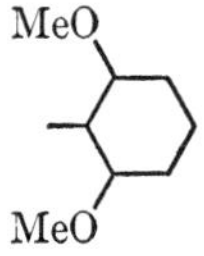 [MeO / MeO cyclohexyl structure]	95.5–96.5	Yellow needles	4
H	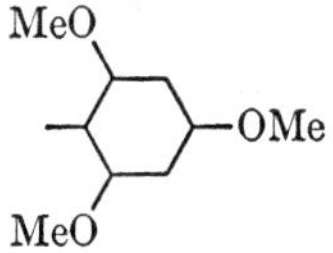 [MeO / OMe / MeO cyclohexyl structure]	83.5–84	Light yellow solid	4
H	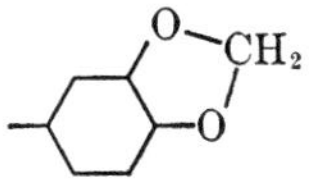 [O—CH$_2$—O dioxole cyclohexyl structure]	167.5	Pale yellow prisms	25
H	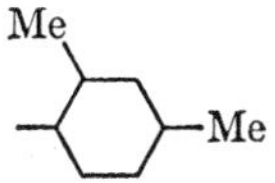 [Me / Me cyclohexyl structure]	56–57 (corr.)	—	3

Table continued

TABLE XXIV-1 (continued)

R_1	R_2	M.p., °C.	Remarks	Ref.
H	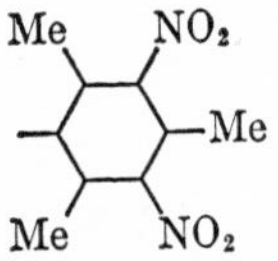 (ring: Me, NO₂, Me, NO₂, Me)	197.5–198	—	4
H	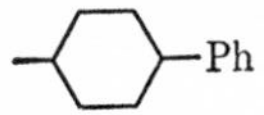 (cyclohexyl-Ph)	128	—	26
H	$C_{10}H_7$-α	114,116– 116.5 (corr.)	Brown solid	3,27
H	$C_{10}H_7$-β	137	—	27
Me	Me	104–106	—	9
Me	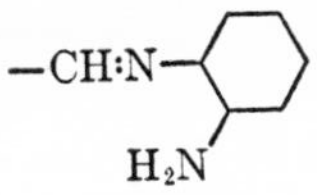 —CH:N— (ring, H_2N)	166	Brown leaflets	28
Me	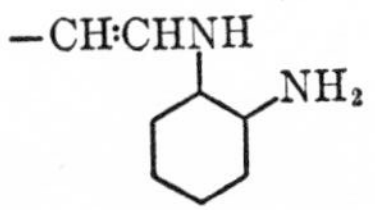 —CH:CHNH— (ring, NH_2)	183	Red cryst. Prepared from AcCOCH:CHOEt	28
Me	Ac (ring, OMe)	87–88	—	29
Me	Ph (ring, OH)	57–58	Conc. H_2SO_4 gives golden color	30
Me	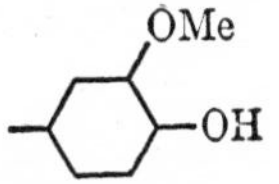 (ring, MeO, OH)	162–163	Yellow hexagons	31
Me	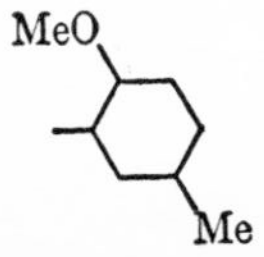 (ring, MeO, Me)	96–97	—	32

R₁	R₂	M.p., °C	Remarks	Ref.
Me	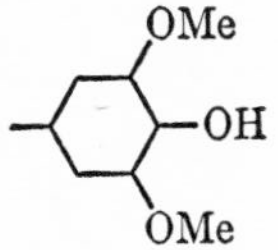 phenyl ring bearing OMe, OH, OMe	161–161.5	Light yellow needles	33
Et	Et	50.5	—	34
Bu^t	Ph	108–109	—	10
Bu^t	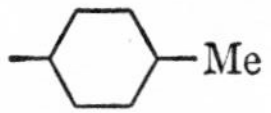 phenyl ring bearing Me (Ph)	109–110	—	10
CH₂Ph	Ph	97	Conc. H_2SO_4 gives orange color	35,36
CH₂Ph	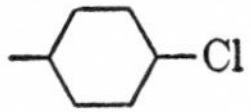 phenyl ring bearing Cl	133,132	—	37,38
CH₂Ph	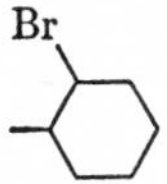 phenyl ring bearing Br, Br	110	—	39
CH₂Ph	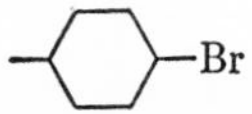 phenyl ring bearing Br	143	—	38
CH₂Ph	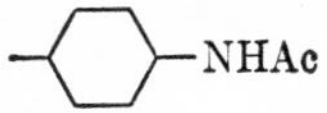 phenyl ring bearing NHAc	199	—	40
CH₂Ph	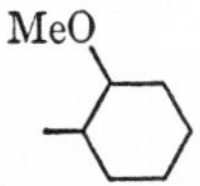 phenyl ring bearing MeO	101.5	—	37
CH₂Ph	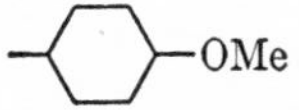 phenyl ring bearing OMe	137,138	—	37,38

Table continued

TABLE XXIV-1 (continued)

R₁	R₂	M.p., °C.	Remarks	Ref.
CH₂Ph	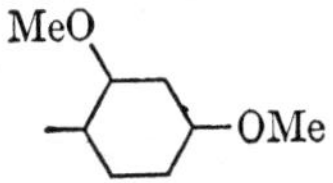 (MeO, OMe, Me-substituted cyclohexyl)	108–109	Conc. H₂SO₄ gives maroon color, changing to orange-red	41
CH₂Ph	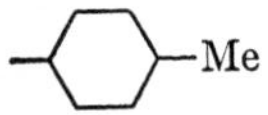 (Me-substituted cyclohexyl)	112–113	—	37
CH₂Ph	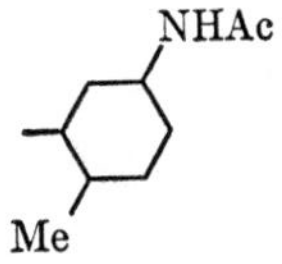 (NHAc, Me-substituted cyclohexyl)	124–125	—	40
CH₂Ph	(Me, Me-substituted cyclohexyl)	126	—	40
CH₂Ph	(Me, Me-substituted cyclohexyl)	106	—	40
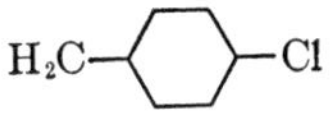 H₂C–(Cl-substituted cyclohexyl)	Ph	142	—	23
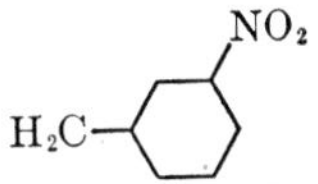 H₂C–(NO₂-substituted cyclohexyl)	Ph	121–122	—	42
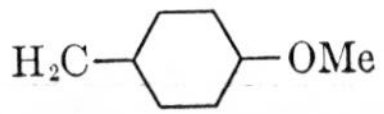 H₂C–(OMe-substituted cyclohexyl)	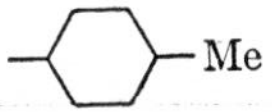 (Me-substituted cyclohexyl)	113–115	—	43

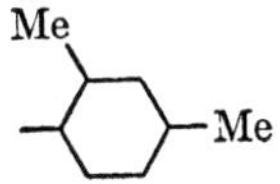

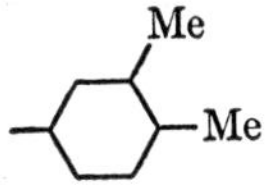

R₁	R₂	M.p., °C.	Remarks	Ref.
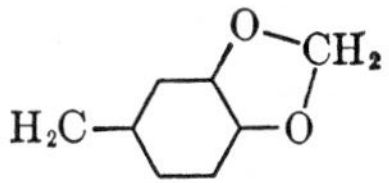 (structure)	Ph	137–138	—	44
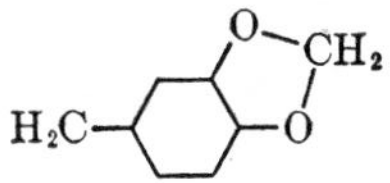 (structure)	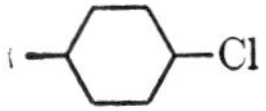 (Cl-cyclohexyl structure)	161	—	38
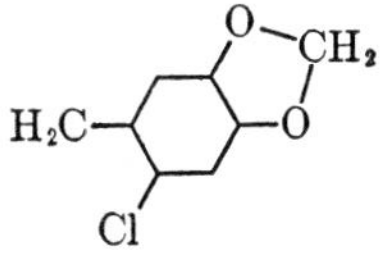 (structure)	Ph	114	—	45
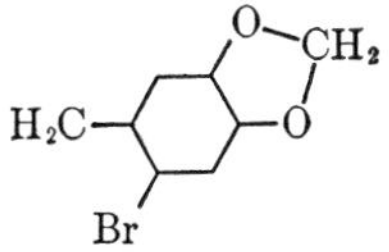 (structure)	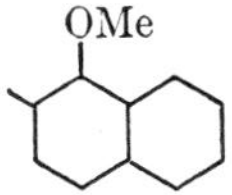 (OMe decalin structure)	203	—	45
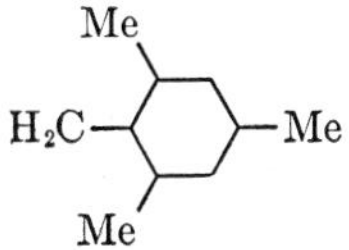 (structure)	Ph	118	—	46
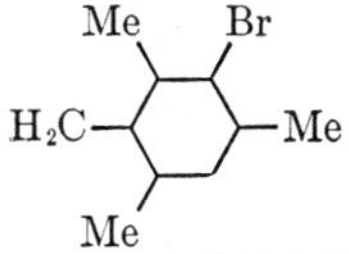 (structure)	Ph	161	—	46

Table continued

TABLE XXIV-1 (*continued*)

R₁	R₂	M.p., °C.	Remarks	Ref.
CH₂Bz	Ph	169–170	Orange cryst.	47
CHClPh	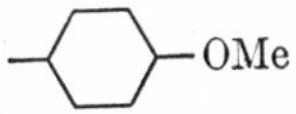 (ring)—OMe	92–93	—	48
CHBrPh	Ph	109–110	Yellow hexagons. Wool dye. Conc. H₂SO₄ gives blood-red color	49
CH(CN)Ph	CH(CN)Ph	227		50
CH(OH)Bz	Ph	187–188 (red liquid)	With MeONa-MeOH gives methyl benzoate and 2-phenyl-3-hydroxymethylquinoxaline	51
CH(OMe)Bz	Ph	131–132	With MeONa-MeOH gives methyl benzoate and 2-phenyl-3-methoxymethylquinoxaline	52
CHPhCHBz₂	Ph	176	With MeOH-Ba(OH)₂ gives 2-phenyl-3,1'-phenyl-2'-benzoyl-ethylquinoxaline, m.p. 148°	49
CHPh₂	Ph	198–199	—	53
CH₂CH₂Bz	CH₂CH₂Bz	166.5–167.5	—	54
O-Mesityl	Ph	182–183	—	51
—C:C(Ph)— / O-Mesityl / —CH₂CHMe (steroid structure, OAc, AcO, OAc)	Ph	217.5–218.5	—	55
Ph	(ring)—NO₂	124	—	9
Ph	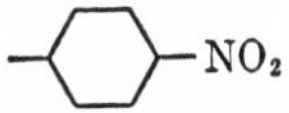 (ring)—NMe₂	161	—	6
Ph	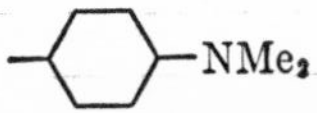 (ring)—NMe₂	120–121	—	9

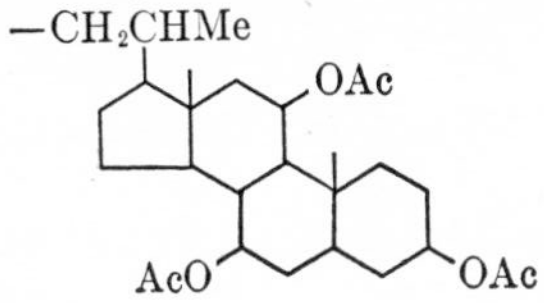

R₁	R₂	M.p., °C.	Remarks	Ref.
Ph	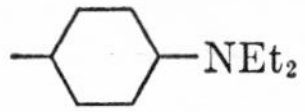 NEt₂	126–127	—	9
Ph	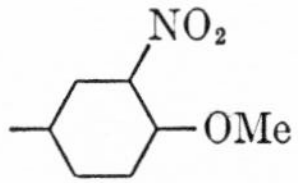 NO₂, OMe	155–157	—	56
Ph	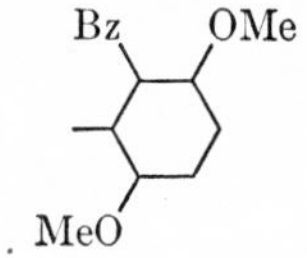 Bz, OMe, MeO	206–207	—	57
Ph	Mesityl (Me, Br, Me, Br, Me, Me)	134–134.5	Light yellow cryst.	58
Ph	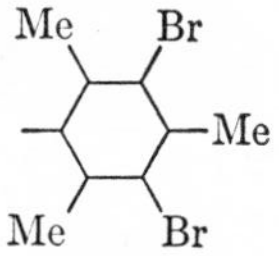 Me, NO₂, Me, Me	187–188	Conc. H₂SO₄ gives dark red color	5
Ph	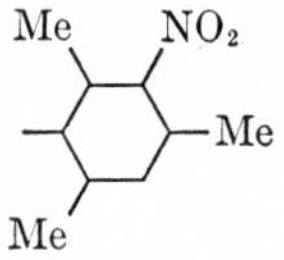 Me, NO₂, Me, Me	151–152 (corr.)	Conc. H₂SO₄ gives dark red color	5
Ph	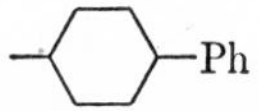 Ph	163	—	59
Ph	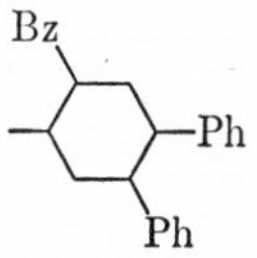 Bz, Ph, Ph	184	—	60

Table continued

TABLE XXIV-1 (continued)

R₁	R₂	M.p., °C.	Remarks	Ref.
Ph	$C_{10}H_7$-α	137–139	Yellowish cryst.	61
Ph	$C_{10}H_7$-β	108–110	Light yellow needles	61
Ph	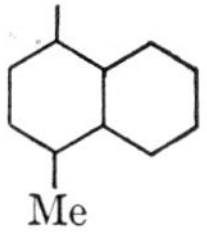 (decalin, Me)	132–133	—	62
Ph	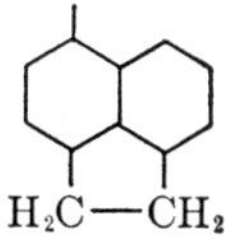 (decalin, H_2C—CH_2)	162	—	63
Ph	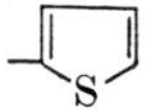 (thiophene)	128	Conc. H_2SO_4 gives yellow color	13
Ph	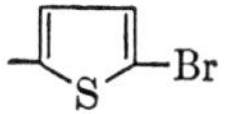 (2-Br-thiophene)	122	Yellow. Conc. H_2SO_4 gives intense violet color	64
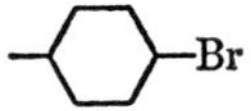 (Br-cyclohexyl)	Mesityl	190–191	Conc. H_2SO_4 gives dark red color	5
(O_2N-cyclohexyl)	(NO_2-cyclohexyl)	168	—	6
(O_2N-cyclohexyl)	(NO_2-cyclohexyl)	186	—	6

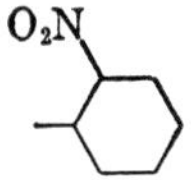

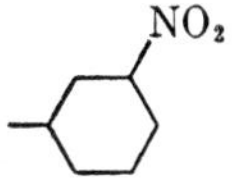

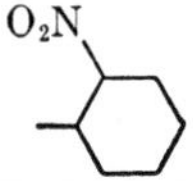

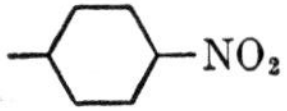

R₁	R₂	M.p., °C.	Remarks	Ref.
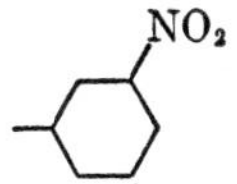 NO₂	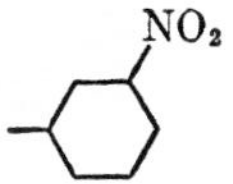 NO₂	208 213	— —	65 66
NO₂	NO₂	221	—	6
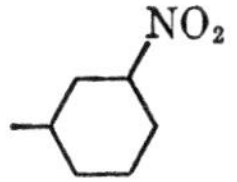 NO₂ (Mesityl)	Me NO₂ Me NO₂	144–146	Conc. H₂SO₄ gives dark red color	5
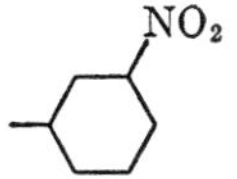 NO₂	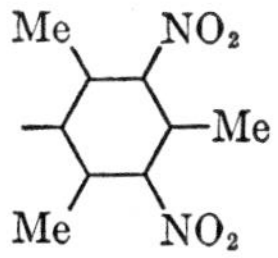 NO₂	188–189 (corr.)	Conc. H₂SO₄ gives dark red color	5
NO₂ (Mesityl)	Me NO₂ Me	201	—	67
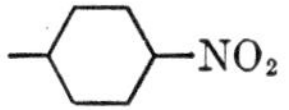 NO₂	NO₂	210–211.5 (corr.)	Conc. H₂SO₄ gives dark red color	5
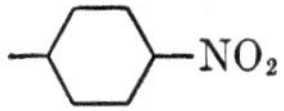 NO₂	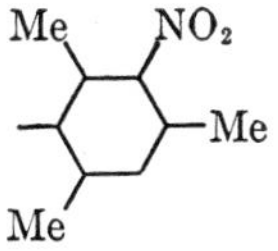 NO₂ Me Me	198–199 (corr.)	Conc. H₂SO₄ gives dark red color	5

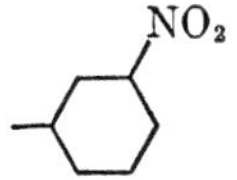

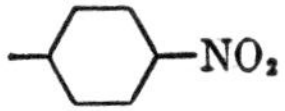

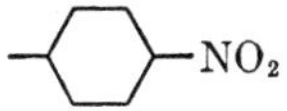

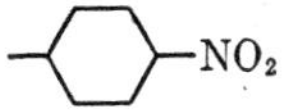

Table continued

TABLE XXIV-1 (*continued*)

R₁	R₂	M.p., °C.	Remarks	Ref.
(dinitro-methylcyclohexane, NO₂, NO₂)	(dinitro-methylcyclohexane, NO₂, NO₂)	274 285	— —	68 66
(amino-methylcyclohexane, NH₂)	(amino-methylcyclohexane, NH₂)	267–268 260–262	Yellow plates; prepared from the dinitro compd. and H₂-Raney Ni	69,70
(hydroxy-methylcyclohexane, OH)	(hydroxy-methylcyclohexane, OH)	326–328	Yellow cryst.	70
(MeO, methylcyclohexane)	(MeO, methylcyclohexane, OMe)	183	Conc. H₂SO₄ gives red color	1
(OMe, methylcyclohexane)	(OMe, methylcyclohexane, OMe)	110	Conc. H₂SO₄ gives red-brown color	1
(OMe, methylcyclohexane)	(MeO, methylcyclohexane, OMe)	149–150 145.5–146	—	9,71
(OMe, methylcyclohexane)	(OMe, methylcyclohexane, OMe)	76–79	Conc. H₂SO₄ gives maroon color changing to cherry-red	41
(OMe, OMe, methylcyclohexane)	(OMe, OMe, methylcyclohexane)	198.5–199	—	72

R₁	R₂	M.p., °C.	Remarks	Ref.
⬡–OCH₂Ph	⬡–OCH₂Ph	156	Conc. H₂SO₄ gives blue-violet color.	12
⬡–OPh	⬡–OPh	153	—	73
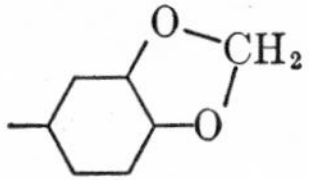 ⬡–O–CH₂–O (methylenedioxy)	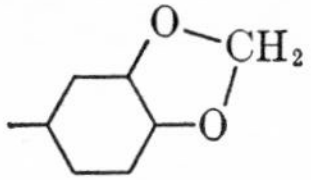 ⬡–O–CH₂–O (methylenedioxy)	204,199–200	Yellow tablets. Conc. H₂SO₄ gives indigo-blue color	7,9
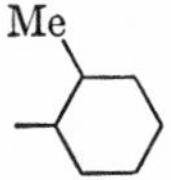 ⬡ (Me, NO₂)	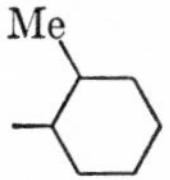 ⬡ (Me)	132–133	Conc. H₂SO₄ gives dark-red color	5
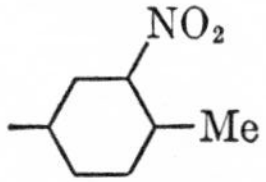 ⬡ (Me)	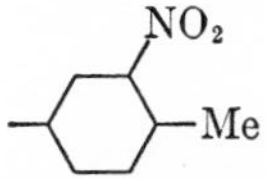 ⬡ (NO₂, Me)	179–180	—	74
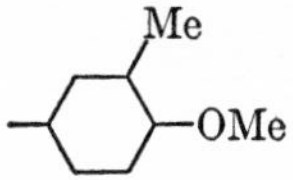 ⬡ (Me, OMe)	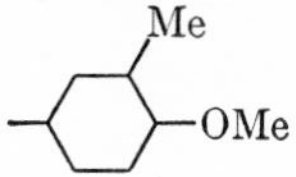 ⬡ (Me, OMe)	139.5–140	Yellow cryst.	75
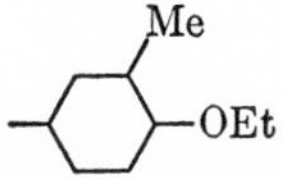 ⬡ (Me, OEt)	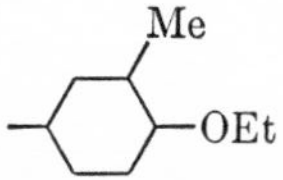 ⬡ (Me, OEt)	172–173	Yellow cryst.	75
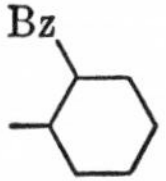 ⬡ (Bz)	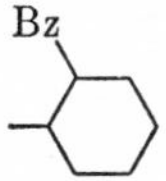 ⬡ (Bz)	237–238	—	76

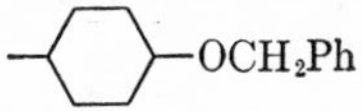

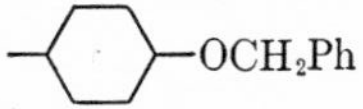

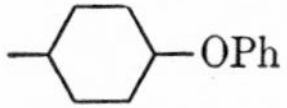

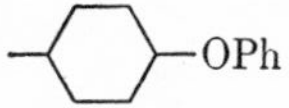

Table continued

TABLE XXIV-1 (continued)

R_1	R_2	M.p., °C.	Remarks	Ref.
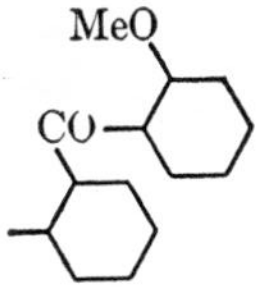 MeO— (CO, cyclohexyl)	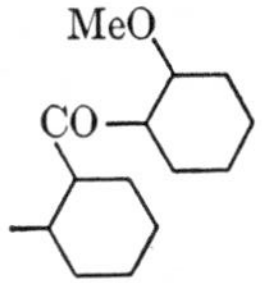 MeO— (CO, cyclohexyl)	250	—	14
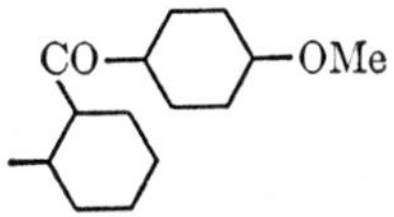 OMe (CO, cyclohexyl)	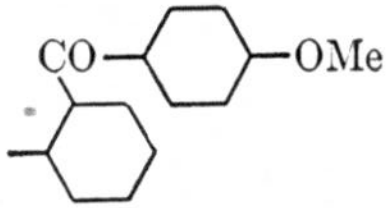 OMe (CO, cyclohexyl)	251	—	14
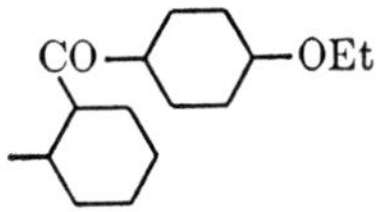 OEt (CO, cyclohexyl)	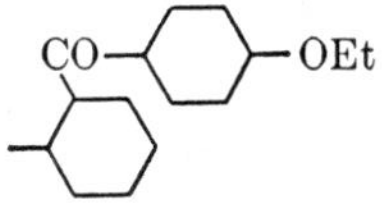 OEt (CO, cyclohexyl)	227.5	—	8
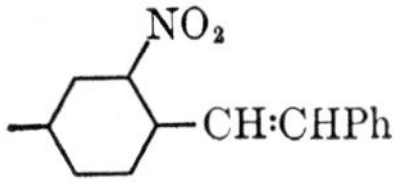 NO_2, CH:CHPh, $C_{10}H_7$-β	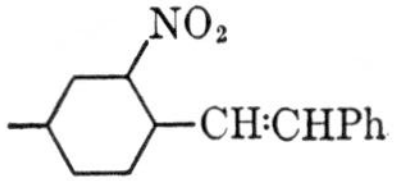 NO_2, CH:CHPh, $C_{10}H_7$-β	207–208	Brilliant yellow leaflets. Conc. H_2SO_4 gives green color	74
		192–193	—	77
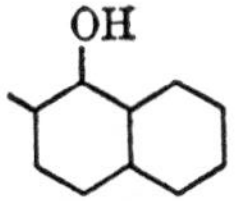 OH	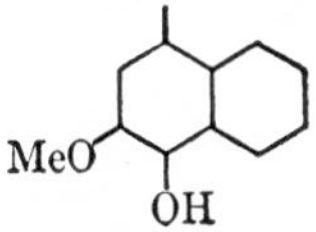 MeO OH	>300 (dec.)	Red cryst. Conc. H_2SO_4 gives dark green color	78

R₁	R₂	M.p., °C.	Remarks	Ref.

R_1	R_2	M.p., °C.	Remarks	Ref.
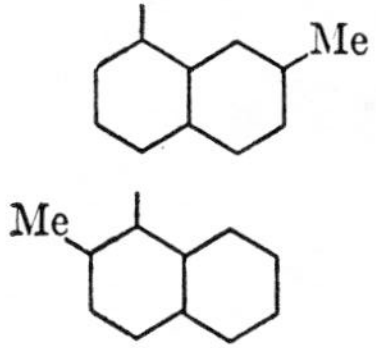 2-Furyl / 2-Indolyl / 3-Indolyl (Me-substituted decalin structures, "or")	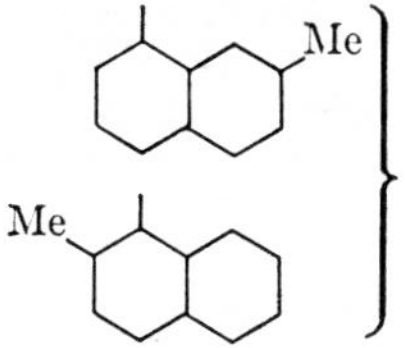 Me (Me-substituted decalin structures)	269 (corr.)	Yellow needles. Conc. H_2SO_4 gives blue-violet color	79
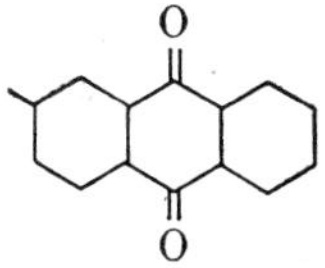 (anthraquinone structure, O=…=O)	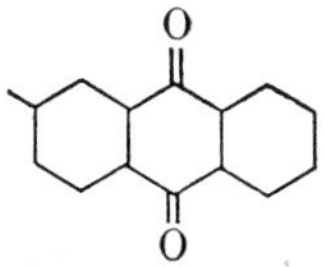 (anthraquinone structure, O=…=O)	326.5	Yellow cryst.	80
2-Furyl / 2-Indolyl / 3-Indolyl	2-Furyl / 2-Indolyl / 3-Indolyl	131–132 / 154 (dec.) / 163 (dec.)	— / — / —	9 / 81 / 81
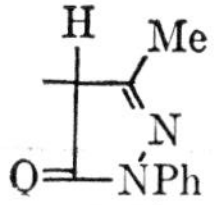 (H Me C—N—NPh, O= structure)	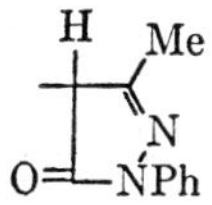 (H Me C—N—NPh, O= structure)	>300	Red needles	82

TABLE XXIV-2. Compounds Substituted in the Benzene Ring 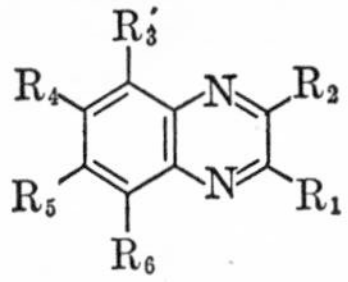   Otherwise as Table XXIV-1

R_1	R_2	R_3	R_4	R_5	R_6	M.p., °C	Remarks	Ref.
H	H	H	NH_2	H	H	158–159	Yellow needles. Conc. H_2SO_4 gives violet color	16
H	H	H	Me	H	H	—	B.p. 245°. Oxalate, m.p. 135–136°	16
H	H	H	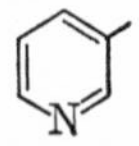 (structure)	H	H	144–145	Pale yellow needles	83
H	{H / Me}	H	AsO_3H_2	H	H	>250	Green solid	84
H	H	H	NH_2	H	H	173	Yellow cryst.	85
Bu^t	H	H	{NO_2 / H} or	H	{H / NO_2}	134.5–135	—	10
$C_4H_8O_4$ / $C_6H_{11}O_5$	H	H	{AsO_3H_2 / H} or	{H / AsO_3H_2}	H		Prepared from maltosone and lactosone	84
Me	Me	H	NH_2	H	H	186–187	—	70
Me	Me	H	OMe	H	H	99–100	—	9
Me	Me	H	Ac	H	H	117–119	—	56
Me	Me	H	AsO_3H_2	H	H	212–215 (dec.)	Pink flakes	86
Me	Me	H	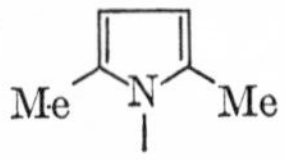 (structure)	H	H	161–163	Straw needles	70
Me	Me	H	CO_2H	Cl	H	260 (corr.)	Yellow needles	87
Me	Me	H	CO_2H	Br	H	278 (dec.)	—	88
Me	Me	CO_2H	Cl	H	H	278 (corr., dec.)	Yellow needles	87

R₁	R₂	R₃	R₄	R₅	R₆	M.p., °C	Remarks	Ref.
CH(CN)Ph	CH(CN)Ph	H	NH₂	H	H	Dec.	Yellow-brown needles. Conc. H₂SO₄ gives violet color	50
CH(CN)Ph	CH(CN)Ph	Me	H	H	H	Dec. >250	Orange-red needles. Wool dye. Conc. H₂SO₄ gives violet color	50
Ph	Ph	H	Cl	H	H	119–121	—	89
Ph	Ph	H	NO₂	H	H	188	Conc. H₂SO₄ gives red color	15
Ph	Ph	H	NH₂	H	H	172–173,175	Yellow cryst. Hydrochloride, red plates, m.p. ~250°. Ac deriv., m.p. 252°. Conc. H₂SO₄ gives red color	15,70
Ph	Ph	H	OMe	H	H	156,154.5–155	Yellow prisms	9,90
Ph	Ph	H	CN	H	H	179–180	Yellow cryst, Conc. H₂SO₄ gives orange color	91
Ph	Ph	H	Buᵗ	H	H	—		92
Ph	Ph	H	Ac	H	H	171–172	Yellow prisms	56
Ph	Ph	H	Ph	H	H	148	Yellow cryst,	93
Ph	Ph	H	PhSO₂	H	H	196	—	94
Ph	Ph	H	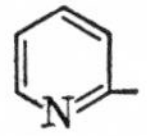 (pyridyl ring structure)	H	H	198–199	Pale yellow prisms	95
Ph	Ph	H	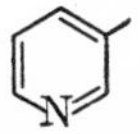 (methyl-pyridyl ring structure)	H	H	194.5–196.5	—	83
Phᵃ	Ph	H	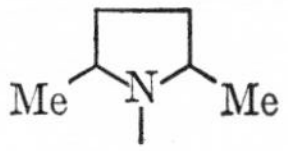 (2,5-dimethylpyrrol-1-yl structure, Me)	H	H	151–153	—	70

Table continued

TABLE XXIV-2 (continued)

R₁	R₂	R₃	R₄	R₅	R₆	M.p., °C	Remarks	Ref.
Ph[b]		H	AsO₃H₂	H	H	—	Pale yellow solid	86
Ph		H	Me	Cl	H	148.5	Conc. H_2SO_4 gives red color	96
Ph		H	CO₂H	Br	H	234.5	—	88
Ph		H	NH₂	NHPh	H	—	—	97
Ph		H	CO₂H	Cl	H	247 (corr.)	—	87
Ph		Cl	OMe	OMe	Cl	251–252	Yellow plates	98
Ph		Cl	H	H	H	214	—	99
Ph		Cl	Me	H	H	143	Yellow-white needles. Conc. H_2SO_4 gives red color	100
Ph		NH₂	H	OMe	H	174–175	Yellow needles	101
Ph		NMe₂	H	H	OMe	233 (dec.)	Pale yellow needles	102
Ph		OMe	H	NO₂	H	207–208	Yellow needles	103
Ph		OMe	NH₂	H	H	—	Hydrochloride, light red needles	104
Ph		OMe	OMe	H	H	139–140	Yellow needles	98
Ph		Me	H	H	OMe	196–197	Gray needles	105
Ph		Me	H	H	Pr^i	136.7–137.3 (corr.)	Conc. H_2SO_4 gives blood-red color	106
Ph		CHO	H	CHO	NH₂	289–290 (dec.)	Orange or yellow cryst.	107
Ph		CO₂H	Cl	H	H	248 (corr.) (dec.)	—	87
Ph	(Cl-/Me-cyclohexyl structure)	H	(2,5-dimethylpyrrol-1-yl structure); NH₂	H	H	178–179	—	70
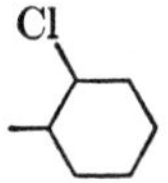 (Cl-/Me-cyclohexyl structure)[a]	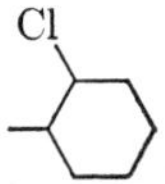 (Cl-/Me-cyclohexyl structure)	H	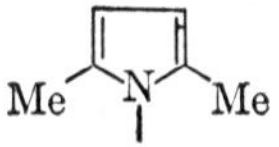 Cl	H	H	211–212	—	70
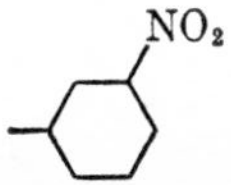 (NO₂-/Me-cyclohexyl structure)	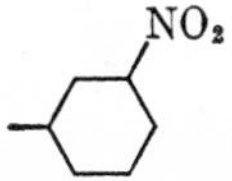 (NO₂-/Me-cyclohexyl structure)	H	Cl	H	H	224–225	With SnCl₂-HCl or Raney Ni gives the corresponding di-NH₂-compd. orange plates, m.p. 80–81°	108

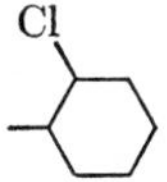

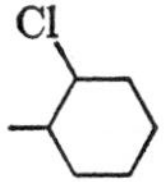

R_1	R_2	R_3	R_4	R_5	R_6	M.p., °C.	Remarks	Ref.
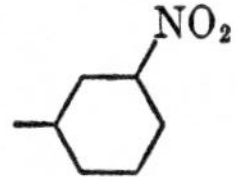 NO_2 (aryl)	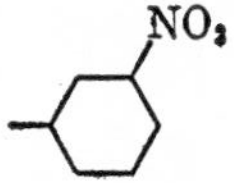 NO_2 (aryl)	H	OPh	H	H	195–196	Yellow cryst.	109
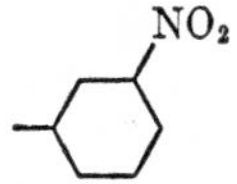 NO_2 (aryl)	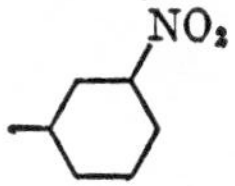 NO_2 (aryl)	H	AsO_3H_2	H	H	>230	—	86
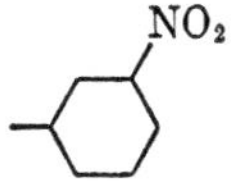 NO_2 (aryl)	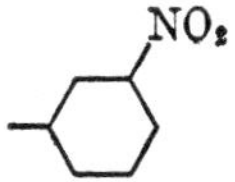 NO_2 (aryl)	Me	H	H	H	208–210	Pale yellow needles	65
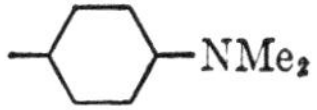 NMe_2 (aryl)	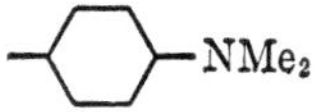 NMe_2 (aryl)	H	AsO_3H_2	H	H	>260	Yellow powder	86
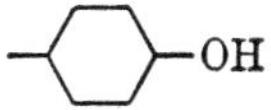 OH (aryl)	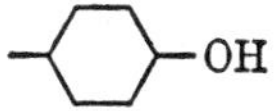 OH (aryl)	H	NH_2	H	H	338–340	—	70
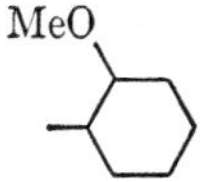 MeO (aryl)	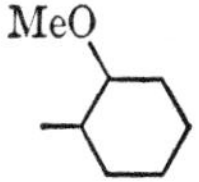 MeO (aryl)	H	Me	H	H	135	Conc. H_2SO_4 gives deep-red color	1
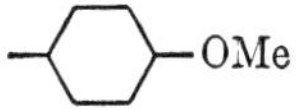 OMe (aryl)	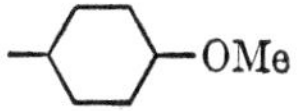 OMe (aryl)	H	NH_2	H	H	194–196	Light brown cryst.	70
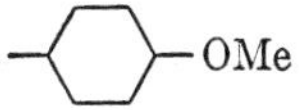 OMe (aryl)	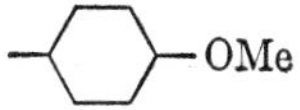 OMe (aryl)	H	OMe	H	H	131–132	—	9
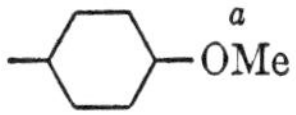 OMe (aryl) [a]	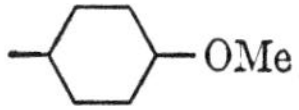 OMe (aryl)	H	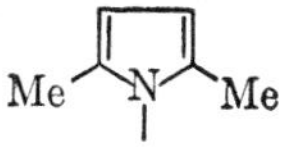 (Me–pyrrol-1-yl–Me ring)	H	H	189–190	—	70

Table continued

TABLE XXIV-2 (*continued*)

R₁	R₂	R₃	R₄	R₅	R₆	M.p., °C.	Remarks	Ref.
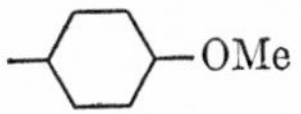 OMe (ring)	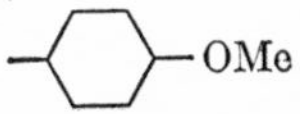 OMe (ring)	H	AsO₃H₂	H	H	—	Yellow needles	86
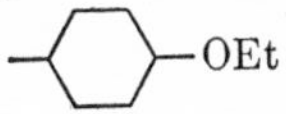 OEt (ring)	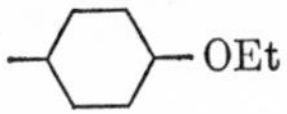 OEt (ring)	H	AsO₃H₂	H	H	—	Yellow needles	86
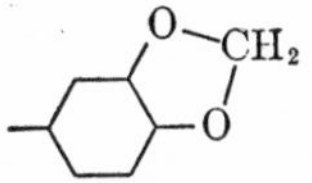 methylenedioxy (O–CH₂–O ring)	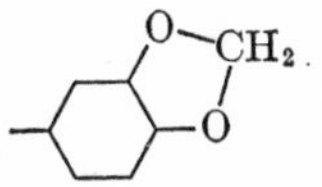 methylenedioxy (O–CH₂–O ring)	H	OMe	H	H	171–172	—	9
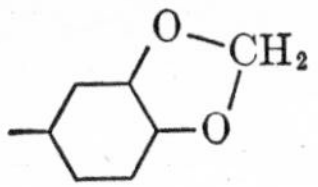 methylenedioxy (O–CH₂–O ring)	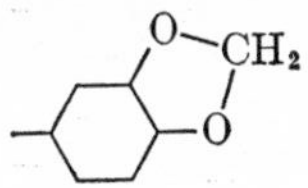 methylenedioxy (O–CH₂–O ring)	H	AsO₃H₂	H	H	—	Yellow powder	86
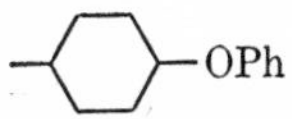 OPh (ring)	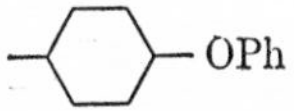 OPh (ring)	H	Me	H	H	149	Conc. H₂SO₄ gives violet color	1,11
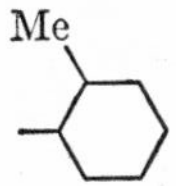 Me (ring)	 Me (ring)	H	NO₂	H	H	197.5–198.5	—	5
2-Furyl	2-Furyl	H	OMe	H	H	109–110	—	9
2-Furyl	2-Furyl	H	AsO₃H₂	H	H	>250	Light brown solid	86

^{a} Prepared from the corresponding 6-NH₂ compound and acetonylacetone in boiling ethanol-acetic acid.
^{b} With boiling AcOH-HX gives the Br₂As and Cl₂As (m.p. 232°) compounds, and thence, with Na₂CO₃, the (HO)₂As compound (m.p. 185–187°).

TABLE XXIV-3. Di- and Triquinoxalines (for 2,5-Bis-2'-quinoxalyl-1,4-diaryl-1,4-dihydropyrazines see Table XXXVI-2)

Structure of compound	Dicarbonyl compd. used	M.p., °C.	Remarks	Ref.
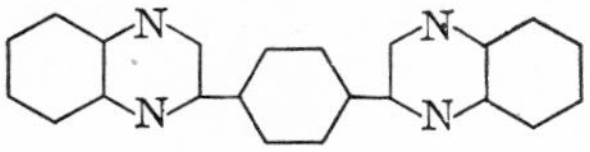 (diquinoxaline structure)	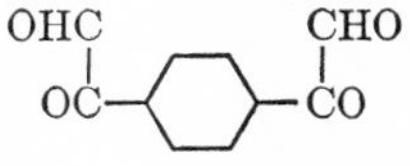 OHC ─ OC─◯─CHO CO	262	Yellow leaflets	110
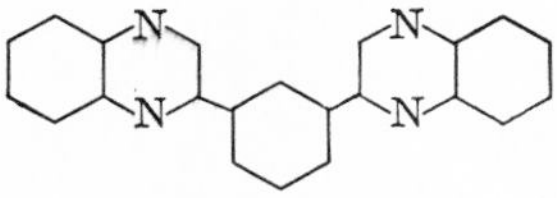 (diquinoxaline structure)	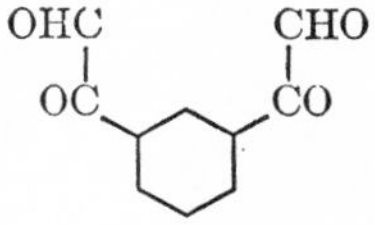 OHC ─ OC─◯─CHO CO	202–203	—	111
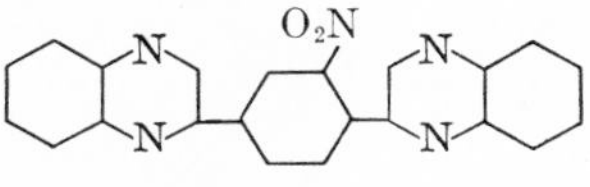 (diquinoxaline structure, O₂N)	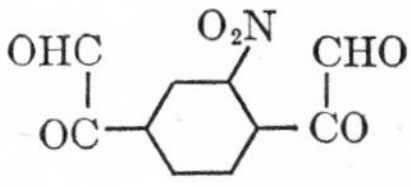 OHC O₂N OC─◯─CHO CO	—	Yellow powder. Impure	110
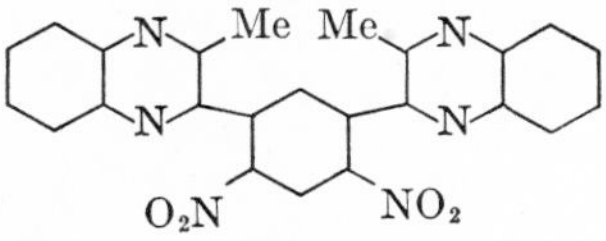 (diquinoxaline structure, Me Me, O₂N NO₂)	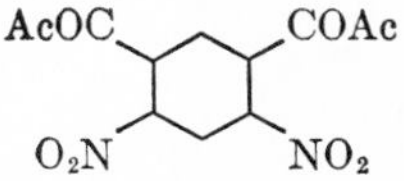 AcOC─◯─COAc O₂N NO₂	238–239	—	112
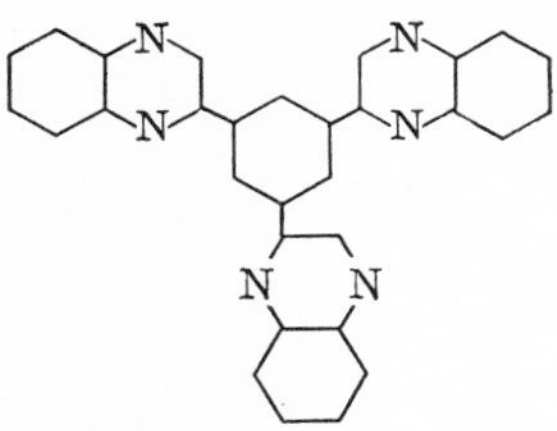 (triquinoxaline structure)	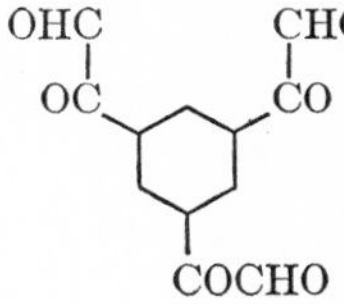 OHC ─ OC─◯─CHO CO COCHO	302–303	—	110
(diquinoxaline structure, X = CHPhCO₂H)	COCH(CN)Ph COCH(CN)Ph	235–236	Yellow-brown solid	113

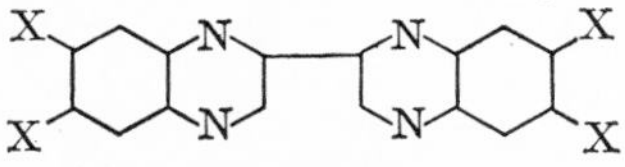

(X = CHPhCO₂H)

References

1. Schönberg and Malchow, *Ber.*, **55**, 3746 (1922).
2. R. Robinson and Tomlinson, *J. Chem. Soc.*, **1935**, 1283.
3. Fuson, Emerson, and Gray, *J. Am. Chem. Soc.*, **61**, 480 (1939).
4. Fuson, McKeever, Rabjohn, and Gray, *J. Am. Chem. Soc.*, **65**, 1028 (1943).
5. Fuson and Soper, *J. Org. Chem.*, **9**, 193 (1944).
6. Chattaway and Coulson, *J. Chem. Soc.*, **1928**, 1080.
7. Greene and R. Robinson, *J. Chem. Soc.*, **1922**, 2182.
8. Brand and Krey, *J. prakt. Chem.*, **110**, 10 (1925).
9. Bost and Towell, *J. Am. Chem. Soc.*, **70**, 903 (1948).
10. Fuson, Gray, and Gouza, *J. Am. Chem. Soc.*, **61**, 1937 (1939).
11. Schönberg and Kraemer, *Ber.*, **55**, 1174 (1922).

12. Schönberg and Bleyberg, *Ber.*, **55**, 3753 (1922).
13. Steinkopf and Bokor, *Ann.*, **540**, 14 (1939).
14. Brand and Hoffmann, *Ber.*, **53**, 815 (1920).
15. Hinsberg, *Ann.*, **292**, 245 (1896).
16. Hinsberg, *Ann.*, **237**, 327 (1887).
17. Gabriel and Sonn, *Ber.*, **40**, 4850 (1907).
18. Fischer and Römer, *Ber.*, **41**, 2350 (1908).
19. Böttcher, *Ber.*, **46**, 3084 (1913).
20. Durio, *Gazz. chim. ital.*, **63**, 747 (1933).
21. Norrish and Griffiths, *J. Chem. Soc.*, **1928**, 2829.
22. W. E. Evans, Jr., Carr, and Krantz, Jr., *J. Am. Chem. Soc.*, **60**, 1628 (1938).
23. Bennett and Willis, *J. Chem. Soc.*, **1928**, 1960.
24. Kipnis, Soloway, and Ornfelt, *J. Am. Chem. Soc.*, **69**, 1231 (1947).
25. Kawai and Ashino, *Bull. Chem. Soc. Japan*, **13**, 480 (1938).
26. Kröhnke and Börner, *Ber.*, **69**, 2006 (1936).
27. Goldyrev and Postovskii, *Chem. Abs.*, **34**, 4732 (1940) [*J. Gen. Chem. U. S. S. R.* **10**, 39 (1940)].
28. Diels and Peterson, *Ber.*, **55**, 3449 (1922).
29. Piutti, *Gazz. chim. ital.*, **66**, 276 (1936).
30. v. Auwers, *Ber.*, **50**, 1177 (1917).
31. Brickman, Hawkins, and Hibbert, *J. Am. Chem. Soc.*, **62**, 2149 (1940).
32. v. Auwers and W. Müller, *Ber.*, **50**, 1149 (1917).
33. Kulka, Hawkins, and Hibbert, *J. Am. Chem. Soc.*, **63**, 2371 (1941).
34. Urion, *Chem. Abs.*, **28**, 2677 (1934) [*Ann. chim.*, **1**, 5 (1934)].
35. Malkin and R. Robinson, *J. Chem. Soc.*, **1925**, 369.
36. Burton and Shoppee, *J. Chem. Soc.*, **1937**, 546.
37. Jörlander, *Ber.*, **50**, 406 (1917).
38. Allen and Frame, *Can. J. Research*, **6**, 605 (1932).
39. Barnes and Payton, *J. Am. Chem. Soc.*, **58**, 1300 (1936).
40. Jörlander, *Ber.*, **50**, 1457 (1917).
41. W. Baker and R. Robinson, *J. Chem. Soc.*, **1932**, 1798.
42. Bodforss, *Ber.*, **49**, 2795 (1916).
43. W. A. Hutchins, Montwani, Mudbhatkal, and Wheeler, *J. Chem. Soc.*, **1938**, 1882.
44. Dodwadmath and Wheeler, *Proc. Indian Acad. Sci.*, **2A**, 438 (1935).
45. Dev and Wheeler, *J. Univ. Bombay*, **7**, 205 (1938).
46. Barnes and R. J. Brown, *J. Am. Chem. Soc.*, **65**, 412 (1943).
47. Lutz and Stuart, *J. Am. Chem. Soc.*, **58**, 1885 (1936).
48. Jörlander, *Ber.*, **49**, 2782 (1916).
49. Kleinfeller and Trommsdorff, *Ber.*, **72**, 256 (1939).
50. Dutt and Sen, *J. Chem. Soc.*, **1922**, 2663.
51. Blatt, *J. Am. Chem. Soc.*, **58**, 1894 (1936).
52. Blatt, *J. Am. Chem. Soc.*, **57**, 1103 (1935).
53. Kohler and Weiner, *J. Am. Chem. Soc.*, **56**, 434 (1934).
54. Wawzonek, *J. Am. Chem. Soc.*, **65**, 839 (1943).
55. R. P. Jacobsen, *J. Am. Chem. Soc.*, **66**, 662 (1944).
56. Borsche and Barthenheier, *Ann.*, **553**, 250 (1942).
57. Koelsch and Prill, *J. Am. Chem. Soc.*, **67**, 1296 (1945).
58. Fuson, Weinstock, Jr., and Ullyot, *J. Am. Chem. Soc.*, **57**, 1803 (1935).
59. Kohler and Nygaard, *J. Am. Chem. Soc.*, **52**, 4128 (1930).
60. Allen and Spanagel, *J. Am. Chem. Soc.*, **55**, 3773 (1933).
61. Ruggli and Reinert, *Helv. Chim. Acta*, **9**, 67 (1926).
62. J. W. Cook and Galley, *J. Chem. Soc.*, **1931**, 2012.

63. Ruggli and Jenny, *Helv. Chim. Acta*, **10**, 228 (1927).
64. Buu-Hoï and Nguyen-Hoan, *Rec. trav. chim.*, **68**, 5 (1949).
65. Boon and Nisbet, *J. Chem. Soc.*, **1929**, 1901.
66. Chattaway and Coulson, *J. Chem. Soc.*, **1927**, 577.
67. Chattaway and Coulson, *J. Chem. Soc.*, **1928**, 1361.
68. Christie and Kenner, *J. Chem. Soc.*, **1926**, 470.
69. Kuhn, Möller, and Wendt, *Ber.*, **76**, 405 (1943).
70. Gilman and Broadbent, *J. Am. Chem. Soc.*, **70**, 2619 (1948).
71. Hobday and Short, *J. Chem. Soc.*, **1943**, 609.
72. Vanzetti, *Gazz. chim. ital.*, **57**, 162 (1927).
73. Asahina and Tanase, *Chem. Abs.*, **34**, 7906 (1940) [*Proc. Imp. Acad. (Tokyo)*, **16**, 297 (1940)].
74. Chardonnens and Venetz, *Helv. Chim. Acta*, **22**, 822 (1939).
75. Shapiro, *Ber.*, **66**, 1370 (1933).
76. Brand and Ludwig, *Ber.*, **53**, 809 (1920).
77. Fulton and R. Robinson, *J. Chem. Soc.*, **1939**, 200.
78. Fries and Leue, *Ber.*, **55**, 753 (1922).
79. Lesser and Gad, *Ber.*, **60**, 242 (1927).
80. de Diesbach and Quinza, *Helv. Chim. Acta*, **17**, 105 (1934).
81. Sanna, *Gazz. chim. ital.*, **52**, 165 (1922).
82. Perroncito, *Gazz. chim. ital.*, **67**, 158 (1937).
83. Coates, A. H. Cook, Heilbron, Hey, Lambert, and Lewis, *J. Chem. Soc.*, **1943**, 406.
84. P. L. Cramer and W. L. Lewis, *J. Am. Chem. Soc.*, **52**, 229 (1930).
85. Platt and Sharp, *J. Chem. Soc.*, **1948**, 2129.
86. W. L. Lewis, P. L. Cramer, and Bly, *J. Am. Chem. Soc.*, **46**, 2058 (1924).
87. Goldstein and Studer, *Helv. Chim. Acta*, **21**, 51 (1938).
88. Goldstein and Gianola, *Helv. Chim. Acta*, **26**, 173 (1943).
89. Mangini and Deliddo, *Gazz. chim. ital.*, **63**, 612 (1933).
90. McCoubrey and Webster, *J. Chem. Soc.*, **1948**, 1719.
91. Borsche, Stackmann, and Makaroff, *Ber.*, **49**, 2222 (1916).
92. Reilly and Hickinbottom, *J. Chem. Soc.*, **1920**, 103.
93. Bell and Kenyon, *J. Chem. Soc.*, **1926**, 2705.
94. Loudon, *J. Chem. Soc.*, **1939**, 902.
95. A. H. Cook, Heilbron, Lambert, and Spinks, *J. Chem. Soc.*, **1943**, 404
96. G. T. Morgan and Challenor, *J. Chem. Soc.*, **1921**, 1537.
97. Kehrmann and Stanoyévitch, *Helv. Chim. Acta*, **8**, 663 (1925).
98. Frisch, Silverman, and Bogert, *J. Am. Chem. Soc.*, **65**, 2432 (1943).
99. Macleod, Pfund, and Kilpatrick, *J. Am. Chem. Soc.*, **44**, 2260 (1922).
100. G. T. Morgan and Glover, *J. Chem. Soc.*, **1921**, 1700.
101. F. E. King and Beer, *J. Chem. Soc.*, **1945**, 791.
102. H. H. Hodgson and J. H. Cook, *J. Chem. Soc.*, **1933**, 825.
103. Borsche, Löwenstein, and Quast, *Ber.*, **50**, 1339 (1917).
104. Fromm and Ebert, *J. prakt. Chem.*, **108**, 75 (1924).
105. Dadswell and Kenner, *J. Chem. Soc.*, **1927**, 580.
106. Doumani and Kobe, *J. Am. Chem. Soc.*, **62**, 562 (1940).
107. Ruggli and Frey, *Helv. Chim. Acta*, **22**, 1403 (1939).
108. Hall and Turner, *J. Chem. Soc.*, **1945**, 699.
109. Oesterlin, *Monatsh.*, **57**, 31 (1931).
110. Ruggli and Gassenmeier, *Helv. Chim. Acta*, **22**, 496 (1939).
111. Ruggli and Theilheimer, *Helv. Chim. Acta*, **24**, 899 (1941).
112. Ruggli and Straub, *Helv. Chim. Acta*, **21**, 1084 (1938).
113. Tiwari and Dutt, *Proc. Natl. Acad. Sci. India*, **7**, 58 (1937).

CHAPTER XXV

Quinoxalines Unsubstituted in the Hetero Ring

If the quinoxaline synthesis from *o*-diamines and 1,2-diketones discussed in the preceding chapter is modified by using glyoxal instead of a diketone, quinoxalines are produced in which the hetero ring carries no substit-

$$R \text{—} \left\langle \underset{NH_2}{\overset{NH_2}{}} \right. + \underset{CHO}{\overset{CHO}{|}} \longrightarrow R \text{—} \left\langle \underset{N}{\overset{N}{}} \right\rangle + 2H_2O \tag{1}$$

uent (Eq. 1). Compounds of this type, prepared by this and other methods, are summarized in Table XXV-1.

Quinoxaline. This compound (I), the parent member of the group, is best prepared using the conditions recommended by Cavagnol and Wiselogle.[1] It is a weak base, $pK_a = \sim 0.8$ in water[2] at 20°, of which the hydrochloride, sulfate, and tetrachloroiodate (see Table XXV-1) have been described. The pure base does not fluoresce in aqueous solution.[3]

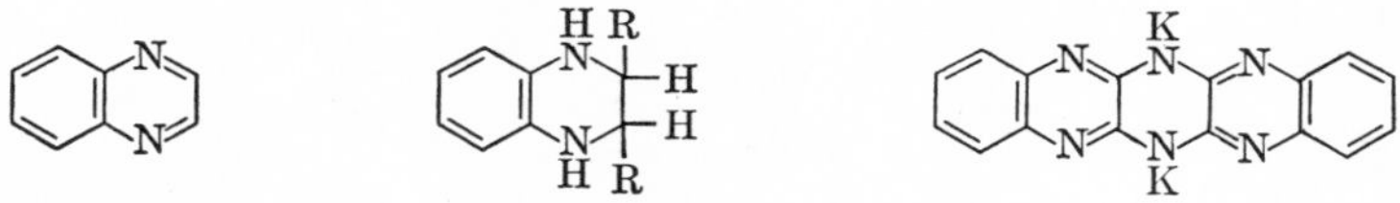

(I)   (II)   (III)

Quinoxaline undergoes additive reactions with bisulfite, hydrogen cyanide, and Grignard reagents, forming compounds of type (II) (see Table XXXVII-4). On reduction, either catalytically or with sodium and alcohol, it yields 1,2,3,4-tetrahydroquinoxaline (II; R = H) (Table XXXVII-4). Quinoxaline condenses with two or more equivalents of potassium amide with formation of the dipotassium salt (III) of fluorubin.[4]

Oxidation of quinoxaline produces results which depend greatly on the reagent used. Thus with permanganate the product is pyrazine-2,3-dicarboxylic acid (IV),[5] which is obtainable in a yield of 66% under suitably controlled conditions.[6] With ammonium persulfate, on the other hand, the product is 2,3-dihydroxyquinoxaline (V) (Chapter XXVII, Section 2)[4]; and hydrogen peroxide in acetic acid gives quinoxaline di-*N*-oxide (VI) (Chapter XXVI)[7].

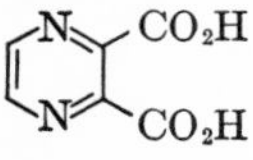

(IV) 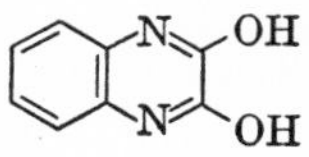   (V) 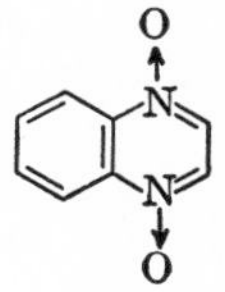   (VI)

6,6′-Diquinoxalyl. This compound (VII) is prepared by condensing glyoxal with 3,3′,4,4′-tetraaminodiphenyl,[8] but its properties have not been described in detail.

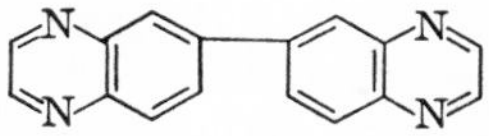

(VII)

TABLE XXV-1. Quinoxalines Unsubstituted in the Hetero Ring[a]

Substituent	Prep.[b]	M.p., °C.	Remarks	Ref.
Nil	A,B	27 30.5– 31.5	B.p. 220–223°/ 760, 44–45°/1 mm. Hydrochloride, dec., 184°; sulfate, m.p. 186–187°; tetrachloroiodate, $C_8H_6N_2$, $HICl_4$, dec. 125–130°	1,3, 9–11
6-Cl	A,C	60 63.8– 64.3	B.p. 117–119°/10 mm.	1,10
6-Br	C	56	—	10
6-NO₂	A	177	Brown needles	11
5-NH₂	A,D	91,92 93–95	Yellow-orange cryst. Hydrate, yellow plates, m.p. 87–88°	12–14
6-NH₂	A	158–159	Intense violet color in conc. mineral acids. Sulfate, hydrochloride, and chloroplatinate are red solids	9,13,14
5-NHAc	A	131 (crude)	—	12
5-NH₂—⬡—SO₂NH	E	169–170 168.5–169.5 163–165[c]	Yellow plates	12–14
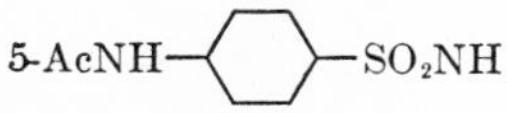 5-AcNH—⬡—SO₂NH	F	228–230 234	—	12,13
6-NH₂—⬡—SO₂NH	E	230–231 231.5–232.5[c] 227–229	Yellow needles	12–15

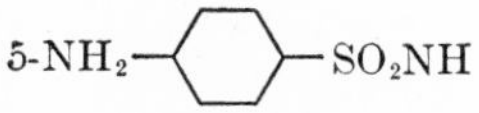

Table continued

TABLE XXV-1. Quinoxalines Unsubstituted in the Hetero Ring[a] (*continued*)

Substituent	Prep.[b]	M.p., °C.	Remarks	Ref.
6-AcNH—⟨ 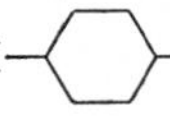 ⟩—SO$_2$NH	F	277 (dec.) 279	—	12,13
6-OMe	A	60	B.p. 128°/7 mm.	1
6-Me	A	<0	B.p. 245°, 86°/1 mm. Oxalate, m.p. 135–136°	1,9
5-NO$_2$-7-OMe	A	182.5–183	—	16
5-NHOH-7-OMe	O	157(dec.)	—	16
5-NH$_2$-7-OMe	A,N	95 94–96 96.5–97	Yellow plates or needles. Dihydrochloride, m.p. 210.5–211	16–18
5-NHAc-7-OMe	G	175–176 174 173.7–174.5	—	16–18
5-NH-tosyl-7-OMe	G	140	—	17
5-NH[CH$_2$]$_2$NEt$_2$-7-OMe	H,I	—	B.p. 165–168°/1 mm., 130–140°/0.01 mm. Dipicrate, m.p. 184–185°. Monopicrate, m.p. 139°. Monohydrochloride, m.p. 169–171°	17,18
5-NH[CH$_2$]$_3$NEt$_2$-7-OMe	H	—	B.p. 185–186°/5 mm. Dipicrate, m.p. 174°	17
5-NH$_2$-7-Me	A	103	Hydrate, yellow needles, m.p. 122° with evolution of H$_2$O and formation of anhyd. base	13
5-NH$_2$—⟨ 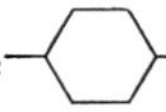 ⟩—SO$_2$NH-7-Me	E	214–216	—	13
5-AcNH—⟨ 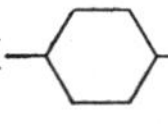 ⟩—SO$_2$NH-7-Me	F	209	—	13
7-NH$_2$-5-Me	A	158–160	Yellow cryst.	13
7-NH$_2$—⟨ 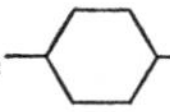 ⟩—SO$_2$NH-5-Me	E	225–227	—	13
7-AcNH—⟨ 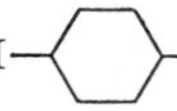 ⟩—SO$_2$NH-5-Me	F	262	—	13
7-NH$_2$-6-Me	A	194–195	Orange cryst.	13
7-NH$_2$—⟨ 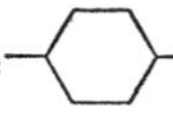 ⟩—SO$_2$NH-6-Me	E	219–220	—	13
7-AcNH—⟨ 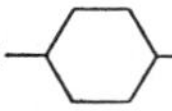 ⟩—SO$_2$NH-6-Me	F	262–265	—	13
6,7-Di-OH	A	>260	Very sparingly sol. in org. solvents	19
6-OH-7-OMe	A,M	238–239	—	19
6-OBz-7-OMe	J	136.5–137.5	—	19
6,7-Di-OMe	A	150–151	—	19

TABLE XXV-1. Quinoxalines Unsubstituted in the Hetero Ring[a] *(continued)*

Substituent	Prep.[b]	M.p., °C.	Remarks	Ref.
5-NO$_2$-6-OH-7-OMe	K	Dec. >235	Structure not certain	19
5-NH$_2$-6,7-di-OMe	A,L	107.5–108.5	—	19
5-NH$_2$—⟨ ⟩—SO$_2$NH-6,7-di-OMe	E	217.5–218.5	—	19
5-AcNH—⟨ ⟩—SO$_2$NH-6,7-di-OMe	F	238.5–239	—	19
5-NH[CH$_2$]$_2$NEt$_2$-6,7-di-OMe	I	—	B.p. 175°/0.5 mm.	19

[a] For Bz-acetoxy- and -methoxyquinoxalines, see F. E. King, Clark, and Davis, *J. Chem. Soc.*, *1949*, 3012.

[b] A, from the *o*-diamine and glyoxal (as bisulfite or sulfate) in aqueous solution, in aqueous sodium acetate and acetic acid (usually at 50–100° and at pH 5–6.5), or in aqueous sodium carbonate.   B, from 2-(*d*-arabo)tetrahydroxybutylquinoxaline by ultraviolet irradiation in 0.5 N sodium hydroxide (5 hours at room temperature). C, from the 2,3-dicarboxylic acid or its ammonium salt by pyrolysis at 220–240°. D, from the 5-acetamido compound by hydrolysis with dilute sulfuric acid at 95°.

E, from the AcNH—⟨ ⟩—SO$_2$NH compound by hydrolysis with hot aqueous

or alcoholic hydrochloric acid, or with hot aqueous sodium hydroxide.   F, from the amino compound and *p*-acetamidobenzenesulfonyl chloride in pyridine.   G, by acylation of the amino compound.   H, from the potassium salt of the tosylamido derivative by reaction with the appropriate alkyl chloride in boiling ethanol, followed by hydrolysis with concentrated sulfuric acid.   I, from the amino compound by direct alkylation in boiling ethanol or in phenol and sodium phenoxide at 100°. J, by acylation of the hydroxy compound.   K, by nitration of 6,7-dimethoxyquinoxaline.   L, by reduction of the dinitro compound which is obtained (impure) by nitration of 6,7-dimethoxyquinoxaline.   M, from 5-amino-6,7-dimethoxyquinoxaline by deamination and demethylation.   N, from the corresponding nitro compound by reduction with sodium hydrosulfite in aqueous alcohol.   O, from the corresponding nitro compound by reduction with alcoholic ammonium sulfide.

[c] M.p. is corrected.

References

1. Cavagnol and Wiselogle, *J. Am. Chem. Soc.*, **69**, 795 (1947).
2. Albert, Goldacre, and J. Phillips, *J. Chem. Soc.*, **1948**, 2240.
3. Kuhn and Bär, *Ber.*, **67**, 898 (1934).
4. Bergstrom and Ogg, Jr., *J. Am. Chem. Soc.*, **53**, 245 (1931).
5. Gabriel and Sonn, *Ber.*, **40**, 4850 (1907).
6. Sausville and Spoerri, *J. Am. Chem. Soc.*, **63**, 3153 (1942).
7. McIlwain, *J. Chem. Soc.*, **1943**, 322.
8. Tiwari and Dutt, *Proc. Natl. Acad. Sci. India*, **7**, 58 (1937).
9. Hinsberg, *Ann.*, **237**, 327 (1887).
10. Chattaway and Humphrey, *J. Chem. Soc.*, **1929**, 645.
11. Hinsberg, *Ann.*, **292**, 245 (1896).
12. Wolf, Beutel, and Stevens, *J. Am. Chem. Soc.*, **70**, 2572 (1948).
13. Platt and Sharp, *J. Chem. Soc.*, **1948**, 2129.
14. Jensen, *Acta Chem. Scand.*, **2**, 91 (1948).
15. Marshall, *J. Pharmacol.*, **84**, 1 (1945).
16. Mizzoni and Spoerri, *J. Am. Chem. Soc.*, **67**, 1652 (1945).
17. Gawron and Spoerri, *J. Am. Chem. Soc.*, **67**, 514 (1945).
18. F. E. King and Beer, *J. Chem. Soc.*, **1945**, 791.
19. Ehrlich and Bogert, *J. Org. Chem.*, **12**, 522 (1947).

CHAPTER XXVI

Quinoxaline N-Oxides

A. Preparation. The conversion of quinoxaline derivatives into the corresponding N-oxides is readily accomplished by warming the quinoxaline compound with hydrogen peroxide in acetic acid at 50–60°. The reaction has not been carried out with a sufficient number of compounds to enable any generalization to be made as to its scope, but whereas quinoxaline and its homologs substituted at C_2 or C_3 yield di-N-oxides, 3-ethoxy- and 3-ethoxy-2-methyl-quinoxaline give only mono-N-oxides under similar conditions.

B. Properties

(1) Di-N-oxides. Quinoxaline-, 2-methylquinoxaline, and 2-methyl-3-n-amylquinoxaline di-N-oxides are yellow crystalline compounds melting at 238–239°, 180–181°, and 107°, respectively.[1] They show both basic and peroxidic properties, liberating iodine from potassium iodide in presence of acetic acid.[1] On reduction with neutral or faintly acid hydrosulfite, the oxides are converted into the parent quinoxalines; reduction with zinc dust in aqueous sulfuric acid, however, produces fission of the hetero ring, as is illustrated by the reductive degradation of quinoxaline di-N-oxide to o-phenylenediamine and acetaldehyde (Eq. 1).[1] This reaction evidently involves pre-

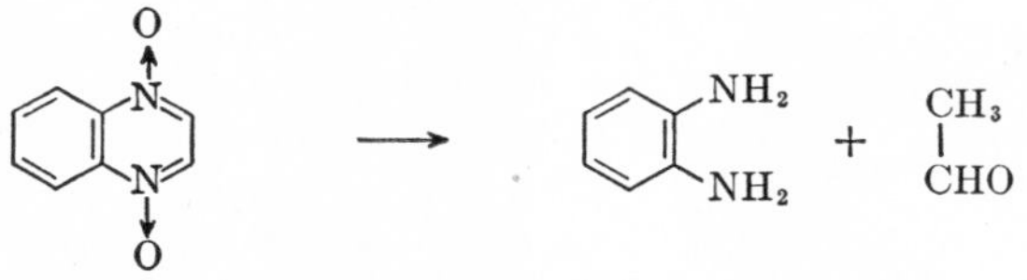

$$(1)$$

liminary reduction of the di-N-oxides to the parent quinoxalines, as the latter substances also undergo the same reaction. 1,2,3,4-Tetrahydroquinoxalines, however, are stable under these conditions, and McIlwain's[1] explanation of the facts is that a 1,4-dihydroquinoxaline is produced, the cation of which can exist as a hybrid of (Ia) and (Ib); further reduction gives the tautomeric form (IIa) of the Schiff base (IIb), whence o-phenylenediamine and the carbonyl compound are formed by hydrolysis.

The di-N-oxides of 2-methylquinoxaline and 2-methyl-3-n-amylquinoxaline also possess acidic properties, forming sodium salts for which the

(Ia) (Ib) 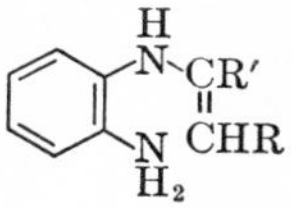 (IIa)

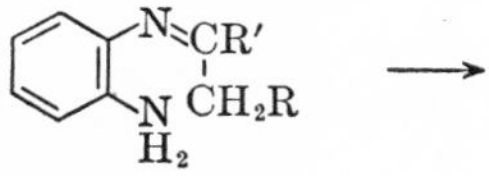

(IIb) 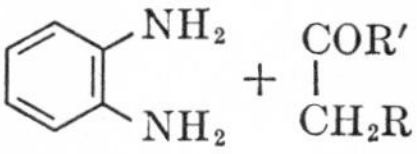 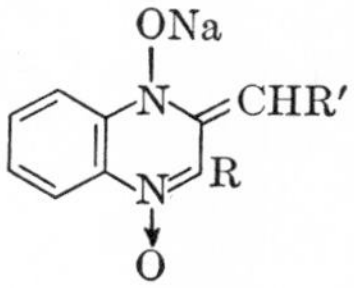 (III)

structure (III) is suggested[1]; this structure is supported by the nonacidic nature of quinoxaline di-*N*-oxide, which cannot yield a sodium salt of type (III).[1] Alkaline solutions of these oxides are light-sensitive, yielding highly colored products of unknown constitution.[1]

The di-*N*-oxide (yellow needles, m.p. 208°) of 2,3-diphenylquinoxaline, in contrast to the foregoing compounds, is stable toward reducing agents.[2]

(2) Mono-*N*-oxides. The *N*-oxide of 3-ethoxyquinoxaline (IV), m.p. 104–106°, liberates iodine from potassium iodide in acetic acid, but is not acidic and shows only weak basic properties.[3] Its structure is considered to be (IV) rather than (V) because on acid hydrolysis it yields 2,3-dihydroxyquinoxaline and not the cyclic hydroxamic acid (VI) which would be expected from (V), and also because 2,3-diethoxyquinoxaline does not yield an oxide under the same conditions.[3]

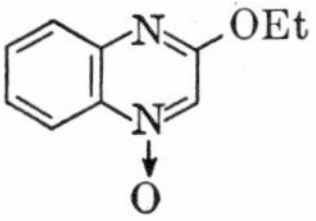

(IV) 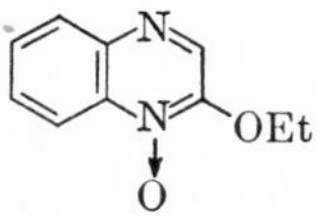 (V) 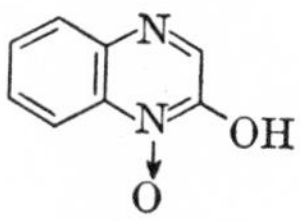 (VI) 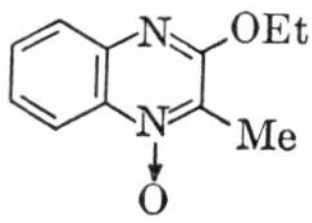 (VII)

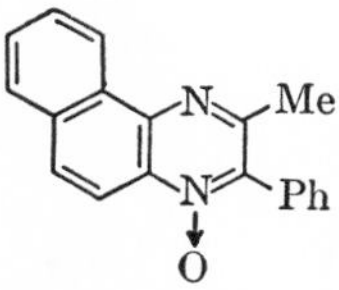

(VIII)
R.I. 1907

3-Ethoxy-2-methylquinoxaline *N*-oxide, m.p. 84–86°, also shows peroxidic properties, and yields 3-ethoxy-2-methylquinoxaline when reduced with hydrosulfite in hot aqueous alcohol. The structure (VII) is assigned to it from analogy with (IV).[3]

2-Phenyl-3-methyl-5,6-benzoquinoxaline forms a monoxide, m.p. 212°, which is formulated as the 1-oxide (VIII), although the alternative 4-oxide structure does not seem to be excluded.[2]

References

1. McIlwain, *J. Chem. Soc.*, **1943**, 322.
2. Maffei, *Gazz. chim. ital.*, **76**, 239 (1946)
3. Newbold and Spring, *J. Chem. Soc.*, **1948**, 519.

CHAPTER XXVII

2-Hydroxy- and 2,3-Dihydroxyquinoxalines

1. 2-Hydroxyquinoxalines

A. Compounds Containing No Additional Substituent in the Hetero Ring

Preparation. 2-Hydroxyquinoxalines of this group (as I) may be prepared by four general methods, *viz.:*

(1) Decarboxylation of the corresponding 3-carboxylic acids (Chapter XXIX).

(2) Reduction of the appropriately substituted *o*-nitrophenylglycine with subsequent oxidation of the initially formed 3,4-dihydroquinoxaline (Eq. 1).

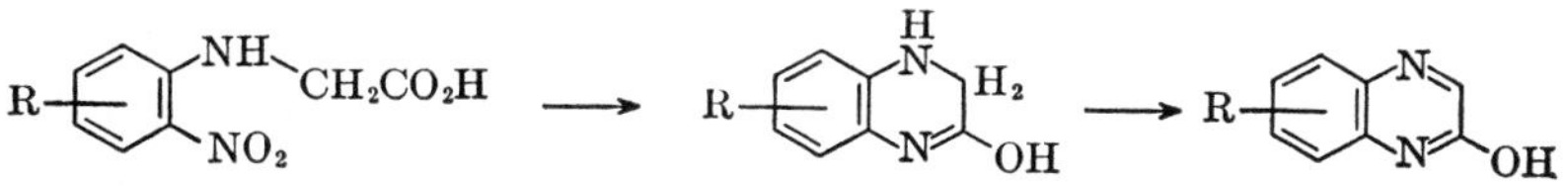

$$R \overset{NH\cdot CH_2CO_2H}{\underset{NO_2}{\bigcirc}} \longrightarrow R \underset{N}{\overset{H}{N}}\text{-}OH \xrightarrow{H_2} R \underset{N}{\overset{N}{\bigcirc}}\text{-}OH \qquad (1)$$

(I)

(3) Interaction of an *o*-diamine with bromoacetic acid. This method has the advantage of using readily accessible starting materials, but is liable to give a mixture of the two possible isomeric products if the amine is substituted at C_3 or C_4, as in the example[1] of equation 2.

$$Me \overset{NH_2}{\underset{NH_2}{\bigcirc}} + CH_2BrCO_2H \longrightarrow Me\underset{N}{\overset{N}{\bigcirc}}OH + Me\underset{N}{\overset{N}{\bigcirc}}OH \qquad (2)$$

(4) Condensation of an *o*-diamine with an ester of glyoxylic acid. Using butyl glyoxylate, this method has been employed extensively by Wolf and his co-workers,[2] but it has the same disadvantage as the foregoing synthesis of giving rise to mixed products from substituted *o*-phenylenediamines (Eq. 3).

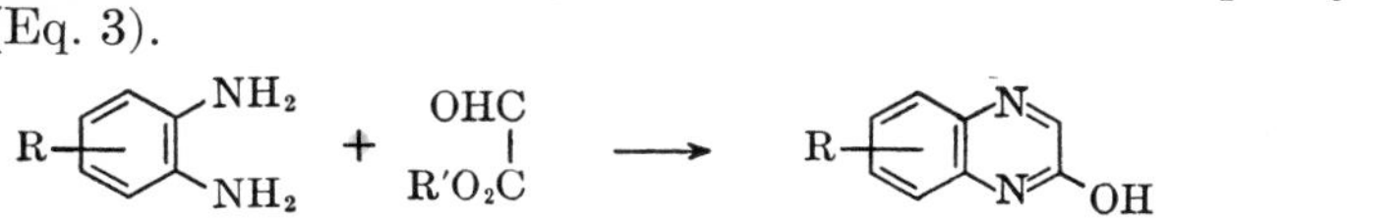

$$R\overset{NH_2}{\underset{NH_2}{\bigcirc}} + \overset{OHC}{\underset{R'O_2C}{|}} \longrightarrow R\underset{N}{\overset{N}{\bigcirc}}OH \qquad (3)$$

Properties. 2-Hydroxyquinoxalines (Table XXVII-1) are high-melting solids which are generally sparingly soluble or insoluble in common organic solvents, but are soluble in dilute sodium or ammonium

hydroxide.[2] On treatment with phosphoryl chloride they are converted
into the corresponding 2-chloroquinoxalines. If phosphorus pentachloride
is used, 2-hydroxyquinoxaline yields 2,3-dichloroquinoxaline,[3] but this behavior is probably exceptional, as Bz-substituted-2-hydroxyquinoxalines
appear to react normally in presence of phosphorus pentachloride.[2] On
oxidation with warm hydrogen peroxide in acetic acid, 2-hydroxy- gives
2,3-dihydroxyquinoxaline.[4]

TABLE XXVII-1. 2-Hydroxyquinoxalines Containing No Additional Substituent
in the Hetero Ring

Substituent	Prep.[a]	M.p., °C.	Remarks	Ref.
Nil	A,B	271, 269, 265	Sub. 200°/0.5 mm.	3,9,28
6-Cl	D	305	—	21
7-Cl	D	270	—	21
7-OMe	D	235–236	—	22
8-SMe	C	227	Structure uncertain	33
5-Me	B,D	286	—	34
6-Me	D	274	Pale yellow plates	1
7-Me	D	270–272, 266–267, 265	—	1,35–37

[a] A, from the o-diamine and ethyl glyoxylate in boiling alcohol. B, by decarboxylation of the corresponding 3-carboxylic acid. C, from PhNHCOCH:NOH by
boiling with phosphoric anhydride in toluene for 3 hours.[33] D, from the appropriate o-nitroarylglycine (or ester) by reduction and (spontaneous) cyclization. If a
3,4-dihydroquinoxaline is first isolated it may be converted into the required product by oxidation with silver nitrate or atmospherically.

B. Compounds Containing an Additional (C₃) Substituent in the Hetero Ring

This group comprises the majority of 2-hydroxyquinoxalines. In addition to the compounds discussed in this section, 2-hydroxyquinoxaline-3-
aldehydes are considered in Chapter XXVIII, 2-hydroxyquinoxaline-3-
carboxylic acids in Chapter XXIX, and 2-hydroxy-3-polyhydroxyalkyl-
quinoxalines in Chapter XXXVI.

Preparation

(1) The most general method is the condensation of a primary o-
diamine with an α-keto acid or its ester, as in equation 4. No intermediate
is normally isolated, but if "Balbiano's acid," which is a tautomeric mix-

$$\text{o-phenylenediamine} + \underset{\underset{(EtO)}{HOCO}}{OCR} \longrightarrow \text{quinoxaline (R, OH)} + H_2O(EtOH) \qquad (4)$$

ture of (II; R = H) and (III), is condensed with o-phenylenediamine the
product is (IV; R = H). The acid (II; R = Me) similarly yields the

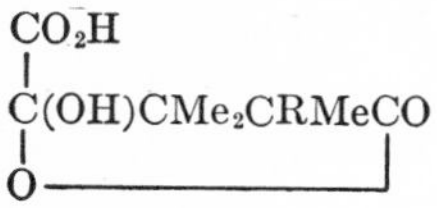

$$
\begin{array}{l}
CO_2H \\
| \\
C(OH)CMe_2CRMeCO \\
| \\
O\underline{\hspace{3cm}}
\end{array}
\qquad
\begin{array}{l}
CO_2H \\
| \\
COCMe_2CHMeCO_2H
\end{array}
$$

(II)   (III)

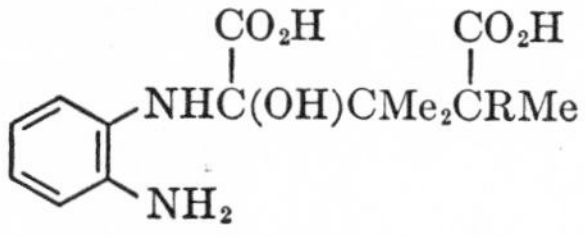

(IV) 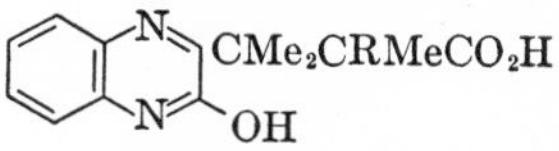   (V)

adduct (IV; R = Me). Ring closure of (IV; R = H and Me) to the quinoxalines (V; R = H and Me) is effected by heating the former compounds slightly above their melting points.[5,6]

A further point of interest in connection with the synthesis of 2-hydroxyquinoxalines from α-keto acids arises with acids of the type RCO-COCO$_2$H. Such compounds may react either as 1,2-diketones or as α-keto acids; thus the ester (VI), reacting as a 1,2-diketone gives (VII),[7] but (VIII) reacts as the derived α-keto acid and yields (IX).[8]

MeCOCOCO$_2$Et

(VI)

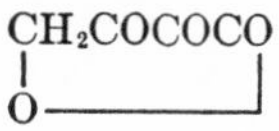

(VIII) 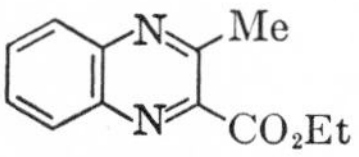   (VII) 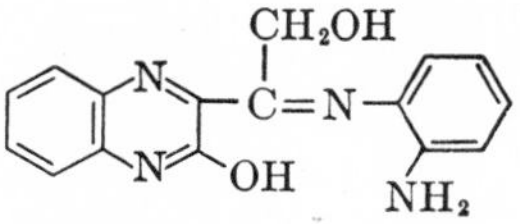   (IX)

Table XXVII-2 contains 3-substituted-2-hydroxyquinoxalines nearly all of which are prepared by the above method. It is to be noted that the use of a substituted o-diamine in the synthesis may give a mixture of products [9,10] or if a single product is formed the structure is uncertain; for example, 3,4-diaminotoluene and benzoylformic acid give a compound (yellow needles, m.p. 196–197°), which may be either 6- or 7-methyl-2-hydroxy-3-phenylquinoxaline.[11]

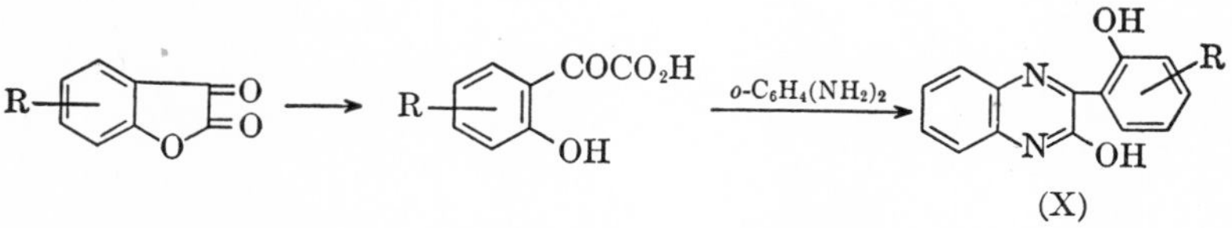

(X)

(2) In a few cases (see Table XXXV-2), 2-hydroxy-3,2'-hydroxyaryl-quinoxalines (X) have been prepared by condensing o-phenylenediamine with coumaran-2,3-diones. This reaction, to which further reference is

made in Chapter XXXV, Section 2B, involves the transformations shown in equation 5.

(*3*) 2-Hydroxy-3-phenylquinoxaline (XI) is obtained by oxidation of 3-phenylquinoxaline-2-carboxylic acid (XII) with chromic anhydride.[12] It is therefore not surprising that it is also formed by similar oxidation of various 3-phenylquinoxalines containing an easily oxidized alkyl residue at C_2. For example, it is produced in small amount, together with 3-phenyl-2-acetylquinoxaline (m.p. 110–111°, 99.5°)[13,14] (XIII), by the oxidation of (XIV; R = CHMeCOPh)[13]; and it also results when (XIV; R = CH_2-COPh, $CH(COPh)_2$, and $CH(OMe)CPh_2OH$), (XV), and (XVI) (m.p. 163–164°) are oxidized.[12,15-17]

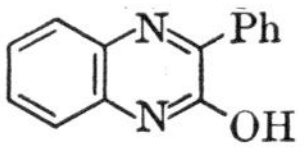

(XI) 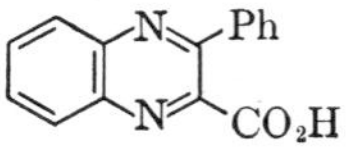   (XII) 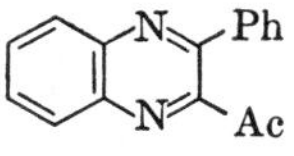   (XIII) 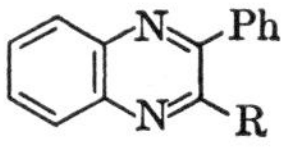   (XIV)

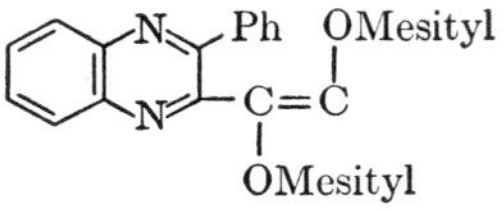

(XV) 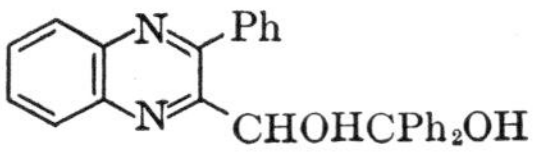   (XVI)

Properties. The physical properties of 3-substituted-2-hydroxy-quinoxalines are summarized in Table XXVII-2. The chemistry of

TABLE XXVII-2. 2-Hydroxyquinoxalines Containing a (3-) Substituent in the Hetero Ring

Substituents	Prep.[a]	M.p., °C.	Remarks	Ref.
3-Me	A,E	245	—	9,38
3-CH_2Cl	B	221–222 (dec.)	—	65
3-$CHBr_2$	A	250	—	39
3-$CMe_2CHMeCO_2H$	A (see text)	223–224	—	6
3-$CMe_2CMe_2CO_2H$	A (see text)	238–239	—	5
3-CH_2Ac	B	257	Yellow cryst.	40
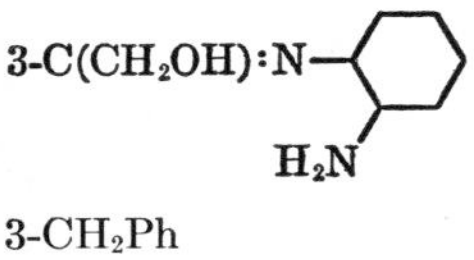 3-$C(CH_2OH)$:N— H_2N	A (see text)	167.5–168.5	Yellow solid Ac deriv., m.p. 233.5°; Ac_2 deriv., m.p. 212–213°; Ac_3 deriv., m.p. 182°	8
3-CH_2Ph	A	196	—	18
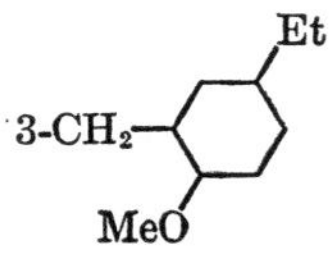 3-CH_2—	A	184–185	—	41

TABLE XXVII-2 (*continued*)

Substituents	Prep.[a]	M.p., °C.	Remarks	Ref.
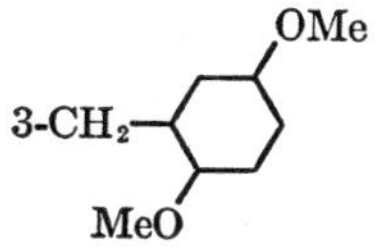 3-CH₂— (OMe, MeO cyclohexyl)	A	179–180 180	—	42
3-CH₂C₁₀H₇-β	A	222–223	—	43
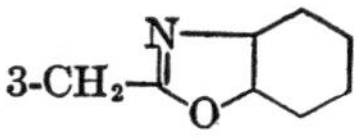 3-CH₂— (oxazole ring)	B	330	—	44
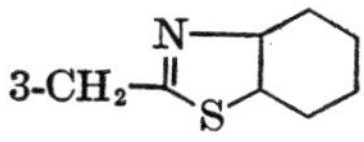 3-CH₂— (thiazole ring)	B	318–320	—	44
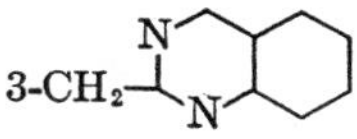 3-CH₂— (pyrimidine ring)	B	315	Yellow-brown needles	45
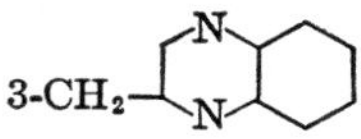 3-CH₂— (pyrazine ring)	B	307–309	Orange-red needles	46
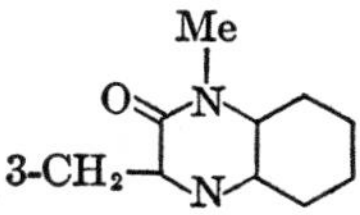 3-CH₂— (N-Me pyrimidinone)	B[b]	355	Dull orange needles. Hot conc. H₂SO₄ gives crimson-violet color	47
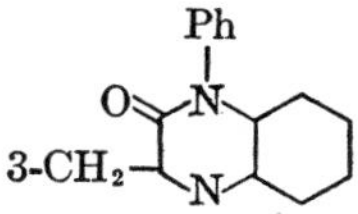 3-CH₂— (N-Ph pyrimidinone)	B[b]	372	Orange needles. Hot conc. H₂SO₄ gives magenta color	47
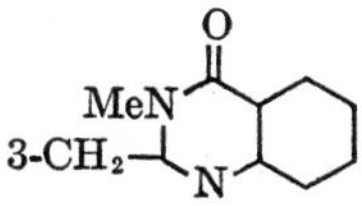 3-CH₂— (MeN pyrimidinone)	B	354	Yellow needles. Hot conc. H₂SO₄ gives pale yellow color	47
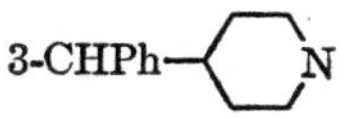 3-CHPh— (piperidine)	B	294–295	—	48
3-Ph	A (also see text)	247	—	49
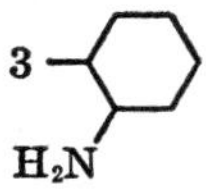 3 — (H₂N cyclohexyl)	D	258–260	—	50–52
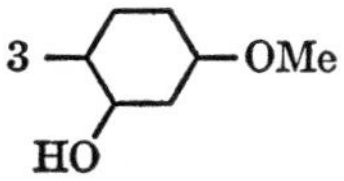 3 — (HO, OMe cyclohexyl)	A	312	Yellow needles. Conc. H₂SO₄ gives deep red color	53

Table continued

TABLE XXVII-2 (*continued*)

Substituents	Prep.[a]	M.p., °C.	Remarks	Ref.
(structure: Br, OMe, HO substituted cyclohexene ring, 3-)	A	360	Yellow needles	53
(structure: OH-substituted decalin, 3-)	A	312	Brick-red needles. Conc. H_2SO_4 gives violet-brown color	54
(structure: bicyclic lactam, 3-)	B	>350	Brick-red cryst. powder	55
(structure: bicyclic thiazolone, 3-)	A	>315	Red cryst.	56
3-CO_2Et	B[c]	175 175.5– 176.5	—	8,28
3-$CONH$–*(cyclohexyl)* H_2N–	B[d]	~350	Sparingly sol. in,[e] and stable to, acids and alk. The Ac_2 deriv. gives 2-hydroxyquinoxaline-3-carboxylic acid with boiling N NaOH	8
3-Me-7-Cl	A,C	265–267	—	65
3-Me-6-OMe	G	243.5– 244.5	—	10
3-Me-7-OMe	G	240– 240.5	—	10
3,6- (or 3,7-) Me_2	A	220 (dec.)	—	57
3,7- (or 3,6-) Me_2	F	238	—	37
3-Ph-6- (or 7-) Me	A	198	Yellow needles	57
3-CO_2Et-6- (or 7-) Me_2	B	199	—	20

[a] A, from the *o*-diamine and $RCOCO_2H$ in water, alcohol, or acetic acid. B, from the *o*-diamine and $RCOCO_2Et$ in alcohol or acetic acid. C, from 3-ethoxy-2-methylquinoxaline-1-oxide and boiling aqueous-alcoholic hydrochloric acid. D, by condensation of *o*-phenylenediamine with acetylisatin, followed by saponification. E, from 2,2′-aminophenylamino-3-methylquinoxaline by hydrolysis with boiling 20% hydrochloric acid. F, from 3,4-diaminotoluene and ethyl 1-chloropropionate, followed by atmospheric oxidation of the initially formed dihydro compound. G, from the *o*-nitroamine and 1-bromopropionic acid (or the ethyl ester), followed by reduction, ring closure, and oxidation (*cf.* method D, Table XXVII-1).
[b] These condensations proceed well in phenol at 100°, or by dry fusion of the components with a trace of ammonium chloride.
[c] *o*-Phenylenediamine:ester = 1:1 in boiling alcohol.
[d] *o*-Phenylenediamine:ester = 2:1 in boiling acetic acid.

[e] This compound is possibly better represented as: *(structure: quinoxalinone with CONH–NH– phenyl bridge)*

these compounds (and of compounds unsubstituted at C_3) has not been studied, apart from qualitative observations of their weakly acidic nature.

Methylation of Hydroxyquinoxalines.   In a number of cases, 2-hydroxyquinoxalines undergo N-methylation when treated with methyl sulfate or iodide and alkali, or with diazomethane, and thus give rise to 1-

(XVII)   (XVIII)   (XIX)

methyl-2-keto-1,2-dihydro derivatives. Thus the compounds (XVIII; R = Me, R' = H), (XVIII; R = $CHBr_2$, R' = H), (XVIII; R = CO_2Et, R' = H), and (XVIII; R = CO_2Et, R' = Me) are prepared by one or other of these methods from the hydroxy compounds (as XVII),[8,18-20] the constitutions being proved by synthesis by alternative routes (see Table XXXVII-2), and 2-hydroxy-3-chloromethylquinoxaline yields what is probably the N-methyl derivative (XVIII; R = CH_2Cl, R' = H) (Table XXXVII-2), although the structure of this compound has not been proved.[4] By the action of methyl sulfate and sodium hydroxide, 2,3-dihydroxyquinoxaline is converted into a compound, m.p. 256–258°, which is formulated as 1,4-dimethyl-2,3-diketo-1,2,3,4-tetrahydroquinoxaline (XIX)[4]; and the 6-chloro, 6-bromo, 6-methoxy-, and 6-methyl analogs of (XIX) (m.p. 192°, 205–206°, 182–183°, and 196–197°, respectively) are prepared similarly.[21,22] These compounds are not identical with the corresponding 2,3-dimethoxyquinoxalines (Table XXXII-2), but the possibility of their being the 1,3-dimethyl isomers, formed by O,N-methylation such as occurs with 1,4-dihydroxyphthalazine (Chapter XIX), appears not to be excluded.

The N-alkylation of 2-hydroxyquinoxalines, however, is not always a facile process. Thus with 2-hydroxy-3-methylquinoxaline, N-ethylation is less satisfactory than N-methylation, and N-benzylation does not occur under moderate conditions.[18] The compound (XVII; R = o-CONHC$_6$-H$_4$NH$_2$, R' = H) (for an alternative formulation see Table XXVII-2) does not react with diazomethane.[8] Furthermore, cases are known where methylation gives O- and not N-derivatives. 3-Amino-2-hydroxyquinoxaline (XVII; R = NH_2, R' = H), for example, gives 3-amino-2-methoxyquinoxaline (Table XXXI-1, on treatment with methyl sulfate and alkali[23]; and 2-hydroxy-3-d-arabotetraacetoxybutylquinoxaline (XVII; R = [CHOAc]$_3$CH$_2$OAc, R' = H) (Table XXXVI-1) yields the 2-methoxy derivative (m.p. 154.5–156.5°, $[\alpha]_D^{20}$ −27.6° in chloroform) by the action of diazomethane.[19]

2. 2,3-Dihydroxyquinoxalines

Preparation. The two general methods by which these compounds (I) may be prepared are (*1*) condensation of the appropriate diamine with oxalic acid in hot aqueous acid or by dry fusion, and (*2*) condensation of the diamine with ethyl oxalate in excess (Eq. 6). 2,3 Dihydroxyquinoxa-

$$R\text{---}\left\langle\begin{array}{c}NH_2\\NH_2\end{array}\right. + \begin{array}{c}CO_2R'\\|\\CO_2R'\end{array} \longrightarrow R\text{---}\left\langle\begin{array}{c}N\\\\N\end{array}\right\rangle\begin{array}{c}OH\\\\OH\end{array} + 2R'OH \qquad (6)$$

$$(R' = H \text{ or } Et) \qquad\qquad\qquad (I)$$

line, the parent compound of the series, has also been prepared by a variety of additional methods involving the hydrolysis or oxidation of a number of 2-hydroxy- or 2-alkoxyquinoxalines (see Table XXVII-3).

TABLE XXVII-3. 2,3-Dihydroxyquinoxalines

Substituent	Prep.[a]	M.p., °C.	Remarks	Ref.
Nil	A,B,C,D,E, F,G,H,I,J	>360, 351–355 (dec.), 410	Sub. 330°. Monobenzoyl deriv., m.p. 176°	3,4, 26–30, 58–60
6-Cl	A,E,K	380, >350	—	32,61
6-Br	E	—	Not purified	22
5-NO$_2$	E	284 (dec.)	Yellow plates	62
6-NO$_2$	A,E	344–346 (dec.) 329–330 (dec.)	—	22,62
5-NH$_2$	L	344	Yellow cryst.	62
6-NH$_2$	L	350	Yellow microneedles	62
6-OMe	E	—	Not purified	22
5-AsO$_3$H$_2$	A	>300	—	63
6-AsO$_3$H$_2$	A,M	>300	—	63,64
6-Me	A	>300	Gives unstable acetate, but no isolable salts with strong mineral acids	57

[a] A, from the *o*-diamine and oxalic acid, by fusion at ~200° or in boiling 4 *N* hydrochloric acid. B, from *o*-phenylenediamine and diethyl diketosuccinate in water, alcohol, or benzene. C, from quinoxaline by oxidation with ammonium persulfate. D, from 2-hydroxy-3-(*d*-arabo)tetrahydroxybutylquinoxaline by oxidation with acid permanganate or hot aqueous periodate. E, from the *o*-diamine and excess ethyl oxalate at 160–170° or under reflux. F, from 3-ethoxyquinoxaline 1-oxide and boiling aqueous-alcoholic hydrochloric acid. G, from 2-chloro-3-ethoxy- or 2,3-diethoxyquinoxaline by refluxing with alcohol and hydrochloric acid. H, from 2-hydroxy-3-ethoxyquinoxaline and warm aqueous acetic acid. I, by oxidation with warm hydrogen peroxide in acetic acid of 2-hydroxyquinoxaline, 2-hydroxy-, or 2-ethoxyquinoxaline-3-carboxylic acid, 2-chloro-3-ethoxyquinoxaline, or quinoxaline-2,3-dicarboxylic acid. J, by hydrolysis of 2-sulfanilamido-3-methoxyquinoxaline. K, from 2,3,6-trichloroquinoxaline by hydrolysis in boiling acetic acid. L, from the nitro compound by reduction with boiling aqueous sodium sulfide. M, from the diamine and oxalyl chloride.

Properties. The physical properties of members of this group are given in Table XXVII-3. The properties of 2,3-dihydroxyquinoxaline, the parent member of the group, have been studied in some detail. This compound is very sparingly soluble in water and organic solvents, and shows strong blue fluorescence in ultraviolet light;[24] it is used in photography (to prevent staining during certain development processes); and it is a group reagent for the alkaline earths as well as a specific reagent for barium.[25] On reduction with zinc and hot dilute hydrochloric acid it yields the 3,4-dihydro derivative (II) (Table XXXVII-3).

$$\text{(II)}$$

2,3-Dihydroxyquinoxaline is soluble in acetic acid,[26] but its characteristic reactions are those of a monobasic acid. It is soluble in sodium carbonate,[26] and dissolves freely in dilute sodium hydroxide,[27,28] although the monosodium salt thus formed has been described as being sparingly soluble in hot water.[29] With hot aqueous potassium carbonate 2,3-dihydroxyquinoxaline gives a monopotassium salt, moderately soluble in water and in alcohol.[30] On the other hand, a hot aqueous solution of the dihydroxy compound yields a di-silver salt when treated with aqueous silver nitrate followed by ammonia.[30] The dihydroxy compound resists acetylation, but with benzoyl chloride in pyridine it gives a monobenzoyl derivative, regarded as the O-rather than as the N-compound by reason of its hydrolysis by dilute alkali at room temperature (hydrolysis by concentrated hydrochloric acid is slower).[30]

$$\text{(III)} \qquad \text{(IV)}$$

If 2,3-dihydroxyquinoxaline or 6-chloro-2,3-dihydroxyquinoxaline is heated with o-aminophenol hydrochloride under suitable conditions, condensation occurs at the 2,3-positions of the pyrazine ring, giving (III; R = H) or (III; R = Cl), respectively.[31] Analogously, 6-chloro-2,3-dihydroxyquinoxaline furnishes (IV; R = H or Cl) by condensation with the hydrochloride of o-phenylenediamine or 4-chloro-o-phenylenediamine, respectively[32] (see volume on *Phenazines*).

References

1. Platt, *J. Chem. Soc.*, **1948**, 1310.
2. Wolf, Pfister, III, Beutel, R. M. Wilson, C. A. Robinson, and J. R. Stevens, *J. Am. Chem. Soc.*, **71**, 6 (1949).
3. Motylewski, *Ber.*, **41**, 800 (1908).
4. Newbold and Spring, *J. Chem. Soc.*, **1948**, 519.
5. Rothstein and Shoppee, *J. Chem. Soc.*, **1927**, 531.
6. Kon, Stevenson, and Thorpe, *J. Chem. Soc.*, **1922**, 650.
7. Wahl and Doll, *Bull. soc. chim.*, **13**, 468 (1913).
8. Ohle and Gross, *Ber.*, **68**, 2262 (1935).
9. Hinsberg, *Ann.*, **292**, 245 (1896).
10. Yolles and Schultz, *J. Am. Chem. Soc.*, **71**, 2375 (1949).
11. Hinsberg, *Ber.*, **18**, 1228 (1885).
12. Blatt, *J. Am. Chem. Soc.*, **57**, 1103 (1935).
13. Lutz and Stuart, *J. Am. Chem. Soc.*, **59**, 2316 (1937).
14. Sachs and Röhmer, *Ber.*, **35**, 3307 (1902).
15. Blatt, *J. Am. Chem. Soc.*, **58**, 1894 (1936).
16. Lutz and Stuart, *J. Am. Chem. Soc.*, **58**, 1885 (1936).
17. Lutz, J. M. Smith, Jr., and Stuart, *J. Am. Chem. Soc.*, **63**, 1143 (1941).
18. A. H. Cook and Perry, *J. Chem. Soc.*, **1943**, 394.
19. Ohle, Gross, and Wolter, *Ber.*, **70**, 2148 (1937).
20. Wellman and Tishler, *J. Am. Chem. Soc.*, **69**, 714 (1947).
21. Crowther, Curd, Davey, and Stacey, *J. Chem. Soc.*, **1949**, 1260.
22. Curd, Davey, and Stacey, *J. Chem. Soc.*, **1949**, 1271.
23. Stevens, Pfister, and Wolf, *J. Am. Chem. Soc.*, **68**, 1035 (1946).
24. Kuhn and Bär, *Ber.*, **67**, 898 (1934).
25. Steigmann, *J. Soc. Chem. Ind.*, **1943**, 42.
26. Glotz, *Bull. soc. chim.*, **3**, 511 (1936).
27. Baxter and Spring, *J. Chem. Soc.*, **1945**, 229.
28. Gowenlock, Newbold, and Spring, *J. Chem. Soc.*, **1945**, 622.
29. M. A. Phillips, *J. Chem. Soc.*, **1928**, 2393.
30. Heller, Buchwaldt, Fuchs, Kleinicke, and Kloss, *J. prakt. Chem.*, **111**, 1 (1925).
31. Kehrmann and Bener, *Helv. Chim. Acta*, **8**, 16 (1925).
32. Kehrmann and Bener, *Helv. Chim. Acta*, **8**, 20 (1925).
33. Brand and Völcker, *Arch. Pharm.*, **272**, 257 (1934).
34. Platt and Sharp, *J. Chem. Soc.*, **1948**, 2129.
35. Leuckart and Hermann, *Ber.*, **20**, 24 (1887).
36. Plöchl, *Ber.*, **19**, 6 (1886).
37. Hinsberg, *Ann.*, **248**, 71 (1888).
38. Durio, *Gazz. chim. ital.*, **63**, 747 (1933).
39. Ohle, *Ber.*, **67**, 155 (1934).
40. Schöpf and Ross, *Ann.*, **546**, 1 (1940).
41. Gulland and Virden, *J. Chem. Soc.*, **1928**, 921.
42. Gulland and Virden, *J. Chem. Soc.*, **1928**, 1478.
43. Fulton and R. Robinson, *J. Chem. Soc.*, **1939**, 200.
44. Borsche and Doeller, *Ann.*, **537**, 53 (1939).
45. Borsche and Doeller, *Ber.*, **76**, 1176 (1943).
46. Borsche and Doeller, *Ann.*, **537**, 39 (1939).
47. A. H. Cook and Naylor, *J. Chem. Soc.*, **1943**, 397.
48. Singh, *J. Chem. Soc.*, **1925**, 2445.

49. Burton and Shoppee, *J. Chem. Soc.*, **1937**, 546.
50. Bednarczyk and Marchlewski, *Bull. Intern. Acad. polon, sci., Classe sci. math. nat.* **1938A**, 529.
51. Marchlewski, *Roczniki Chem.*, **18**, 698 (1938).
52. Bednarczyk and Marchlewski, *Biochem. Z.*, **300**, 46 (1938).
53. Fries and Saftien, *Ann.*, **442**, 284 (1925).
54. Fries and Pusch, *Ann.*, **442**, 272 (1925).
55. Wislicenus and Bubeck, *Ann.*, **436**, 113 (1924).
56. Hart and Smiles, *J. Chem. Soc.*, **1924**, 876.
57. Hinsberg, *Ann.*, **237**, 327 (1887).
58. Bergstrom and Ogg, Jr., *J. Am. Chem. Soc.*, **53**, 245 (1931).
59. Shriner and Upson, *J. Am. Chem. Soc.*, **63**, 2277 (1941).
60. Ohle and Noetzel, *Ber.*, **76**, 624 (1943).
61. Haworth and S. Robinson, *J. Chem. Soc.*, **1948**, 777.
62. Huntress and Gladding, *J. Am. Chem. Soc.*, **64**, 2644 (1942).
63. M. A. Phillips, *J. Chem. Soc.*, **1928**, 3134.
64. W. L. Lewis and Bent, *J. Am. Chem. Soc.*, **48**, 949 (1926).
65. Dawson, Newbold, and Spring, *J. Chem. Soc.*, **1949, 2579**.

CHAPTER XXVIII

Quinoxaline-2-aldehydes

A. Preparation. The modes of preparation of this small group of compounds are outlined in Table XXVIII-1, the most general method being the degradation of the corresponding 2-polyhydroxyalkylquinoxaline (I) by means of phenylhydrazine; an excess of the reagent is commonly used, the phenylhydrazone (II) of the aldehyde thus being the final product (Eq. 1). This rather unusual reaction is described more fully in Chapter XXXVI, Section 2C.

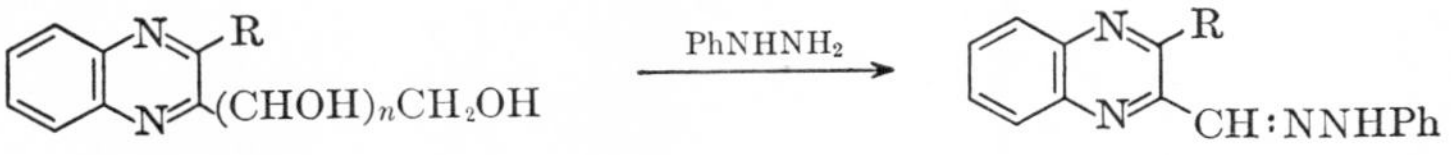

$$\text{(I)} \xrightarrow{\text{PhNHNH}_2} \text{(II)} \tag{1}$$

The amino-anil (III) of 3-methylquinoxaline-2-aldehyde (Table XXIV-1) is the product of the reaction between o-phenylenediamine and acetylglyoxal in water at room temperature.

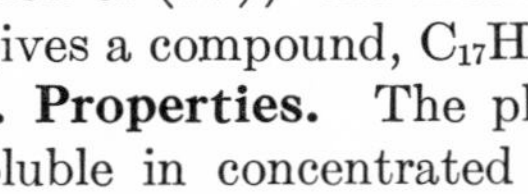

The phenylhydrazone of quinoxaline-2-aldehyde cannot be prepared by fission of (IV); the method works well with the quinoline analog, but (IV) gives a compound, $C_{17}H_{12}O_2N_4$, of unknown structure.[1]

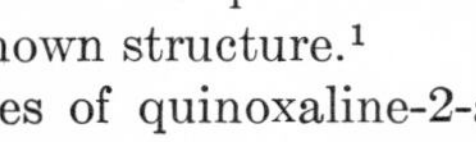

B. Properties. The phenylhydrazones of quinoxaline-2-aldehydes are soluble in concentrated sulfuric acid giving characteristic green or greenish-blue solutions.[2,3] Insufficient data are available to make possible a general discussion of these compounds, but 3-hydroxyquinoxaline-2-aldehyde (see below) has been studied in some detail.

C. 3-Hydroxyquinoxaline-2-aldehyde. Ohle and Noetzel,[4] to whom our knowledge of this compound is due, state that it is best prepared from 3-hydroxy-2-(d-arabo)tetrahydroxybutylquinoxaline by oxidation with aqueous potassium periodate, either (a) by leaving overnight in the dark at room temperature or (b) by heating at 100° for 10 minutes in

TABLE XXVIII-1. Quinoxaline-2-aldehydes

Substitution at C$_3$	Prep. (as aldehyde or phenyl-hydrazone)^a	M.p. of aldehyde, °C.	M.p. of phenyl-hydrazone, °C.	Remarks	Ref.
Nil	A,B,C	110, 108	229–230,231	Semicarbazone, m.p. 251°. Oxime, m.p. 197–198° (204–205°), is sol. in alk., and stable to hot mineral acids. Hydrazone, m.p. 151°. Azine, m.p. 265°. 2,4-Dinitrophenylhydrazone, m.p. 234–235°. Meth-one, m.p. 231°. Anil, m.p. 130°. 4'-Carboxy-anil, m.p. 285° (dec.). 4'-Carbethoxyanil, m.p. 137°. 4'-Carbonamido-anil, m.p. 244–252°. 4'-Sulfonamidoanil, m.p. 220°	1,6, 7–10
OH	C,D. Also see text	71–72	Red prisms, m.p. 282, and orange-red needles, m.p. 278	Cryst. as pentahydrate. Anil, m.p. 216°; oxime, m.p. 265° (dec.); dime-don deriv., m.p. 215–217°; hydrazone, m.p. 222–223° (dec.); methyl-phenylhydrazone, m.p. 250°	4,11, 12
OMe	C^b	145	—	Orange-red needles	12
Ph	C	—	176	—	2

^{a} A, from 2-methylquinoxaline and selenium dioxide; a little 2-carboxylic acid is also formed. B, from 2-(d-arabo)tetrahydroxybutylquinoxaline and lead tetraace-tate in benzene-acetic acid (yield 67%). C, from the corresponding 2-polyhydroxy-alkyl (usually tetrahydroxybutyl)quinoxaline by treatment with phenylhydrazine. D, from the corresponding 2-dibromomethylquinoxaline by condensation with phenylhydrazine.
^{b} By use of 1 mole phenylhydrazine.

the presence of sodium bicarbonate (if the alkali is omitted, the concentra-tion of periodic acid becomes high, iodine is liberated, and 2,3-dihydroxy-quinoxaline is produced).

The pentahydrate (see Table XXVIII-1) crystallizes in colorless prisms which become reddish-brown in the light but not in the dark.   The anhy-drous aldehyde is yellow.   The aldehyde is not oxidized by the atmosphere, probably owing to stabilization by hydrogen bonding, and it reacts only slowly with hot Fehling solution, but it reduces Schiff and Tollens reagents. In addition to the derivatives mentioned in Table XXVIII-1, the aldehyde forms an alcoholate and a bisulfite compound.   The dimedon derivative gives an anhydride [+0.5 AcOH, m.p. 319–321° (dec.); +3H$_2$O, m.p. 309–317° (dec.)] when it is boiled with 50% aqueous acetic acid.

The hydrazone (Table XXVIII-1) of the aldehyde is unstable, being converted in boiling alcohol into the aldazine hydrate (V); this is a yellow substance, m.p. 253° (dec.), which with sodium hydroxide yields a reddish-orange sodium salt. The deepening of color associated with conversion of (V) into the sodium salt is attributed by Ohle and Noetzel to the resonating anion, to which (VI) is a contributing structure. A deepening of color also accompanies the conversion of the yellow phenylhydrazone of quinoxaline-2-aldehyde into its sodium salt, and in explanation of this it is suggested

(V)    (VI)

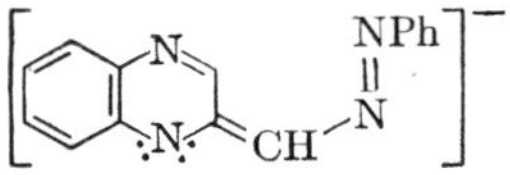

(VII) 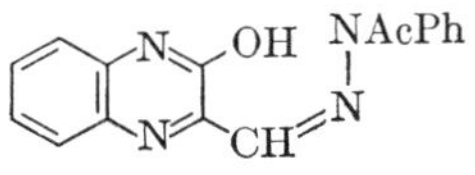   (IX)

that the structure (VII) makes a major contribution to the mesomeric anion.[4,5] On the other hand, the situation is reversed in the case of the phenylhydrazone of 3-hydroxyquinoxaline-2-aldehyde. Here, the red phenylhydrazone gives only an orange-yellow sodium salt, and this is explained[4] in terms of the extra resonance in the free phenylhydrazone which

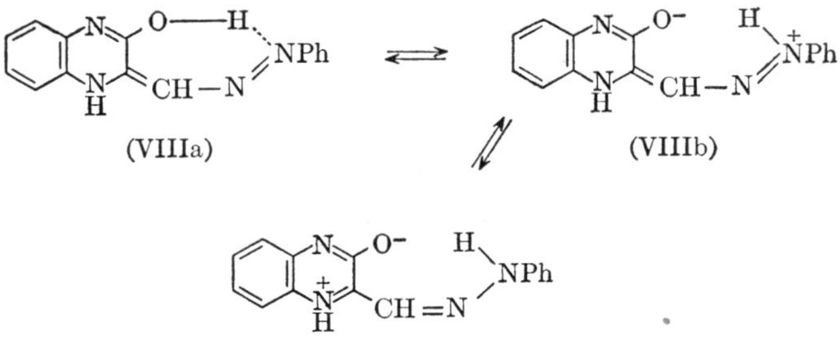

(VIIIa)   (VIIIb)

(VIIIc)

results from hydrogen bonding (VIII a-b-c); clearly this hydrogen bonding would be prevented, and the resonance energy diminished, by conversion into the sodium salt. Acetylation of the phenylhydrazone gives the N-acetyl derivative (IX) (yellow needles, m.p. 284°). The structure of (IX) follows from its alternative preparation from the aldehyde and as-acetyl-phenylhydrazine, and both the lightening of color and also the position of acetylation are readily understood on the basis of structures (VIII, a–c).

References

1. Borsche and Doeller, *Ann.*, **537,** 39 (1939).
2. Ohle and Hielscher, *Ber.*, **74,** 18 (1941).
3. Ohle and Melkonian, *Ber.*, **74,** 279 (1941).
4. Ohle and Noetzel, *Ber.*, **76,** 624 (1943).
5. Ohle and Iltgen, *Ber.*, **76,** 1 (1943).
6. Müller and Varga, *Ber.*, **72,** 1993 (1939).
7. Varga, *Magyar Biol. Kutatointezet Munkai*, **12,** 359 (1940).
8. Ohle and Hielscher, *Ber.*, **74,** 13 (1941).
9. Kjaer, *Acta Chim. Scand.*, **2,** 455 (1948).
10. Karrer and Schwyzer, *Helv. Chim. Acta*, **31,** 777 (1948).
11. Ohle, *Ber.*, **67,** 155 (1934).
12. Ohle, Gross, and Wolter, *Ber.*, **70,** 2148 (1937).

CHAPTER XXIX

Quinoxaline-2-carboxylic and -2,3-Dicarboxylic Acids

1. Quinoxaline-2-carboxylic Acids

A. Preparation. Methods for preparing quinoxaline-2-carboxylic acids vary considerably and depend on whether or not the acid contains a 3-substituent, and, if so, on its nature. Broadly speaking, the following general procedures are suitable (see Table XXIX-1).

(*1*) The ethyl ester of the acid, if available by a convenient method, is hydrolyzed in alkaline solution.

(*2*) Quinoxaline derivatives with suitable substituents at C_2 may be oxidized under various conditions giving the 2-carboxylic acids.

(*3*) An *o*-diamine is condensed with alloxan, and the resulting anil (I) is subjected to alkaline hydrolysis, yielding a 3-hydroxyquinoxaline-2-carboxylic acid (II). The question whether the initial condensation products are correctly represented as (I) or as the isomeric hydroxyureido-quinoxalines (III) remained unsettled for many years.[1-6] H. Rudy and K.-E. Cramer,[7] however, found that *o*-amino derivatives of tertiary, as well as those of primary and secondary, aromatic amines undergo similar

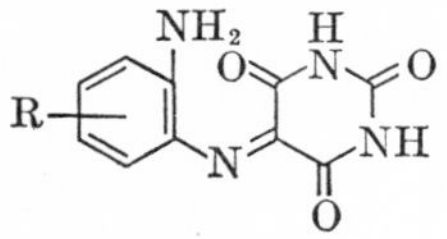

(I) 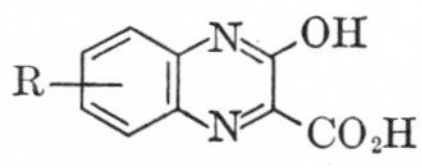   (II) 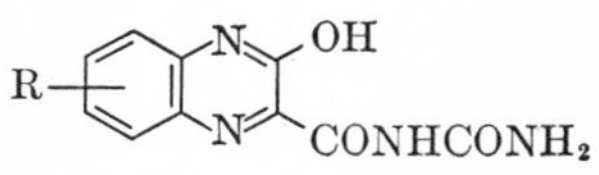   (III)

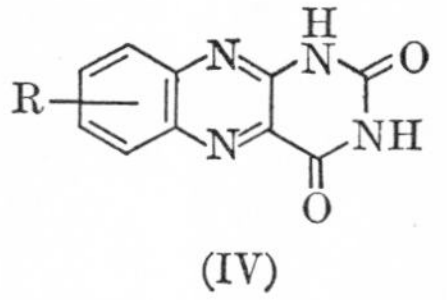

(IV) 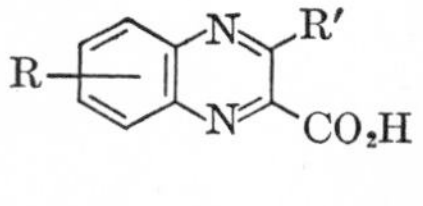   (V)

condensations with alloxan; the primary products must thus be anils (I) and not quinoxalines (III), and there is now no reason to believe that a compound of structure (III) has been prepared.

(*4*) Alloxazines (IV) are hydrolyzed in alkaline solution, yielding, according to conditions, 3-amino-(V; R′ = NH₂) or 3-hydroxy-(V; R′ = OH)-quinoxaline-2-carboxylic acids.

(*5*) An *o*-diamine is condensed with mesoxalic acid or its ester. If the diamine is substituted at C₄, the formation of both the possible isomers may be expected, as in equation 1.[8]

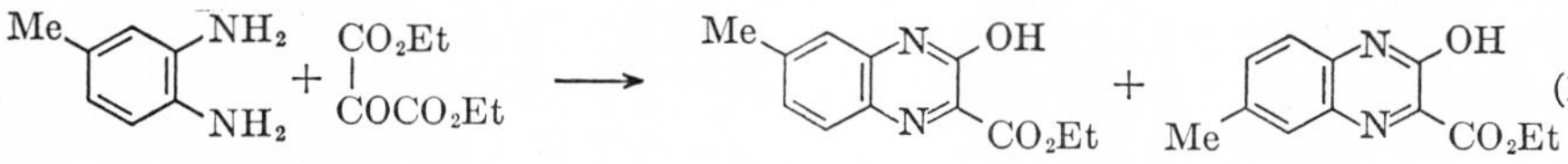

$$(1)$$

TABLE XXIX-1. Quinoxaline-2-carboxylic Acids

Substituents	Prep.[a]	M.p., °C.	Remarks	Ref.
Nil	A,B,C, D,E,W	212,210 208–209	Sol. in hot water, alc., chloroform, acetone. Aq. soln. gives reddish-violet FeSO₄ reaction. Loses CO₂ at m.p. with formation of quinoxaline. Acid chloride, m.p. 115°; Me ester, m.p. 113°; Et ester, m.p. 85°; anilide, m.p. 180°; xylidide, m.p. 132°; tetrahydroanilide, m.p. 154°. Phenyl ester, m.p. 104°; *o*-hydroxy-, m.p. 167°; *m*-hydroxy-, m.p. 175°; and *p*-hydroxyphenyl ester, m.p. 184°, are formed by heating quinoxaline-2,3-dicarboxylic anhydride with the appropriate phenol at 170° (ref. 14). Hydrazide, m.p. 204°, and phenylhydrazide, m.p. 186°, are prepared from foregoing aryl esters and N₂H₄ or PhNHNH₂ (ref. 14)	16–20, 39
3-Cl	F	146–147 (dec.)	Yellow prisms. Distn. at 0.1 mm. gives 2-chloroquinoxaline. Et ester, m.p. 42.5°. Amide, m.p. 215°	21
3-NH₂	G,H,I, J	210 (dec.), 212–213 (dec.)	Yellow needles. Me ester, m.p. 218–219° [hydrochloride, m.p. 188–189° (dec.); acetyl deriv. m.p. 143–144°]. Et ester, m.p. 165–166°. Amide, yellow needles, m.p. 263–264°; 3-carbethoxyaminoamide, dec.>300°; 3-acetamidoamide, m.p. 207° (dec.)	9,21–24
3-OH	K,L,M, N,U	265 (dec.), 200 (dec.)	Yellow needles. Loses CO₂ at m.p., yielding 2-hydroxyquinoxaline. Oxidation with warm AcOH-H₂O₂ gives 2,3-dihydroxyquinoxaline (ref. 28). Et ester, m.p. 175.5–176.5°	6,21,22, 25–27

Table continued

TABLE XXIX-1. Quinoxaline-2-carboxylic Acids (*continued*)

Substituents	Prep.[a]	M.p., °C.	Remarks	Ref.
3-OEt	O	120–121	Loses CO_2 at 180° giving 2-eth-oxyquinoxaline. Et ester, m.p. 25°	21
3-Me[b]	P,V[b]	73, [b]74	—	23,29
3-Et[b]	P[b]	64[b]	—	29
3-Pr[n][b]	P[b]	83–84[b]	—	29
3-Ph	Q,R	153	Dec. at the m.p. into CO_2 and 2-phenylquinoxaline	17,30, 31
3-OH-6 (and 7-) Me	S	214	Loses CO_2 at the m.p. giving a product, m.p. 247°, which is a mixt. of 3-OH-6- and 7-methyl-quinoxaline (refs. 8,33); the acid is thus a mixt. of the 6- and 7-Me isomers. Amide,[c] m.p. 286–287° (ref. 34).	4,32
3-OH-8-Me	T	230 (dec.)	Yellow prisms. Gives 2-hy-droxy-5-methylquinoxaline at m.p., hence its structure. Et ester, m.p. 225°	35
3-NH_2-6,7-Me_2	H	—	Gives 2-amino-6,7-dimethyl-quinoxaline in boiling $PhNO_2$	36

[a] A, by oxidation of 2-(*d*-arabo)tetrahydroxybutylquinoxaline with 6% hydrogen peroxide and aqueous sodium hydroxide (80°; 1 hour); yield, 70%. B, by alkaline decomposition of various degradation products of 2-(*d*-arabo)tetrahydroxybutylquinoxaline (Chapter XXXVI, Section 2B). C, by oxidation of glucazidone with permanganate in boiling acetone, and of glucazidone-3-sulfonic acid with hot aqueous permanganate (see Chapter XXXVIII, Section 1C). D, by oxidation of quinoxaline-2-aldehyde with hydrogen peroxide and sodium hydroxide. E, by oxidation of 2-methylquinoxaline with selenium dioxide (major product is quinoxaline-2-aldehyde). F, by hydrolysis (1% aqueous methanolic sodium carbonate at the b.p.) of the ethyl ester, which is prepared from ethyl 3-hydroxyquinoxaline-2-carboxylate (Table XXIX-1) by treatment with phosphorus oxychloride. G, by Hofmann degradation of 3-carbonamidoquinoxaline-2-carboxylic acid (Table XXIX-3). H, by selective hydrolysis of the corresponding alloxazine with concentrated ammonia at 170–175°. I, by hydrolysis of the corresponding amide (prepared from ethyl 3-chloroquinoxaline-2-carboxylate and methanolic ammonia at 150°) with boiling 10% aqueous sodium hydroxide. J, from 2,3-dicarbonamido-quinoxaline (Table XXIX-3) by treatment with 1 mole of potassium hypobromite. K, from alloxazine by alkaline hydrolysis. L, from alloxan-2-aminoanil by alkaline hydrolysis (for reaction, see text). M, from 3-aminoquinoxaline-2-carboxylic acid by high-temperature alkaline hydrolysis. N, by hydrolysis with hot 3 N aqueous sodium hydroxide of the ethyl ester (for preparation see Table XXVII-2) or of ethyl 3-chloroquinoxaline-2-carboxylate. O, from the ethyl ester [prepared from ethyl 3-chloroquinoxaline-2-carboxylate (Table XXX-1) and boiling alcoholic sodium ethoxide] by hydrolysis with boiling 1% alcoholic potash. P, from *o*-phenylenediamine hydrochloride and the appropriate AlkCOCOCO₂Et in aqueous-alcoholic sodium acetate. Q, from 10-phenyl-9,10-dihydroglucazidone (Chapter XXXVIII, Section 1C) by oxidation with permanganate in acetone. R, from 3-phenyl-2-phenacyl- or 3-phenyl-2-dibenzoylmethylquinoxaline by boiling for a short time with chromic anhydride in acetic acid. S, preparation as in method L, but starting with 3,4-diaminotoluene. T, by hydrolysis (10% sodium hydroxide at 95°) of the ethyl ester, which is prepared by condensing mesoxalic ester with 2,3-diaminotoluene. U, from the diamine hydrochloride and mesoxalic acid in hot aqueous solution. V, from *o*-phenylenediamine and ethyl 1-chloro-2-ketopropane 1-carboxylate in aqueous solution (in presence of CaCO₃). W, from 2-tribromo-methylquinoxaline and aqueous-alcoholic silver nitrate (3.7 moles) at the b.p.

[b] These entries refer to the ethyl esters, the free acids being unknown.

[c]Prepared by condensing 3,4-diaminotoluene with formyldichloroacetamide, CHO·CCl₂·CONH₂ (prepared *in situ* from asparagine and chloramine-T).

B. Properties. The constants of these acids, and those of their simple derivatives, are summarized in Table XXIX-1. Little can be said by way of a general statement of properties, as these are greatly influenced by the nature of the substituent adjacent to the carboxyl group. The acids in which this substituent is a chloro or an amino group display considerable activity, particularly the latter compound and its derivatives. Thus the amide (VI) gives the urethan (VII) when heated under reflux with ethyl chloroformate, whence alloxazine (VIII) is produced in high yield by treatment with hot alcoholic sodium ethoxide.[9] Again, interaction of the methyl ester (IX) with acetic anhydride gives the acetyl derivative (X) and thence, by methanolic ammonia, the amide (XI), which is converted in boiling acetic anhydride into the benzopteridine (XII; R = Ac). The same compound, together with the hydroxy analog (XII: R = H), is produced when (VI) is boiled with acetic anhydride.[9]

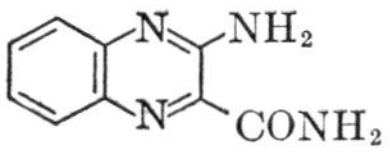

(VI) 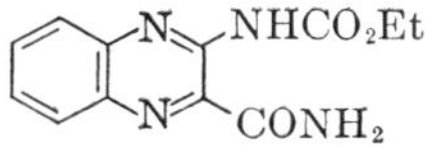   (VII) 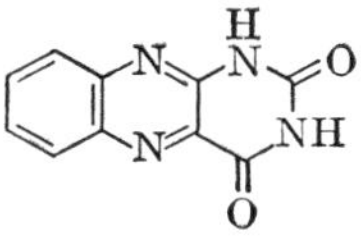   (VIII)

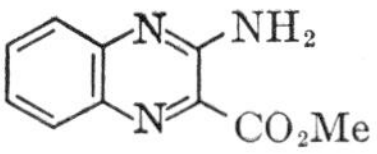

(IX) 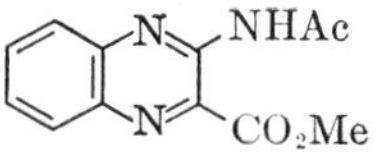   (X) 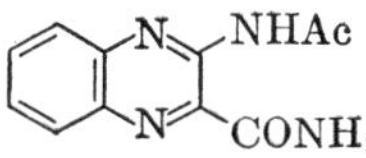   (XI)

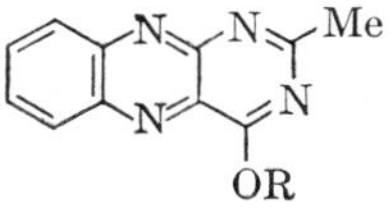

(XII) 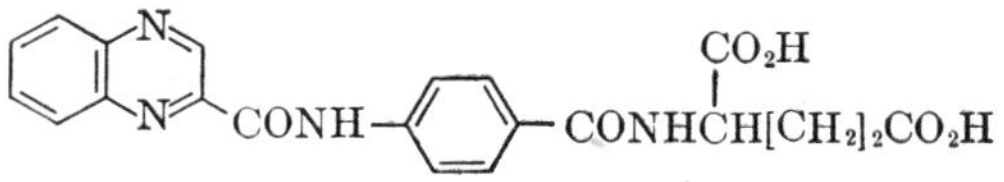   (XIII)

The compound (XIII), which bears a close formal structural resemblance to folic acid is formed by condensing the acid chloride of quinoxaline-2-carboxylic acid with N-p-aminobenzoylglutamic acid in a mixture of ether and aqueous sodium hydroxide. It forms pale yellow crystals, m.p. 145°, and shows some antagonistic action against folic acid when assayed with *Lactobacillus casei*, but no antagonism using various other bacteria.[10]

2. Quinoxaline-2,3-dicarboxylic Acids

A. Preparation

(1) The general method of preparing these compounds is to condense an o-diamine with diketosuccinic (dihydroxytartaric) acid or the sodium salt thereof in hot aqueous or aqueous-alcoholic solution (2). Hinsberg

$$(2)$$

(III)
R.I. 2834

(IV)

and König, to whom this synthesis is due, assumed[11] that the reaction led directly to (II; R = H). It was subsequently shown, however,[12] that this is not so; working with (I; R = H, Cl, and Br), it was found that the reaction proceeded by way of the intermediates (III) or (IV), the former being formed if the condensation is carried out in neutral solution, and the latter by working in a faintly acid medium. Strong acidification of a solution of either (III) or (IV) gives (II). One may note that the melting point of (IV) is almost identical with that of (III) in each of the three cases (R = H, Cl, and Br), suggesting that, at the melting point, (IV) undergoes dehydration to (III).

(2) Quinoxaline-2,3-dicarboxylic acid is also obtained by the oxidation of phenazine with alkaline potassium permanganate.[13]

B. Properties. The melting points of quinoxaline-2,3-dicarboxylic acids and their simple derivatives are given in Table XXIX-2. The parent compound (II; R = H) has been converted into various other derivatives which are given in Table XXIX-3.

Decarboxylation of this group of acids occurs readily. Thus if the parent acid or its 6-chloro or 6-bromo analog, or, better, their diammonium salts, are heated at 220–240°, the corresponding quinoxalines are formed.[12] If quinoxaline-2,3-dicarboxylic acid anhydride is heated with various phenols at 170°, partial decarboxylation occurs and the aryl esters of quinoxaline-2-carboxylic acid are produced (Table XXIX-1). Similarly, attempts to produce phenolphthalein analogs from the acid and a phenol in presence of concentrated sulfuric acid, phosphoric acid, or aluminum chloride lead only to quinoxaline-2-carboxylic acid,[14] although several compounds of the type (V; R = OH and NEt₂) and (VI) are stated to result from interaction of the dicarboxylic acid with the appropriate polyhydric phenol or aminophenol in presence of zinc chloride at 150–190°; these products, however, have not been thoroughly characterized and are only briefly described.[15]

On oxidation with hot alkaline permanganate, quinoxaline-2,3-dicarboxylic acid gives pyrazinetetracarboxylic acid (VII).[12]

TABLE XXIX-2. Quinoxaline-2,3-dicarboxylic Acids

Substituent	Acid	M.p., °C.			Ref.
		Anhydride	EtH ester	Et$_2$ ester	
Nil	190 (evolves CO$_2$)	235,[a] 251 (dec.), dec. 250–260	—	83[b]	11,12, 23,24
6-Cl	175 (dec.)	dec. 230–240[a]	159[c]	60[d]	12
6-Br	172 (dec.)	dec. 235–245[a]	161[c]	69[d]	12
6-Me	dec. 145 (anhyd.), 130 (hydrate)	—	—	—	4,32
7-Cl-6-Me	173 (dec.)	—	—	—	37

[a] Prepared from the acid and boiling acetic anhydride.
[b] Prepared from the acid by Fischer-Speier esterification.
[c] From the acid anhydride and ethanol.
[d] From the acid anhydride, ethanol, and hydrogen chloride.

TABLE XXIX-3. Derivatives (Other Than Those in Table XXIX-2) of Quinoxaline-2,3-dicarboxylic Acid

Derivative	Prep.[a]	M.p., °C.	Remarks	Ref.
Me$_2$ ester	A	130	—	23,26
	B	325		
Diamide	C	328 (dec.)	With 2 moles KOBr gives alloxazine; with 1 mole KOBr gives 3-aminoquinoxaline - 2-carboxylic acid (Table XXIX-1)	23
Monoamide	D	190–195 (dec.) 225 (dec.)	With KOBr gives 3-aminoquinoxaline - 2-carboxylic acid	12,24
Imide	E	dec. 260	—	12
N-Acetylimide	F	dec. 220	—	12
(Mono) o-aminophenylamide	G	168	—	38

Table continued

TABLE XXXIX-3. *(continued)*

Substituents	Prep.[a]	M.p., °C.	Remarks	Ref.
(Mono) *o*-acetamidophenyl-amide	H,I	217	—	38
o-Acetamidophenylimide	J	310–315	Treatment with dil. NaOH aq. gives the *o*-acetamidophenylamide	38
Acid phenyl ester	K	157	—	14
Acid *o*-hydroxyphenyl ester	K	162	—	14
Acid *m*-hydroxyphenyl ester	K	202	—	14
Acid *p*-hydroxyphenyl ester	K	168	—	14

[a] A, from the acid by Fischer-Speier esterification. B, from *o*-phenylenediamine and methyl dihydroxymaleate, using quinone as *in situ* oxidant. C, from the dimethyl ester (m.p. 130°) and dry methanolic ammonia. D, from the anhydride and dry ammonia in benzene. E, from the monoamide by heating at 185–205°. F, from the imide and acetic anhydride. G, from the anhydride and *o*-phenylenediamine in boiling alcohol. H, from the *o*-amino compound by acetylation with acetyl chloride. I, from the anhydride and *o*-aminoacetanilide. J, from the *o*-amino- or *o*-acetamidophenylamide and boiling acetic anhydride. K, from the anhydride and the appropriate phenol at 110°/0.25 hour. If reaction temperature is 170°, CO_2 is evolved and the corresponding esters of quinoxaline-2-carboxylic acid are formed (Table XXIX-1).

References

1. Bednarczyk and Marchlewski, *Bull. intern. acad. polon. sci., Classe sci. math. nat.* 1938A, 529.
2. Marchlewski, *Roczniki Chem.*, **18**, 698 (1938).
3. Bednarczyk and Marchlewski, *Biochem. Z.*, **300**, 46 (1938).
4. Hinsberg, *Ber.*, **18**, 1228 (1885).
5. Kühling, *Ber.*, **26**, 540 (1893).
6. Hinsberg, *Ann.*, **292**, 245 (1896).
7. Rudy and Cramer, *Ber.*, **71**, 1234 (1938).
8. Platt, *J. Chem. Soc.*, **1948**, 1310.
9. Gowenlock, Newbold, and Spring, *J. Chem. Soc.*, **1948**, 517.
10. Woolley and Pringle, *J. Biol. Chem.*, **174**, 327 (1948).
11. Hinsberg and König, *Ber.*, **27**, 2181 (1894).
12. Chattaway and Humphrey, *J. Chem. Soc.*, **1929**, 645.
13. Puskareva and Agibalova, *J. Gen. Chem., U. S. S. R.*, **8**, 151 (1938).
14. Piutti and Marini, *Gazz. chim. ital.*, **66**, 270 (1936).
15. Dutta, *Ber.*, **65**, 1791 (1932).
16. Maurer and Boettger, *Ber.*, **71**, 1383 (1938).
17. Maurer, Schiedt, and Schroeter, *Ber.*, **68**, 1716 (1935).
18. Maurer and Schiedt, *Ber.*, **70**, 1857 (1937).
19. Müller and Varga, *Ber.*, **72**, 1993 (1939).
20. Borsche and Doeller, *Ann.*, **537**, 39 (1939).
21. Gowenlock, Newbold, and Spring, *J. Chem. Soc.*, **1945**, 622.
22. Weijlard, Tishler, and Erickson, *J. Am. Chem. Soc.*, **66**, 1957 (1944)
23. Baxter and Spring, *J. Chem. Soc.*, **1945**, 229.
24. A. Phillips, *Ber.*, **28**, 1655 (1895).
25. Kuhn and Bär, *Ber.*, **67**, 898 (1934).
26. Ohle and Gross, *Ber.*, **68**, 2262 (1935).
27. Kühling, *Ber.*, **24**, 2363 (1891).

28. Newbold and Spring, *J. Chem. Soc.*, **1948,** 519.
29. Wahl and Doll, *Bull. Soc. Chim.*, **13,** 468 (1913).
30. Lutz and Stuart, *J. Am. Chem. Soc.*, **58,** 1885 (1936).
31. Lutz, J. M. Smith, Jr., and Stuart, *J. Am. Chem. Soc.*, **63,** 1143 (1941).
32. Hinsberg, *Ann.*, **237, 327** (1887).
33. Hinsberg, *Ann.*, **248, 71** (1888).
34. Dakin, *Biochem. J.*, **11, 79** (1917).
35. Platt and Sharp, *J. Chem. Soc.*, **1948,** 2129.
36. Wolf, Beutel, and Stevens, *J. Am. Chem. Soc.*, **70,** 2572 (1948).
37. G. T. Morgan and Challenor, *J. Chem. Soc.*, **1921,** 1537.
38. Crippa and Aguzzi, *Gazz. chim. ital.*, **67,** 352 (1937).
39. B. R. Brown, *J. Chem. Soc.*, **1949,** 2577.

CHAPTER XXX

2-Chloro- and 2,3-Dichloroquinoxalines

1. 2-Chloroquinoxalines

Preparation

(*1*) Simple 2-chloroquinoxalines are prepared by acting upon the corresponding hydroxy compound with phosphorus oxychloride. It is to be noted that interaction of 2-hydroxyquinoxaline and phosphorus pentachloride gives 2,3-dichloroquinoxaline.[1]

(*2*) A number of 3-*sec*-amino-2-chloroquinoxalines have been prepared from 2,3-dichloroquinoxaline by selective amination, *e.g.*, by treatment with the appropriate amine[2] at 0–15°.

TABLE XXX-1. 2-Chloroquinoxalines

Substituent	Prep.[a]	M.p., °C.	Remarks	Ref.
Nil	A,B,C	46–47	Insol. in H_2O; easily sol. in org. solvents and in 5 N HCl. Hydrochloride separates from soln. in conc. HCl	11
6-Cl	A	159–160	—	9
7-Cl	A	141	—	9
3-NH_2	D	139	Hydrochloride, m.p. >400°	2
6-Cl-3-NH_2	D	221	Structure not proved, but based on assumption that anionoid substitution replaces Cl at C_3 in 2,3,6-trichloroquinoxaline (ref. 9)	2
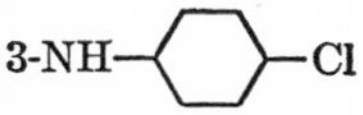 3-NH—⟨ ⟩—Cl	E	133–134	Yellow needles	2
3-$NH(CH_2)_2NEt_2$	F	—	B.p. 160–170°/0.01 mm. Picrate, m.p. 153–154°	2
3-$NH(CH_2)_3NEt_2$	F	—	B.p. 180–182°/0.015 mm. Picrate, m.p. 159°. Dihydrobromide, m.p. 165°	2
6-Cl-3-$NH(CH_2)_2NEt_2$	F	83–84	Structure based on assumption (ref. 9) that anionoid substitution replaces Cl at C_3 in 2,3,6-trichloroquinoxaline. Hydrochloride, m.p. 246° (dec.)	2

TABLE XXX-1. 2-Chloroquinoxalines (*continued*)

Substituent	Prep.[a]	M.p., °C.	Remarks	Ref.
3-OMe	G	74–75	—	15
7-OMe	A	102	—	10
3-OEt	G	71–73	Sub. 70°/10⁻³ mm.	4
3-Me	A	86–87	Sub. 85°/10⁻³ mm.	4,6,
		84–86		7
5-Me	A	95	—	7
6-Me	A	105–107	—	5
7-Me	A	76,77	Insol. in H₂O; easily sol. in org. solvents; salts with conc. acids are hydrolyzed by water	5,8
3-CO₂H	H	146–147 (dec.)	—	11
3-CO₂Et	A	42.5	—	11
3-CONH₂	I	215	—	11

[a] A, from the corresponding hydroxy compound by refluxing with phosphorus oxychloride. B, from the 3-carboxylic acid (Table XXX-1) by distillation at 0.1 mm. C, from 2-hydroxyquinoxaline-3-carboxylic acid (Table XXIX-1) by refluxing with phosphorus oxychloride. D, from the appropriate 2,3-dichloroquinoxaline by refluxing with alcoholic ammonia (saturated at 0°). E, from 2,3-dichloroquinoxaline, p-chloroaniline, and dilute hydrochloric acid (reflux). F, from the appropriate 2,3-dichloroquinoxaline and amine at 0–15°. G, from 2,3-dichloroquinoxaline and alcoholic sodium alkoxide (1 mole) under reflux. H, from the ethyl ester by hydrolysis with 1% aqueous methanolic sodium carbonate. I, from the ethyl ester and ethanolic ammonia at 0° [at 150° the product of reaction is 3-carbonamido-2-aminoquinoxaline (Table XXIX-1)].
[b] Erroneously formulated by the authors as the 3,4-dihydro derivative.

Properties. Melting points and other data for a number of 2-chloroquinoxalines are given in Table XXX-1; a number of new compounds (not given in Table XXX-1) have also recently been prepared.[3] No systematic study of these compounds as a group has been made, but in general their physical characteristics are insolubility in water, ready solubility in organic solvents, and low melting point. The compounds appear to be somewhat weak bases, but no quantitative data are available. The chlorine atom at C_2 is replaceable by other groups; 2-chloroquinoxaline, for example, easily yields 2-ethoxy- (Chapter XXXII, Section 1) and 2-aminoquinoxaline (Chapter XXXI, Section 1A), but this characteristic reactivity is affected to some extent by the presence of other substituents attached to C_3 or to the Bz ring.[2–8] One may note in particular the production of the compounds (III; R = H) [m.p. 155–156°; dihydrochloride, m.p. 206° (dec.)], (III; R = Cl) (m.p. 187–188°), and (IV) (m.p. 147°) by elimination of ethyl chloride, which occurs when (I; R = H and Cl) and (II), respectively, are heated[2] to 190–200°; and other examples of the same reaction have been described recently.[9]

2. 2,3-Dihalogenoquinoxalines

R—[quinoxaline structure]—NH(CH₂)₂NEt₂ with Cl

(I)

[quinoxaline structure]—NH(CH₂)₃NEt₂ with Cl

(II)

R—[quinoxaline structure with H, N, H₂, H₂, Et]

(III)
R.I. 1877

[quinoxaline structure with H, N—CH₂, CH₂, N—CH₂, Et]

(IV)

A. 2,3-Dichloroquinoxalines

Preparation. 2,3-Dichloroquinoxalines are usually prepared (see Table XXX-2) by heating the corresponding 2,3-dihydroxy compound with phosphorus oxychloride or pentachloride. The use of phosphorus pentachloride sometimes effects the chlorination of the Bz ring also; thus 2,3-dihydroxy-6-methoxyquinoxaline yields[10] with this reagent 2,3,x-trichloro-6-methoxyquinoxaline, m.p. 188°.

Properties. Both chlorine atoms in 2,3-dichloroquinoxalines are reactive. Thus 2,3-dihydroxy- and 6-chloro-2,3-dihydroxyquinoxaline are formed from the chloro compounds by treatment with boiling dilute mineral acid or alkali, or with boiling acetic acid, respectively,[2] and under normal reaction conditions the same two dichloroquinoxalines yield 2,3-dialkoxy, 2,3-diaryloxy, and 2,3-diprimary, and *sec*-amino derivatives.[2,4,11-13] With ethylenediamine, 2,3-dichloroquinoxaline yields[14] the

TABLE XXX-2. 2,3-Dichloroquinoxalines

Substituent	Prep.[a]	M.p., °C.	Ref.
Nil	A,B,C,D	150,147–150, 149–150,148	1,2,15, 20,21
6-Cl	A	143–144,144	2,22
6-Br	A	132	10
6-NO₂	A	152	10
6-OMe	E	160	10
6-Me	A,E	114–115	10,23

[a] A, from the 2,3-dihydroxy compound and phosphorus pentachloride at *ca.* 150–180°. B, from 2-hydroxyquinoxaline and phosphorus pentachloride. C, from 3-hydroxy-1-benzyl-2-keto-1,2-dihydroquinoxaline (Table XXXVII-2) and phosphorus pentachloride at 160° (the other product of reaction is benzyl chloride). D, from 3-hydroxy-1-methyl-2-keto-1,2-dihydroquinoxaline (Table XXXVII-2) and phosphorus pentachloride. E, from the 2,3-dihydroxy compound and phosphoryl chloride at 120–130°.

substance (I), m.p. > 350°, and both chlorine atoms react with the appropriate Grignard reagent to give 2,3-dimethyl- and 2,3-di-*n*-propylquinoxaline (Chapter XXXIII, Section 2).[14]   Under appropriate conditions, however, it is possible to prepare 2-chloro-3-amino derivatives[2] and 2-chloro-3-alkoxy compounds.[2,4,15]   Unsuccessful attempts to prepare 2-chloro-3-phenoxyquinoxaline have been reported.[13]

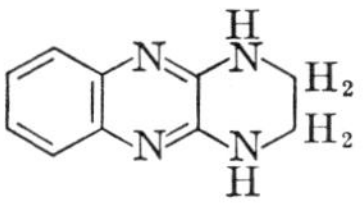

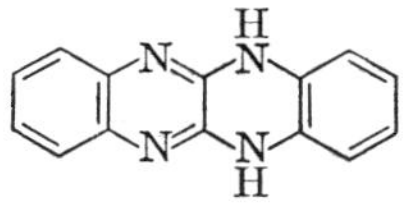

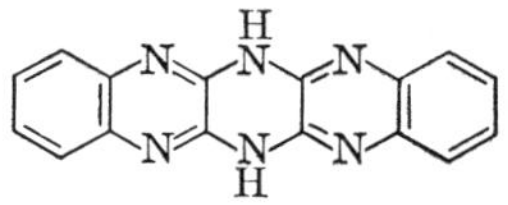

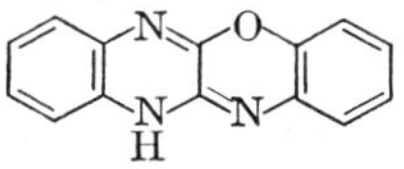

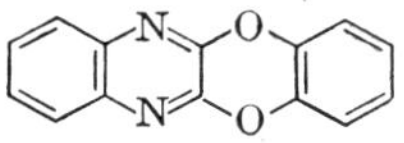

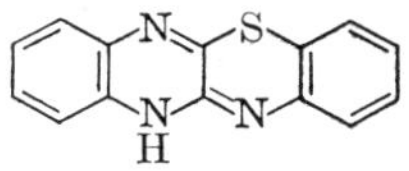

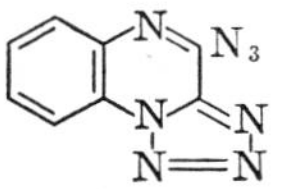

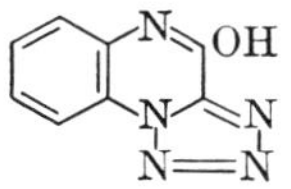

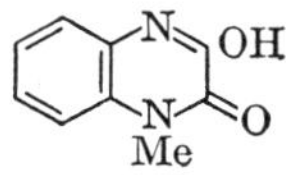

2,3-Dichloroquinoxaline condenses with *o*-phenylenediamine to give fluoflavin (II), and with 2,3-diaminoquinoxaline to give fluorubin (III)[12]; it reacts with *o*-aminophenol, yielding (IV)[16]; with catechol, the product is (V)[16]; and *o*-aminothiophenol yields (VI).[17]   On treatment with sodium azide, 2,3-dichloroquinoxaline furnishes the substance (VII), hydrolysis of which yields (VIII)[18] (Chapter XXXVIII, Section 2E).

For 2,3-dichloro-5,6-benzoquinoxaline, see Table XXXVIII-1.

B. 2,3-Dibromoquinoxaline

2,3-Dibromoquinoxaline, m.p. 171–174°, is formed when 3-hydroxy-1-methyl-2-keto-1,2-dihydroquinoxaline (IX) is treated with phosphorus pentabromide.[19]

References

1. Motylewski, *Ber.*, **41**, 800 (1908).
2. Haworth and S. Robinson, *J. Chem. Soc.*, **1948**, 777.
3. Wolf, Pfister, III, Beutel, R. M. Wilson, C. A. Robinson, and J. R. Stevens, *J. Am. Chem. Soc.*, **71**, 6 (1949).

4. Newbold and Spring, *J. Chem. Soc.*, **1948,** 519.

5. Platt, *J. Chem. Soc.*, **1948,** 1310.

6. Wolf, Beutel, and Stevens, *J. Am. Chem. Soc.*, **70,** 2572 (1948).

7. Platt and Sharp, *J. Chem. Soc.*, **1948,** 2129.

8. Leuckart and Hermann, *Ber.*, **20,** 24 (1887).

9. Crowther, Curd, Davey, and Stacey, *J. Chem. Soc.*, **1949,** 1260.

10. Curd, Davey, and Stacey, *J. Chem. Soc.*, **1949,** 1271.

11. Gowenlock, Newbold, and Spring, *J. Chem. Soc.*, **1945,** 622.

12. Hinsberg and Schwantes, *Ber.*, **36,** 4039 (1903).

13. Lockhart and Turner, *J. Chem. Soc.*, **1937,** 424.

14. Ogg, Jr., and Bergstrom, *J. Am. Chem. Soc.*, **53,** 1846 (1931).

15. Stevens, Pfister, and Wolf, *J. Am. Chem. Soc.*, **68,** 1035 (1946).

16. Kehrmann and Bener, *Helv. Chim. Acta*, **8,** 16 (1925).

17. Walter, Hübsch, and Pollak, *Monatsh.*, **63,** 186 (1933).

18. Stollé and Hanusch, *J. prakt. Chem.*, **136,** 9 (1933).

19. Usherwood and Whiteley, *J. Chem. Soc.*, **1923,** 1069.

20. Hinsberg and Pollak, *Ber.*, **29,** 784 (1896).

21. Hinsberg, *Ann.*, **292,** 245 (1896).

22. Kehrmann and Bener, *Helv. Chim. Acta*, **8,** 20 (1925).

23. Hinsberg, *Ann.*, **237,** 327 (1887).

CHAPTER XXXI

2-Amino- and 2,3-Diaminoquinoxalines

1. 2-Aminoquinoxalines

A. *Primary Amino Compounds*

Preparation

(*1*) The most general method is the treatment of the appropriate 2-chloroquinoxaline with alcoholic ammonia under pressure at temperatures ranging from 70 to 170° approximately.

(*2*) The appropriate alloxazine (I) is heated with concentrated or slightly aqueous sulfuric acid at 200° or higher, yielding the corresponding aminoquinoxaline (II) (Eq. 1).

(I)   (II)

Properties. Primary 2-aminoquinoxalines are pale yellow crystalline bases. In general, they readily yield 2-acylamido compounds, but the acylation of 2-amino-3-hydroxyquinoxaline is only brought about with difficulty (the 4'-nitrobenzenesulfonamido derivative has been prepared; see Table XXXI-3), and 2-aminoquinoxaline-3-carboxylic acid does not condense with acetylsulfanilyl chloride.[1]

A number of isolated observations indicate that the 2-amino group is easily susceptible to acid or alkaline hydrolysis. Thus 2-amino-3-hydroxyquinoxaline is prepared by mild acid hydrolysis of the 2,3-diamino compound or of 3-acetylsulfanilamido-2-aminoquinoxaline (Table XXXI-3); 2-sulfanilamido-3-methoxyquinoxaline under similar conditions gives 2,3-dihydroxyquinoxaline[2]; and 2-amino- yields 2-hydroxyquinoxaline-3-carboxylic acid by high-temperature alkaline hydrolysis.[3] No general study of the reaction has been made, but it is of interest that 4-aminocinnolines are stable under similar acid conditions (Chapter VI), and no hydrolysis of 1-aminophthalazines (Chapter XXI) appears to be recorded.

TABLE XXXI-1. Primary 2-Aminoquinoxalines

Substituents	Prep.[a]	M.p., °C.	Remarks	Ref.
Nil	A,B,C	155–156 155–157	Yellow needles. Ac deriv., m.p. 192–193.5° (193–194°). p-Nitrobenzoyl deriv., m.p. 211°, is reduced (H_2-Raney Ni) to p-aminobenzoyl deriv., m.p. 229–230°	3,11,15
6- or 7-Cl	D	197–200	—	15
3-OH	E	>350	—	2
3-OMe	F,G	264–270	—	2
3-Me	A,H	163–165	Pale yellow needles	15,16
5-Me	A,I	201–202	—	16
6-Me	A	181–182	Pale yellow cryst. Picrate, m.p. 278–280° (dec.)	17
7-Me	A	178–180	Pale yellow cryst. Picrate, m.p. 259–262° (dec.)	17
8-Me	I	129	Pale yellow cryst.	16
3-CO_2H			See Table XXIX-1	
6,7-Me_2	D(b)	275–278	—	15

[a] A, from the 2-chloro compound and alcoholic ammonia at temperatures ranging from 150 to 175°.   B, from the 3-carboxylic acid by decarboxylation (by heating at 250° or by refluxing for 10 minutes in nitrobenzene).   C, from alloxazine by hydrolysis with 95% sulfuric acid (10 minutes at 240–250°).   D, from the corresponding alloxazine (a) by hydrolysis with 75% (v/v) sulfuric acid at 200°, or (b) by hydrolysis with concentrated ammonia at 170–175°, followed by decarboxylation of the resultant (crude) 3-carboxylic acid in boiling nitrobenzene.   E, from 2,3-diamino- or 2-amino-3-acetylsulfanilamidoquinoxaline by hydrolysis with hot 2.5 N hydrochloric acid.   F, by methylation (methyl sulfate and alkali) of 3-hydroxy-2-aminoquinoxaline.   G, from 2-chloro-3-methoxyquinoxaline (Table XXX-1) and methanolic ammonia at 165° (2,3-diaminoquinoxaline is also formed).   H, from 2-chloro-3-methylquinoxaline and liquid ammonia in alcohol at 120°.   I, from the corresponding alloxazine by hydrolysis with concentrated sulfuric acid at 230–240°.

B. Secondary Amino Compounds

The compounds given in Table XXXI-2 are prepared, except where otherwise stated, by interaction of chloroglyoximes (III) or chloroisonitrosoketones (IV) with excess of o-phenylenediamine in alcoholic solution (cf. Chapter XXIV), the excess base furnishing the 2,2'-aminoanilino substituent.   2,2'-Aminoanilino-3-methylquinoxaline is hydrolyzed in boiling 20%

$$
\begin{array}{cc}
\text{HON:CR} & \text{OCR} \\
| & | \\
\text{HON:CCl} & \text{HON:CCl} \\
\text{(III)} & \text{(IV)}
\end{array}
$$

hydrochloric acid to 2-hydroxy-3-methylquinoxaline[4] [cf. hydrolysis of primary 2-amino- to 2-hydroxyquinoxalines (Section A)].   Numerous dialkylaminoalkylaminoquinoxalines, prepared by direct condensation of the appropriate chloroquinoxaline and amine, have been recently described by Curd and his co-workers.[5,6]

TABLE XXXI-2. Secondary 2-Aminoquinoxalines

Substituents	M.p., °C.	Remarks	Ref.
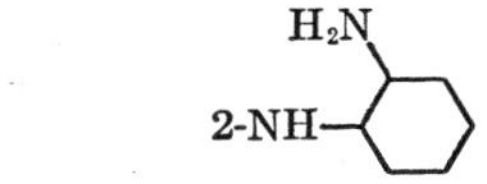 2-NH— (H₂N)	169–170	—	4
2-NHCH₂Ph[a]	62–64	Hydrochloride, m.p. 255–256°	8
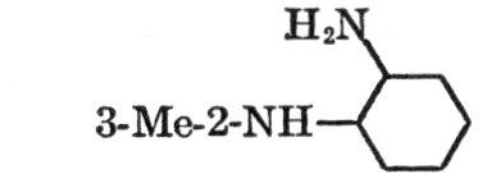 3-Me-2-NH— (H₂N)	242 (dec.)	Hydrolyzed to 2-hydroxy-3-methylquinoxaline by boiling 20% HCl	4
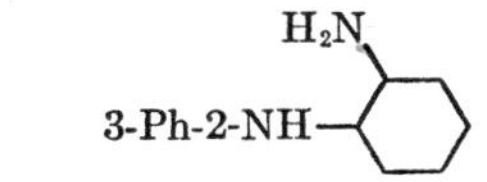 3-Ph-2-NH— (H₂N)	217–218 (dec.)	—	4
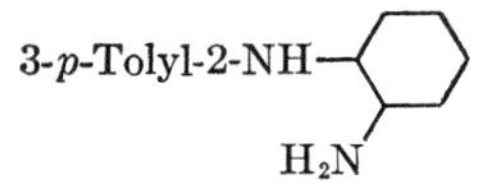 3-p-Tolyl-2-NH— (H₂N)	217 (dec.)	—	4

[a] Prepared from 2-aminoquinoxaline, benzyl chloride, and sodium hydride in boiling benzene.

C. 2-Sulfonamidoquinoxalines

A number of these compounds, which have been prepared by reason of their possible chemotherapeutic value, are given in Table XXXI-3, and biological data in Appendix III. Sulfonamidoquinoxalines derived from Bz-aminoquinoxalines are described in Chapters XXV and XXXIII, Section 1. A large number of Bz substituted-2-sulfanilamidoquinoxalines have recently been prepared by Wolf and his co-workers.[7]

D. Tertiary Amino Compound

The compound (V) (hydrochloride, m.p. 217–218°) is prepared[8] by condensing 2-chloroquinoxaline with the requisite amine at 140–150°.

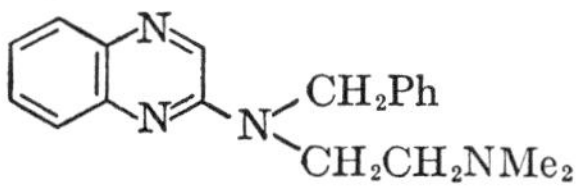

(V)

2. Diaminoquinoxalines

A. Diprimary Amino Compounds

2,3-Diaminoquinoxaline. This compound may be prepared (a) by condensing o-phenylenediamine with cyanogen[2,9,10]; (b) by reacting

2,3-dichloroquinoxaline (Chapter XXX) with either liquid[2] or alcoholic[11] ammonia at 150°; and (c) by reacting 2-chloro-3-methoxyquinoxaline (Chapter XXX) with methanolic[2] ammonia at 165°. It crystallizes from pyridine in yellow plates or needles, m.p.[2,11] 328–330° (dec.), > 340°.

TABLE XXXI-3. 2-Sulfonamidoquinoxalines

(References and methods of preparation[a] are in parentheses after the melting points.)

| R | M.p., °C., for R' equals | | | | | |
	3'-NO₂	4'-NO₂	3'-NH₂	4'-NH₂	4'-NHAc	Other groups
Nil	200–202 [b] (A,18)	—	231–232 [b] (B,18)	247–248 250–252 (F,G,3,16)	243–244 (D,3)	4' - Caproyl-amido, m.p. 199–200; 4'-succinamido, m.p. 234–235; 4' - benzam-ido, m.p. 259–260 (H,3). 4'-Amino-methyl, m.p. 228 (I, 19)
6- (or 7-) Cl	—	—	—	241–242 (F,15)	266–268 (D,15)	—
3-NH₂	—	—	—	dec. 275–280 (F,2)	dec. 260 (D,2)	—
3-OH	—	310 (dec.) (A,2)	—	275–278 (B,2)	—	—
3-OMe	—	—	—	263–264 (C,2)	—	—
3-Me	—	—	—	210–212 207–209 (F,G,15,16)	244–245 (D,15)	—
5-Me	—	—	—	202–204 (F,G,16)	—	—
3-CO₂H	—	—	—	238–239 (E,3)	—	—
3-CO₂Et	—	—	—	—	236–237 (D,3)	—
6,7-Me₂	—	—	—	246–247 (F,15)	239–240 (D,15)	—

[a] A, from the aminoquinoxaline and nitrobenzenesulfonyl chloride in pyridine. B, from the nitro compound by reduction (ammonium sulfide, or iron and alcoholic hydrochloric acid). C, from the chloroquinoxaline and acetylsulfanilamide, potassium carbonate, and copper bronze (in boiling nitrobenzene), followed by hydrolysis. D, from the aminoquinoxaline and acetylsulfanilyl chloride in pyridine. E, from 3-carbethoxy-2-acetylsulfanilamidoquinoxaline by hydrolysis. F, from the acetamido compound by hydrolysis (usually with alcoholic hydrochloric acid). G, from the chloroquinoxaline and sulfanilamide, potassium carbonate, potassium iodide, and copper bronze (autoclave, 160–190°). H, from 2-sulfanilamidoquinoxaline by acylation. I, from 2-aminoquinoxaline and p-phthalimidomethylbenzenesulfonyl chloride, followed by hydrolytic removal of the phthaloyl residue.
[b] M.p. is corrected.

The fine structure of 2,3-diaminoquinoxaline is unknown, for whereas its synthesis from cyanogen and *o*-phenylenediamine is suggestive of structure (I), its preparation from 2,3-dichloroquinoxaline and ammonia provides equally strong evidence for structure (II). The compound may be a tautomeric mixture of (I) and (II); but its condensation reactions clearly show that it reacts as a true diamine. Thus it reacts with benzil, pyruvic acid, and oxalic acid to yield (III), (IV), and (V), respectively[9]; it may be

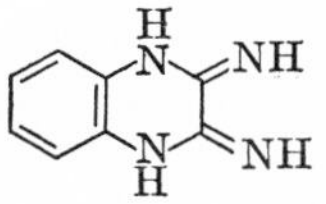

(I) 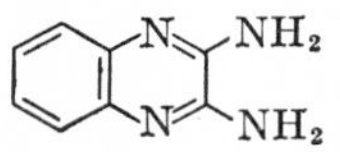   (II) 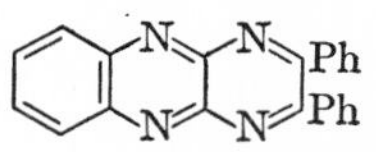   (III)

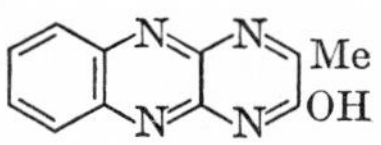

(IV) 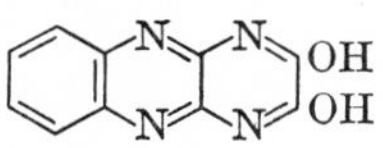   (V) 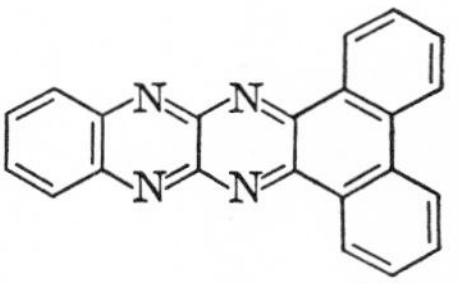   (VI)

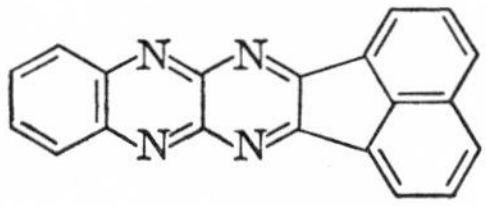

(VII) 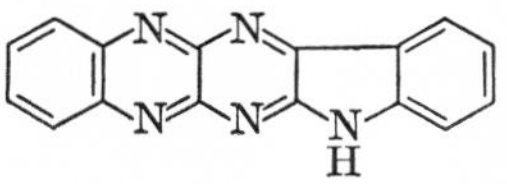   (VIII) 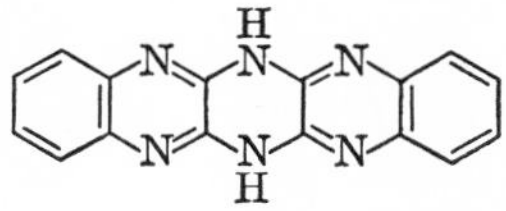   (IX)

condensed with substituted phenanthraquinones, acenaphthenquinones, and isatins to form products of types (VI), (VII), and (VIII)[9,12,13]; and on fusion with 2,3-dichloroquinoxaline it yields fluorubin[9] (IX).

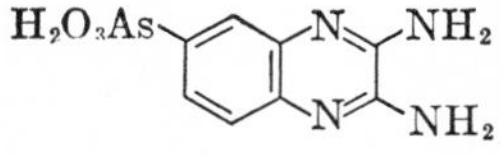

(X)

2,3-Diaminoquinoxaline-6-arsonic Acid. (X) is an orange solid (dec. 200–205°) which is formed by passing cyanogen into a warm methanolic solution of 3,4-diaminophenylarsonic acid.[14]

B. *Primary-Secondary Amino Compounds*

Table XXXI-4 summarizes the preparation and properties of these compounds.

TABLE XXXI-4. Primary-Secondary Diaminoquinoxalines

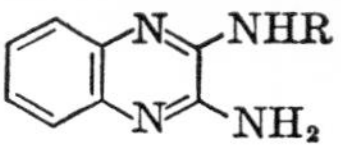

R	Other substituents	Prep.[a]	M.p., °C	Remarks	Ref.
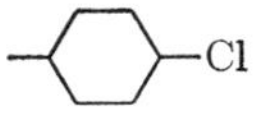 —C6H4—Cl	Nil	A	193–194	Yellow prisms	20
(CH2)2NEt2	Nil	A	114–115	—	20
(CH2)3NEt2	Nil	A	141–142	—	20
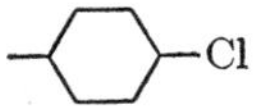 —C6H4—Cl	6-Cl	A	239 (dec.)	Yellow needles	20
(CH2)2NEt2	6-Cl	A	124.5–125.5	—	20

[a] A, from the appropriate 3-chloro-2-aminoquinoxaline (Table XXX-1) and amine (p-chloroaniline at 140–190°, dialkylaminoalkylamines at 100°).

TABLE XXXI-5. Disecondary Aminoquinoxalines

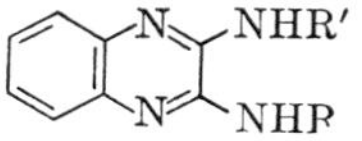

R	R'	Other substituents	Prep.[a]	M.p., °C	Remarks	Ref.
Et	Et	Nil	A	156	—	9
Ph	Ph	Nil	A	223,123	Yellow needles (+AcOH). Solvent-free, m.p. 138–139°. Hydrochloride, m.p. 248–250°	20,21
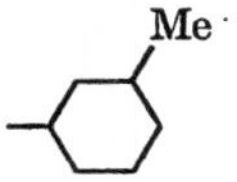 —C6H4(Me)	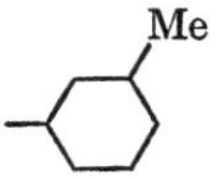 —C6H4(Me)	Nil	A	225	Yellow plates	21
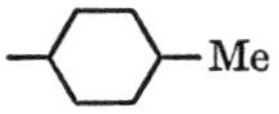 —C6H4—Me	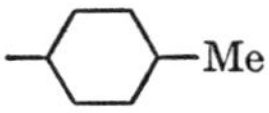 —C6H4—Me	Nil	A	254	Yellow needles	21
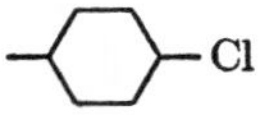 —C6H4—Cl	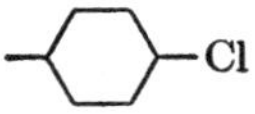 —C6H4—Cl	Nil	A	232	—	20
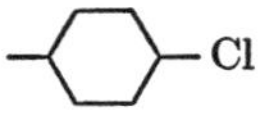 —C6H4—Cl	(CH2)2NEt2	Nil	B	90–92	—	20
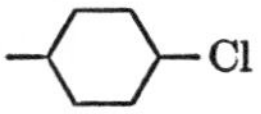 —C6H4—Cl	(CH2)3NEt2	Nil	B	94–95	—	20
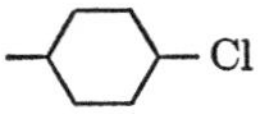 —C6H4—Cl	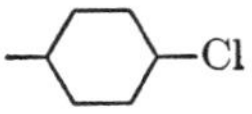 —C6H4—Cl	6-Cl	A	182–183	Yellow needles. M.p. is presumably that of solvent-free compd. Solvates: +COMe2, m.p. 84°; +1/2 C6H6, m.p. 135°; both solidify above m.p. and re-melt at ∼182–183°	20
(CH2)2NEt2	(CH2)2NEt2	6-Cl	A	95–97	Probably impure	20
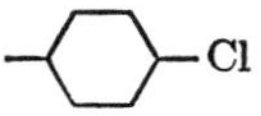 —C6H4—Cl	(CH2)3NEt2	6-Cl	B	82–83	—	20

[a] A, from the appropriate 2,3-dichloroquinoxaline and excess amine (at the b.p. or at 120–140°). B, from the appropriate 2-chloro-3-dialkylaminoalkylamino-quinoxaline (Table XXX-1) and arylamine in boiling dilute hydrochloric acid.

C. *Disecondary Amino Compounds*

These compounds are listed in Table XXXI-5. Compounds in which both amino groups contain the same substituent are prepared from a 2,3-dichloroquinoxaline and excess of the primary amine, and substances containing one *N*-alkyl and one *N*-aryl group are made by selective amination of the dichloroquinoxaline, the alkyl substituent being introduced first (see Table XXX-1).

References

1. Gowenlock, Newbold, and Spring, *J. Chem. Soc.*, **1948**, 517.
2. Stevens, Pfister, and Wolf, *J. Am. Chem. Soc.*, **68**, 1035 (1946).
3. Weijlard, Tishler, and Erickson, *J. Am. Chem. Soc.*, **66**, 1957 (1944).
4. Durio, *Gazz. chim. ital.*, **63**, 747 (1933).
5. Crowther, Curd, Davey, and Stacey, *J. Chem. Soc.*, **1949**, 1260.
6. Curd, Davey, and Stacey, *J. Chem. Soc.*, **1949**, 1271.
7. Wolf, Pfister, III, Beutel, R. M. Wilson, C. A. Robinson, and J. R. Stevens, *J. Am. Chem. Soc.*, **71**, 6 (1949).
8. Gardner and J. R. Stevens, *J. Am. Chem. Soc.*, **71**, 1868 (1949).
9. Hinsberg and Schwantes, *Ber.*, **36**, 4039 (1903).
10. Bladin, *Ber.*, **18**, 666 (1885).
11. Gowenlock, Newbold, and Spring, *J. Chem. Soc.*, **1945**, 622.
12. De and Dutta, *Ber.*, **64**, 2598 (1931).
13. Dutta and De, *Ber.*, **64**, 2602 (1931).
14. W. L. Lewis, P. L. Cramer, and Bly, *J. Am. Chem. Soc.*, **46**, 2058 (1924).
15. Wolf, Beutel, and Stevens, *J. Am. Chem. Soc.*, **70**, 2572 (1948).
16. Platt and Sharp, *J. Chem. Soc.*, **1948**, 2129.
17. Platt, *J. Chem. Soc.*, **1948**, 1310.
18. English, Clark, Shepherd, Marson, Krapcho, and Roblin, *J. Am. Chem. Soc.*, **68**, 1039 (1946).
19. Wolf, R. M. Wilson, and Tishler, *J. Am. Chem. Soc.*, **68**, 151 (1946).
20. Haworth and S. Robinson, *J. Chem. Soc.*, **1948**, 777.
21. Lockhart and Turner, *J. Chem. Soc.*, **1937**, 424.

CHAPTER XXXII

2-Alkoxy-, 2,3-Dialkoxy-, and 2,3-Diaryloxyquinoxalines

1. 2-Alkoxyquinoxalines

As indicated in Table XXXII-1, a number of these compounds have been described in earlier chapters. Nearly all the compounds given in Table XXXII-1 contain an additional 3-substituent; this may be introduced either before or after the 2-alkoxy group, but in either event the alkoxy compound is prepared from the appropriate 2-chloroquinoxaline, usually by treatment with the requisite sodium alkoxide and alcohol.

No general study has been made of 2-alkoxyquinoxalines. In a few cases [3-hydroxy-2-ethoxy- and 2-ethoxy-3-methylquinoxaline (see Table XXXII-1), and 3-sulfanilamido-2-methoxyquinoxaline (Table XXXI-3)] it has been found that the compounds are readily hydrolyzed to the corresponding 2-hydroxyquinoxalines in acid solution.

TABLE XXXII-1. 2-Alkoxyquinoxalines

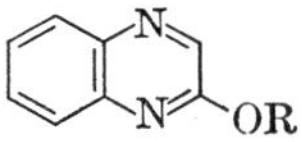

R	Other substituents	Prep.[a]	M.p., °C.	Remarks	Ref.
Me	3-Cl			See Table XXX-1	
Me	3-NH$_2$			See Table XXXI-1	
Me	3-Sulfanilamido			See Table XXXI-3	
Me	7-Me	A	71	Sol. in hot water, org. solvents, and conc. acids (salts are hydrolyzed by water). Erroneously formulated in literature as 3,4-dihydro compd.	1
Me	3-(CHOH)$_3$CH$_2$OH			See Table XXXVI-1	
Me	3-CHO			See Table XXVIII-1	
Et	Nil	A,B	56–58	Yields the 4-oxide with H$_2$O$_2$-AcOH at 56° (ref. 2)	3
Et	3-Cl			See Table XXX-1	
Et	3-OH	C	197–199	Yields 2,3-dihydroxy-quinoxaline in AcOH aq. at 56°	2

Table continued

TABLE XXXII-1. 2-Alkoxyquinoxalines (*continued*)

R	Other substituents	Prep.[a]	M.p., °C.	Remarks	Ref.
Et	3-Me	A	55–57	Picrate, m.p. 116–118°. Gives 2-hydroxy-3-methylquinoxaline with boiling HCl-EtOH aq. Gives the 4-oxide with H_2O_2 and AcOH at 56°	2
Et	7-Me	D	67	Sol. in hot water, org. solvents, and conc. acids (salts are hydrolyzed by water). Erroneously formulated in literature as 3,4-dihydro compd.	1
Et	3-CO_2H			See Table XXIX-1	

[a] A, from the 2-chloro compound and sodium alkoxide in boiling alcohol.   B, from the 3-carboxylic acid by decarboxylation at 180°.   C, from 3-chloro-2-ethoxy-quinoxaline (Table XXX-1) and 20% aqueous-alcoholic potassium hydroxide at the b.p.   D, from the 2-chloro compound and boiling alcoholic potassium hydroxide.

2. 2,3-Dialkoxy- and 2,3-Diaryloxyquinoxalines

The preparation and properties of these compounds are given in Table XXXII-2.   As will be seen from the table, even less is known of their properties than of those of the 2-alkoxyquinoxalines.

TABLE XXXII-2.   2,3-Dialkoxy- and 2,3-Diaryloxyquinoxalines

R	R'	Prep.[a]	M.p., °C.	Remarks	Ref.
Me	H	A	92–93, 92–94	—	2,4
Et	H	B	78	Unaffected by boiling 0.2 N aq.-alc. KOH	3
Ph	H	C	160	Does not react with MeI (8 hrs. at 100°)	5
⟨⟩–Cl	H	C	153	—	5
⟨⟩–OMe	H	C	193–194	—	5
⟨⟩–Me	H	C	145–146	—	5
Me	Cl	B	110–111	—	6
Me	Br	B	114–115	—	7
Me	OMe	B	125–126	—	7
Me	Me	B	82–83	—	7

[a] A, from 2,3-dichloroquinoxaline and methanolic sodium methoxide at the b.p.; if only 1 mole of sodium methoxide is used, the products are unchanged chloro compound, 3-chloro-2-methoxy-, and 2,3-dimethoxyquinoxaline.   B, from the appropriate 2,3-dichloroquinoxaline and boiling alcoholic sodium alkoxide.   C, from 2,3-dichloroquinoxaline and the potassium aryloxide at 100–120°,

References

1. Leuckart and Hermann, *Ber.*, **20**, 24 (1887).
2. Newbold and Spring, *J. Chem. Soc.*, **1948**, 519.
3. Gowenlock, Newbold, and Spring, *J. Chem. Soc.*, **1945**, 622.
4. Stevens, Pfister, and Wolf, *J. Am. Chem. Soc.*, **68**, 1035 (1946).
5. Lockhart and Turner, *J. Chem. Soc.*, **1937**, 424.
6. Crowther, Curd, Davey, and Stacey, *J. Chem. Soc.*, **1949**, 1260.
7. Curd, Davey, and Stacey, *J. Chem. Soc.*, **1949**, 1271.

CHAPTER XXXIII

2-Methyl- and
2,3-Dimethylquinoxalines

1. 2-Methylquinoxalines

The great majority of analogs of 2-methylquinoxaline (I; R = H) contain a substituent in the 3-position, and only a few 2-methylquinoxa-

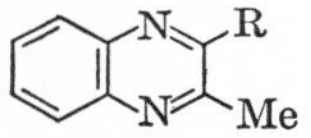

(I) — quinoxaline, N, R, Me

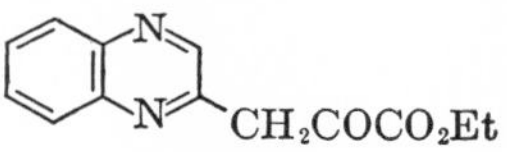

(II) — quinoxaline, N, N, CH_2COCO_2Et

lines are known with substituents in the Bz ring. Most of the 3-substituted compounds have been described in other chapters—the compounds

I; R = Ac, Ph, —(OMe, OH ring), —(OMe, OH, OMe ring), $-CH:N-$(ring, NH_2),

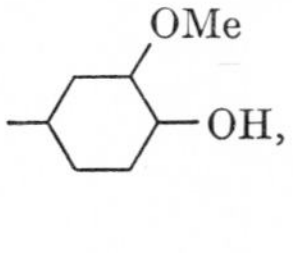

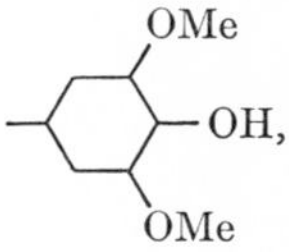

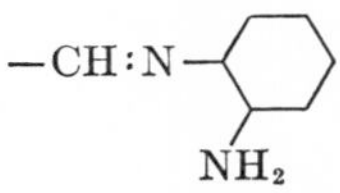

and $-CH:CHNH-$(ring, NH_2)

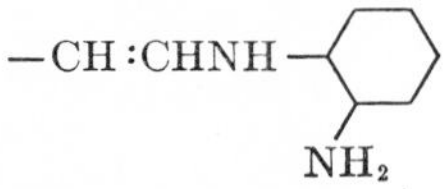

(I; R = Ac), Ph, are mentioned in Table XXIV-1; (I; R = OH), its 6- and 7-methoxy derivatives, and its 6- and 7-methyl derivatives in Table XXVII-2; (I; R = CO_2Et) in Table XXIX-1; (I; R = Cl) in Table XXX-1; (I; R = NH_2) and (I; R = sulfanilamido) in Tables XXXI-1 and 3; and (I; R = OEt) in Table XXXII-1.

2,6- (or 2,7) Dimethylquinoxaline, m. p. 54°, b.p. 267–268°, is formed by condensing 3,4-diaminotoluene with chloroacetone in warm aqueous solution.[1]

6- (or 7-) Amino-2-methylquinoxaline, m.p. 173°, is prepared[2] from 1,2,4-triaminobenzene dihydrochloride and methylglyoxal in aqueous sodium carbonate at 95°. Condensation with acetylsulfanilyl chloride yields 6- (or 7-) acetylsulfanilamido-2-methylquinoxaline, m.p. 283–285°, whence the free sulfanilamido compound, m.p. 258°, is formed by acid hydrolysis.[2]

TABLE XXXIII-1. Condensation Products of 2-Methylquinoxaline

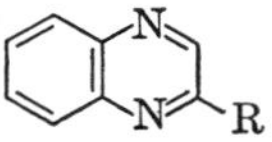

R	Prep.[a]	M.p., °C.	Remarks	Ref.
—CH₂COCO₂Et	A	161–162	Yellow needles. Picrate, red needles, m.p. 134°; methiodide, red solid, dec. 176°; *O*-Bz deriv., m.p. 94–98°; oxime, m.p. 146–148°; 2,4 - dinitrophenylhydrazone, m.p. 136–137°; hydrazone-hydrazide, dec. 225°. Oxime-acid (by alk. hydrolysis of oxime-ester), m.p. 191–192° (dec.)	4

R	Prep.[a]	M.p., °C.	Remarks	Ref.
(structure: —C(=NNHPh)COCO₂Et)	B	158–160	Orange-yellow needles	4
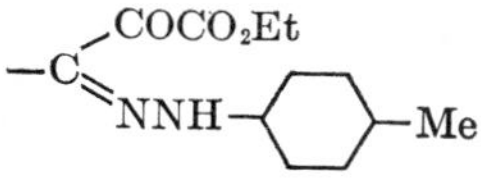 (structure: —C(=NNH—C₆H₄—Me)COCO₂Et)	B	149–150	Red cryst.	4
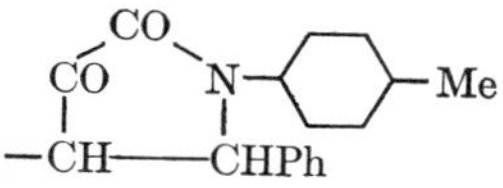 (structure: ring —CH—CHPh with CO—CO—N—C₆H₄—Me)	C	283–285	Red prisms	4
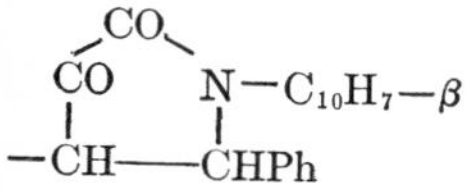 (structure: ring —CH—CHPh with CO—CO—N—C₁₀H₇-β)	C	dec. 290–292	Red powder	4
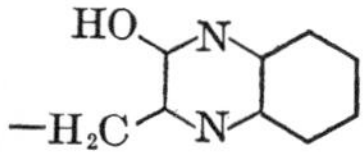 (structure: —H₂C with HO-quinoxaline fused ring)	D	307–309	Orange-red needles. Conc. H₂SO₄ gives dark green soln.	4
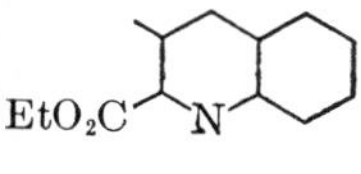 (structure: EtO₂C-quinoxaline fused ring)	E	152–154	Derived acid (hydrolysis by alc. NaOH), dec. 181°, gives Me ester, m.p. 172–173°	4
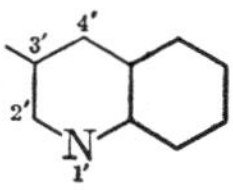 (structure: fused ring)	F	214–215	Monopicrate, m.p. 238–239°; monomethiodide, dec. 268–269°	4
—CH₂CN	G	116–117	Yellow needles	4
—CH(CN)COCH₃	H	228–229	Yellow tablets	4
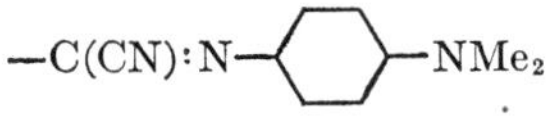 —C(CN):N—C₆H₄—NMe₂	I	251	Violet-red needles	4

TABLE XXXIII-1. Condensation Products of 2-Methylquinoxaline (*continued*)

R	Prep.[a]	M.p., °C.	Remarks	Ref.
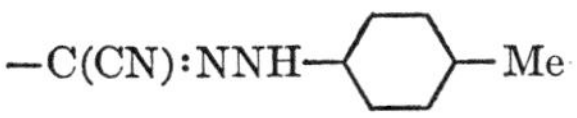 —C(CN):NNH—⬡—Me	J	187–188	Orange-yellow needles	4
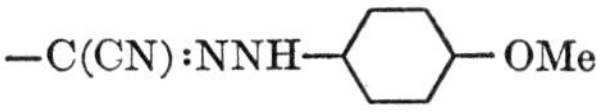 —C(CN):NNH—⬡—OMe	J	188–190	Yellow-red needles	4
—C(CN):CHPh	K	146–147	Yellow needles	4
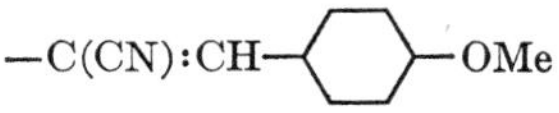 —C(CN):CH—⬡—OMe	K	162–163	Yellow needles	4
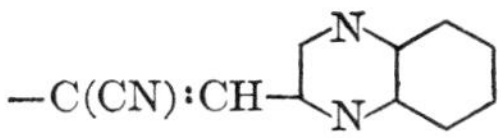 —C(CN):CH—(quinoxaline)	K	245	Yellow needles	4
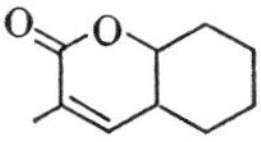 (coumarin structure)	L	196–197	Colorless needles	4
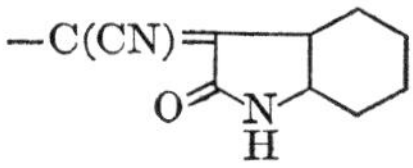 —C(CN)=(oxindole structure)	M	306–308	—	4
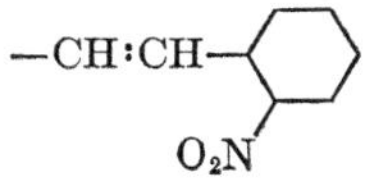 —CH:CH—⬡ (O_2N)	N	156	—	5
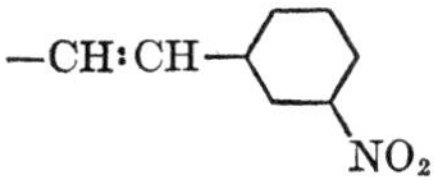 —CH:CH—⬡ (NO_2)	N	199.5	—	5
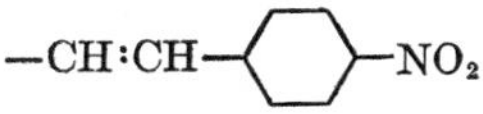 —CH:CH—⬡—NO_2	N	200	—	5
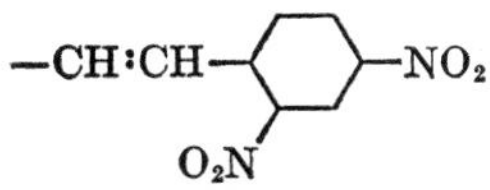 —CH:CH—⬡—NO_2 (O_2N)	N	219–220 (dec.)	—	5

[a] A, from 2-methylquinoxaline, ethyl oxalate, and potassium ethoxide in alcohol-ether. B, from ethyl 2-quinoxalylpyruvate and the aryldiazonium chloride and sodium acetate in alcohol. C, from ethyl 2-quinoxalylpyruvate, benzaldehyde, and the appropriate arylamine. D, from ethyl 2-quinoxalylpyruvate and o-phenylene-diamine. E, from ethyl 2-quinoxalylpyruvate and o-aminobenzaldehyde at 130–140°/12 mm. F, from the 2'-carboxylic acid (dec. 181°) by decarboxylation at 200–205° *in vacuo*. G, from the oxime [m.p. 191–192° (dec.)] of 2-quinoxalylpyruvic acid and acetic anhydride at 45°. H, prepared as in method G, but at reflux temperature. I, from 2-cyanomethylquinoxaline and p-nitrosodimethylaniline in boiling methanol. J, from 2-cyanomethylquinoxaline, sodium acetate, and the aryldiazonium chloride. K, from 2-cyanomethylquinoxaline and the appropriate aldehyde in alcohol containing piperidine. L, from 2-cyanomethylquinoxaline salicylaldehyde, and piperidine (1 drop) at 100°. M, from 2-cyanomethylquin-oxaline and isatin in methanol containing piperidine. N, from 2-methylquinoxa-line (1 mole) and the appropriate aldehyde (1 mole) in boiling acetic anhydride (5–6 moles).

TABLE XXXIII-2. Condensation Products of Substituted 2-Methylquinoxaline

R'	R	Prep.[a]	M.p., °C.	Remarks	Ref.
Ph	—CH:CHPh	A	149	Yellow needles	5
Ph	—CH:CH—⟨ ⟩—NO$_2$	A	233	Yellow needles	5
Ph	—CH:CH—⟨ ⟩—NO$_2$ O$_2$N	A	215	Yellow needles	5
H	—CPh:CH—⟨ ⟩—NO$_2$	A	149	Pale yellow needles	5

[a] A, from the appropriate quinoxaline and aldehyde in boiling acetic anhydride.

2-Methylquinoxaline, b.p. 242–245°/760 mm., is conveniently prepared on a large scale from *o*-phenylenediamine and isonitrosoacetone (*cf.* Chapter XXIV).[3,4]   In contrast to the analogs mentioned above, in which the reactivity of the 2-methyl group has not in general been investigated, 2-methylquinoxaline has been studied in some detail from this aspect. Thus, Bennett and Willis[5] have shown that styryl derivatives (see Table XXXIII-1) are formed by condensation with aldehydes in acetic anhydride;   and Borsche and Doeller[4] have prepared quinoxaline-2-aldehyde (Chapter XXVIII) by oxidation with selenium dioxide, and ethyl 2-quinoxalylpyruvate (II) by condensation with ethyl oxalate.   From this ester and from the derived 2-cyanomethylquinoxaline a large number of derivatives have been prepared[4] by reactions which demonstrate the extreme reactivity of the methylene group in these compounds (see Table XXXIII-1).

In connection with these condensation reactions of 2-methylquinoxaline and its derivatives, it is important to note that the reactivity of the 2-methyl- (or 2-methylene-) group is much influenced by substituents either in the methyl group itself or at the adjacent (C$_3$) position.   Thus, 3-hydroxy-2-methylquinoxaline does not condense with ethyl oxalate in presence of potassium ethoxide.[6]   In contrast to the behavior of ethyl 2-quinoxalylpyruvate (II), the 3-methyl analog (III) does not react with diazonium salts, with *o*-aminobenzaldehyde, or with primary arylamines and aromatic aldehydes.[4]   Again, 3-phenyl-2-benzylquinoxaline (IV) fails to react with several aromatic aldehydes in boiling acetic anhydride[5]; 2-benzylquinoxaline, however, gives the expected product with *p*-nitrobenzaldehyde (see Table XXXIII-2).   3-Phenyl-2-methylquinoxaline also

(III)   (IV)   (V)

gives styryl derivatives with several aldehydes (see Table XXXIII-2). Both 2-cyanomethylquinoxaline (V; R = H) and the 3-methyl analog (V; R = Me) contain a reactive methylene group and yield the anticipated products on reaction with aromatic aldehydes, diazonium salts, and *p*-nitrosodimethylaniline (Tables XXXIII-1 and 3). Condensation products of 2,3-dimethylquinoxaline are described below (Section B), and methyl group reactivity in reduced quinoxalines is mentioned in Chapter XXXVII, Section 1B.

On bromination (in acetic acid containing sodium acetate at 100°), 2-methylquinoxaline gives *2-tribromomethylquinoxaline*,[5,19] m.p. 109°, whence is obtained *2-dibromomethylquinoxaline*, m.p. 118°, by partial debromination with aqueous-alcoholic silver nitrate.[19] As with the condensation reactions mentioned above, the results obtained on attempted bromination, under similar conditions, of 2-methylquinoxalines are greatly dependent on substitution. Thus 2,3-dimethylquinoxaline gives the bis-(dibromomethyl) derivative (*vide infra*); 3-phenyl-2-methyl- gives 3-phenyl-2-dibromomethylquinoxaline, m.p. 148°; 3-phenyl-2-benzyl- and 3-phenyl-2-*p*-chlorobenzylquinoxaline give acetoxy derivatives (as VI), m.p. 126 and 119°, respectively; and 3-phenyl-2-*p*-methoxybenzylquinoxaline is unchanged.[5]

(VI)   (VII)

Oxidation of 2-methylquinoxaline with alkaline permanganate at 50° yields 5-methylpyrazine-2,3-dicarboxylic acid (VII).[7]

2. 2,3-Dimethylquinoxalines

2,3-Dimethylquinoxaline, m.p. 106° [hydrate, m.p. 85°; sulfate, m.p. 151–152° (dec.); chloroaurate, dec. 130°; picrate, m.p. 189°],[8,9] has a dipole moment[10] $\mu = \sim 0.6 \times 10^{-18}$. It is formed by the action of methyl-magnesium iodide on 2,3-dichloroquinoxaline,[11] but is most conveniently prepared from *o*-phenylenediamine by condensation with diacetyl or diacetyl monoxime.[8,9] From the latter reaction an adduct (I) of 2,3-dimethylquinoxaline and diacetyl dioxime has been isolated (the dioxime arises *via* the hydroxylamine liberated by interaction of the monoxime with *o*-phenylenediamine); the compound (I) melts partially at 182° with dissociation into its components, and the same decomposition occurs on treatment with acid or alkali.[12]

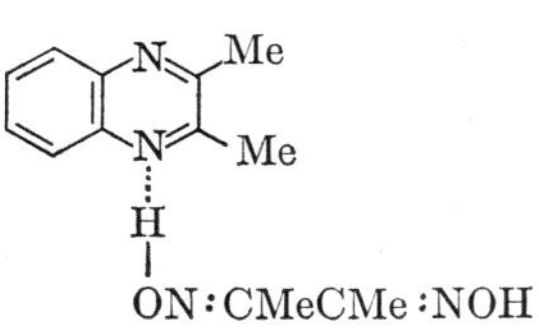

ON:CMeCMe:NOH

(I) 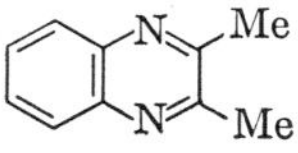   (II) 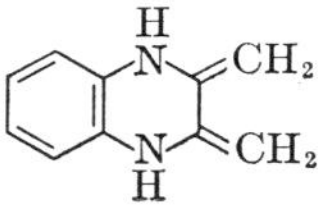   (III) 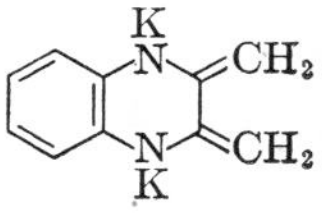   (IV)

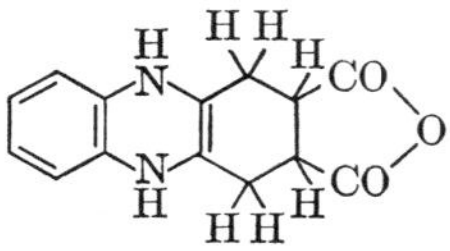

(V) 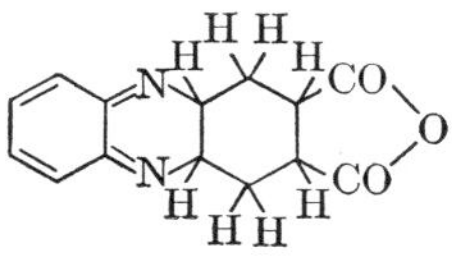   (VI)

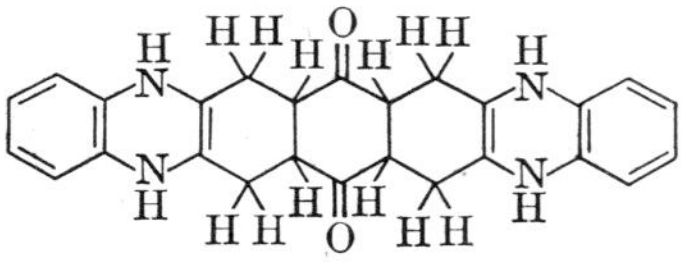

(VII) 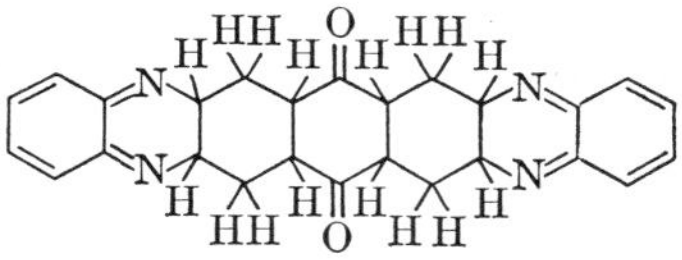   (VIII)

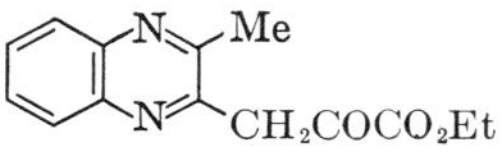

(IX) 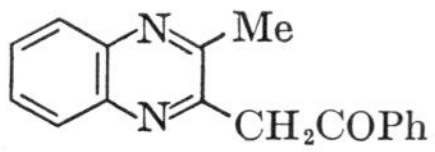   (X)

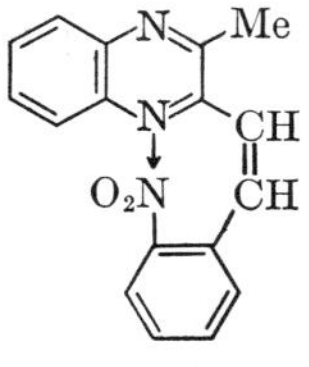

(XI) 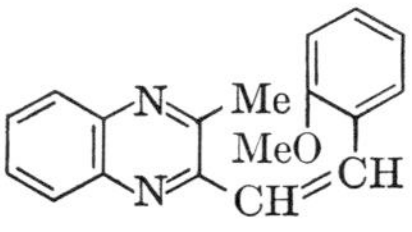   (XII) 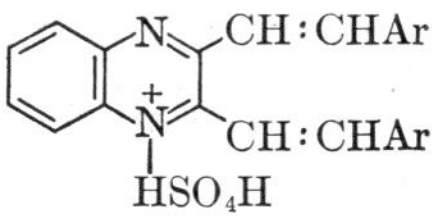   (XIII)

In some of its reactions, 2,3-dimethylquinoxaline (II) behaves in a manner consistent with the view that it can react as the tautomer (III). With potassium amide in liquid ammonia, for example, a crystalline dipotassium salt is formed, which clearly must be (IV)[11]; on treatment with ethyl iodide this salt gives *2,3-di-n-propylquinoxaline*, m.p. 42.9° (corr.), identical with the compound obtained from 2,3-dichloroquinoxaline and pro-

TABLE XXXIII-3. Condensation Products of 2,3-Dimethylquinoxaline

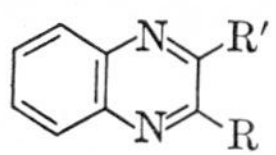

R	R'	Prep.[a]	M.p., °C.	Remarks	Ref.
—CH₂COCO₂Et	Me	A	129,129–130	Orange-yellow needles. Picrate, m.p. 140–141°; O-Bz deriv., m.p. 119–122°; oxime, m.p. 181–182°; p-nitrophenylhydrazone, m.p. 189°; 2,4-dinitrophenylhydrazone, m.p. 179–180°. Gives brownish-green color with FeCl₃. Oxime-acid, dec. 197–199° (crude)	4,5
—CH₂COCO₂H	Me	B	dec. 223–225	Yellow needles	4
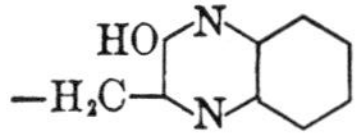 (structure)	Me	C	dec. 355	Red needles. Conc. H₂SO₄ gives green color	4
—CH₂CN	Me	D	131–133	—	4
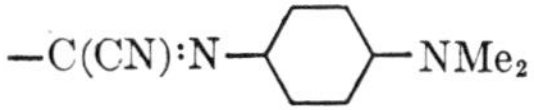 —C(CN):N-⟨⟩-NMe₂	Me	E	183–184	Wine-red needles	4
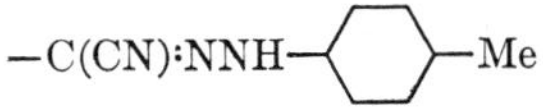 —C(CN):NNH-⟨⟩-Me	Me	F	223–224	Yellow needles	4
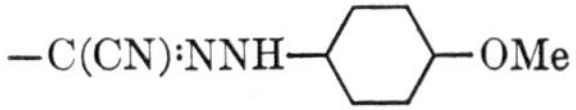 —C(CN):NNH-⟨⟩-OMe	Me	F	204	Yellow needles	4
—C(CN):CHPh	Me	G	138	—	4
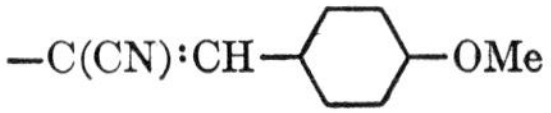 —C(CN):CH-⟨⟩-OMe	Me	G	143	Yellow needles	4
—CH:CHPh	—CH:CHPh	H	190.5	Yellow needles	5

Table continued

TABLE XXXIII-3. Condensation Products of 2,3-Dimethylquinoxaline (*continued*)

R	R'	Prep.[a]	M.p., °C.	Remarks	Ref.
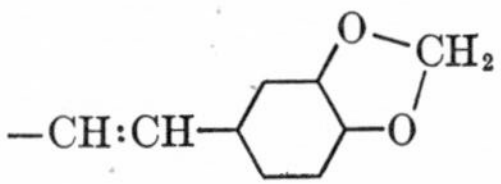 —CH:CH— (benzodioxole)	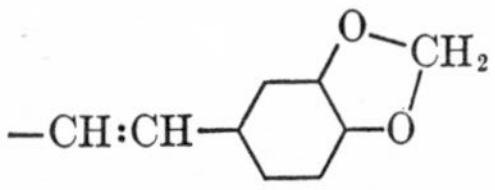 —CH:CH— (benzodioxole)	H	208	Yellow needles	5
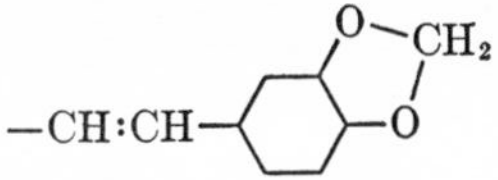 —CH:CH— (benzodioxole)	Me	I	150	Yellow needles	5
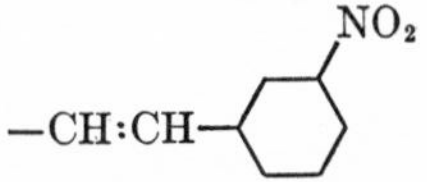 —CH:CH— (NO₂-cyclohexyl)	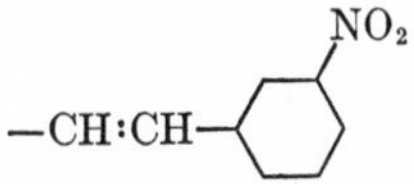 —CH:CH— (NO₂-cyclohexyl)	I,J	237	Yellow cryst.	5
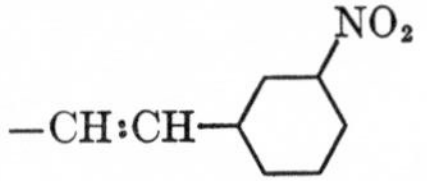 —CH:CH— (NO₂-cyclohexyl)	Me	I	184	~Colorless needles	5
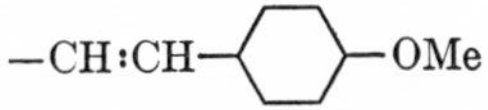 —CH:CH— (OMe-cyclohexyl)	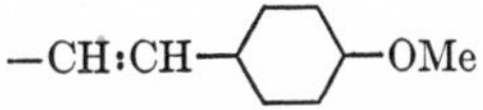 —CH:CH— (OMe-cyclohexyl)	I	163	Yellow needles	5,18
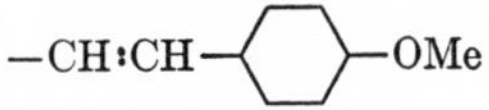 —CH:CH— (OMe-cyclohexyl)	Me	I	122.5	Yellow needles	5,18
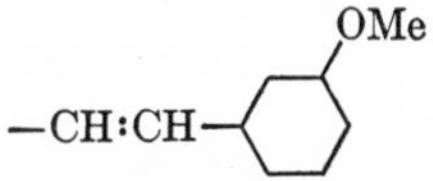 —CH:CH— (OMe-cyclohexyl)	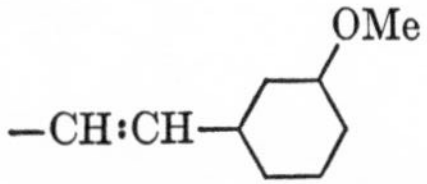 —CH:CH— (OMe-cyclohexyl)	K	126	Yellow prisms	5
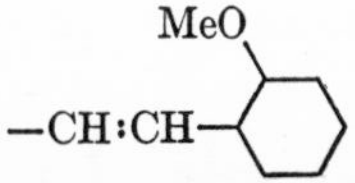 —CH:CH— (MeO-cyclohexyl)	Me	K	112	Yellow cryst.	5

R	R'	Prep.[a]	M.p., °C.	Remarks	Ref.
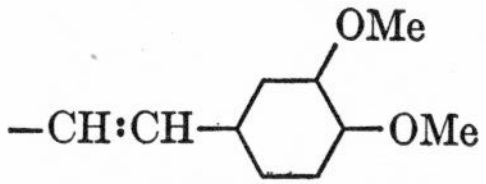 —CH:CH— (3,4-dimethoxyphenyl, OMe/OMe)	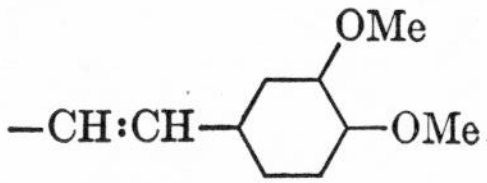 —CH:CH— (3,4-dimethoxyphenyl, OMe/OMe)	K	208	Yellow needles	5
—CH:CH-furyl-α	—CH:CH-furyl-α	K	169	Yellow cryst.	5
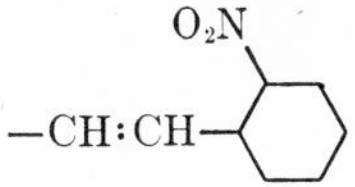 —CH:CH— (O_2N-phenyl)	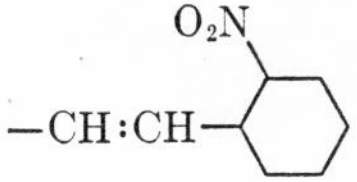 —CH:CH— (O_2N-phenyl)	K	194.5	—	5
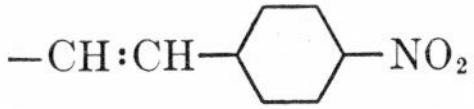 —CH:CH— (phenyl-NO_2)	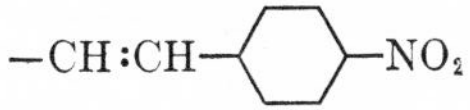 —CH:CH— (phenyl-NO_2)	K	288 (dec.)	Deep yellow cryst.	5
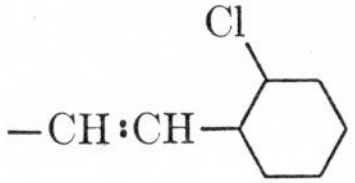 —CH:CH— (Cl-phenyl)	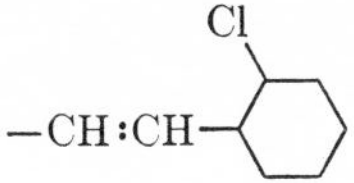 —CH:CH— (Cl-phenyl)	K	189.5	Yellow needles	5
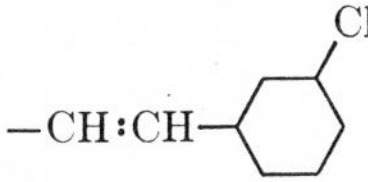 —CH:CH— (Cl-phenyl)	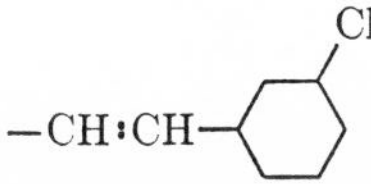 —CH:CH— (Cl-phenyl)	K	149	Yellow needles	5
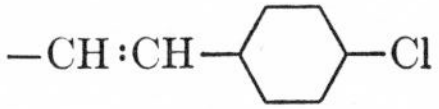 —CH:CH— (phenyl-Cl)	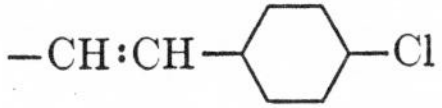 —CH:CH— (phenyl-Cl)	K	218	—	5
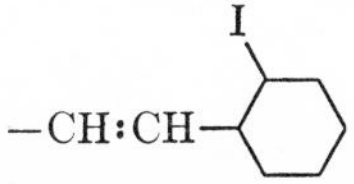 —CH:CH— (I-phenyl)	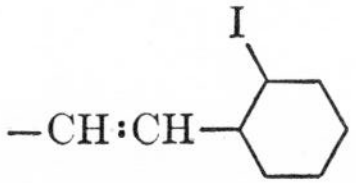 —CH:CH— (I-phenyl)	K	179	Yellow plates	5
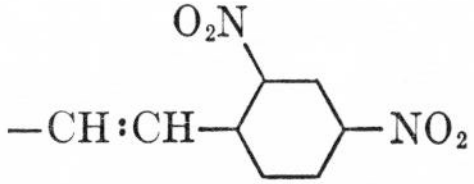 —CH:CH— (O_2N-phenyl-NO_2)	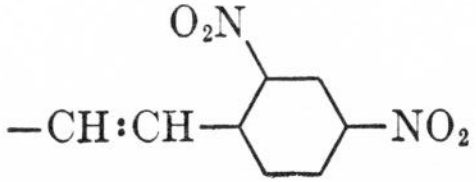 —CH:CH— (O_2N-phenyl-NO_2)	L	295–297 (dec.)	Brown needles	5

Table continued

TABLE XXXIII-3. Condensation Products of 2,3-Dimethylquinoxaline (*continued*)

R	R'	Prep.[a]	M.p., °C.	Remarks	Ref.
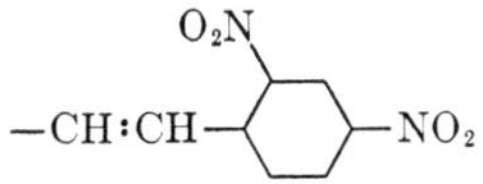 O₂N ... —CH:CH—	Me	K	224–225 (dec.)	Orange-yellow cryst.	5
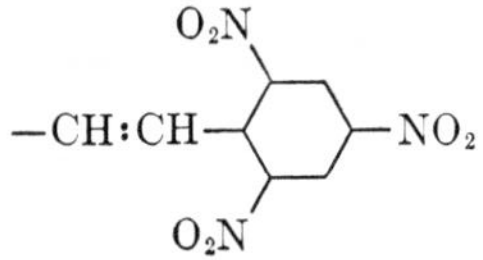 O₂N ... —CH:CH— ... O₂N	Me	K	250–251	Brown cryst.	5
—CH₂COPh		M	125.5–126.5	—	14

[a] A, from 2,3-dimethylquinoxaline, ethyl oxalate, and sodium or potassium ethoxide in ether-alcohol or ether-xylene. B, from the ester by treatment with potassium ethoxide in ether-alcohol at 100°. C, from ethyl 3-methylquinoxal-2-ylpyruvate and o-phenylenediamine at 100°. D, from the oxime-acid (dec. 197–199°; *vide supra*) and warm acetic anhydride. E, from 3-methyl-2-cyanomethylquinoxaline as in method I, Table XXXIII-1. F, from 3-methyl-2-cyanomethylquinoxaline as in method J, Table XXXIII-1. G, from 3-methyl-2-cyanomethylquinoxaline as in method K, Table XXXIII-1. H, from 2,3-dimethylquinoxaline and excess aldehyde at the b.p. I, from 2,3-dimethylquinoxaline (1 mole) and the appropriate aldehyde (1 mole) in boiling acetic anhydride. J, from 3-methyl-2,3'-nitrostyrylquinoxaline and m-nitrobenzaldehyde in boiling acetic anhydride. K, from 2,3-dimethylquinoxaline (1 mole) and the appropriate aldehyde (2 moles) in boiling acetic anhydride. L, as in method K, but with 3 moles of aldehyde. M, from 2,3-dimethylquinoxaline and ethyl benzoate (with sodamide in liquid ammonia).

pylmagnesium iodide.[11] Again, the fact that 2,3-dimethylquinoxaline gives adducts, m.p. >. 305 and 190°, with maleic anhydride and benzoquinone, respectively, suggests that here also the tautomer (III) is involved, the products being formulated as (V) or (VI) and (VII) or (VIII), respectively.[13]

2,3-Dimethylquinoxaline condenses with only 1 mole of ethyl oxalate, giving ethyl 3-methylquinoxal-2-ylpyruvate (IX),[4,5] the methyl and methylene groups of which are unreactive (see Section 1). Similarly, the base condenses with ethyl benzoate to give mainly 3-methyl-2-phenacylquinoxaline (X) (a little of the diphenacyl (?) derivative is also formed.)[14] The methyl group in 3-methyl-2-cyanomethylquinoxaline is unreactive, but the methylene group displays normal reactivity (see Table XXXIII-3).

In reactions with aldehydes, on the other hand, both methyl groups of 2,3-dimethylquinoxaline usually participate, distyryl derivatives being formed (Table XXXIII-3). Under standard conditions of reaction in boiling acetic anhydride the yields of styryl compounds are variable, depending on the nature of the aldehyde[5]; in a few cases monostyryl derivatives are also formed, at times even to the exclusion of the production of distyryl compounds. Bennett and Willis[5] explain these results in terms of steric configuration; the unusually ready formation of 2,3-di-o-nitrostyrylquinoxaline, for example, is regarded as the result of bonding between the ring nitrogen and the nitro group in the monostyryl derivative (XI), the 3-methyl group being thus fully exposed to attack by the aldehyde; whereas in (XII), which is the only product of reaction with o-anisaldehyde, a configuration of the type shown—protecting the 3-methyl group against attack—is enforced by the mutual repulsion between N_1 and the methoxyl group. Bennett and Willis have obtained support for these views by studying the halochromy which is observed with solutions of these styryl quinoxalines in concentrated sulfuric acid.[15] The colors of the acid solutions become progressively deeper in the order nitrostyryl < unsubstituted styryl < methoxystyryl; as the halochromy is due to salt formation (XIII), these results indicate that a nitro group (in the styryl nucleus) hinders, and a methoxyl group assists, the coordination between N_1 and the acid, which is what would be expected on the basis of (XI) and (XII).

Bromination of 2,3-dimethylquinoxaline in chloroform gives a dibromo compound, m.p. 150°, regarded as *2,3-di(bromomethyl)quinoxaline.*[12,16] In acetic acid containing sodium acetate, however, the product[5,16] is *2,3-bis(dibromomethyl)quinoxaline,* m.p. 228°.

Oxidation of 2,3-dimethylquinoxaline with alkaline permanganate at 95° gives 5,6-dimethylpyrazine-2-carboxylic acid.[8]

2,3,6-Trimethylquinoxaline, m.p. 91°, b.p. 270–271°, is prepared by condensation of 3,4-diaminotoluene with diacetyl or diacetyl monoxime in warm aqueous acetic acid.[5,17]   On condensation with aromatic aldehydes in boiling acetic anhydride it yields 2-mono- and 2,3-distyryl derivatives (Table XXXIII-4).

TABLE XXXIII-4.[5] Condensation Products of 2,3,6-Trimethylquinoxaline[a]

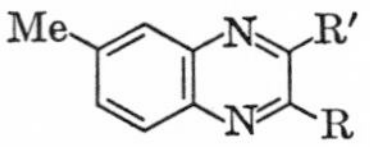

R	R'	M.p., °C.
Ph	Ph	163
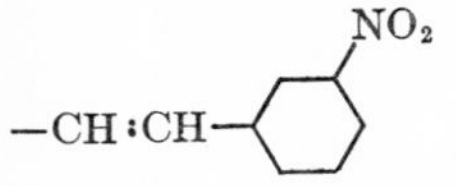 —CH:CH—(NO₂-phenyl)	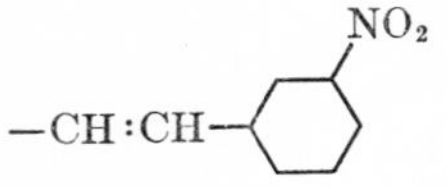 —CH:CH—(NO₂-phenyl)	244.5
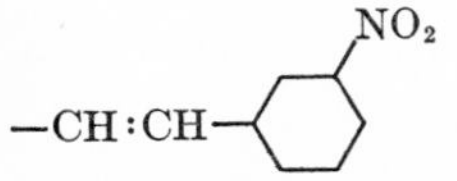 —CH:CH—(NO₂-phenyl)	Me	165
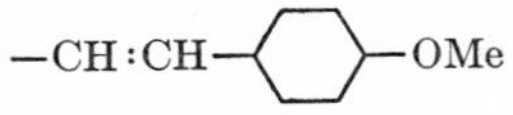 —CH:CH—(OMe-phenyl)	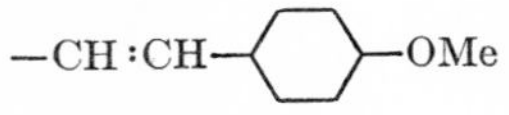 —CH:CH—(OMe-phenyl)	136
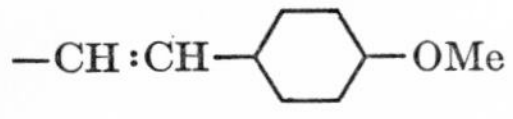 —CH:CH—(OMe-phenyl)	Me	116
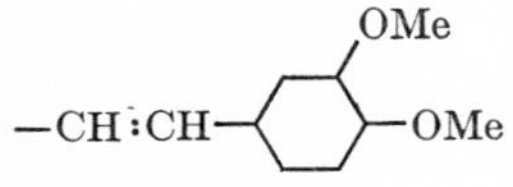 —CH:CH—(di-OMe-phenyl)	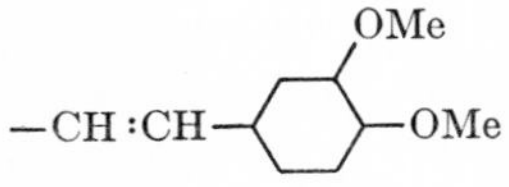 —CH:CH—(di-OMe-phenyl)	205
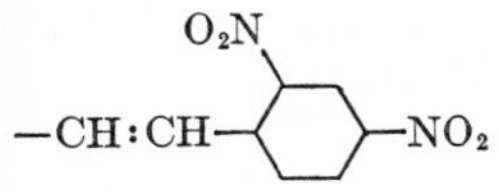 —CH:CH—(O₂N-,NO₂-phenyl)	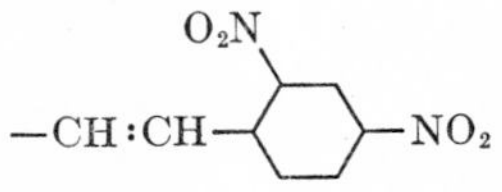 —CH:CH—(O₂N-,NO₂-phenyl)	251–253 (dec.)
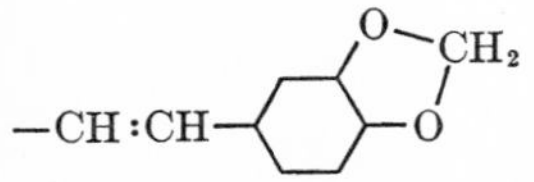 —CH:CH—(methylenedioxyphenyl)	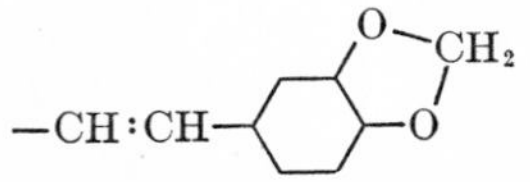 —CH:CH—(methylenedioxyphenyl)	168

[a] Yellow or orange-yellow compounds.

References

1. Hinsberg, *Ann.*, **237**, 327 (1887).
2. Platt and Sharp, *J. Chem. Soc.*, **1948**, 2129.
3. Böttcher, *Ber.*, **46**, 3084 (1913).
4. Borsche and Doeller, *Ann.*, **537**, 39 (1939).
5. Bennett and Willis, *J. Chem. Soc.*, **1928**, 1960.
6. A. H. Cook and Naylor, *J. Chem. Soc.*, **1943**, 397.
7. Leonard and Spoerri, *J. Am. Chem. Soc.*, **68**, 526 (1946).
8. Gabriel and Sonn, *Ber.*, **40**, 4850 (1907).
9. Bost and Towell, *J. Am. Chem. Soc.*, **70**, 903 (1948).
10. van Arkel and Snoek, *Rec. trav. chim.*, **52**, 719 (1933).
11. Ogg, Jr., and Bergstrom, *J. Am. Chem. Soc.*, **53**, 1846 (1931).
12. S. T. Henderson, *J. Chem. Soc.*, **1929**, 466.
13. Schönberg and Mostafa, *J. Chem. Soc.*, **1943**, 654.
14. Bergstrom and Moffat, *J. Am. Chem. Soc.*, **59**, 1494 (1937).
15. Bennett and Willis, *J. Chem. Soc.*, **1929**, 256.
16. Bennett and Willis, *J. Chem. Soc.*, **1930**, 1709.
17. von Pechmann, *Ber.*, **21**, 1411 (1888).
18. McKee, McKee, and Bost, *J. Am. Chem. Soc.*, **69**, 468 (1947).
19. B. R. Brown, *J. Chem. Soc.*, **1949**, 2577.

CHAPTER XXXIV

Quinoxaline Quaternary Salts

A. Preparation

(*1*) By addition of an alkyl ester to a quinoxaline. This standard method of preparing quaternary salts from the corresponding bases is of limited application in the quinoxaline field. Simple quinoxalines, *e.g.*, quinoxaline itself and 6-methylquinoxaline, readily yield quaternary salts by this method (Table XXXIV-1), but substituents in the hetero ring tend to inhibit the reaction; the methiodide of 2,3-dimethylquinoxaline, for example, is formed only by using drastic conditions,[1,2] and 2,3-diphenoxy-quinoxaline does not react[3] with methyl iodide at 100°. 2,3-Dimethyl-quinoxaline may be quaternized by reaction with alkyl sulfates, alkyl arylsulfonates, and Grignard reagents, but not with benzyl chloride, 4-nitro- or 2,4-dinitrobenzyl chloride, ethyl iodide, or propyl iodide.[2]

The question of whether N_1 or N_4 is involved in the formation of quaternary salts of quinoxalines (I) having two different substituents in the hetero ring has received but little attention. The crude methiodide from

(I) (II) (III) (IV)

3-phenyl-2-methylquinoxaline condenses with aldehydes, but the pure salt does not, and it therefore appears that this base gives mainly the N_4 quaternary salt (II) with a little of the N_1 isomer (III).[2] If 3-hydroxy-2-methylquinoxaline is treated with methyl iodide, quaternization is accompanied by methylation at N_4, but methyl sulfate gives the N_1 quaternary salt (IV).[4,5]

(*2*) By direct synthesis from an *o*-aminodiphenylamine or -*N*-alkyl-aniline and a 1,2-diketone in presence of hydrochloric acid. This interesting reaction, discovered by F. Kehrmann and J. Messinger,[6] gives rise to quinoxaline quaternary salts (V) containing substituents (usually phenyl) at C_2 and C_3 (Eq. 1). For reasons which cannot now be regarded as satisfactory, O. N. Witt and C. Schmidt[7] proposed the name "stilbazonium" salts for quaternary quinoxaline salts prepared by this method, and the

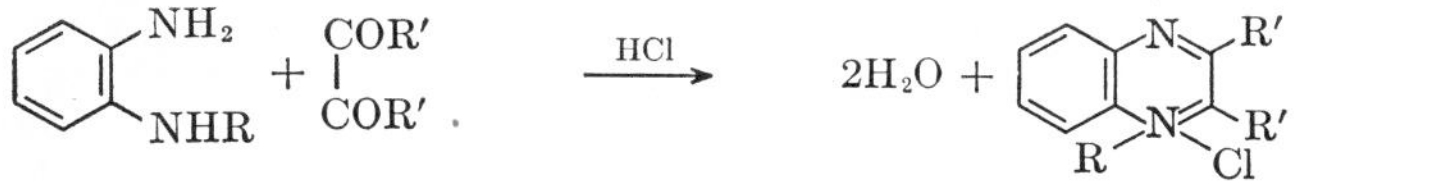

$$2H_2O + \quad (V) \qquad (1)$$

name has persisted to some extent in the literature[8,9]; its continued use serves no useful purpose, however, and merely tends to cause confusion between these quinoxalinium salts and the quaternary salts derivable from the true stilbazoles (bases obtained from 2- and 4-methylpyridine by condensation with aromatic aldehydes).

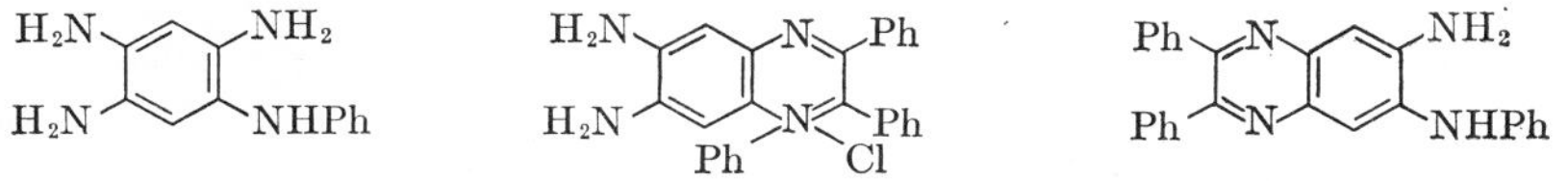

(VI)

(VII)

(VIII)

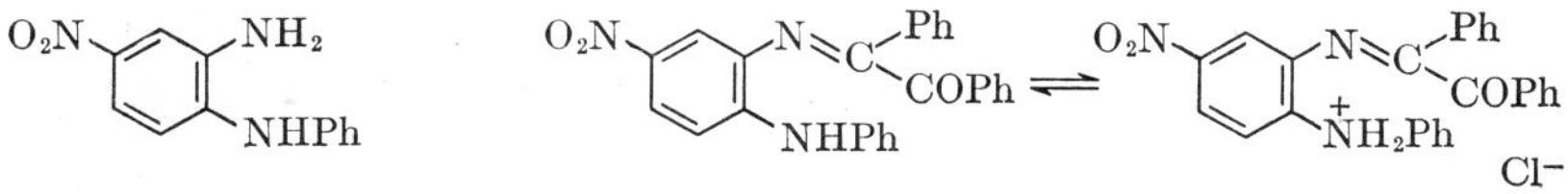

(IX)

(X)

(XI)

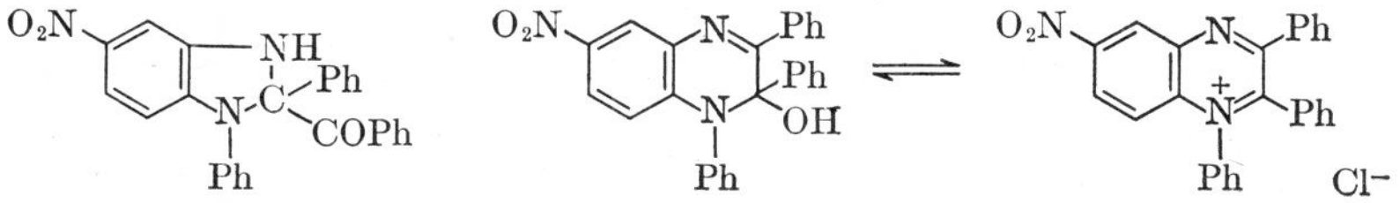

(XIV)

(XIII)

(XII)

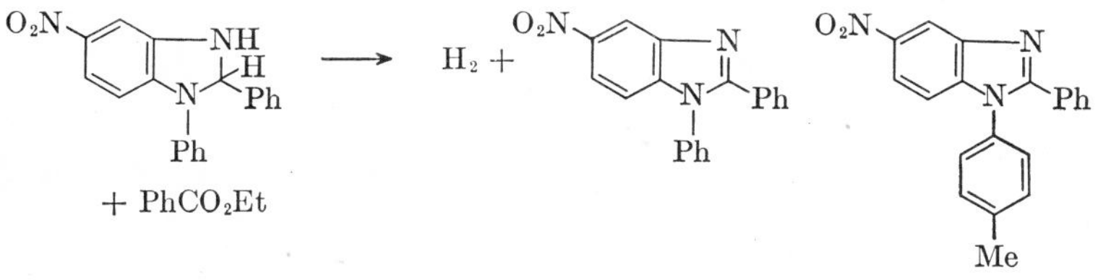

(XV)

+ PhCO₂Et

(XVI)

(XVII)

Two points of interest may be noted in connection with this reaction. First it has been observed that, using the amine (VI), the product of reaction consists almost entirely of (VII), only a very little of the compound (VIII) being formed[10]; quaternary salt formation thus occurs to the almost complete exclusion of the alternative o-phenylenediamine condensation which might also have been expected to occur.

Second, the course of the reaction is greatly modified if the amine component contains a nitro group in the p-position to the secondary amino group, as in (IX). Brand and Wild[11] have studied the behavior of (IX) and its analogs, and have found that the expected quaternary salt (XII) is not obtained by interaction of (IX) and benzil in alcoholic hydrochloric acid, but that the products are the pseudo base (XIII) and 5-nitro-1,2-diphenylbenziminazole (XVI). The initial product is the anil (X), which in acid solution is considered to be in equilibrium with (XI) and (XII). The latter does not separate from acid solution, and on reduction of the acidity immediately passes into the pseudo base (XIII). In boiling alcoholic hydrochloric acid, (X) and (XIII) give the benziminazole (XVI) and ethyl benzoate *via* the intermediates (XIV) and (XV); the hydrogen which is eliminated is not evolved in the free state, and is assumed to reduce one of the entities in the reaction mixture. 5-Nitro-2-phenyl-1-p-tolylbenziminazole (XVII) is similarly formed from the p-tolyl analog of (IX).

The authors[11] consider that these deviations from the normal reaction are the result of the instability conferred by the nitro group on the quaternary ring nitrogen of the salt (XII). The salt (XIX), with a methyl instead of a phenyl group attached to N_1, is sufficiently stable to be isolated, but if the parent amine (XVIII) is refluxed with benzil in alcoholic hydrochloric acid the reaction still follows an abnormal course and yields a mixture of the pseudo base (XX) and 6-nitro-2,3-diphenylquinoxaline (XXI) (in the formation of which demethylation occurs). If the nitro group in (IX) is replaced by chlorine, the labilizing effect is removed, and the normal reaction occurs, giving 6-chloro-1,2,3-triphenylquinoxalinium chloride, and thence the pseudo base.

(XVIII)

(XIX)

(XX)

(XXI)

B. Properties. The quaternary quinoxalinium salts are crystalline solids which decompose on heating (in many cases, particularly the 1-phenyl salts, no decomposition or melting points are recorded in the literature). They form double salts (*e.g.*, with ferric chloride and platinic

TABLE XXXIV-1. Quinoxaline Quaternary Salts

(structure: quinoxaline N–R, X)

R	X	Nuclear Substituents	Prep.[a]	M.p.,° C.	Remarks	Ref.
Me	I	Nil	A	175 (dec.)	Yellow-red plates	15
Et	I	Nil	A	146 (dec.)	Red needles	15
Et	I	6-Me	A	176 (dec.)	Yellow-red cryst.	15
Me	I	2,3-Me₂	B	192	Green-yellow needles	1,2
Ph	Cl	2,3-Ph₂	C	—	Forms double salts $C_{26}H_{19}N_2Cl$, $FeCl_3$ and $(C_{26}H_{19}N_2Cl)_2$, $PtCl_4$	6
Ph	Cl	2,3-[CH(CN)Ph]₂	D	—	Yellow needles. Conc. H_2SO_4 gives orange-yellow color	19
α-C₁₀H₇	Cl	2,3-[CH(CN)Ph]₂	D	—	Red needles. Conc. H_2SO_4 gives red-violet color.	19
α-C₁₀H₇	Cl	2,3-[CH(CN)Ph]₂-6-Me	D	—	Brown needles. Conc. H_2SO_4 gives orange-brown color	19
Ph	Cl	2,3-[CH(CN)Ph]₂-6-NHPh	D	—	Blue-brown needles. Conc. H_2SO_4 gives green color	19
Ph	Cl	2,3-Ph₂-6,7-(NH₂)₂	D	—	Chloroplatinate	10
Ph	Cl	2,3-Ph₂-6-NH₂-7-NHPh	D	—	Green needles	13
Ph	Cl	2,3-Ph₂-7-Cl	D	—	Green-yellow needles	8
Ph	Cl	2,3-Ph₂-7-NHPh	E	—	Brown-violet needles	8
Ph	Cl	2,3-Ph₂-7-NMe₂	E	—	—	8
(cyclohexyl, I)	Cl	2,3-Ph₂-7-Me	D	166–168	Yellow-green micro-needles. Conc. H_2SO_4 gives cherry-red color	17
Ph	I	2,3-Me₂	F	204 (dec.)	—	5
Me	NO₃	2,3-Ph₂	G	120 (not sharp)	—	12
Ph	Cl	6-NH₂-2,3-Ph₂	D	—	—	12

[a] A, from the base and alkyl iodide at room temperature. B, from the anhydrous base and excess methyl iodide at 90°. C, from o-aminodiphenylamine and benzil in alcoholic hydrochloric acid. D, from $o\text{-}C_6H_4\langle{}^{NH_2}_{NHAr}$ and $(RCO)_2$ in acetic acid (or alcohol) containing hydrochloric acid. E, from the 7-chloro compound and the appropriate amine at 150–180°. F, from o-aminodiphenyl-amine and diacetyl in cold alcohol, followed by addition of hydriodic acid. G, from the pseudo base (Table XXXVII-3) and nitric acid.

chloride)[6,10,12] which are often highly crystalline and may be used for characterization, as also may the pseudo bases (*vide infra*) obtainable from the quaternary salts.

The quaternary salts are all more or less highly colored compounds. The color is particularly marked in compounds containing an anilino or dimethylamino group at C_7 by reason of the resonance between the conventional form (with quaternary N_1) and the quinonoid form (as XXII); compounds of this type are in fact quinoxaline analogs of the aposafranine dyes.[8,13]

(XXII)   (XXIII)   (XXIV)

Treatment of 1,2,3-triphenylquinoxalinium bromide with ethylmagnesium iodide gives 1,2,3-triphenyl-2-ethyl-1,2-dihydroquinoxaline (Table XXXVII-1).[14]

C. Decomposition by Alkali. Alkiodides of quinoxaline and 6-methylquinoxaline are said to be decomposed by alkali with the production of volatile material having an unpleasant odor,[15,16] but the reaction has not been further studied. Salts with a phenyl group on the quaternary ring nitrogen are decomposed even by mild alkali (sodium carbonate or ammonia) yielding the corresponding pseudo bases (as XXIII),[6,8,9,17] the properties of which (low melting point, solubility in organic solvents; see Table XXXVII-3) obviously indicate a covalent and not a quaternary hydroxide structure. 6-Amino-7-anilino-1,2,3-triphenylquinoxalinium chloride gives what is probably the anhydro base (XXIV) (Chapter XXXVII, Section 2) on treatment with sodium carbonate.[13]

D. Quinoxaline Cyanines. Cyanine dyes containing one or two quinoxaline nuclei have been prepared and studied by A. H. Cook and his co-workers[2,4,5,18] Thus, condensation of the appropriate 2,3-dimethylquinoxalinium salt and aldehyde in a cold mixture of pyridine and acetic anhydride[2] yields the dyes (XXV; R = Me) (iodide, m.p. 244°; methosulfate, m.p. 182–183°), (XXV; R = Et) (ethosulfate, m.p. 170–171°), and (XXVI; R = Me) (iodide, m.p. 189–190°). The phenyl analogs (XXV; R = Ph) (chloride, dec. 320°) and (XXVI; R = Ph) (acetate, m.p. 154°) and the symmetrical dye (XXVII; R = Ph) (chloride, dec. above 300°; acetate, m.p. 161°) are obtained by way of the unstable methylene base (XXVIII) prepared by interaction of diacetyl with o-aminodiphenylamine in absence of mineral acid.[2,5] The methyl analog of the last-named dye (XXVII; R = Me) (iodide, m.p. 204–205°) is prepared by condensing

1,2,3-trimethylquinoxalinium iodide with sodium formate in acetic anhydride. Condensation of the same quinoxalinium salt with the requisite heterocyclic anilinovinyl quaternary salt in acetic anhydride containing a large excess of sodium acetate yields the benzoxazole dye (XXIX) (dec. above 300°) and the quinoline analog (XXX) (m.p. > 360°). The dye (XXXI) (dec. above 300°) is prepared *via* the methylene base (XXXII). Other dyes, for details of which the original papers[4,18] should be consulted, have been prepared from quaternary salts of reduced quinoxalines, e.g., (XXXIII; R = Me, Ph; R' = Me, Et) (Chapter XXXVII, Section 1B).

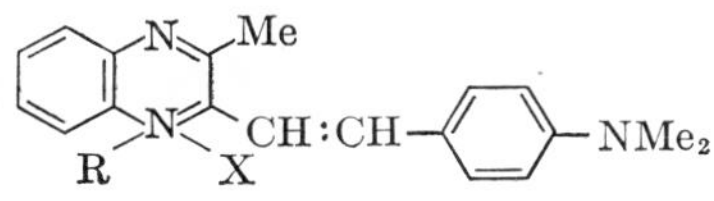

(XXV)

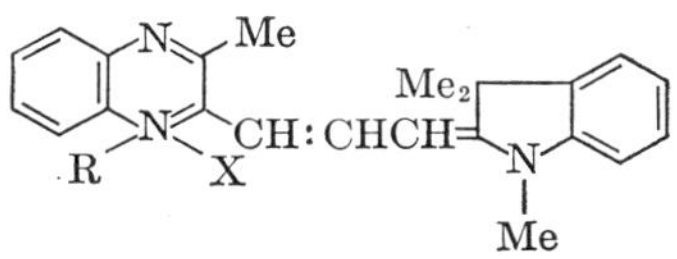

(XXVI)

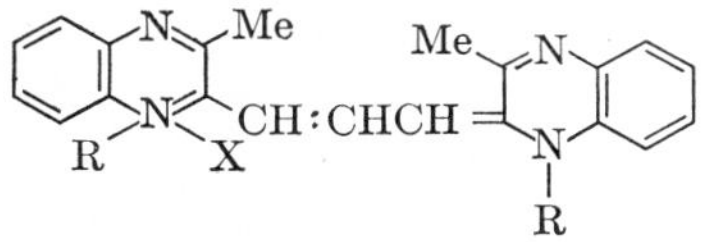

(XXVII)

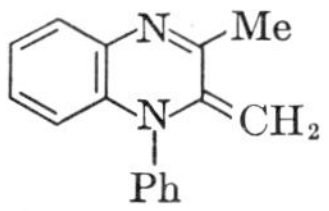

(XXVIII)

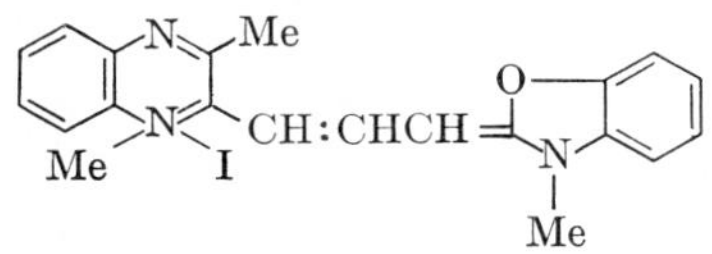

(XXIX)

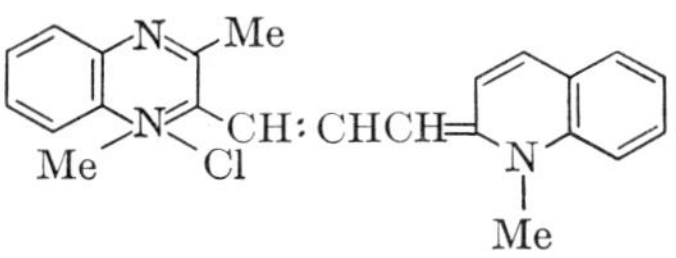

(XXX)

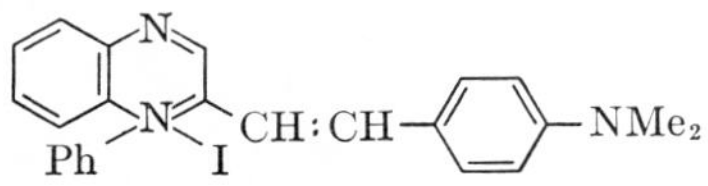

(XXXI)

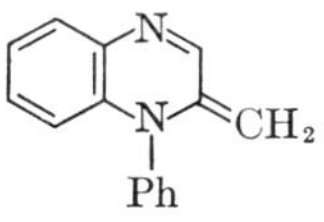

(XXXII)

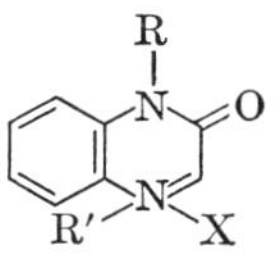

(XXXIII)

In these cyanine dyes the quinoxaline nucleus has a marked bathochromic effect in comparison with other heterocyclic nuclei. The colors of the dyes are reversibly discharged by alkali. Although stable in very dilute acid, the dyes are in general acid-sensitive, and can only be satisfactorily prepared under the mild conditions given above.

References

1. Bennett and Willis, *J. Chem. Soc.*, **1928**, 1960.
2. A. H. Cook, Garner, and Perry, *J. Chem. Soc.*, **1942**, 710.
3. Lockhart and Turner, *J. Chem. Soc.*, **1937**, 424.
4. A. H. Cook and Perry, *J. Chem. Soc.*, **1943**, 394.
5. Anker and A. H. Cook, *J. Chem. Soc.*, **1944**, 489.
6. Kehrmann and Messinger, *Ber.*, **24**, 1239 (1891).
7. Witt and Schmidt, *Ber.*, **25**, 1013 (1892).
8. Kehrmann and Falke, *Helv. Chim. Acta*, **7**, 981 (1924).
9. P. Jacobson, *Ann.*, **287**, 97 (1895).
10. Kehrmann and Stanoyévitch, *Helv. Chim. Acta*, **8**, 663 (1925).
11. Brand and Wild, *Ber.*, **56**, 105 (1923).
12. Kehrmann and Messinger, *Ber.*, **25**, 1627 (1892).
13. Kehrmann, *Ber.*, **50**, 554 (1917).
14. Freund and Richard, *Ber.*, **42**, 1101 (1909).
15. Hinsberg, *Ann.*, **292**, 245 (1896).
16. Hinsberg, *Ann.*, **237**, 327 (1887).
17. P. Jacobson, *Ann.*, **427**, 142 (1922).
18. A. H. Cook and Naylor, *J. Chem. Soc.*, **1943**, 397.
19. Dutt and Sen, *J. Chem. Soc.*, **1922**, 2663.

CHAPTER XXXV

Formation of Quinoxalines from Compounds Containing a Furan Ring

1. Conversion of 5-Hydroxy-2,5-diphenyl-4-keto-4,5-dihydrofurans and Related Compounds into Quinoxalines

The transformations described in this section have been carried out chiefly by R. E. Lutz and his co-workers during a study of the relationships existing between 1,4-diphenylbutane-1,2,4-trione derivatives and the furans named in the title.

5-Hydroxy-2,5-diphenyl-4-keto-4,5-dihydrofuran (I) stands in tautomeric relationship to 1,4-diphenylbutane-1,2,4-trione (II), and on condensation with o-phenylenediamine would therefore be expected to give 3-phenacyl-2-phenylquinoxaline (III).

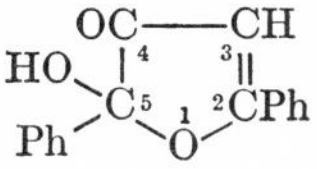

(I) 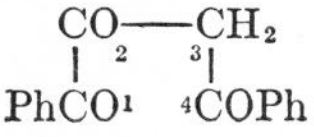   (II) 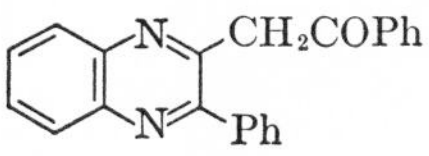   (III)

The questions of whether compounds of types (I) and (II) are interconvertible and of whether a particular entity is best represented by the cyclic or open-chain structure are without relevance here. The point which is important for the present discussion is that, although prototropy can be prevented, and the open-chain form stabilized, by the introduction of suitable substituents (Table XXXV-1, first column), the removal of the mobile hydrogen does not prevent the more or less facile conversion of these open-chain derivatives into quinoxalines. The conversion of the cyclic (furan) derivatives into quinoxalines is also readily effected. These facts are summarized in Table XXXV-1; the acyclic and furan compounds given in the first and second columns, respectively, yield the quinoxalines shown in the third column by treatment with o-phenylenediamine in one of the lower alcohols. It will be seen that the potential or actual 1,2-diketone group originates from C_1 and C_2 of the acyclic compound (i.e., from C_5 and C_4 of the dihydrofuran), and that the C_3 side chain of the quinoxaline arises from the C_3-C_4 fragment of the butanetrione derivatives (i.e., from the C_2-C_3 portion of the furans).

TABLE XXXV-1

Structure of butanetrione	Structure of related dihydrofuran	Structure of resultant quinoxaline	M.p., etc., of quinoxaline	Ref.
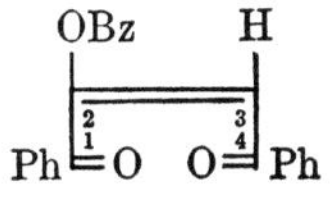 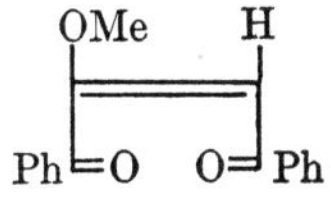 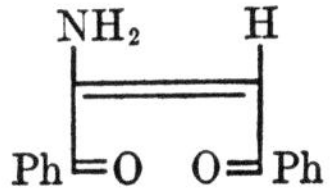 OBz, H, Ph≡O, O=Ph	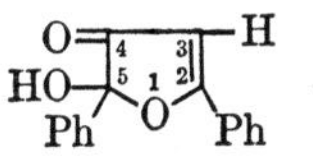 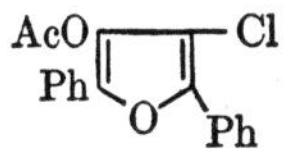 H, Ph, O=, HO, Ph	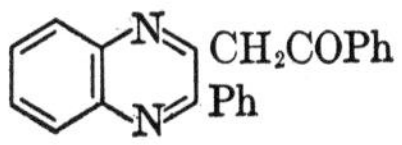 CH₂COPh, Ph (quinoxaline)	Orange crystals, m.p. 169–170°	6
OMe, H, Ph≡O, O=Ph	Cl, Ph, AcO, Ph			
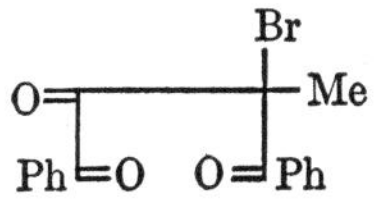 NH₂, H, Ph≡O, O=Ph	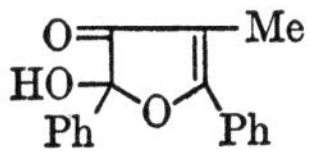 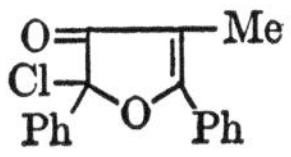 Me, Ph, O=, HO, Ph	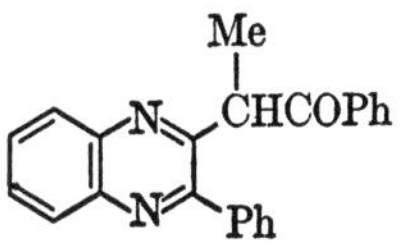 Me, CHCOPh, Ph (quinoxaline)	155.5–156° (corr.)	7
Br, Me, O=, Ph≡O, O=Ph	Me, Ph, O=, Cl, Ph			

Structure of butanetrione	Structure of related dihydrofuran	Structure of resultant quinoxaline	M.p., etc., of quinoxaline	Ref.
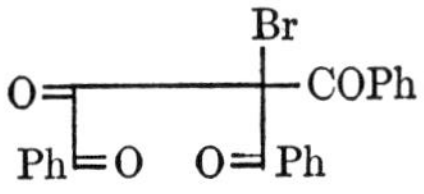 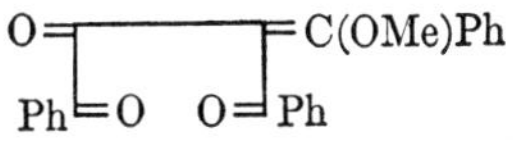 Br–COPh / O=C Ph–O O=Ph	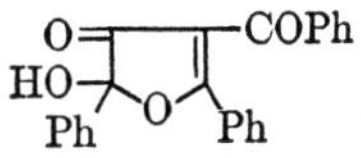 O= , HO–Ph, COPh, Ph–O	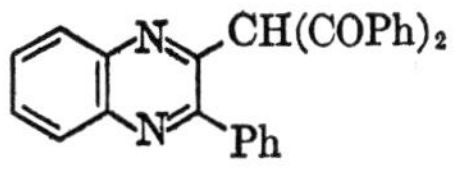 CH(COPh)$_2$ / Ph (IV)	157°	1
C(OMe)Ph / Ph=O O=Ph				
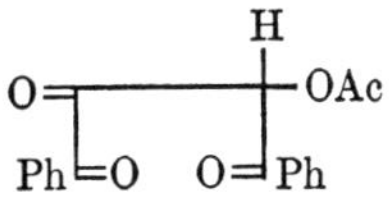 H–OAc / O= Ph O=Ph	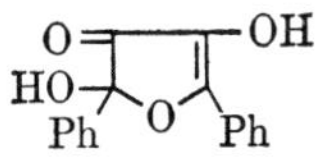 O= , HO–Ph, OH, Ph–O	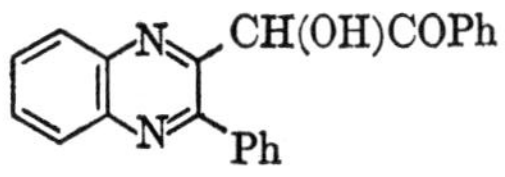 CH(OH)COPh / Ph	187–188°	8
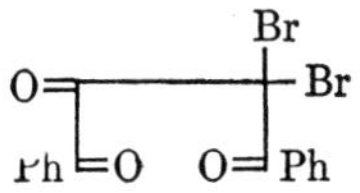 Br–Br / O= Ph rh O=Ph	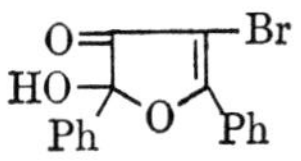 O= , HO–Ph, Br, Ph–O	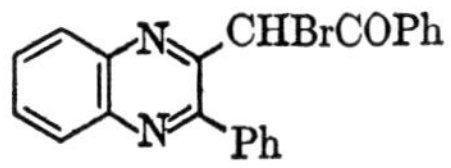 CHBrCOPh / Ph	Light yellow crystals, m.p. 191–192° (corr.)	9

The structure of 2-phenyl-3-dibenzoylmethylquinoxaline (Table XXXV-1, formula IV) follows from the fact that on acid hydrolysis it yields (III).[1]

2. Conversion of Coumaran-3-ones into Quinoxalines

A. 2-Hydroxy- and 2-Bromo-coumaran-3-ones. Several investigators have observed that coumaran-3-ones (I) containing suitable substituents at C_2 yield 3,2′-hydroxyarylquinoxalines (II) when they are condensed with *o*-phenylenediamine in boiling alcohol or acetic acid. A

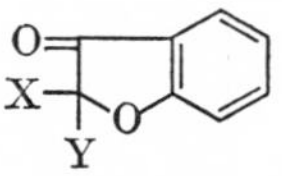

(I) 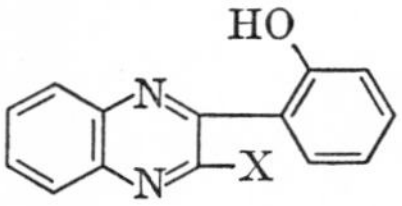   (II) 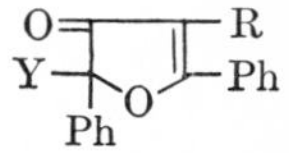   (III)

comparison of the structure (I) with that of the dihydrofurans (III) discussed in the preceding section obviously suggests a connection between the two quinoxaline syntheses, and an examination of the available data indicates that the reactions are in fact intimately related.

Coumaranone (I; X = Y = H) and 2-bromo-2-alkylcoumaranones (I; X = alkyl; Y = Br) do not react with *o*-phenylenediamine,[2,3] but analogs of (I) in which Y is halogen or hydroxyl and X is alkyl or a hydrogen atom react to form quinoxalines of the general formula (II; X = H or alkyl). From Table XXXV-1 it is seen that the dihydrofurans which yield quinoxalines are compounds of type (III) in which Y is likewise hydroxyl or chlorine, and a comparison of the data given in Table XXXV-1 with those in Table XXXV-2 shows that the dihydrofurans react in precisely the same manner as the comparable coumaranones.

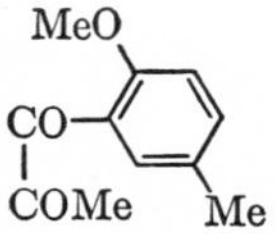

(V)

The structure of (IV) (Table XXXV-2) follows from its conversion into the methyl ether, also produced by independent synthesis from *o*-phenylenediamine and the diketone (V) (Table XXIV-1).

TABLE XXXV-2

Structure of coumaranone	Structure of resultant quinoxaline	M.p., etc., of quinoxaline	Ref.
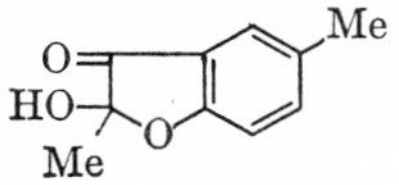 (structure)	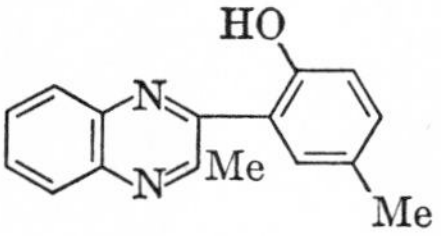 (structure) (IV)	194–195°. Amphoteric	2
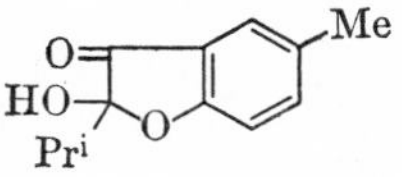 (structure)	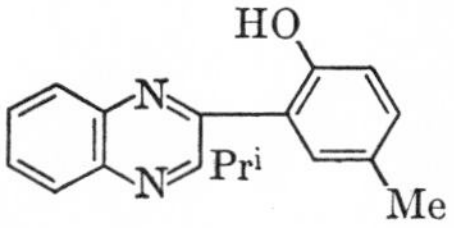 (structure)	161–162°. Amphoteric	2
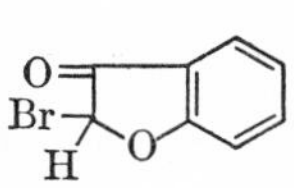 (structure)	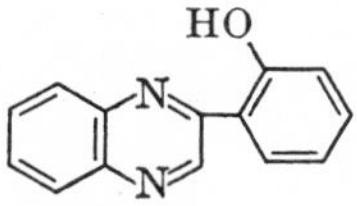 (structure)	189°. Yellow needles. Conc. H₂SO₄ gives brown-red- color	3
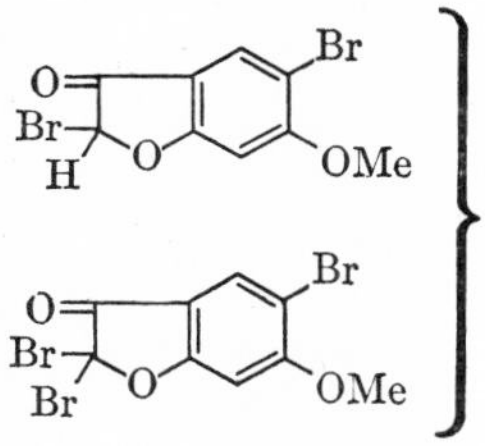 (structures, bracketed)	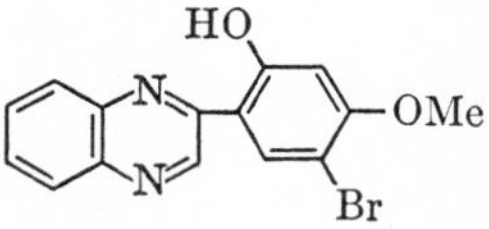 (structure)	240°. Yellow needles. Conc. H₂SO₄ gives deep blue color. OBz deriv., m.p. 212°	3
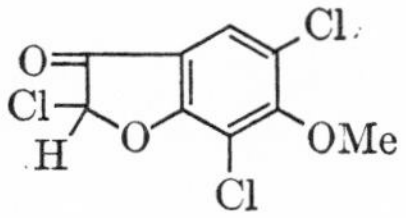 (structure)	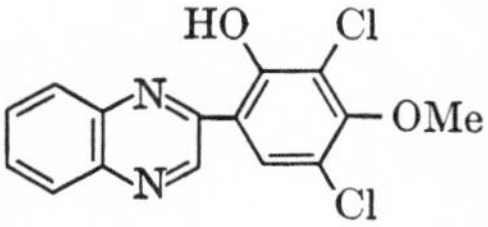 (structure)	237°. Yellow needles. Conc. H₂SO₄ gives intense red color	3
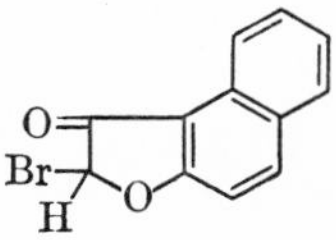 (structure)	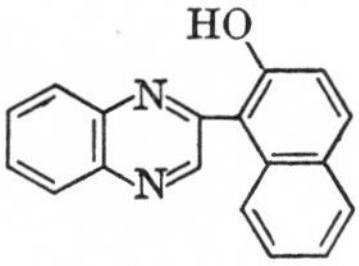 (structure)	142°. Orange-red crystals. OBz deriv., m.p. 156°	5
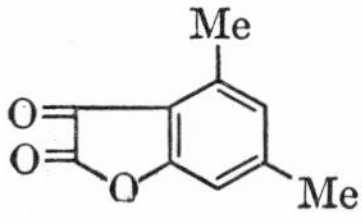 (structure)	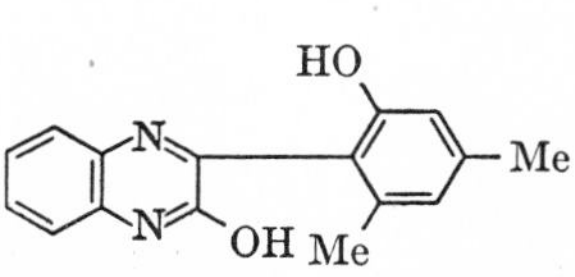 (structure)	260°. Yellow needles	4

Table continued

TABLE XXXV-2. (*continued*)

Structure of coumaranone	Structure of resultant quinoxaline	M.p., etc., of quinoxaline	Ref.
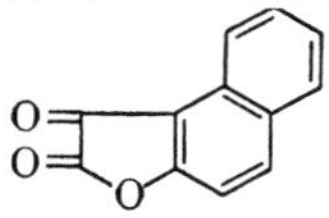	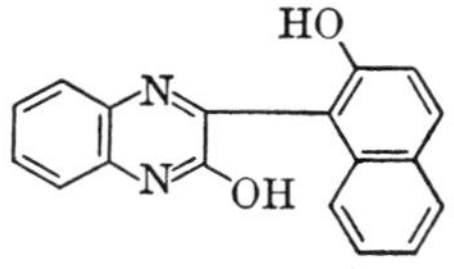 (X)	287°. Orange-yellow needles Conc. H_2SO_4 gives blue color. Ac_2 deriv., m.p. 227°	5
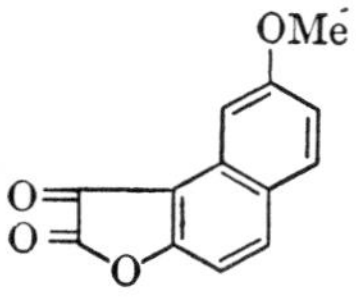	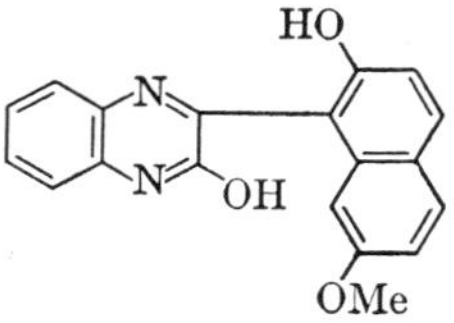	275–276°. Yellow needles. Conc. H_2SO_4 gives violet color	10

B. Coumaran-2,3-diones. Examination of the structure of coumaran-2,3-diones, *e.g.*, (VI), suggests that condensation with *o*-phenylene-diamine might occur in either of two possible ways. A reaction analogous to those already considered would lead, by fission of the O—C linkage in the manner shown, to the corresponding 2-hydroxy-3,2′-hydroxyaryl-quinoxaline (VII) *via* the intermediate (VIII). Alternatively the coumarandione might function simply as a 1,2-diketone and yield a benzofurano-quinoxaline (IX). Experiment shows, as indicated in Table XXXV-2, that only the first of these reactions occurs. At 290–300°, however, (VII)

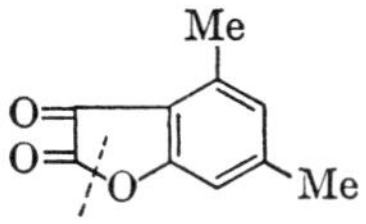

(VI) 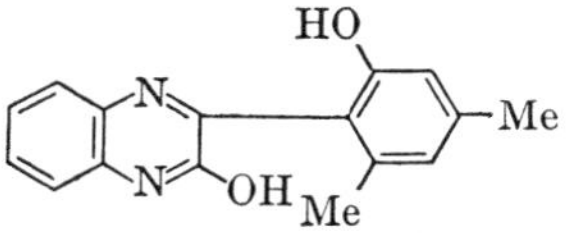   (VII) 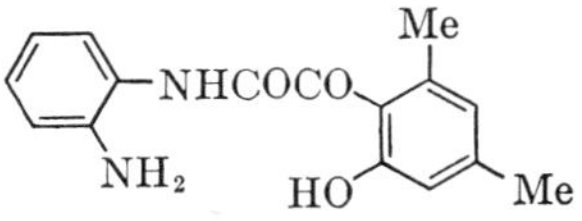   (VIII)

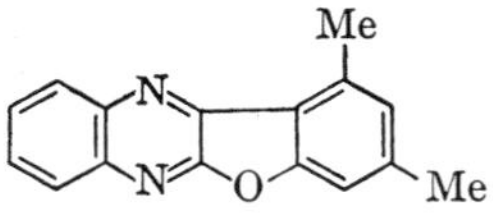

(IX)   (XI)
R.I. 2459   *R.I.* 3088

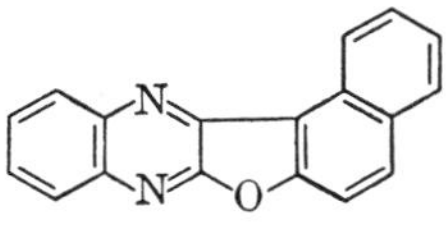

undergoes dehydration to (IX) (m.p. 206°), and (X) (Table XXXV-2) yields (XI) (yellow needles, m.p. 218°, giving a blue color with concentrated sulfuric acid).[4,5]

References

1. Lutz, J. M. Smith, Jr., and Stuart, *J. Am. Chem. Soc.*, **63**, 1143 (1941).
2. von Auwers and W. Müller, *Ber.*, **50**, 1149 (1917).
3. Fries and Saftien, *Ann.*, **442**, 284 (1925).
4. Fries and Bartens, *Ann.*, **442**, 254 (1925).
5. Fries and Pusch, *Ann.*, **442**, 272 (1925).
6. Lutz and Stuart, *J. Am. Chem. Soc.*, **58**, 1885 (1936).
7. Lutz and Stuart, *J. Am. Chem. Soc.*, **59**, 2316 (1937).
8. Blatt, *J. Am. Chem. Soc.*, **58**, 1894 (1936).
9. Lutz and Stuart, *J. Am. Chem. Soc.*, **59**, 2322 (1937).
10. Lesser and Gad, *Ber.*, **60**, 242 (1927).

CHAPTER XXXVI

2-Polyhydroxyalkylquinoxalines

1. Synthesis

It has long been known that o-phenylenediamine may be condensed with aldoses (I) to give quinoxalines (II) or benziminazoles (III),[1,2] and in recent years the condensation of o-diamines with many sugars and sugar derivatives has been studied in detail, and the scope of the reaction considerably extended, by a number of German workers.

CHO
|
CHOH(CHOH)$_n$CH$_2$OH

(I)

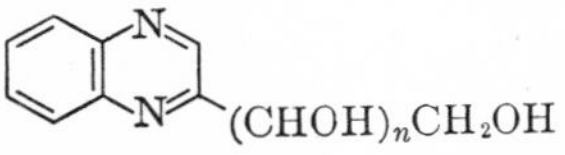

(CHOH)$_n$CH$_2$OH

(II)

(CHOH)$_{n+1}$CH$_2$OH

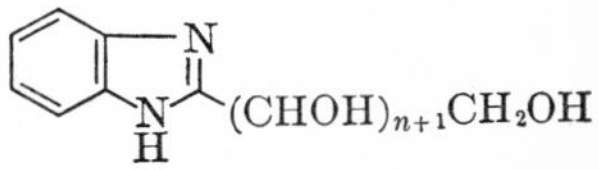

(III)

CO$_2$R
|
CO(CHOH)$_3$CH$_2$OH

(IV)

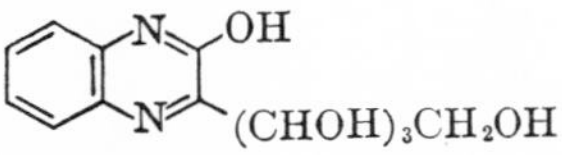

OH / (CHOH)$_3$CH$_2$OH

(V)

COPh
|
CO(CHOH)$_3$CH$_2$OH

(VI)

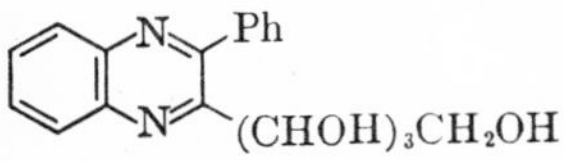

Ph / (CHOH)$_3$CH$_2$OH

(VII)

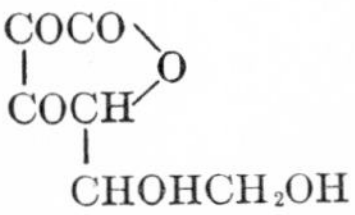

COCO
|
COCH
|
CHOHCH$_2$OH

(VIII)

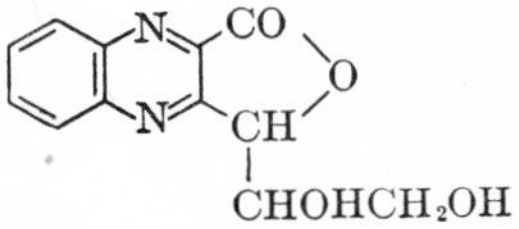

CO
CH
|
CHOHCH$_2$OH

(IX)
R.I. 1688

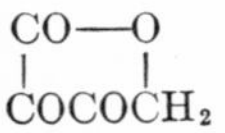

CO—O
| |
COCOCH$_2$

(X)

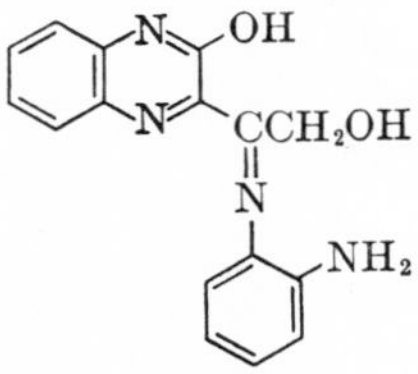

OH
CCH$_2$OH
‖
N

NH$_2$

(XI)

(CHOH)$_3$CH$_2$OH

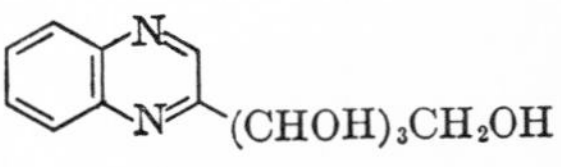

(XII)

Standard quinoxaline syntheses of the types discussed in earlier chapters may be effected by the interaction of o-diamines with suitably substituted sugar derivatives, e.g., α-keto acids or 1,2-diketones (the use of

300

these derivatives has the additional advantage of preventing benziminazole formation which might otherwise occur[3]).   Thus the sodium or potassium salt of d-glucosonic acid (as IV) yields 3-hydroxy-2-d-arabotetrahydroxy-butylquinoxaline (V) with o-phenylenediamine in dilute hydrochloric acid[4] (*cf.* Chapter XXVII), and the stereoisomer of (V) similarly results from the methyl ester of l-glucosonic acid.[5]   Again, 1-phenyl-d-fructosone (VI) undergoes a normal 1,2-diketone reaction and yields 3-phenyl-2-d-arabo-tetrahydroxybutylquinoxaline (VII),[6] and a solution of 2,3-diketogluconic acid lactone (VIII) likewise gives 2-d-erythrotrihydroxypropylquinoxaline-3-carboxylic acid lactone (IX)[7,8] (*cf.* Chapter XXIV).   This last reaction, involving condensation at C_2-C_3 of (VIII), should be contrasted with the reaction of (X), where condensation occurs at C_1-C_2 after opening of the lactone ring, the product being (XI) (Table XXVII-2).

In contrast to the foregoing, the reaction between o-phenylenediamine and glucose is not a "standard" quinoxaline synthesis, because the formation of the product, 2-d-arabotetrahydroxybutylquinoxaline (XII) involves elimination of both hydrogen and water.   In addition to its formation from glucose,[1] (XII) has also been prepared from glucosamine,[9] glucosone,[10] and sucrose.[11]   The preparation of (XII) has also been studied in the presence of hydrazine, and this, as shown below, has led to improved yields and also to an understanding of the probable mechanism of reaction.

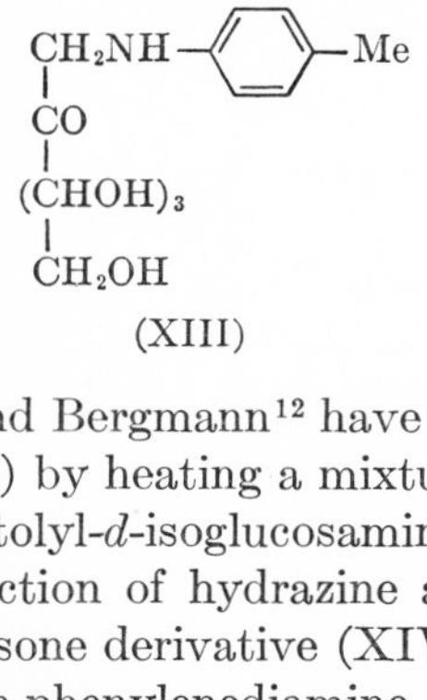

$$
\begin{array}{ll}
\begin{array}{l}
CH_2NH \\
| \\
CO \\
| \\
(CHOH)_3 \\
| \\
CH_2OH
\end{array}
&
\begin{array}{l}
CH\!:\!NNH_2 \\
| \\
C\!:\!NNH_2 \\
| \\
(CHOH)_3 \\
| \\
CH_2OH
\end{array}
\\
\quad\quad (XIII) & \quad\quad (XIV)
\end{array}
$$

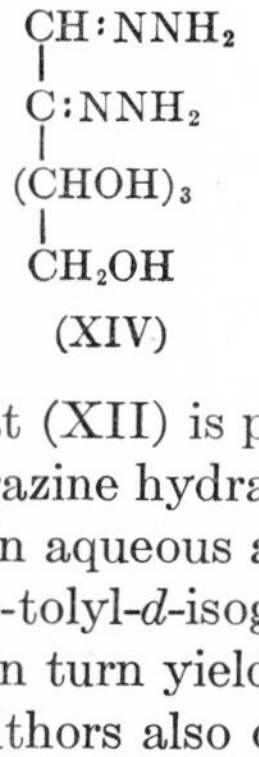

Weygand and Bergmann[12] have shown that (XII) is produced in very high yield (90%) by heating a mixture of hydrazine hydrate, o-phenylene-diamine, and p-tolyl-d-isoglucosamine (XIII) in aqueous acetic acid; furthermore, the action of hydrazine alone on p-tolyl-d-isoglucosamine furnishes the glucosone derivative (XIV), which in turn yields (XII) by condensation with o-phenylenediamine.   These authors also observe that hydrazine dehydrogenates fructose, but not glucose, in weakly acid or alkaline medium.   On the basis of these results they have proposed a mechanism for the conversion of glucose into (XII) (Scheme 1).   In this scheme, (XV), the initial product of reaction between o-phenylenediamine and glucose, is converted *via* the Amadori rearrangement into an analog (XVI) of (XIII); condensation of this with hydrazine yields (XVIII), which by loss of ammonia in two successive stages (the hydrazine thus functioning as hydrogen acceptor) furnishes (XII).

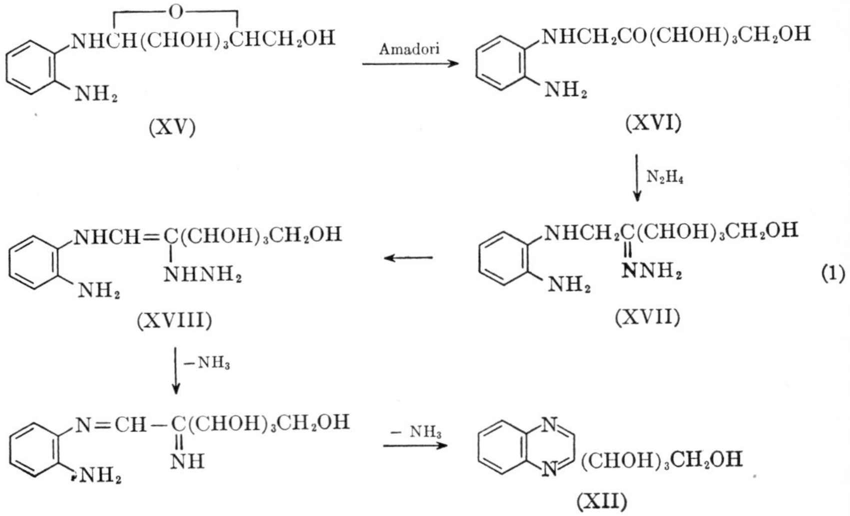

The beneficial effect of hydrazine has also been observed by Ohle and Hielscher,[13] who favor the use of boric acid in the reaction mixture. Under these conditions (XII) may be obtained in 35% yield directly from glucose, but with fructose the yield is much higher (60–70%). The use of substituted hydrazines (methyl- and phenylhydrazine, sym- and asym-dimethylhydrazine, sym- and asym-diphenylhydrazine, and phenylhydrazine-p-sulfonic acid) does not produce markedly different effects, and hydroxylamine gives inferior results.[13] When phenylhydrazine is used in the preparation of (XII), further reactions occur (Section 2C) unless the experimental conditions are carefully controlled.

It has already been stated (vide supra) that aldoses may give either benziminazoles or quinoxaline derivatives by condensation with o-phenylenediamine. By means of the hydrazine-boric acid reaction medium, however, quinoxalines* may be obtained[14] from sugars (e.g., l-arabinose, d-galactose) which under other conditions yield only benziminazoles. These findings may invalidate the earlier statement of Maurer et al.[3] that substituted o-diamines, viz., toluylenediamine and o-diaminobenzoic acid, yield only benziminazoles irrespective of the sugar used.

2. Properties and Reactions

A. General. 2-Polyhydroxyalkylquinoxalines are crystalline, optically active solids (see Table XXXVI-1) which may be acetylated at the hydroxylated side chain. The anticipated susceptibility to oxidizing

---

* In these cases the formation of quinoxalines was diagnosed by conversion of the crude products (in solution) into flavazoles (Chapter XXXVIII, Section 2C) and not by isolation of the quinoxalines themselves.

TABLE XXXVI-1. 2-Polyhydroxyalkylquinoxalines

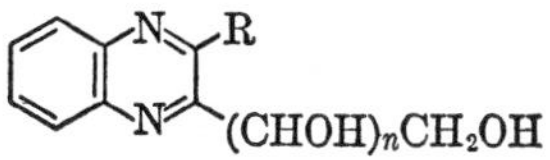

R / (CHOH)$_n$CH$_2$OH structure

n	Configuration	R	Prep.[a]	M.p., °C.	$[\alpha]_D$	Remarks	Ref.
3	d-arabo-	OH	A	199–200	—	Gives Ac$_4$ deriv. Reduces Fehling soln. and hypoiodite	4
3	l-xylo-	OH	A	170 (dec.)	−62° (H$_2$O)	—	5
2	d-erythro-	CONH$_2$	B	167	−86.8° (C$_5$H$_5$N)	γ-Lactone of hydroxy acid, m.p. 187°, $[\alpha]_D$ +151° (C$_5$H$_5$N), −18.56° (Na-OH); gives Ac$_2$ deriv. Hydrazide, m.p. 171°, $[\alpha]_D$ −77.96° (C$_5$H$_5$N)	7
3	d-arabo-	Ph	A	198	−156°, −145° (C$_5$H$_5$N)	—	19,6
3	d-arabo-	H	A,C,D, E,F,G	194 (dec.) 192–193	−85.8° (4 N HCl)	Hydrate, m.p. 187–188°, $[\alpha]_D$, −75.2° (5 N HCl). Gives Ac$_4$ deriv., m.p. 121° (120°), $[\alpha]_D$ −30.3° (−29.2°) (CHCl$_3$)	1,3,4,9–11
3	d-arabo-	OMe	H	183	−13.7° (C$_5$H$_5$N)	—	5

[a] A, see text. B, from the lactone (see text for prepn.) and methanolic ammonia at 20°. C, from o-phenylenediamine and glucose. D, from o-phenylenediamine and mannose. E, from o-phenylenediamine and d-glucosamine hydrochloride in presence of cupric acetate in aqueous acetic acid at 50°. F, from o-phenylenediamine and glucosone in dilute sodium hydroxide (room temperature). G, from o-phenylenediamine and cane sugar. H, from the tetraacetoxy compound by hydrolysis.

agents is illustrated by the conversion of 2-d-arabotetrahydroxybutyl quinoxaline (I) in high yield into quinoxaline-2-carboxylic acid with alkaline hydrogen peroxide (Table XXIX-1) and by that of the 3-hydroxy analog into 2,3-dihydroxyquinoxaline by oxidation with acid permanganate.[4] 2-Polyhydroxyalkylquinoxalines are also oxidized by Fehling solution and by hypoiodite[4,5,7,8]; 2-polyhydroxyalkylbenziminazoles, on the other hand, are not oxidized by these reagents[3,4] and a simple means is thus at hand of distinguishing between the two possible types of product formed by condensation of sugars with o-diamines (Section 1).

On treatment with hot sulfuric acid, 2-d-arabotetrahydroxybutylquinoxaline is converted into glucazidone (Chapter XXXVIII, Section 1C) by cyclodehydration.

B. Decomposition by Alkali.   3-Hydroxy-2-d-arabotetrahydroxybutylquinoxaline is completely resinified if it is boiled for a short time with 0.1 N sodium hydroxide.[15]

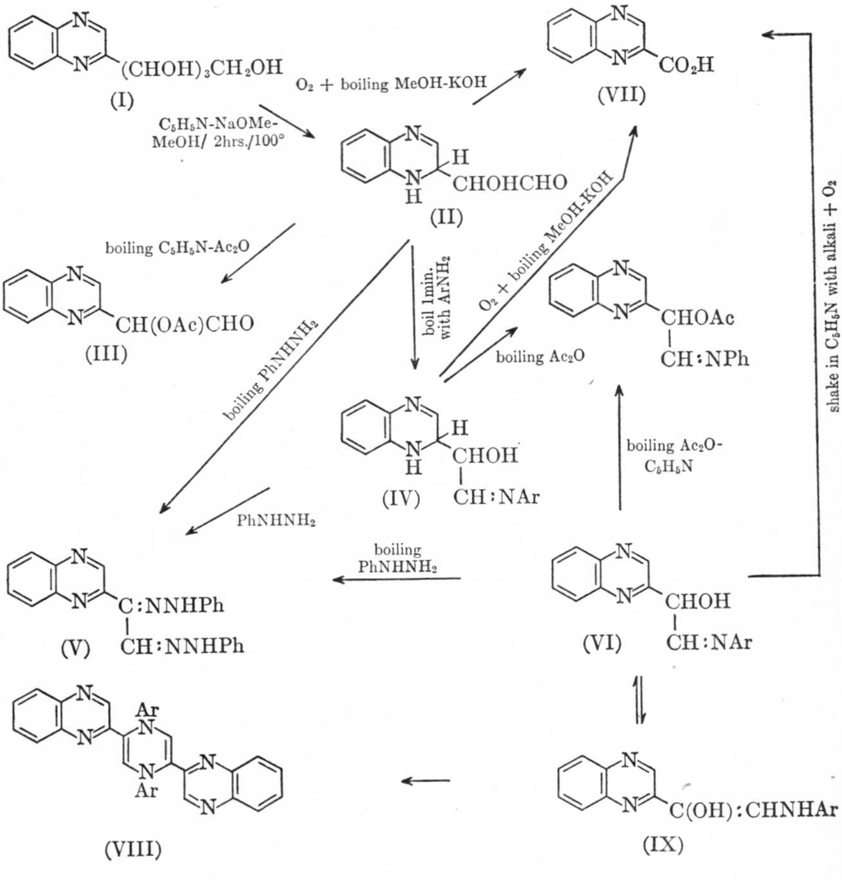

Maurer and Boettger[16] have shown that 2-d-arabotetrahydroxybutyl-quinoxaline (I) may be subjected to alkaline oxidation in well-defined stages which are indicated in the appended reaction scheme. The initial product (II) may be transformed as shown (see also Table XXXVI-2) to (IV) and (VI); all these compounds on further oxidation give quinoxaline-2-carboxylic acid (VII), which also results from more drastic alkaline oxidation of (I) (Section 2A). Table XXXVI-2 summarizes the products obtained by this series of reactions. The 2,5-bis-2'-quinoxalyl-1,4-diaryl-1,4-dihydropyrazines (VIII) are formed along with compounds of type (VI) during dehydrogenation of the compounds (IV), and are considered to arise by condensation of two molecules of (IX) [the enolic form of (VI)].

TABLE XXXVI-2. Compounds Arising from Alkaline Degradation of 2-d-arabo-tetrahydroxybutylquinoxaline

Structure	M.p., °C.	Remarks
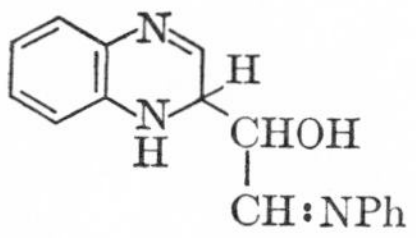	188	Red needles. Gives red-violet color in alk. soln., turning colorless on exposure to air with formation of quinoxaline-2-carboxylic acid. Easily dehydrogenated (H_2O_2-Me_2CO at room temp., PbO_2-$CHCl_3$ at room temp., or PhMe alone at 100°) to compd. (VI; Ar = Ph)
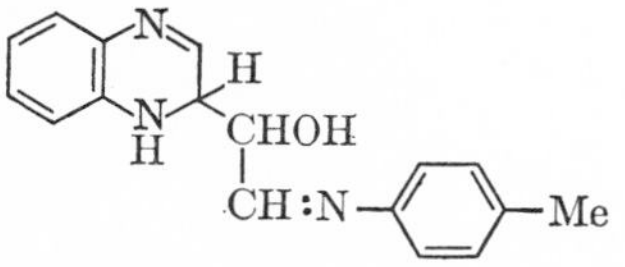	150	Red needles
	166	Red needles
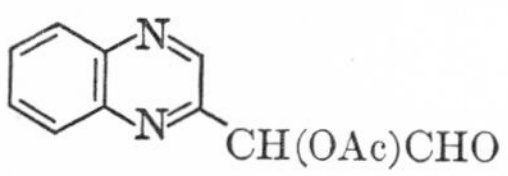	117	Gives red soln. in alkali; reduces Fehling soln.
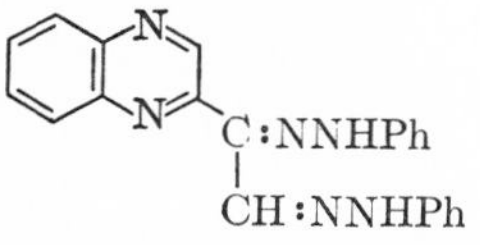	243	Yellow cryst.
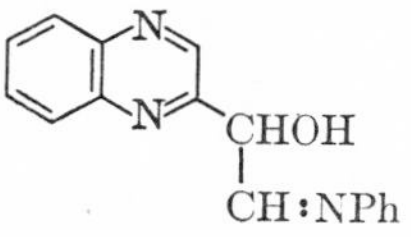	208	Yellow cryst. Insol. in alk. (contrast the above 1,2-dihydro deriv., m.p. 188°). In C_5H_5N gives red soln. on adding alk.; shaking with air then gives colorless soln. with formation of PhNC and quinoxaline-2-carboxylic acid

Table continued

TABLE XXXVI-2. (*continued*)

Structure	M.p., °C.	Remarks
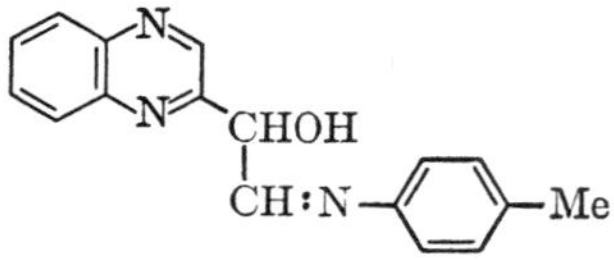 CHOH / CH:N—⟨⟩—Me	190	—
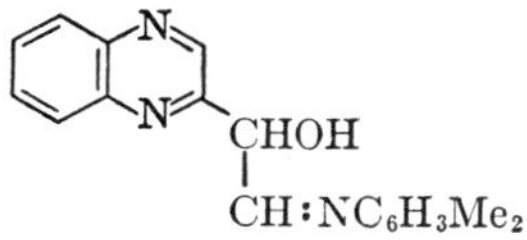 CHOH / CH:NC₆H₃Me₂	187	Yellow leaflets
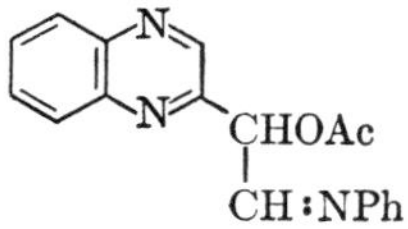 CHOAc / CH:NPh	134	Colorless needles
(VIII; Ar=Ph)	253	Orange leaflets
(VIII; Ar=—⟨⟩—Me) 	267	Red cryst.
(VIII; Ar=C₆H₃Me₂)	276	—

C. Reactions with Phenylhydrazine

(*i*) *In Neutral or Alkaline Solution.* Treatment of 2-tetrahydroxy-butylquinoxalines (X) with phenylhydrazine in neutral or alkaline solution produces the corresponding quinoxaline-2-aldehydes (XI). Although this removal of three carbon atoms *via* the agency of phenylhydrazine may well be highly specific for compounds of type (X), it is worthwhile from a broader aspect to compare this reaction with other examples of fission of heterocyclic compounds containing polyhydroxyalkyl side chains. Thus, oxidation of the furan and pyrrole derivatives (XII) and (XIII) with lead tetraacetate brings about the removal of three carbon atoms from the side chain,[17,18] and quinoxaline-2-aldehyde (XI; R = H) may be similarly prepared from (X; R = H).[17,18] Again, the conversion of (X; R = H) into quinoxaline, and the similar removal of the side chain from riboflavin, may be brought about by irradiation with ultraviolet light (Table XXV-1), and it has been suggested[19] that this formation of quinoxaline may proceed by an initial elimination of three carbon atoms to give quinoxaline-2-alde-hyde followed by a Cannizzaro reaction and decarboxylation of the result-ant acid. On the other hand, only traces of benziminazole are obtained by

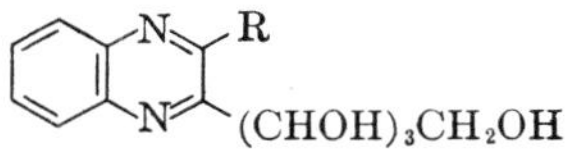

(X) 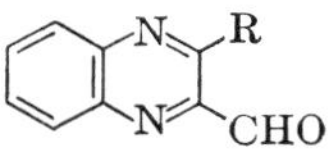 (XI) 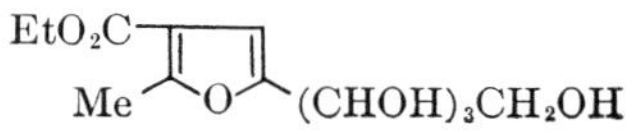 (XII)

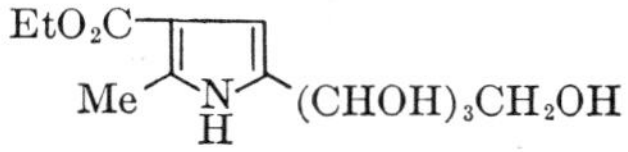

(XIII) 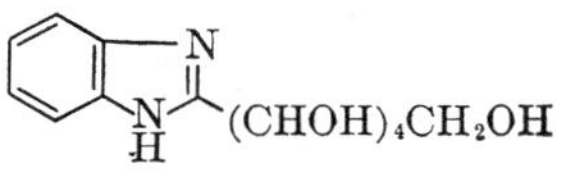 (XIV)

similar irradiation of the compound (XIV) derived from galactose[19] and neither this compound nor its arabinose analog yields benziminazole-2-aldehyde on oxidation with lead tetraacetate.[17,18]

The reaction with phenylhydrazine has been carried out with several compounds of type (X). Thus, using not less than 3 moles of aqueous phenylhydrazine at 100°, 2-d-arabotetrahydroxybutylquinoxaline (X; R = H) and its 3-phenyl analog (X; R = Ph) give about 20% of the phenylhydrazones of the aldehydes (XI; R = H and Ph), but the reactions are incomplete and unchanged material is recovered.[6,13] The compound (XV) (see Table XXXVII-2) similarly yields the phenylhydrazone (XVI),[5] and 3-methoxy-2-d-arabotetrahydroxybutylquinoxaline (X; R = OMe) gives the free aldehyde (XI; R = OMe) when treated with 1 mole phenylhydrazine.[5]

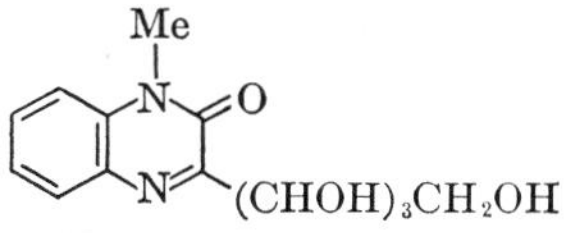

(XV) 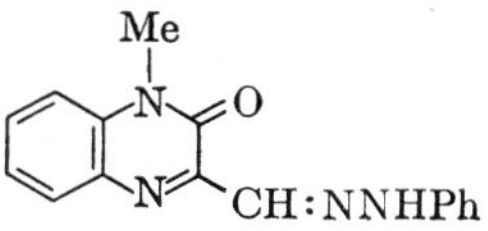 (XVI)

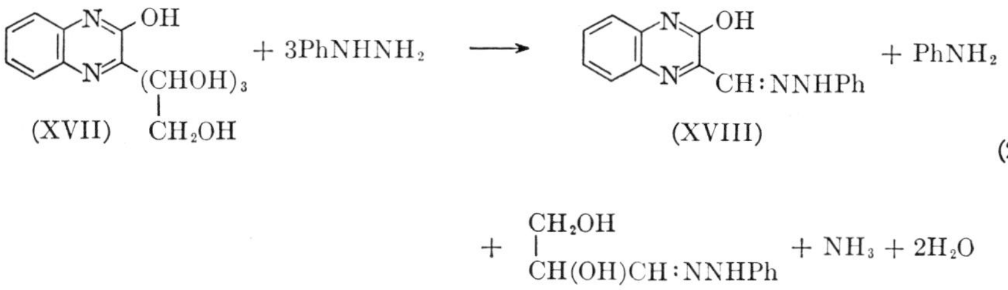

(XVII) (XVIII)

(2)

$$+ \begin{array}{c} CH_2OH \\ | \\ CH(OH)CH:NNHPh \end{array} + NH_3 + 2H_2O$$

(XIX)

The reaction has been carried out with both the d-arabo- and the l-xylo forms of the 3-hydroxy compound (X; R = OH), and in each case the phenylhydrazone of 3-hydroxyquinoxaline-2-aldehyde is produced.[4,5]

Ohle and his co-workers,[15] in a detailed study of the reaction with the d-arabo-isomer, have found that if 3 or more moles of phenylhydrazine (in aqueous solution at 100°) are used the reaction proceeds according to equation 2.   Under these conditions the yield of (XVIII) is 85%, but in 0.1 N sodium hydroxide it falls to 65% [methylglyoxal bisphenylhydrazone (XX) is also formed in this case], and in N-sodium hydroxide it is only 49%. If the phenylhydrazine is replaced by hydrazine or methylphenylhydrazine, the corresponding hydrazones of (XI; R = OH) are produced, but the use of aniline instead of a hydrazine gives the anil (XXI) [m.p. 267° (dec.)] of 3-hydroxy-1,4-dihydroquinoxaline-2-aldehyde; on treatment with boiling phenylhydrazine, this anil is smoothly converted into the true quinoxaline derivative (XVIII).   From this and other evidence Ohle and his associates[15] conclude that the decomposition of (XVII) in aqueous phenylhydrazine involves the following successive stages: (a) conversion of (XVII) into (XXII) by means of hydrogen ions and hydroxyl ions;   (b) fission of (XXII) into glyceraldehyde and 3-hydroxy-1,4-dihydroquinoxaline-2-aldehyde;   (c) conversion of these aldehydes into, respectively, the phenylhydrazone (XIX) and 3-hydroxy-1,4-dihydroquinoxaline-2-aldehyde phenylhydrazone;   and (d) dehydrogenation of the last-named compound to (XVIII) by means of phenylhydrazine.

CH:NNHPh
|
C:NNHPh
|
CH₃

(XX)   (XXI)   (XXII)

The conversion of 2-tetrahydroxybutylquinoxalines into aldehydes by means of phenylhydrazine appears to be a general reaction which is, however, favored by the presence of a free hydroxyl group at C_3 of the quinoxaline nucleus.   It is considered[15] that the function of this acidic hydroxyl in promoting the reaction is to act as an extra source of protons and thus to facilitate the conversion of (XVII) into (XXII).

(ii) *In Acid Solution.*   Treatment of 2-d-arabotetrahydroxybutylquinoxaline (X; R = H) with phenylhydrazine in acetic acid solution gives 1-phenyl-3-d-erythro-1′,2′,3′-trihydroxypropylflavazole (XXIII). This compound and its analogs are described in Chapter XXXVIII, Section 2C.

Similar treatment of the 3-hydroxy analog (XVII) produces an entirely different reaction.   The yield of (XVIII)—which, as mentioned above, is the major product in neutral or moderately alkaline solution—is suppressed to 33%, and the main product is a compound of formula $C_{18}H_{18}O_4N_4$ (XXIV).[15]   This compound, in the formation of which no fis-

(CHOH)$_2$CH$_2$OH

(XXIII)

(CHOH)$_2$CH$_2$OH

(XXIV)

(XXV)   (XXVa)   (XXVb)

sion of the side chain has occurred, crystallizes in orange-red needles, m.p. 220° (dec.), and yields a diacetyl derivative (orange-red leaflets, m.p. 158°) which gives a violet solution in concentrated sulfuric acid. On treatment with methanolic ammonia, the diacetyl derivative is mainly hydrolyzed to (XXIV), but decomposition to (XVIII) also occurs to a small extent. With boiling aqueous-alcoholic sodium hydroxide, however, the diacetyl derivative gives as sole product a yellow compound, m.p. 260° (+0.5 mole C$_2$H$_5$OH), which yields only a monoacetyl derivative (colorless needles, m.p. 244°). The formula, C$_{18}$H$_{14}$O$_2$N$_4$, of this yellow compound indicates that its formation from the diacetyl derivative involves dehydration as well as deacetylation, and it is considered[15] to be a pyridazine derivative having one of the structures (XXV), (XXVa), or (XXVb), where R is 3′-hydroxy-2′-quinoxalyl.

References

1. Griess and Harrow, *Ber.*, **20**, 2205 (1887).
2. Griess and Harrow, *Ber.*, **20**, 3111 (1887).
3. Maurer, Schiedt, and Schroeter, *Ber.*, **68**, 1716 (1935).
4. Ohle, *Ber.*, **67**, 155 (1934).
5. Ohle, Gross, and Wolter, *Ber.*, **70**, 2148 (1937).
6. Ohle and Hielscher, *Ber.*, **74**, 18 (1941).
7. Erlbach and Ohle, *Ber.*, **67**, 555 (1934).
8. Ohle and Gross, *Ber.*, **68**, 2262 (1935).
9. Lohmar and Link, *J. Biol. Chem.*, **150**, 351 (1943).
10. Bond, Knight, and Walker, *Biochem. J.*, **31**, 1033 (1937).
11. Maurer and Schiedt, *Ber.*, **67**, 1980 (1934).
12. Weygand and Bergmann, *Chem. Ber.*, **80**, 255 (1947).
13. Ohle and Hielscher, *Ber.*, **74**, 13 (1941).
14. Ohle and Liebig, *Ber.*, **75**, 1536 (1942).
15. Ohle, Hielscher, Noetzel, and Wolter, *Ber.*, **76**, 1051 (1943).
16. Maurer and Boettger, *Ber.*, **71**, 1383 (1938).
17. Müller and Varga *Ber.*, **72**, 1993 (1939).
18. Varga, *Magyar Biol. Kutatóintézet Munkái*, **12**, 359 (1940).
19. Kuhn and Bär, *Ber.*, **67**, 898 (1934).

CHAPTER XXXVII

Reduced Quinoxalines

1. 1,2- and 1,4-Dihydroquinoxalines

A. Compounds Containing No Hydroxyl or Carbonyl Group in the Hetero Ring

This group comprises a small number of miscellaneous compounds for which there is no general method of preparation. Their properties are summarized in Table XXXVII-1, pages 312–313.

B. Compounds Containing a Hydroxyl or Carbonyl Group in the Hetero Ring

(*a*) *1-Substituted-2-keto-1,2-dihydroquinoxalines*

Preparation

(*a*) The most general method of preparing these compounds (II) is to condense an *N*-substituted *o*-phenylenediamine (I) with an α-keto acid (or keto ester). The reaction may be carried out with the amine hydrochloride in aqueous solution, or with the free base in an organic solvent (Eq. 1). This method was developed by Kehrmann and Messinger,[1] and

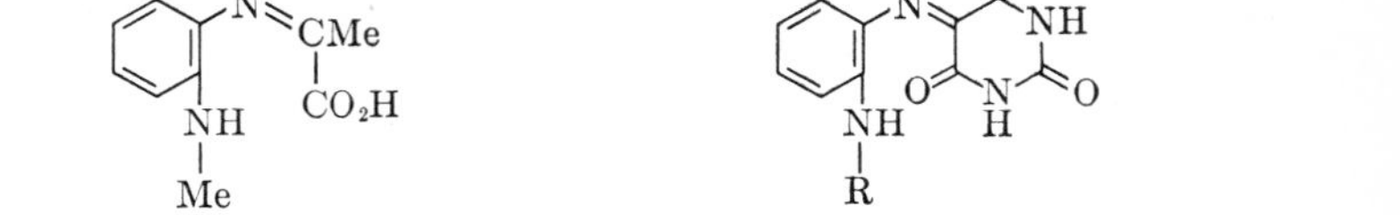

$$(1)$$

(I)   (II)

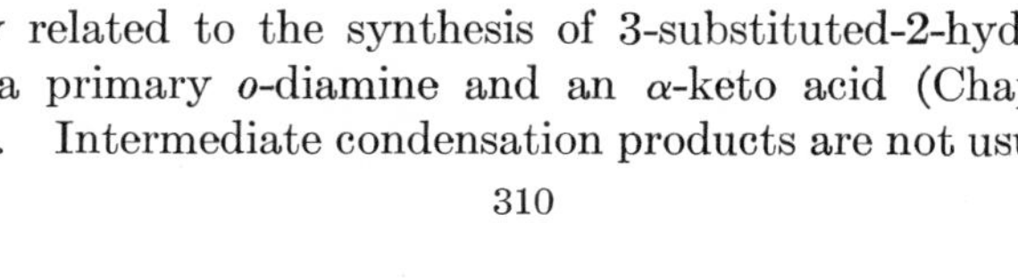

(III)   (IV)

is obviously related to the synthesis of 3-substituted-2-hydroxyquinoxalines from a primary *o*-diamine and an α-keto acid (Chapter XXVII, Section 1B). Intermediate condensation products are not usually isolable, but the anil (III) results when N-methyl-o-phenylenediamine and pyruvic acid react in acetic acid, whereas in aqueous hydrochloric acid the product is (II; R = R' = Me).[2]

(b) Condensation of (I) with alloxan, followed by alkaline hydrolysis of the product (IV), gives derivatives having a carboxyl group at C_3 (II; R' = CO_2H) (cf. Chapter XXIX, Section 1), and such compounds may also be made from the esters (II; R' = CO_2Et) prepared according to method (a) using ethyl mesoxalate. Decarboxylation of (II; R' = CO_2H) occurs readily, yielding 2-keto-1,2-dihydroquinoxalines substituted only at N_1 in the hetero ring.

(c) Some 1-methyl-2-keto-1,2-dihydroquinoxalines may be prepared from 2-hydroxyquinoxalines by methylation with diazomethane, or with methyl sulfate or methyl iodide and alkali.

Properties. As with so many classes of heterocyclic compounds, a few scattered observations of the properties of 1-substituted-2-keto-1,2-dihydroquinoxalines are recorded in the literature, but no systematic study of the group has been made.

The compounds (V; R = Me and Ph) contain an active 3-methyl group and yield the pyruvic esters (VI; R = Me and Ph), m.p. 170 and 224°, respectively, by condensation with ethyl oxalate in presence of potassium ethoxide[3] (cf. Chapter XXXIII, Section 1). The methiodide (VII), m.p. 178° (dec.), is slowly formed at 100° from (V; R = Me) and methyl iodide,[4] and crude quaternary salts of (V; R = Me and Ph) have also been prepared.[4,5] In agreement with these observations, (V; R = Me and Ph) exhibit basic properties, dissolving in strong mineral acids. 3-Hydroxy-1-phenyl-2-keto-1,2-dihydroquinoxaline condenses with the hydrochlorides of o-phenylenediamine and o-aminophenol to give the compounds (VIII) and (IX) (m.p. 207.5–208.5°), respectively.[6,7]

The reactions of the N-oxide (X) are of interest. This compound (pale yellow prisms, m.p. 191°) is formed by oxidative cyclization of isonitrosomalonodimethylanilide (XII)[8]; the reaction may be carried out by treatment of (XII) with chromic anhydride in acetic acid, with fuming nitric acid and chloroform at the boiling point, or with nitrosyl chloride in chloroform. The compound may also be made directly from malonodimethyl-

TABLE XXXVII-1. 1,2-Dihydroquinoxalines Containing No Hydroxyl or Carbonyl Group in the Hetero Ring

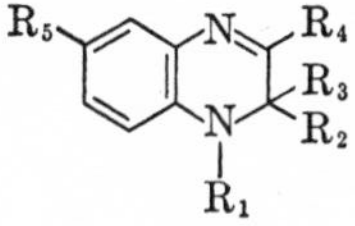

R₁	R₂	R₃	R₄	R₆	R₅	Prep.[a]	M.p., °C.	Remarks	Ref.
H	H	H	NH₂	AsO₃H₂	H	H	226	AsO₃H₂ assumed, but not proved, to be at C₆ rather than at C₇. Bz deriv., m.p. 234°	32
H	H	CONH₂	NH₂	AsO₃H₂	H	I	—	AsO₃H₂ assumed, but not proved, to be at C₆ rather than at C₇	32
H	H	Ph	Ph	H	H	A,B	146	Yellow plates. Gives NO deriv., m.p. 138°	33
H	H	—CHOH CH:NAr	H	H	H			See Chapter XXXVI (Table 2 and Section 2B)	
H	Ph	Ph	Cl	H	H	D	204	—	30
H	Ph	Ph	NH₂	H	H	E	287	Structure uncertain. Does not react with HNO₂ or alc. HCl at 150°	34
Ph	Ph	Et	Ph	H	H	G	198–199	Yellow tablets	35
Ph	Ph	—CH₂—	Me	H	H	C	—	Unstable. For reactions see Chapter XXXIV	36,5
CH₂ CH₂OH	=NCONH₂	CO₂H	NO₂			F	232–235 (dec.)	—	37

Table footnote on facing page

a A, by reduction of 2,3-diphenylquinoxaline with stannous chloride and hydrochloric acid (at the b.p.). B, from o-phenylenediamine and benzoin. C, from o-aminodiphenylamine and diacetyl in the absence of mineral acid. D, from 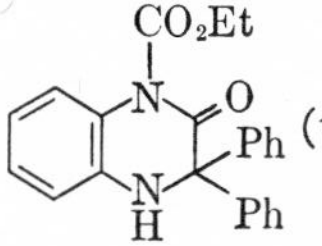 (this Chapter,

Section 2B) and phosphorus pentachloride in benzene. E, from 2,3-diphenylquinoxaline and potassium amide in liquid ammonia at 130–140°. F, from 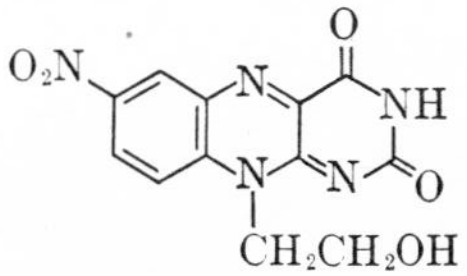 by hydrolysis with $N/40$ sodium hydroxide at 75°. G, from 1,2,3-triphenylquinoxalinium bromide and ethylmagnesium iodide. H, from the o-diamine and $CH_2ClCONH_2$ in boiling aqueous sodium hydroxide. I, from the o-diamine and $CHBr(CONH_2)_2$ in boiling aqueous sodium hydroxide.

TABLE XXXVII-2. 1-Substituted-2-keto-1,2-dihydroquinoxalines

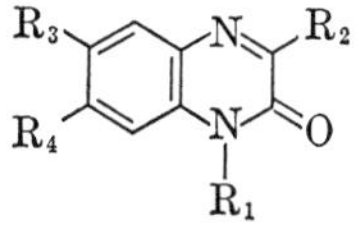

R_1	R_2	R_3	R_4	Prep.[a]	M.p., °C.	Remarks	Ref.
Me	H	H	H	G	122	—	38
Me	H	Me	Me	G	174–175, 176	A degradation prod. of lumiflavin (ref. 41,42)	39,40
Me	OH	H	H	B,P	281–283	With PX_5 gives 2,3-Cl_2- or Br_2-quinoxaline	8
Me	Me	H	H	A,M,N	87	Hydrate, m.p. 63°	1,2,4
Me	Me	Cl	H	A,N	144–145	—	65
Me	CH_2Cl	H	Cl	N	227–229	—	65
Me	$CHBr_2$	H	H	A,M	228–230	—	9
Me	CH:NNHPh	H	H	K,L	187	—	2
Me	CO_2H	H	H	H,I	198	—	2
					174,173–174 (dec.)	Red needles	8,38
Me	CO_2Et	H	H	M	125–126	—	43
Me	CO_2H	Me	Me	F,H	212–214 (dec.)	A degradation prod. of lumiflavin (ref. 41,42)	39,40
Me	CO_2Et	Me	Me	C,O	125–126	—	39
Me	NPhMe	H	H	Q	135	Red prisms. Gives chloroplatinate; methiodide, m.p. 205° (dec.); NO-deriv., m.p. 197°	8
Me	$-(CHOH)_3-CH_2OH$	H	H	J	187	$[\alpha]_D^{17}\ -61.1°\ (C_5H_5N)$. Reduces boiling Fehling soln.	2
Me	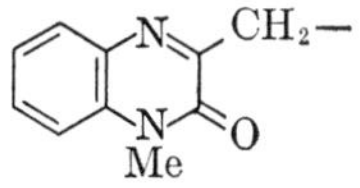 (structure: 1-methyl-3-methylene-2-oxoquinoxaline, labels CH_2, Me, O)	H	H	D	331	Scarlet micro-crystals. Hot conc. H_2SO_4 gives violet color	3

R₁	R₂	R₃	R₄	Prep.ᵃ	M.p., °C.	Remarks	Ref.
Me	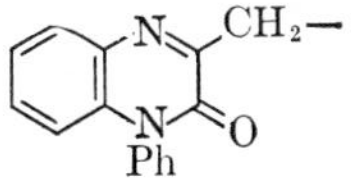 (CH₂– N=, N–Ph, C=O ring structure)	H	H	E	300	Orange needles. Hot conc. H₂SO₄ gives magenta color	3
Me	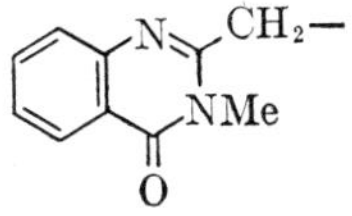 (CH₂– N=, NMe, C=O ring structure)	H	H	D	293	Yellow needles. Hot conc. H₂SO₄ gives yellow color	3
Et	Me	H	H	A	96–97	Hydrate, m.p. 77°	1
(CH₂)₃NEt₂	Me	OMe	H	A	Oil	B.p. 195–197°/3 mm.	44
CHMe(CH₂)₃NEt₂	Me	H	H	A	Oil	B.p. 144°/0.06 mm. Dipicrate, m.p. 168–169° (corr.)	45
CH₂Ph	OH	H	H	B	265	Gives 2,3-dichloroquinoxaline and PhCH₂Cl with PCl₅ at 160°	12
CH₂Ph	Me	H	H	A	99–100	—	1
Ph	OH	H	H	B	302–303	—	6
Ph	Me	H	H	A	195	Insol. in dil. acid	1,4
Ph	CH₂Ph	H	H	A	166	—	4
Ph	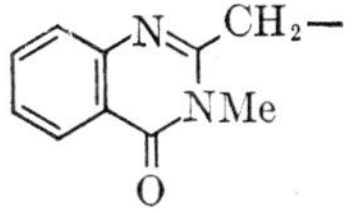 (CH₂– N=, NMe, C=O ring structure)	H	H	D	265	Yellow needles	3

Table footnote on following page

TABLE XXXVI-2. (*continued*)

 a A, from the *N*-substituted-*o*-phenylenediamine hydrochloride (or amine and hydrochloric acid) and RCOCO$_2$H in water (reaction is usually exothermic) or in alcohol-borax, or from the free amine and RCOCO$_2$H in ether or boiling *p*-cymene. B, from the *N*-substituted-*o*-phenylenediamine and oxalic acid at 160–180°. C, from the *N*-substituted-*o*-phenylenediamine and ethyl mesoxalate in boiling alcohol. D, from the *N*-substituted-*o*-phenylenediamine and the appropriate acid or ester in phenol at 100°, or by fusion of the components with a trace of ammonium chloride. E, as for method D, but prepared both from *o*-aminodiphenylamine and also from *N*-methyl-*o*-phenylenediamine. F, from the corresponding ester by hydrolysis with alcoholic sodium ethoxide at room temperature. G, from the 3-carboxylic acid by decarboxylation (at the m.p. of the acid). H, from the *N*-substituted-*o*-phenylene-

diamine by condensation with alloxan followed by hydrolysis of the resultant anil. I, from

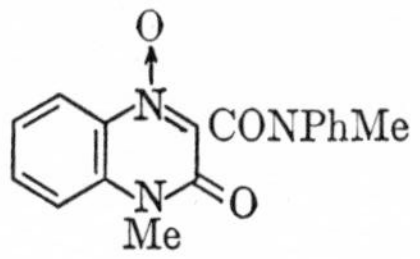

CONPhMe (see text). J,

from *N*-methyl-*o*-phenylenediamine and methyl *d*-glucosonate in alcoholic boric acid containing sodium acetate (reflux 5 hours in hydrogen). K, from the 3-[CHOH]$_3$CH$_2$OH compound (see table) by decomposition with phenylhydrazine. L, from the 3-dibro-momethyl compound (see table) by reaction with phenylhydrazine. M, from the appropriate 3-substituted-2-hydroxyquinoxaline and diazomethane. N, from the appropriate 3-substituted-2-hydroxyquinoxaline, methyl sulfate, and alkali. O, from the appropriate 3-substituted-2-hydroxyquinoxaline, methyl iodide, and boiling alcoholic sodium ethoxide. P, from the 4-oxide (for prepara-

tion, see text) by reduction with zinc and acetic acid. Q, from

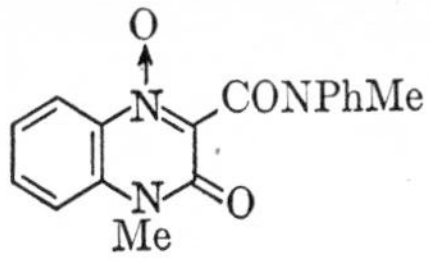

CONPhMe   or CH(NO$_2$)(CONMePh)$_2$ by addition to

cold concentrated sulfuric acid.

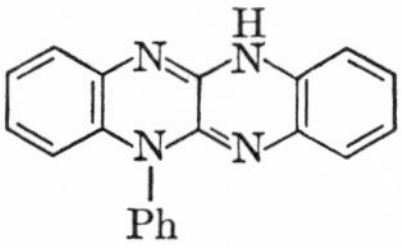

(VIII)
R.I. 2643

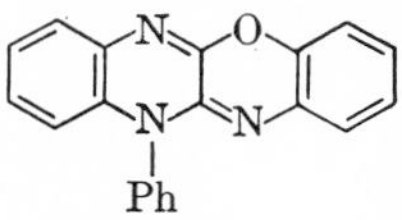

(IX)
R.I. 2607

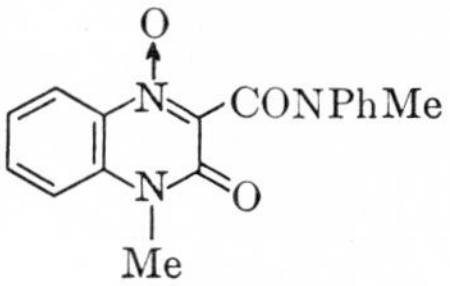

(X)

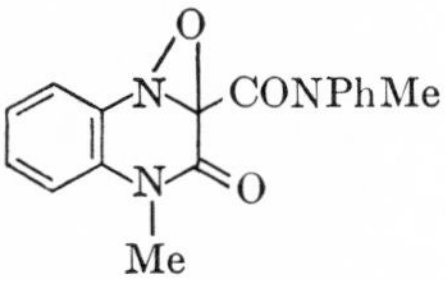

(XI)

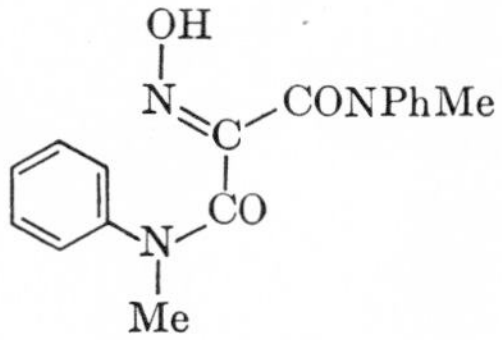

(XII)

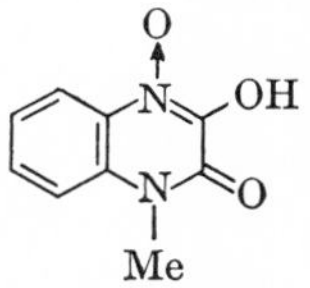

(XIII)

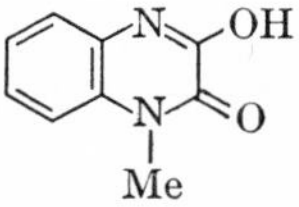

(XIV)

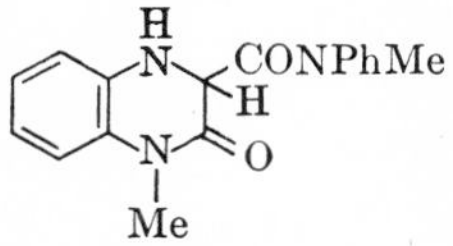

(XV)

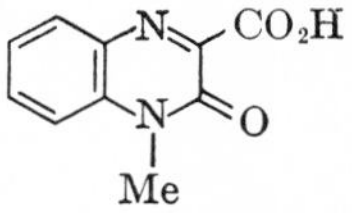

(XVI)

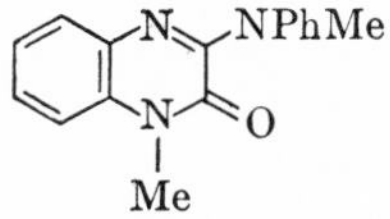

(XVII)

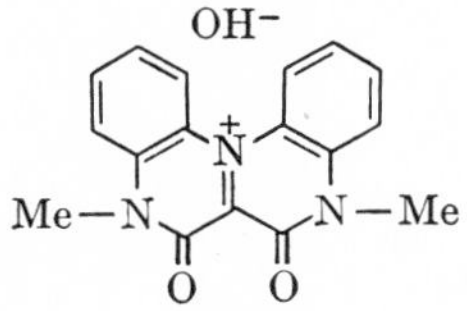

(XVIII)

NPhMeCO₂H

(XIX)

anilide by treatment with nitrosyl chloride and nitric acid. Usherwood and Whiteley[8] formulate the compound as (XI), but its reactions are equally explicable on the basis of structure (X) which is its modern equivalent.

Treatment of (X) with warm alcoholic sodium ethoxide gives formic acid, methylaniline, and the hydroxy oxide (cyclic hydroxamic acid) (XIII), m.p. 257° (dec.), which yields an ethyl ether, m.p. 167–168°, and on reduction with zinc and acetic acid is converted into (XIV). Oxidation of (X) with permanganate produces methylphenyloxamic acid (XIX). Reduction of (X) with cold zinc and acetic acid gives the tetrahydroquinoxaline derivative (XV), m.p. 185°, from which the side chain is removed by the action of warm alcoholic sodium ethoxide with formation of the known acid (XVI). When added to cold concentrated sulfuric acid, (X) is converted into (XVII) by elimination of carbon dioxide, but if the acid is added to the solid the product is a derivative of the quaternary base (XVIII) (Chapter XXXVIII, Section 2B).

When treated with alcoholic hydrochloric acid, (X) yields a chloro compound, m.p. 240–241°, of formula $C_{17}H_{16}O_2N_3Cl$; a chlorine-containing product, $C_{19}H_{18}O_3N_3Cl$, m.p. 226°, is also formed from (X) by reaction with acetyl chloride (although reaction does not occur with benzoyl chloride, benzenesulfonyl chloride, or acetic anhydride). Each of these chloro compounds is stable toward reducing agents, suggesting the absence of the N-oxide grouping, and gives methylaniline on hydrolysis. Usherwood and Whiteley[8] were unable to explain the formation of these products from the parent compound of formula $C_{17}H_{15}O_3N_3$; it is, however, possible that the reactions involved are related to the transformation of 3-ethoxy-2-methyl-quinoxaline-1-oxide (XX) into 3-hydroxy-2-chloromethylquinoxaline (XXI), which has recently been found to occur when (XX) is treated with alcoholic hydrochloric acid.[9]

(XX)   (XXI)

(b) 1,2- and 1,4-Dihydroquinoxalines Having Hydroxyl Groups at C_2 or C_3

Preparation

(a) The appropriate o-nitrophenylglycine is reduced by catalytic or chemical means. This method gives compounds unsubstituted at N_1 and C_2, and hydroxylated at C_3, and has the advantage of avoiding ambiguity as to the orientation of Bz-substituted derivatives (XXII → XXIII) (Eq. 2).

(XXII)   (XXIII)

(b) α-Halogeno esters are heated with the appropriate o-diamine at about 95° for many hours; no solvent is used (Eq. 3). This synthesis also yields compounds of type (XXIII), but suffers from the disadvantages (1) that two isomers may result from a nuclear-substituted o-diamine, *e.g.*, (XXIV) may give (XXV) and (XXVI), and (2) that alkylation of the

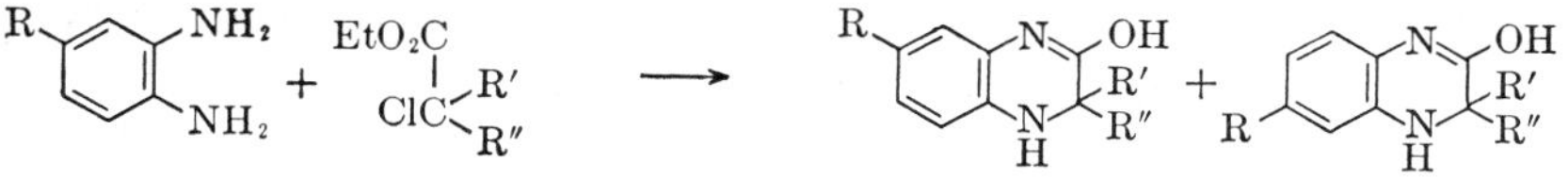

$$ \text{(3)} $$

(XXIV)   (XXV)   (XXVI)

hetero ring by the chloro ester is liable to occur, although this can be suppressed by using excess of the diamine.

(c) 1 - Substituted - 2 - hydroxy - 2,3 - diphenyl - 1,2 - dihydroquinoxalines (XXVIII) are prepared from the quaternary salts (XXVII). It is not necessary to isolate these salts; they may be prepared in solution by condensing benzil with an N-substituted-o-phenylenediamine in presence of hydrochloric acid (cf. Chapter XXXIV), and yield the pseudo bases (XXVIII) on basification (a mild alkali such as sodium carbonate or ammonia usually suffices) (Eq. 4). If the quaternary salt contains a primary

$$ \text{(4)} $$

(XXVII)   (XXVIII)

or secondary amino group at C_7 the formation of an anhydro base is theoretically possible. This has been observed with the salt (XXIX) (or XXX), which yields the compound (XXXI) (green leaflets, m.p. 235°, giving a blue-green color with concentrated sulfuric acid) on treatment with hot aqueous sodium carbonate.[10]

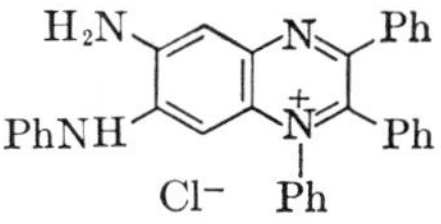

(XXIX) 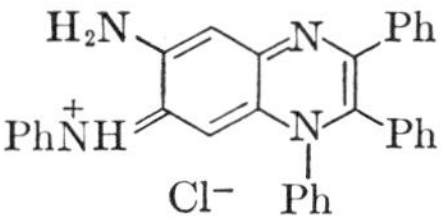   (XXX) 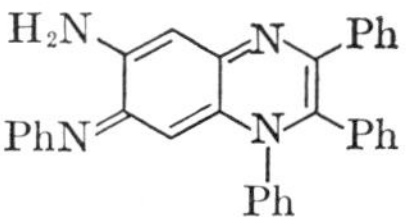   (XXXI)

(d) Miscellaneous compounds. The compound (XXXII) and the 1,4-dihydro derivative (XXXIII) are described in Chapter XXXVI, Section 2C. 3 - Hydroxy - 4 - methyl - 1,2 - epoxy - 1,4 - dihydroquinoxaline (XXXIV), m.p. 192–194°, is a by-product resulting from the addition of nitromalonodimethylanilide to concentrated sulfuric acid (cf. Table XXXVII-2, preparation Q). Its structure implies that it is a tautomeric form of (XXXV) (Table XXXVII-2), and it is soluble in sodium hydroxide,[8] but the two compounds are not identical. The compound (XXXVI; R = 6- or 7-Me), m.p. 147°, is prepared by heating equimolecular proportions of 3,4-diaminotoluene and ethyl chloroacetate on the water bath.[11] Its structure must be accepted with some reserve, because the compound prepared from o-phenylenediamine by an analogous reaction and originally[12] formulated as (XXXVI; R = H) was later[13] shown more probably to have the structure (XXXVII) (Table XXXVII-3).

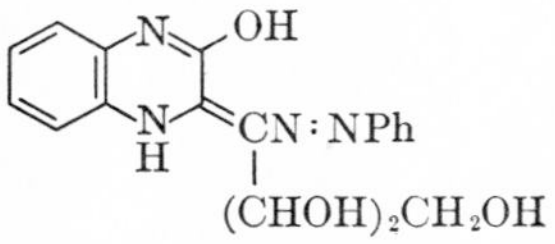

(XXXII) 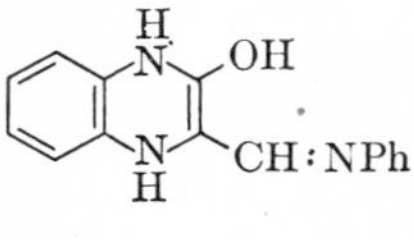   (XXXIII) 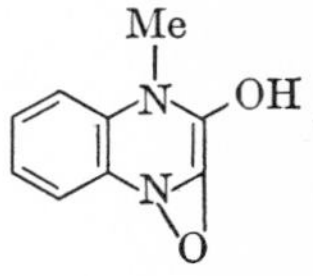   (XXXIV)

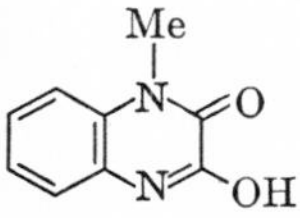

(XXXV) 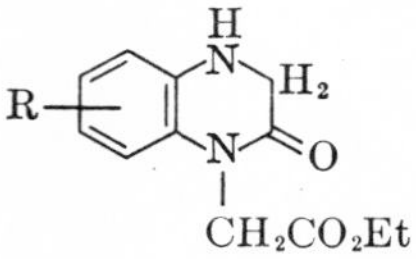   (XXXVI) 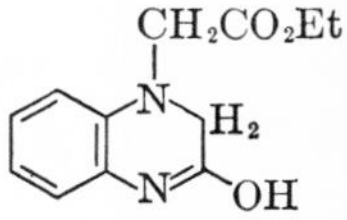   (XXXVII)

The compounds (XXXVIII) and (XXXIX) are formed by an unusual synthesis in which the appropriate dinitrodiethylaniline (as XL) is heated with zinc chloride and acetic acid or acetic anhydride (if the anhydride is used, water is added during the working-up of the product).[14]   The use of zinc chloride and acetic anhydride, and exclusion of moisture throughout, yields the corresponding acetylated compounds, formulated by the authors

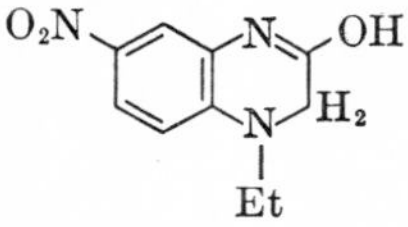

(XXXVIII) 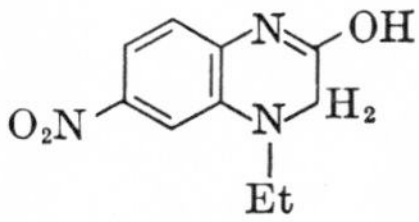   (XXXIX)

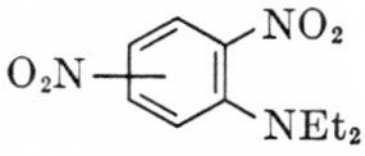

(XL) 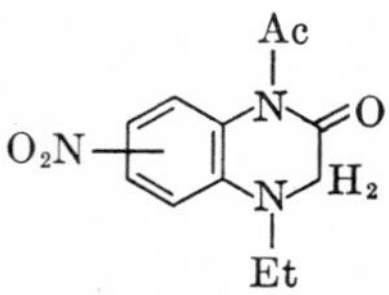   (XLI) 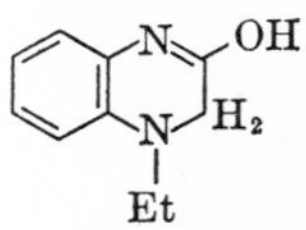   (XLII)

as N$_4$-acetyl derivatives (XLI).[14]   Reduction and deamination of (XXXVIII) yield (XLII), identical with the compound prepared from (XXIII; R = H) by heating with ethyl iodide at 100°.[15]

TABLE XXXVII-3. 1,2-Dihydroquinoxalines Having Hydroxyl Groups at C_2 or C_3

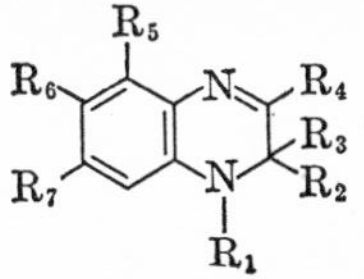

R_1	R_2	R_3	R_4	R_5	R_6	R_7	Prep.[a]	M.p., °C.	Remarks	Ref.
H	H	H	OH	H	H	H	C,D,E,F	130,132–133,138	Hydrate, m.p. 93–94, 96–97°. Ac_2 m.p. 166°; Bz m.p. 210–211°. NO, m.p. 164°, 178° (dec.). EtI at 100° gives 1-Et deriv.	13,15, 19,23, 46
H	H	H	OH	H	H	Cl	C	184	—	17
H	H	H	OH	H	Cl	H	C	214–215 (dec.)	—	17
H	H	H	OH	H	OMe	H	C	169–171	—	18
H	H	H	OH	H	Me	H	M	100–130	—	21
H	H	H	OH	H	NH_2	H	C	181	—	47
H	H	H	OH	H	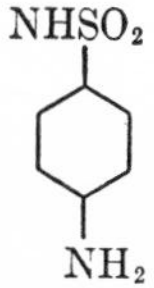 $NHSO_2$(cyclohexyl)NH_2	H	K	188	—	48
H	H	H	OH	H	PO_3H_2	H	A	—		49
H	H	CHOHPh	OH	H	H	H	O	167.5	Ac_2 deriv., m.p. 171–172°	64
H	Me	Me	OH	H	H	H	B,J	175–176, 177	Boiling with conc. HCl gives (probably) unstable o-NH_2-$C_6H_4NHCMe_2CO_2H$ which readily regenerates original compd.	24, 12
H	Me	Me	OH	H	H	Me at C_6 or C_7	J	227	Ac, m.p. 206°; NO, m.p. 153–154° (dec.); $(NO_2)_2$, m.p. > 280°	21

Table continued

TABLE XXXVII-3. 1,2-Dihydroquinoxalines Having Hydroxyl Groups at C_2 or C_3 (continued)

R_1	R_2	R_3	R_4	R_6	R_7	Prep.[a]	M.p., °C.	Remarks	Ref.
H	—CHPh—		OH	H	H	L	210	Tautomeric with 3-hydroxy-2-benzylquinoxaline m.p. 196° (Chapter XXVII, Table II); the compds. may be identical	50
Me	Ph	OH	Ph	H	H	N	dec. 70	—	1
Me	Ph	OH	Ph	NO_2	H	N	195	Yellow leaflets. Continued recrystn. from EtOH gives 4,2,1-NHMe$(NO_2)C_6H_3$N:-CPhCOPh	51
Et	H	H	OH	H	H	See text	98–99	—	15
Et	H	H	OH	H	NO_2	See text	206	Ac, m.p. 127°	14
Et	H	H	OH	NO_2	H	See text	157	Ac, m.p. 166–167°	14
—CH_2	H	H	OH	H	H	G,H	212,232 (dec., corr.)	—	12,13
—CO_2H CH$_2$—	H	H	OH	H	H	I	163	—	12,13
—CO_2Et	Ph	OH	Ph	H	H	N	134–135	Yellow prisms	52
Ph	Ph	OH	Ph	H	Cl	N	164–166	Yellow cryst.	53,54
Ph	Ph	OH	Ph	H	NHPh	N	—	—	53
Ph	Ph	OH	Ph	Cl	H	N	164	Yellow needles	51
Ph	Ph	OH	Ph	NH_2	H	N	98	—	1
Ph	Ph	OH	Ph	Me	OEt	N	136	Yellow plates	55
 4-Me_2N·C_6H_4—	Ph	OH	Ph	H	OEt	N	187–190	Yellow needles	56
 4-Me_2N·C_6H_4—	Ph	OH	Ph	OEt	H	N	187–190	—	56

R₁	R₂	R₃	R₄	R₅	R₆	R₇	Prep.ᵃ	M.p., °C.	Remarks	Ref.
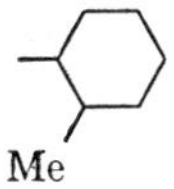 (methylcyclohexyl)	Ph	OH	Ph	H	Me	OEt	N	153	Yellow needles	55
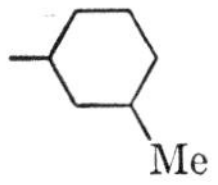 (methylcyclohexyl)	Ph	OH	Ph	H	H	OEt	N	176	Yellow needles	55
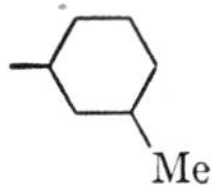 (methylcyclohexyl)	Ph	OH	Ph	H	Me	OEt	N	137.5–140·	Yellow cryst.	55
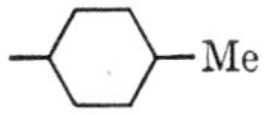 (methylcyclohexyl)	Ph	OH	Ph	H	Me	OEt	N	146–149	Yellow needles	55
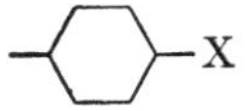 (methylcyclohexyl, X)	Ph	OH	Ph	H	H	Y	N	144–146	Yellow needles. X = Me (or OEt); Y = OEt (or Me)	55
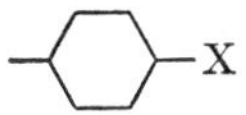 (methylcyclohexyl, X)	Ph	OH	Ph	Me	H	Y	N	176–179	Yellow needles. X = Me (or OEt); Y = OEt (or Me)	55

H_2O_3P—(benzene ring with NO_2)—$NHCH_2CO_2H$

ᵃ A, from the monosodium salt of [structure above] by reduction with H₂-Raney Ni. B, from o-phenylenediamine and chlorotone (CCl₃CMe₂OH) in boiling alcoholic potassium hydroxide. C, from the appropriate nitroarylglycine by reduction with tin and hydrochloric acid or catalytically. D, from o-phenylenediamine, zinc dust, and chloro- or bromoacetic acid (spontaneous reaction). E, from 2,3-dihydroxyquinoxaline by reduction with zinc and hot aqueous hydrochloric acid. F, from o-phenylenediamine, chloroacetic acid, and aqueous ammonia at 100° for 1 hour (this is the best method of preparation; yield 70%). Omission of the ammonia gives the 1-CH₂CO₂H derivative also. G, from the 1-unsubstituted compound and chloroacetic acid. H, from the 1-CH₂CO₂Et compound and alcoholic potassium hydroxide. I, from o-phenylenediamine and ethyl chloroacetate at 95° (24 hours, without solvent). J, from the o-diamine and ethyl α-bromoisobutyrate at 95–100° (24 hours, without solvent). K, from the amino compound and acetylsufanilyl chloride in pyridine, followed by boiling aqueous sodium hydroxide. L, from o-phenylenediamine and the β (enol) form of PhCH₂COCO₂Et at room temperature. M, from 4,2,1-MeC₆H₃(NO₂)NHCH₂CO₂H by reduction with tin and hydrochloric acid. N, from the quaternary salt by alkaline decomposition. O, from o-NH₂C₆H₄NHCH(CO₂Et)CH-(OH)Ph or the corresponding acid by treatment with hot dilute sulfuric acid, or by heating the acid at 200°.

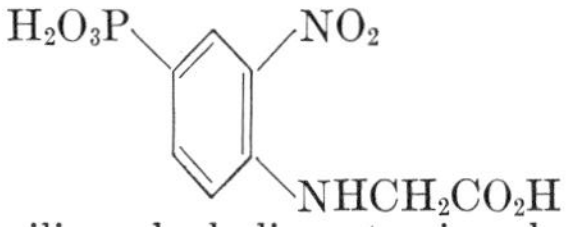

Properties. 1,2-Dihydroquinoxalines containing a pair of hydrogen atoms at N_1 and C_2 are very readily oxidized to true quinoxalines. A simple illustration of this is the fact that o-phenylenediamine and phenacyl bromide in alcoholic solution yield 3-phenylquinoxaline and not the 1,2-dihydro derivative thereof[12]; similarly, true quinoxalines are the only products isolated from the condensation of 3,4-diaminotoluene with phenacyl chloride and chloroacetone.[16] So characteristic is this behavior that the reduction of o-nitroarylglycines, which yields in the first instance 3-hydroxy-1,2-dihydroquinoxalines (XXIII), is also a general practical route to 3-hydroxyquinoxalines[17,18] (Chapter XXVII, Section 1A); indeed, Plöchl[19] and Leuckart and Hermann[20] isolated only 3-hydroxy-6-methylquinoxaline, which they incorrectly took to be the 1,2-dihydro compound, from the reduction of 2-nitro-4-methylphenylglycine. The dihydro compound, has, however, been isolated from this reduction,[21] although attempts to prepare it by an alternative route, namely by condensation of ethyl chloroacetate with 3,4-diaminotoluene,[11,16] appear to give rise to both the possible isomers.[22]

3-Hydroxy-1,2-dihydroquinoxaline (XLIII) may be oxidized to 3-hydroxyquinoxaline merely by distillation or by boiling its alcoholic solution with charcoal, or by boiling an alcoholic solution of its 1-nitroso derivative; it also gives the hydroxyquinoxaline when oxidized with aqueous permanganate, but acid dichromate yields 2,3-dihydroxyquinoxaline.[13,19,23] The 6-methyl analog as (XLIV) is oxidized to 3-hydroxy-6-methylquinoxaline by silver nitrate, nitrous acid, or atmospheric oxygen.[21] The sub-

(XLIII)   (XLIV)   (XLV)

(XLVI)   (XLVII)   (XLVIII)

stance (XLIV; Me = 6 or 7), m.p. 124°, which is formed from 3,4-diaminotoluene and ethyl chloroacetate, undergoes similar oxidation with atmospheric oxygen in alkaline solution, or with silver nitrate or other mild agents in neutral solution.[11]

In contrast to the above behavior, 1,2-dihydroquinoxalines in which C_2 carries no hydrogen atom [e.g., (XLV), (XLVI), and pseudo bases of the type (XLVII) derived from quaternary salts] do not show any tendency to undergo oxidation.

The oxidizable 1,2-dihydroquinoxalines (XLIII) and (XLIV) are amphoteric, being soluble both in caustic alkali and in acids.[11,19,23] The sodium and potassium salts are easily soluble in water, but in excess of alkali the sodium salt, in contrast to the potassium salt, is only sparingly soluble. The metal salts are moderately stable, but those with acids are somewhat unstable.[23] The compounds (XLV) and (XLVI), on the other hand, are also bases but are devoid of acid properties,[21,24] and it is therefore possible that they exist in the keto tetrahydro form (as XLVIII), enolization of which is for some reason inhibited. These compounds clearly differ from the alkali-soluble (XLIII) and (XLIV) in the fact that they are fully substituted at C_2; substitution at C_2 is not, however, the only factor which determines the acidic properties of such reduced hydroxyquinoxalines, because (XXXVIII) and (XXXIX), in which C_2 is not substituted, are likewise insoluble in alkali but soluble in dilute acids.[14]

2. 1,2,3,4-Tetrahydroquinoxalines

A. 1,2,3,4-Tetrahydroquinoxalines Containing No Oxygen Atom Attached to the Hetero Ring

Preparation

(1) Compounds in which the hetero ring is either unsubstituted or carries alkyl or aryl groups on C_2 and C_3 are prepared from the corresponding quinoxalines by reduction, either catalytically or with sodium and alcohol.

(2) Compounds in which the hetero ring carries substituents are made either from the quinoxaline by means of a suitable additive reaction [e.g., compounds of type (I) in which R is alkyl, aryl, CN, or SO$_3$Na], or, in the case of 1- and 4-alkyl and -acyl derivatives (II; R and R' = alkyl or acyl), by introduction of the substituent into the corresponding 1,2,3,4-tetrahydroquinoxaline.

(I) (II)

(3) The compound (III), a brown solid, m.p. 272° (corr.), is prepared from o-phenylenediamine by reaction 5.[25]

(5)

(III)
R.I. 3484

Properties. Compounds of this group are summarized in Table XXXVII-4. They have well-defined basic properties, yielding crystalline picrates, oxalates, or acyl derivatives. In general, compounds in which N_1 and N_4 are both unsubstituted undergo diacylation and dialkylation so readily as to make the isolation of monosubstituted derivatives impossible. Cavagnol and Wiselogle[26] have studied this question with 1,2,3,4-tetrahydroquinoxaline; they find that the two dissociation constants of the base are $k_1 = 6.8 \times 10^{-2}$ and $k_2 = 1.4 \times 10^{-5}$, and explain the difficulty of obtaining monosubstitution products on the grounds that k_1 and k_2 are too close together to allow of a high ratio between singly charged cations and free base. However, monobenzenesulfonyltetrahydroquinoxaline may be prepared, and from this, by alkylation and hydrolysis, various monoalkyl derivatives are obtainable[26] (Table XXXVII-4).

Stereoisomerism of 1,2,3,4-Tetrahydroquinoxalines. 1,2,3,4-Tetrahydroquinoxalines in which C_2 or C_3 carries a substituent as well as a hydrogen atom should be resolvable into optically active forms. This problem has been investigated in several cases by Gibson and his co-workers, the results being summarized in Table XXXVII-5. Numerous salts and acyl derivatives of the various stereoisomers have also been prepared, for particulars of which the original papers should be consulted. The β-base, m.p. 97–98°, from 2,3,6-trimethylquinoxaline could not be resolved.[27] As would be expected, the products obtained from quinoxaline and methyl- or phenyl-magnesium halide (Table XXXVII-4) are the *dl*-forms of the 2,3-disubstituted-1,2,3,4-tetrahydroquinoxalines (Table XXXVII-5).

1,4-Endoalkylene-1,2,3,4-tetrahydroquinoxalines. By condensing 6-methyl-1,2,3,4-tetrahydroquinoxaline with the appropriate

(IV)

alkylene dihalide, Moore and Doubleday[28] have prepared the colorless bases (IV; $n = 1$), m.p. 150° (dec.), (IV; $n = 2$), m.p. 175° (dec.), and (IV; $n = 3$), m.p. 192° (dec.); the first compound was also prepared

TABLE XXXVII-4. 1,2,3,4-Tetrahydroquinoxalines Containing No Oxygen Atom Attached to the Hetero Ring

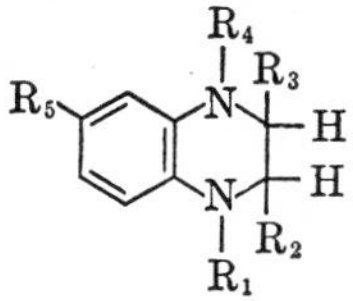

R_1	R_2	R_3	R_4	R_5	Prep.[a]	M.p., °C.	Remarks	Ref.
H	H	H	H	H	A,F,L	97.5,98.5-99	B.p. 153-154°/14 mm. Picrate, m.p. 128.5-129.5°. Ac_2, m.p. 147-147.5. Bz_2, m.p. 201.5°, 206-207°. $(CO_2Et)_2$, m.p. 42-44°	26,57,58
H	H	H	H	Cl	F	113-114	Bz_2, m.p. 168.5-169	26
H	H	H	H	OMe	F	80.5-81	Bz_2, m.p. 138.5-138.8°. Picrate, m.p. 134-135°	26
H	H	H	H	Me	F	104.5-105.5	Bz_2, m.p. 105.2-106.2°. Ac_2, m.p. 141-142°. $(PhSO_2)_2$, m.p. 124-125°. Picrate, m.p. 148-148.5°	26
H	H	H	SO_2Ph	H	B	138-139	Ac, m.p. 111.5-112°	26
H	CH_2NEt_2	H	H	H	G	—	B.p. 175°/3.5 mm.	59
H	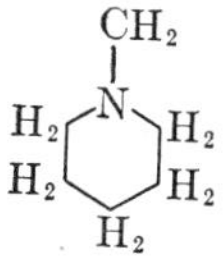 CH_2-N(piperidine)	H	H	H	G	—	B.p. 170-180°/2.8 mm.	59
H	CN	CN	H	H	J	168.5	Dec. by alk. into HCN and quinoxaline	60
H	Me	Me	H	H	K	101 (corr.)	—	60
H	Ph	Ph	H	H	K	106 (corr.)	—	60
H	SO_3Na	SO_3Na	H	H	H	—	Dec. by heat or treatment with bases	60
H	SO_3Na	SO_3Na	H	AsO_3H_2	I	—	Dec. by HCl	61
Me	H	H	H	H	E	—	B.p. 108.5°/2 mm. Bz, m.p. 109-110°. Picrate, m.p. 123-126.5°	26

Table continued

TABLE XXXVII-4. 1,2,3,4-Tetrahydroquinoxalines Containing No Oxygen Atom Attached to the Hetero Ring (*continued*)

R₁	R₂	R₃	R₄	Prep.[a]	M.p., °C.	Remarks	Ref.
Me	H	H	SO₂Ph	C	88–89	Methiodide, m.p. 168–169°	26
Et	H	H	H	E	—	B.p. 89–90°/1 mm. Bz, m.p. 123–124°. Picrate, m.p. 111.5–112°. Oxalate, m.p. 130–131°	26
Et	H	H	SO₂Ph	C	118.5–119.5	—	26
Prⁿ	H	H	H	E	—	B.p. 113.5°/1.5 mm. Bz, m.p. 88–89°. Picrate, m.p. 135–136°	26
Prⁱ	H	H	H	E	—	B.p. 107.5°/1.5 mm. Bz, m.p. 114–115°. Picrate, m.p. 131–132°	26
Prⁿ	H	H	SO₂Ph	C	119.5–120	—	26
Prⁱ	H	H	SO₂Ph	C	142.5–143.5	—	26
Buⁿ	H	H	H	E	—	B.p. 107.5°/1 mm. Bz, m.p. 87–88°. Picrate, m.p. 130–131.5°. Oxalate, m.p. 142.5–143.5°	26
Buⁿ	H	H	SO₂Ph	C	95–95.5	—	26
CH₂Ph	H	H	H	E	50.5–52.5	B.p. 178–179°/1.5 mm. Bz, m.-p. 123.3–123.8°. Picrate, m.-p. 150–151.5°	26
CH₂Ph	H	H	SO₂Ph	C	134–135	—	26
SO₂Ph	H	H	SO₂Ph	D	180,180–181	—	26,58

[a] A, by addition of a 2% alcoholic solution of quinoxaline to a large excess of sodium. B, from 1,2,3,4-tetrahydroquinoxaline, benzenesulfonyl chloride, and sodium hydroxide. C, from 4-benzenesulfonyl-1,2,3,4-tetrahydroquinoxaline, the appropriate alkyl iodide, and sodium carbonate in boiling alcohol. D, from $o\text{-}C_6H_4(NHSO_2Ph)_2$ ethylene bromide, and alcoholic sodium ethoxide. E, from the 4-SO₂Ph compound by hydrolysis with conc. sulfuric acid. F, from the appropriate quinoxaline by reduction with H_2-PtO_2. G, from o-phenylenediamine, $CH_2BrCHBrCH_2N{\langle}^X_Y$, and potassium carbonate in boiling acetone (under nitrogen). H, from quinoxaline and sodium bisulfite. I, from 3,4-diaminophenylarsonic acid and glyoxal bisulfite. J, from quinoxaline and alcoholic HCN at 100°. K, from quinoxaline and the appropriate Grignard reagent. L, from the 1,4-dibenzenesulfonyl derivative by hydrolysis with alcoholic hydrochloric acid at 160–170°.

TABLE XXXVII-5. Stereoisomeric 1,2,3,4-Tetrahydroquinoxalines

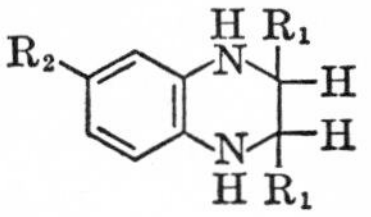

R₁	R₂	M.p., °C.	d, $[\alpha]_{5461}^{20}$	M.p., °C.	l, $[\alpha]_{5461}^{20}$	dl, m.p., °C.	meso, m.p., °C.	Ref
Me	H	94.5	+181.9°	94.5	−181.4°	101–102	111–112	62
Ph	H	135–135.5	+155.7°	135–135.5	−156.2°	105–106, 106	142.5, 142–143	63,33
Me	Me	α-form 61.5–62.5	+206.9°	α-form 61.5–62.5	−206.9°	α-form 71	—	27
		—	—	—	—	β-form 97–98	—	27

using paraformaldehyde as the alkylating agent. The bases give colorless solutions in benzene and nitrobenzene, in which solvents they are bimolecular; the solutions in acetic acid, on the other hand, are red, and in this solvent the bases are monomolecular. Other salts of the bases are usually colored also.

B. 1,2,3,4-Tetrahydroquinoxalines Containing an Oxygen Atom Attached to the Hetero Ring

1,2'-Carbethoxyphenyl-2-keto-1,2,3,4-tetrahydroquinoxaline (V), m.p. 152–153°, is prepared from 2-aminodiphenylamine-2'-carboxylic acid (VI)

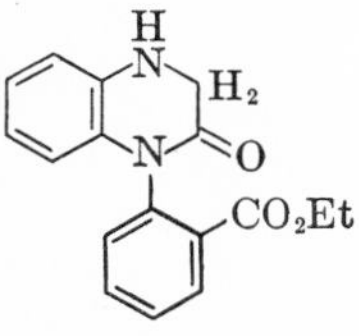

(V)

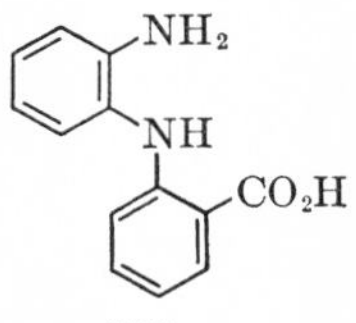

(VI)

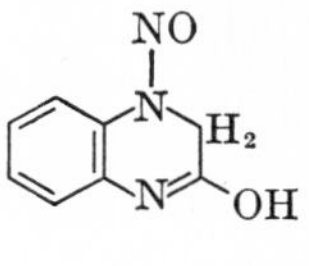

(VII)

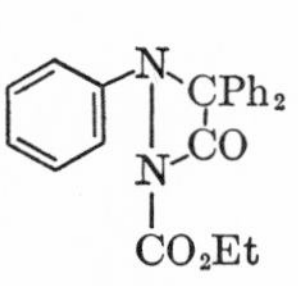

(VIII)

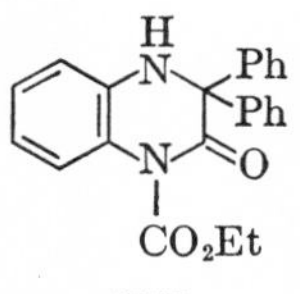

(IX)

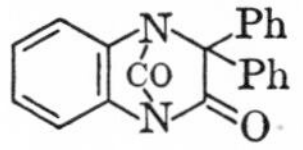

(X)
R.I. 1368

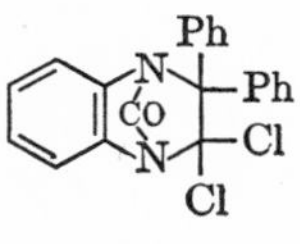

(XI)
R.I. 1368

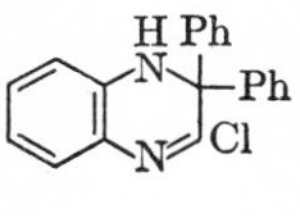

(XII)

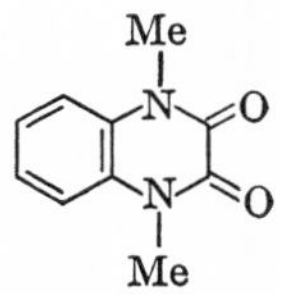

(XIII)

by *N*-alkylation (with formaldehyde, sodium bisulfite, and potassium cyanide) followed by simultaneous cyclization of the product and esterification of the 2′-carboxyl group by means of alcoholic hydrogen chloride.[29] It forms a 4-nitroso derivative, m.p. 117°, which [and also the simpler nitroso analog (VII)] gives rise to condensation products described in Chapter XXXVIII, Section 1D.

3,3-Diphenyl-1-carbethoxy-2-keto-1,2,3,4-tetrahydroquinoxaline   (IX), m.p. 168°, is formed by isomerization in hot alcoholic hydrochloric acid of the adduct (VIII) which is produced by addition of diphenylketene to ethyl benzeneazo-carboxylate.[30]   The conversion of (VIII) into (IX), as pointed out by the authors, may be regarded as an example of the *o*-semidine change characteristic of di-*tert*-hydrazines,[31] *viz.:*

$$Ph_2N \cdot NPh_2 \longrightarrow o\text{-}NHPh \cdot C_6H_4NPh_2$$

The compound gives an acetyl derivative, m.p. 190–191°, from which (IX) is regenerated by acid or alkaline hydrolysis.

When (IX) is treated with a mixture of phosphorus pentachloride and oxychloride under reflux, ethyl chloride is eliminated and the endocarbonyl compound (X), m.p. 335°, is produced in low yield, together with a small quantity of a dichloro compound, m.p. 246°, of probable structure (XI).[30] If the phosphorus oxychloride is replaced by benzene, however, a different reaction occurs, and the sole isolable product is (XII) (Table XXXVII-1).

1,4-Dimethyl-2,3-diketo-1,2,3,4-tetrahydroquinoxaline (XIII) and its 6-chloro, 6-bromo, 6-methoxy, and 6-methyl analogs are prepared by treatment of the appropriate 2,3-dihydroquinoxaline with methyl sulfate and alkali.[9,17,18] For further details regarding these compounds, the structures of which are not fully proved, reference should be made to the section on the methylation of hydroxyquinoxalines (Chapter XXVII, Section 1B).

References

1. Kehrmann and Messinger, *Ber.*, **25**, 1627 (1892).
2. Ohle, Gross, and Wolter, *Ber.*, **70**, 2148 (1937).
3. A. H. Cook and Naylor, *J. Chem. Soc.*, **1943**, 397.
4. A. H. Cook and Perry, *J. Chem. Soc.*, **1943**, 394.
5. Anker and A. H. Cook, *J. Chem. Soc.*, **1944**, 489.
6. Kehrmann and Bener, *Helv. Chim. Acta*, **8**, 16 (1925).
7. Kehrmann and Bener, *Helv. Chim. Acta*, **8**, 20 (1925).
8. Usherwood and Whiteley, *J. Chem. Soc.*, **1923**, 1069.
9. Newbold and Spring, *J. Chem. Soc.*, **1948**, 519.
10. Kehrmann, *Ber.*, **50**, 554 (1917).
11. Hinsberg, *Ber.*, **18**, 2870 (1885).
12. Hinsberg, *Ann.*, **292**, 245 (1896).
13. W. H. Perkin and Riley, *J. Chem. Soc.*, **1923**, 2399.
14. van Romburgh and Huyser, *Rec. trav. chim.*, **49**, 165 (1930).
15. van Romburgh and Deys, *Proc. Acad. Sci. Amsterdam*, **34**, 1004 (1931).

16. Hinsberg, *Ann.*, **237**, 327 (1887).
17. Crowther, Curd, Davey, and Stacey, *J. Chem. Soc.*, **1949**, 1260.
18. Curd, Davey, and Stacey, *J. Chem. Soc.*, **1949**, 1271.
19. Plöchl, *Ber.*, **19**, 6 (1886).
20. Leuckart and Hermann, *Ber.*, **20**, 24 (1887).
21. Hinsberg, *Ann.*, **248**, 71 (1888).
22. Platt, *J. Chem. Soc.*, **1948**, 1310.
23. Motylewski, *Ber.*, **41**, 800 (1908).
24. Banti, *Gazz. chim. ital.*, **59**, 819 (1929).
25. Radulescu, *Chem. Abstracts*, **18**, 2343 (1924) [*Bull. Soc. stiinte Cluj*, **1**, 356 (1922)].
26. Cavagnol and Wiselogle, *J. Am. Chem. Soc.*, **69**, 795 (1947).
27. Gibson, Nutland, and Simonsen, *J. Chem. Soc.*, **1928**, 108.
28. T. S. Moore and Doubleday, *J. Chem. Soc.*, **1921**, 1170.
29. Clemo, W. H. Perkin, Jr., and R. Robinson, *J. Chem. Soc.*, **1924**, 1751.
30. Ingold and Weaver, *J. Chem. Soc.*, **1925**, 378.
31. Wieland, *Ann.*, **381**, 200 (1911).
32. W. L. Lewis and Bent, *J. Am. Chem. Soc.*, **48**, 949 (1926).
33. Hinsberg and König, *Ber.*, **27**, 2181 (1894).
34. Ogg, Jr., and Bergstrom, *J. Am. Chem. Soc.*, **53**, 1846 (1931).
35. Freund and Richard, *Ber.*, **42**, 1101 (1909).
36. A. H. Cook, Garner, and Perry, *J. Chem. Soc.*, **1942**, 710.
37. Hippchen, *Chem. Ber.*, **80**, 263 (1947).
38. Kühling and Kaselitz, *Ber.*, **39**, 1314 (1906).
39. Wellman and Tishler, *J. Am. Chem. Soc.*, **69**, 714 (1947).
40. Kuhn and Reinemund, *Ber.*, **67**, 1932 (1934).
41. Kuhn and Rudy, *Ber.*, **67**, 892 (1934).
42. Kuhn, Reinemund, and Weygand, *Ber.*, **67**, 1460 (1934).
43. Ohle and Gross, *Ber.*, **68**, 2262 (1935).
44. McKee, McKee, and Bost, *J. Am. Chem. Soc.*, **68**, 2116 (1946).
45. Kipnis, Weiner, and Spoerri, *J. Am. Chem. Soc.*, **66**, 1989 (1944).
46. Heller, Buchwaldt, Fuchs, Kleinicke, and Kloss, *J. prakt. Chem.*, **111**, 1 (1925).
47. Waldmann, *J. prakt. Chem.*, **91**, 190 (1915).
48. Raiziss, Clemence, and Freifelder, *J. Am. Chem. Soc.*, **63**, 2739 (1941).
49. Arnold and Hamilton, *J. Am. Chem. Soc.*, **63**, 2637 (1941).
50. Gault and Weick, *Bull. Soc. Chim.*, **31**, 993 (1922).
51. Brand and Wild, *Ber.*, **56**, 105 (1923).
52. Kehrmann and Messinger, *Ber.*, **24**, 1239 (1891).
53. Kehrmann and Falke, *Helv. Chim. Acta*, **7**, 981 (1924).
54. Jacobson and Strübe, *Ann.*, **303**, 305 (1898).
55. P. Jacobson, *Ann.*, **287**, 97 (1895).
56. P. Jacobson, *Ann.*, **427**, 142 (1922).
57. Meisenheimer and Wieger, *J. prakt. Chem.*, **102**, 45 (1921).
58. Hinsberg and Strupler, *Ann.*, **287**, 220 (1895).
59. Benoit and Bovet, *Bull. sci. pharmacol.*, **45**, 97 (1938).
60. Bergstrom and Ogg, Jr., *J. Am. Chem. Soc.*, **53**, 245 (1931).
61. P. L. Cramer and W. L. Lewis, *J. Am. Chem. Soc.*, **52**, 229 (1930).
62. Gibson, *J. Chem. Soc.*, **1927**, 342.
63. Bennett and Gibson, *J. Chem. Soc.*, **1923**, 1570.
64. Culvenor, Davies, Maclaren, Nelson, and Savige, *J. Chem. Soc.*, **1949**, 2573.
65. Dawson, Newbold, and Spring, *J. Chem. Soc.*, **1949**, 2579.

CHAPTER XXXVIII

Condensed Quinoxalines

1. Quinoxalines Condensed with Carbocyclic Rings

A. 5,6-Benzoquinoxalines (R.I. 1907)

Compounds of this group, containing an additional benzene ring fused to the quinoxaline ring system at C_5-C_6, are prepared by the standard methods discussed in previous chapters (see Table XXXVIII-1).

Quaternary salts are available starting from 1-amino-2-arylamino-naphthalenes (*cf.* Chapter XXXIV). Thus the condensation of (I; Ar = Ph) with benzil in acetic acid, followed by addition of dilute hydrochloric acid, yields the crystalline salt (II), which also forms a crystalline nitrate,[1] and (I; Ar = *p*-tolyl) similarly gives (III).[2] If dihydroxytartaric acid is

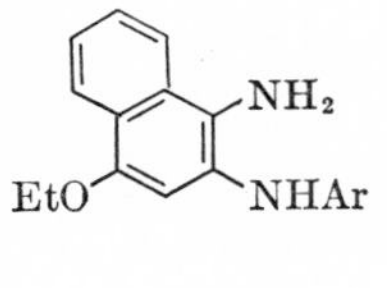

(I) 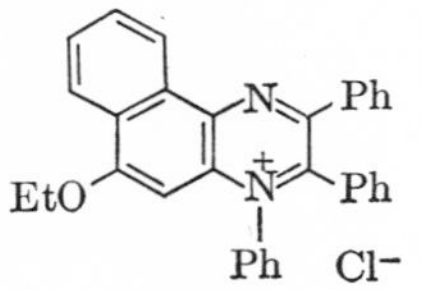   (II) 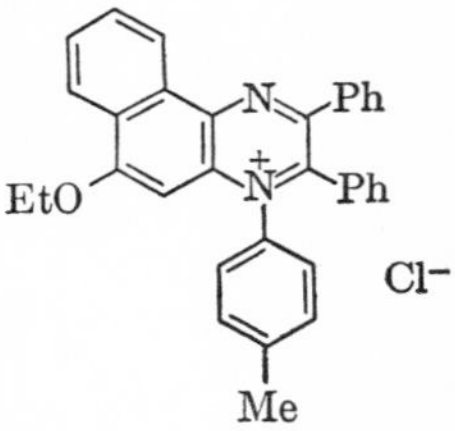   (III)

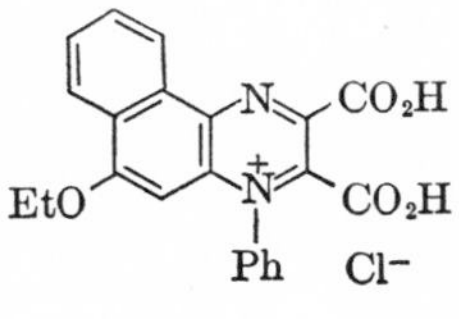

(IV) 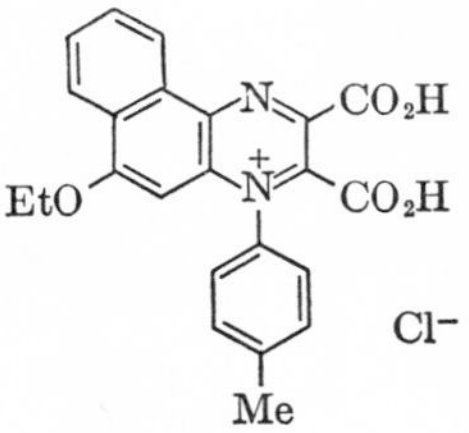   (V)

used in place of benzil, (I; Ar = Ph) gives rise to (IV), and (I; Ar = *p*-tolyl) furnishes (V); the last-mentioned compound forms red needles, and is obtained by treatment of an intermediate acid anhydride with water.[2]

332

TABLE XXXVIII-1. 5,6-Benzoquinoxalines

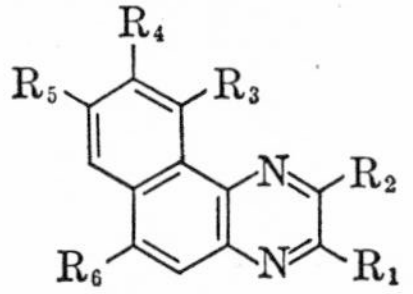

R$_1$	R$_2$	R$_3$	R$_4$	R$_5$	R$_6$	Prep.^{a}	M.p., °C.	Remarks	Ref.
H	H	H	H	H	NHAc	C	252–253	Pale yellow needles	49
H	H	H	H	H	NAc(CH$_2$)$_2$NEt$_2$	D	—	Monopicrate, m.p. 195–197° (dec.)	49
H	NH$_2$	H	H	H	H	E	150–152	{Structures uncertain; positions of NH$_2$ groups should possibly be reversed	50
NH$_2$	H	H	H	H	H	E	215–217		50
Cl	Cl	H	H	H	H	G	142	Pale yellow cryst. Not hydrolyzed by 10% KOH at 100°	51
Cl	NH$_2$	H	H	H	H	H	222	Positions of Cl and NH$_2$ should possibly be reversed	51
OH	OH	H	H	H	H	F	>300	—	51,52
CH(CN)Ph	CH(CN)Ph	H	H	H	H	A	230	Orange-yellow needles. Conc. H$_2$SO$_4$ gives violet color	53
CH(CN)Ph	CH(CN)Ph	H	H	SO$_3$H	H	A	Dec. >270	Yellow needles. Conc. H$_2$SO$_4$ gives violet color	53
CH(CN)Ph	CH(CN)Ph	OH	SO$_3$H	H	H	A	Dec.	Brown amorph. powder. Conc. H$_2$SO$_4$ gives red-violet color	53
CH$_2$CO$_2$H	H	H	H	H	H	I	206	—	8
Ph	Ph	H	H	H	NH$_2$	B	245	Yellow needles	54
Ph	Ph	H	H	H	NHAc	A	245	Yellow needles. Conc. H$_2$SO$_4$ gives red color	54
CH:CHPh	CH:CHPh	H	H	H	H	K	166	—	4

Table continued

TABLE XXXVIII-1. Benzoquinoxalines (*continued*)

R_1	R_2	R_3	R_4	R_5	R_6	Prep.^{a}	M.p., °C.	Remarks	Ref.
Ph	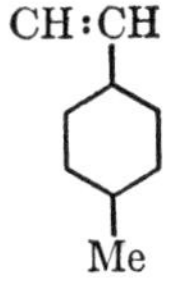 CH:CH (ring, Me)	H	H	H	H	K	178	—	4
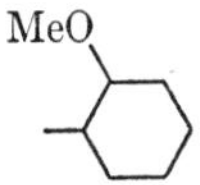 MeO (ring, Me)	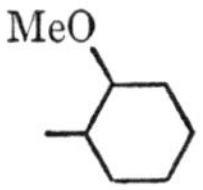 OMe (ring, Me)	H	H	H	H	A	180	Conc. H$_2$SO$_4$ gives violet color	55
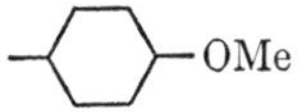 OMe (ring, Me)	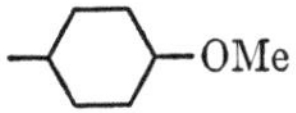 OMe (ring, Me)	H	H	H	H	A	161	Conc. H$_2$SO$_4$ gives blue color	55,56
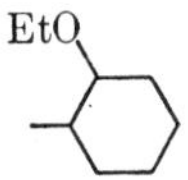 EtO (ring, Me)	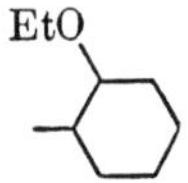 OEt (ring, Me)	H	H	H	H	A	180	Conc. H$_2$SO$_4$ gives blue-violet color	55
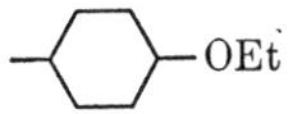 OEt (ring, Me)	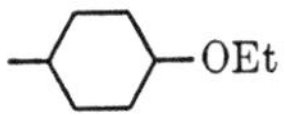 OEt (ring, Me)	H	H	H	H	A	155	Conc. H$_2$SO$_4$ gives blue color	56
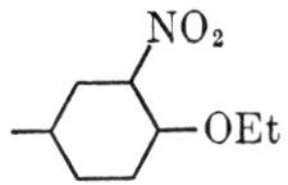 NO$_2$, OEt (ring, Me)	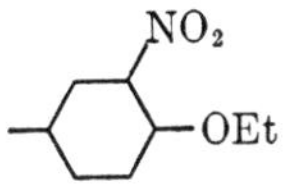 NO$_2$, OEt (ring, Me)	H	H	H	H	A	178	Conc. H$_2$SO$_4$ gives red-violet color	56
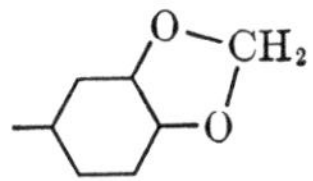 O-CH$_2$-O (ring, Me)	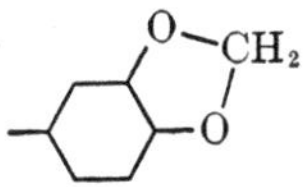 O-CH$_2$-O (ring, Me)	H	H	H	H	A	205	Conc. H$_2$SO$_4$ gives blue color	55,56
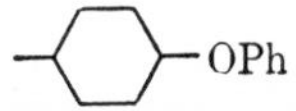 OPh (ring, Me)	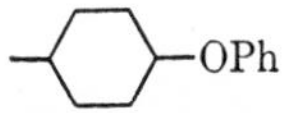 OPh (ring, Me)	H	H	H	H	A	157	Conc. H$_2$SO$_4$ gives blue color	55,56

R₁	R₂	R₃	R₄	R₅	R₆	Prep.ᵃ	M.p., °C.	Remarks	Ref.
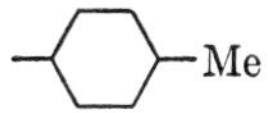 —Me	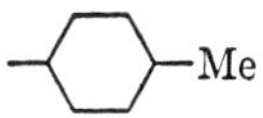 —Me	H	H	H	H	A	183	Conc. H₂SO₄ gives blue-violet color	55,56
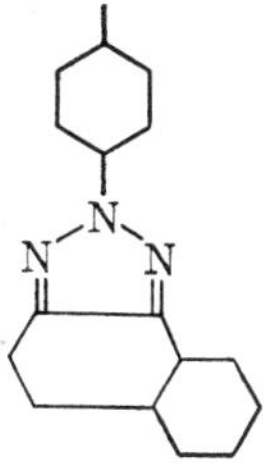	H	H	H	H	H	J	299	—	6

ᵃ A, from the appropriate o-diamine and 1,2-diketone (see Chapter XXIV for general conditions of condensation). B, from the acetamido compound by hydrolysis with 60% sulfuric acid at 95°. C, from the o-diamine and glyoxal sodium bisulfite in boiling water. D, from the acetamido compound, 2-diethylaminoethyl chloride, and sodamide in boiling toluene. E, from the benzalloxazine by hydrolysis with concentrated aqueous ammonia at 170–175°, followed by decarboxylation of the resultant amino acid in boiling nitrobenzene (cf. Table XXXI-1). F, from the o-diamine and oxalic acid at 140–160°. G, from the dihydroxy compound and PCl₅ in a sealed tube at 120°. H, from the dichloro compound and excess of alcoholic ammonia in a sealed tube. I, from the ethyl ester (Table XXXVIII-2) by hydrolysis. J, from compound No. 6, Table XXXVIII-2, by catalytic dehydrogenation with copper in paraffin. K, from compound No. 3, Table XXXVIII-2, and the appropriate aldehyde.

Synthesis of 5,6-Benzoquinoxalines from 2-Amino-1-phenylazonaphtha-
lene. This novel synthesis, which has been studied by Crippa and his co-
workers, consists in the condensation of 2-amino-1-phenylazonaphthalene
(VI) with a ketone of type ArCOCH$_2$R at 165–180° in the presence of a
little concentrated hydrochloric acid; the azo grouping is split, aniline is
eliminated, and a 2-aryl-5,6-benzoquinoxaline (VII) is produced (Eq. 1).

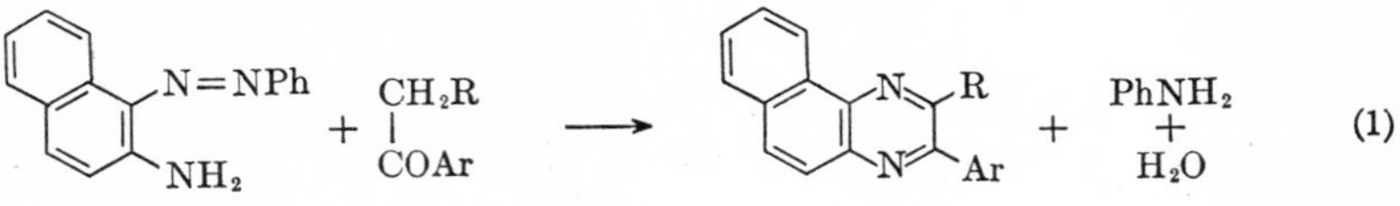

(VI)   (VII)

The course of the reaction was demonstrated[3] by condensing acetophenone with (VI) and also with 2-amino-1-(3′-nitrophenylazo)naphthalene
(VIII); 2-phenyl-5,6-benzoquinoxaline (IX) was formed in each case, and
in the latter reaction *m*-nitroaniline was also identified. The 2-aryl group
in (VII) is thus derived from the ketone used.

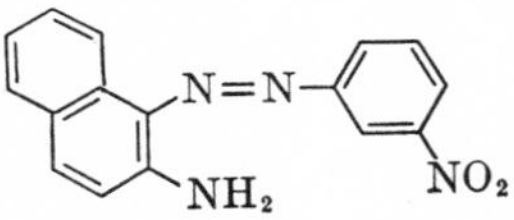

(VIII) 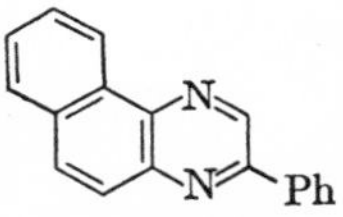   (IX)

The compounds which have been made by this synthesis are shown in
Table XXXVIII-2. As pointed out by Crippa,[4] the method has the
great advantage of yielding products (VII) of unambiguous constitution,
whereas condensation of 1,2-diaminonaphthalene with a diketone
ArCOCOR (or variations of this method) could conceivably give rise to
(X) in addition to (VII). This is illustrated by the preparation of 2-
phenyl-5,6-benzoquinoxaline (IX), m.p. 163°, by Crippa's procedure; condensation of 1,2-diaminonaphthalene with isonitrosoacetophenone, on the
other hand, gives, in addition to (IX), an isomer, m.p. 153°,[5] which must
therefore be 3-phenyl-5,6-benzoquinoxaline (X; R = H, Ar = Ph).

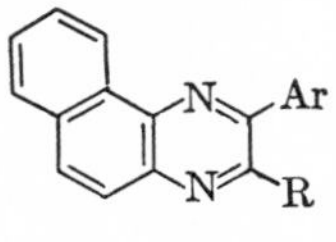

(X) 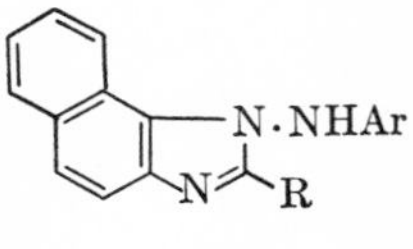   (XI)

As indicated in Table XXXVIII-2, ethyl acetoacetate reacts in the expected manner with (VI); pyruvic acid, however, undergoes decarboxylation and then yields the iminazole (XI; Ar = Ph, R = Me), analogous to
the compounds formed from (VI) and other aldehydes.[4]

TABLE XXXVIII-2   5,6-Benzoquinoxalines   Prepared   from   2-Amino-1-phenyl-azonaphthalene

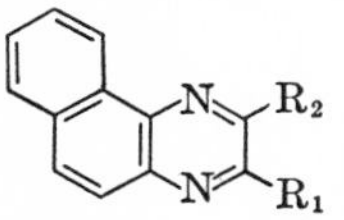

R_1	R_2	Ketone used	M.p., °C.	Ref.
—CH_2CO_2Et	H	$CH_2COCH_2CO_2Et$	96	8
Ph	H	PhCOMe	161–162, 163	3,7
Ph	Me	PhCOEt	121	4
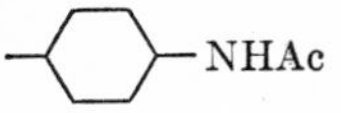 —⟨ ⟩—NHAc	H	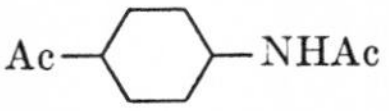 Ac—⟨ ⟩—NHAc	235	6
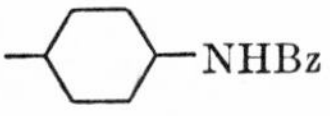 —⟨ ⟩—NHBz	H	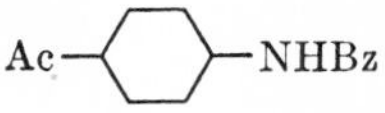 Ac—⟨ ⟩—NHBz	246	6
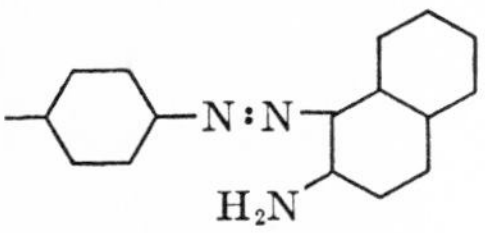 —⟨ ⟩—N:N— (decalin, H_2N)	H	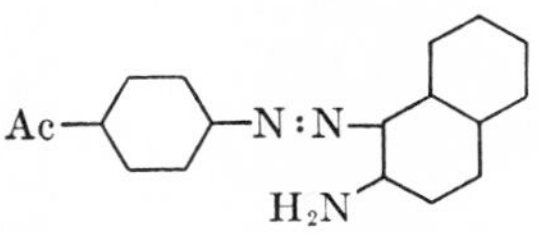 Ac—⟨ ⟩—N:N— (decalin, H_2N)	258	6
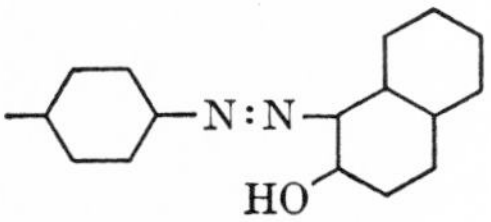 —⟨ ⟩—N:N— (decalin, HO)	H	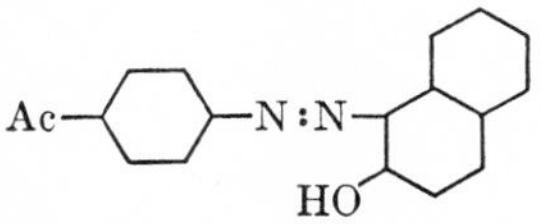 Ac—⟨ ⟩—N:N— (decalin, HO)	294	6
—$C_{10}H_7$-α	H	α-$C_{10}H_7Ac$	161.5	4
—$C_{10}H_7$-β	H	β-$C_{10}H_7Ac$	162.5	4

Some of the 5,6-benzoquinoxalines available by this synthesis are readily oxidized by chromic anhydride in boiling acetic acid to quinones (XII), which by condensation with o-phenylenediamine give rise to phen-

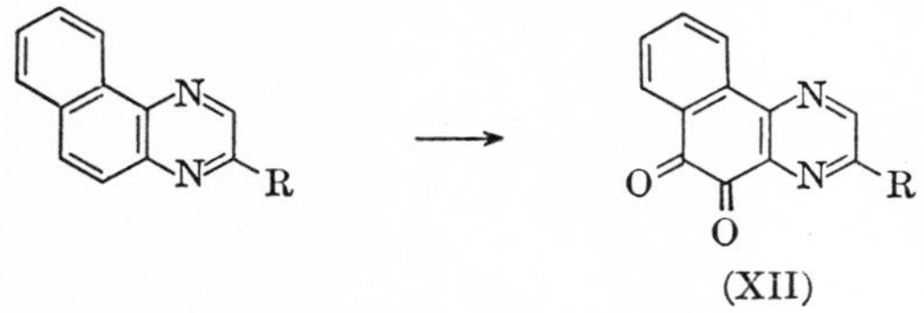

(XII) 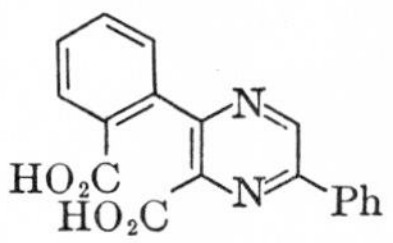   (XIII)

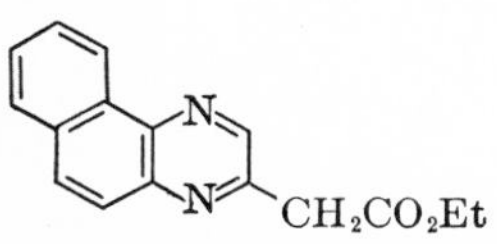

(XIV) 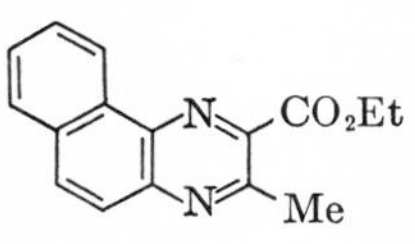   (XV)

azine derivatives.[3,6,7]   The compound (XII;   R = Ph), m.p. 211°, gives the acid (XIII) on oxidation with alkaline permanganate (and thence, by decarboxylation, the known 2,5-diphenylpyrazine).[7] If the acid corresponding to the benzoquinoxaline formed from (VI) and ethyl acetoacetate is oxidized with permanganate, the product is a tribasic acid, m.p. 146°, indicating that the parent quinoxaline contains only one substituent in the hetero ring: it is therefore formulated as (XIV) rather than (XV).[8]

B. 5,6,7,8-Dibenzoquinoxalines (R.I. 2672)

Compounds of this group are prepared by standard methods and are listed in Table XXXVIII-3.

TABLE XXXVIII-3. 5,6,7,8-Dibenzoquinoxalines

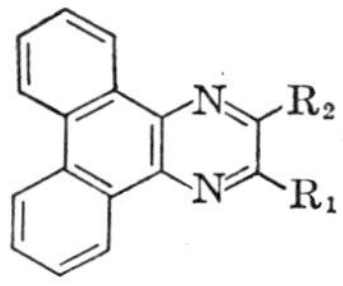

R_1	R_2	Prep.[a]	M.p., °C.	Remarks	Ref.
H	NH_2	A	249	Sulfanilamido deriv., m.p. 258–260°; acetylsulfanilamido deriv., m.p. 265–267°	57
NH_2	CO_2H	B	220–222	—	57
OH	Me	C	>360	Yellow needles. Conc. H_2SO_4 gives red-brown color	20
Me	Me	C	203	Yellow needles. Conc. H_2SO_4 gives brown-orange color	20
Me	Ac	C	212	Yellow needles. Conc. H_2SO_4 gives brown-orange color	20
Ph	Ph	C	272	Conc. H_2SO_4 gives violet color. Dehydrogenated by heating with $AlCl_3$ to 1,2,3,4,5,6,7,8-tetrabenzophenazine	20

[a] A, from the 3-carboxylic acid by decarboxylation at 250°. B, from 5,6,7,8-dibenzalloxazine by hydrolysis with aqueous sodium hydroxide at 225–235° for 20 hours (compare Table XXIX-1). C, from 9,10-diaminophenanthrene and the appropriate dicarbonyl compound.

C. Glucazidone and Derivatives (R.I. 1895)

Glucazidone. This base (XVII) is the main product formed[9] when 2-*d*-arabotetrahydroxybutylquinoxaline (XVI) (Chapter XXXVI) is heated with concentrated or 80% sulfuric acid at 100° (Eq. 2).

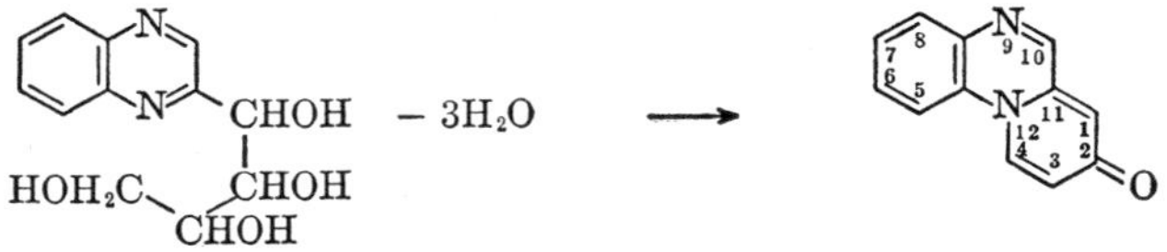

(XVI)   (XVII)   (2)

The nomenclature and numbering of this group of compounds, which have been studied in some detail, are due to Maurer and his co-workers.[9-11]

Glucazidone melts at 104°, and may be distilled without decomposition. It is optically inactive and does not reduce Fehling solution. It dissolves in concentrated mineral acids giving red solutions from which the free base may be precipitated by dilution with water. It forms a hydrochloride, m.p. 184°, and a monomethiodide, m.p. 213° (dec.); in the formation of this quaternary salt N_9 is presumed to be the reactive center, and the structure (XVIII) is therefore ascribed to a compound, m.p. 181°, derived from the salt by oxidation with alkaline ferricyanide. Glucazidone does not react with acylating reagents; the carbonyl group is inert; and it is stable toward alkali (30% at 170°). Oxidation with permanganate yields quinoxaline-2-carboxylic acid.

Bromination and nitration of glucazidone yield monosubstitution products, m.p. 127 and 215°, respectively; a monosulfonic acid is also obtainable, and in all three cases the molecule is attacked at the same point, probably C_3 (*vide infra*). Reduction of the nitro compound is accompanied by reaction at the nucleus. 3-Bromoglucazidone is stable toward ammonia and amines under drastic conditions; interaction with methanolic potash gives an impure halogen-free product which is not identical with 3-hydroxyglucazidone (*vide infra*).

(XVIII)   (XIX)

10-Phenylglucazidone. On treatment with phenylmagnesium bromide, glucazidone yields 10-phenyl-9,10-dihydroglucazidone, as evidenced by the conversion of this substance into 3-phenylquinoxaline-2-carboxylic acid on oxidation with permanganate. Dehydrogenation of the dihydro derivative to 10-phenylglucazidone (XIX; R = Ph), m.p. 125°, occurs readily when it is heated above its melting point, when it is rapidly distilled or refluxed in tetralin, or when the unstable nitroso derivative, m.p. 158° (dec.), of 10-phenyl-9,10-dihydroglucazidone is warmed with acetic acid. 10-Phenylglucazidone yields a monobromo derivative, m.p. 170°, and a mononitro derivative, m.p. 235°.

10-Methylglucazidone (XIX; R = Me), m.p. 98°, and *10-benzylglucazidone* (XIX; R = CH$_2$Ph), m.p. 94°, are similarly obtained from glucazidone by reaction with the appropriate Grignard reagent followed by distillation of the resultant dihydro derivatives.

Glucazidone-3-sulfonic Acid. This compound is prepared by treatment of glucazidone with 20% oleum, and crystallizes as a hydrate, m.p. 275° (dec.). On nitration the sulfonic acid group is replaced by a nitro group, the product, m.p. 215°, being identical with that obtained by nitration of glucazidone itself (*vide supra*). The same nitro compound is also formed by nitration of the bromoglucazidone, m.p. 127°, prepared by bromination of glucazidone. It follows that the same position of the glucazidone molecule is attacked in the three substitution reactions; and as the sulfonic acid gives quinoxaline-2-carboxylic acid when oxidized with hot aqueous permanganate, the position in question must be in the oxygenated ring. The likely position is regarded as C_3, although C_1 is not excluded.[11]

In aqueous solution the sulfonic acid is stable in the dark, but decomposes in the light with formation of an amorphous oxidation product Oxidation of the acid with Br water gives 1,3-dihydroxyglucazidone (XX)

(XX)   (XXI)   (XXII)

1,3-Dihydroxyglucazidone. This compound, prepared as described above, crystallizes in yellow needles, m.p. 206°; it yields a phenylhydrazone (red needles, m.p. 202°), but does not give a crystalline acetyl or benzoyl derivative. It is readily oxidized, being attacked by air in alkaline solution, by Fehling solution, and by permanganate in acetone. Interaction with ethereal diazomethane involves addition of the reagent as well as methylation; according to the amount of reagent used, the product is either a dimethoxy compound, m.p. 99–100°, formulated as (XXI) or (XXII), or an alkali-soluble analog, m.p. 186°, of this substance, in which only one hydroxyl group has been methylated.

3-Hydroxyglucazidone. This compound (XXIII) is a by-product in the preparation of glucazidone from 2-*d*-arabotetrahydroxybutylquinoxaline. It forms reddish-yellow needles, m.p. 159°, and shows amphoteric properties. It gives an acetyl derivative, m.p. 103°; a benzoyl derivative, m.p. 128°; and (with diazomethane) a methyl ether, m.p. 139°, which like glucazidone, reacts with phenylmagnesium bromide forming a product which is readily dehydrogenated to 3-methoxy-10-phenylglucazidone, m.p. 99°. With phenylmagnesium bromide, 3-hydroxyglucazidone yields 3-hydroxy-10-phenyl-9,10-dihydroglucazidone, m.p. 147° (diacetyl derivative, m.p. 150°). 3-Hydroxyglucazidone condenses with *o*-phenylenediamine in dilute acetic acid forming a compound (XXIV), m.p. 325°, which is identical with the product of dehydrogenation of the substance (XXV) resulting from interaction between *o*-phenylenediamine (2 moles) and 2-hydroxymethyl-5-hydroxy-4-pyrone (XXVI).[10]

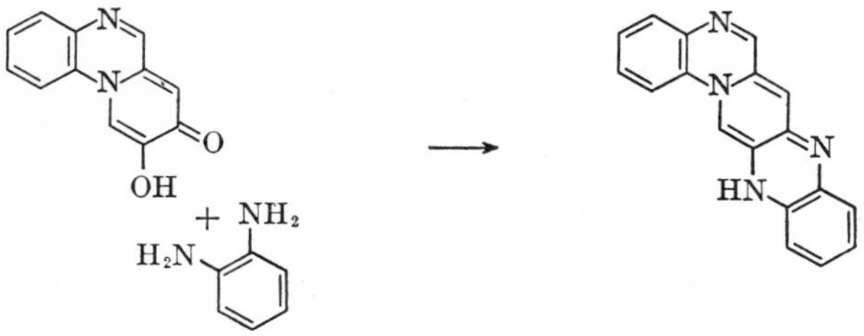

(XXIII)   (XXIV)

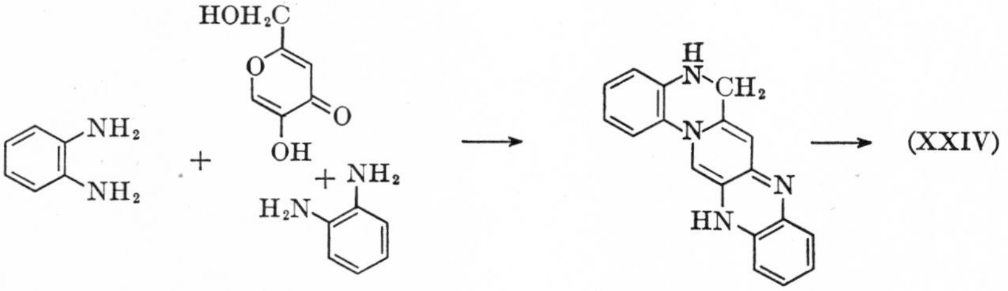

(XXVI)   (XXV)

10-Hydroxyglucazidone. This compound, m.p. 264°, is produced by dehydration of 3-hydroxy-2-*d*-arabotetrahydroxybutylquinoxaline (Chapter XXXVI). It does not react with Grignard reagents.[10]

D. *Other Condensed Quinoxalines*

Compounds (XXVIa)–(XLVI), containing a 5-membered ring attached to C_2-C_3 of the quinoxaline nucleus, are prepared by condensation of *o*-phenylenediamine (or other 1,2-diamine) with the appropriate 1,2-diketone under the usual conditions (*cf.* Chapter XXIV).

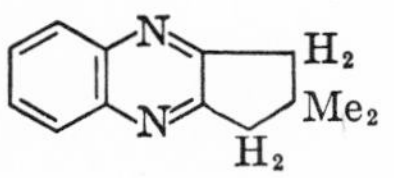

M.p. 123.5°[12] (XXVIa)
(*R.I.* 1752)

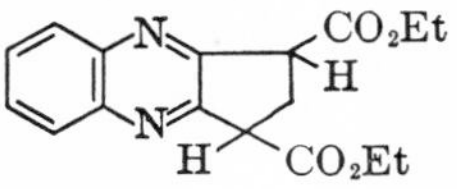

M.p. 202–203°[13] (XXVII)
(*R.I.* 1752)

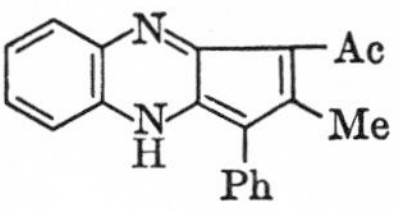

Purple needles, m.p. 250°.
Conc. H_2SO_4 gives purple color[14] (XXVIII) (*R.I* 1753)

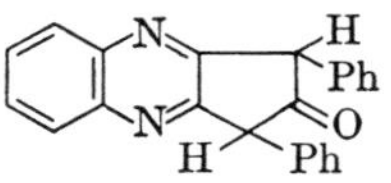

Yellow rods, m.p. 249–250°[15] (XXIX)
(*R.I.* 1752)

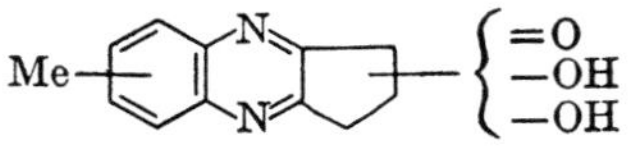

Green needles, dec. on heating[16] (XXX)
(*R.I.* 1752)

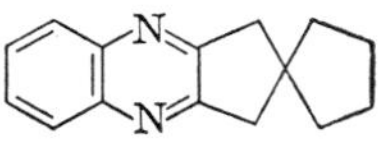

M.p. 95–96°[12] (XXXI) (*R.I.* 2315)

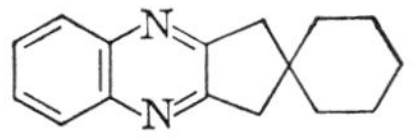

M.p. 99–100°[12] (XXXII) (*R.I.* 2315)

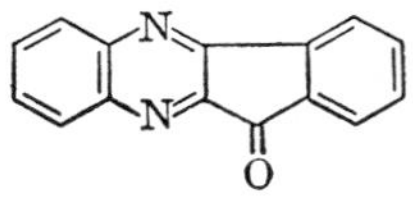

Yellow prisms, m.p. 218–219°[14] (XXXIII) (*R.I.* 2517)

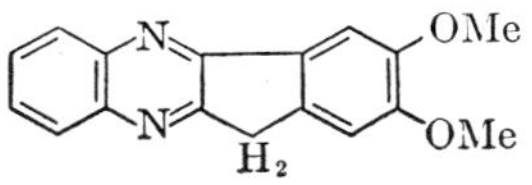

Yellow needles, m.p. 177–178°. Conc. H_2SO_4 gives deep violet color; orange sulfate formed on dilution with water[17] (XXXIV) (*R.I.* 2517)

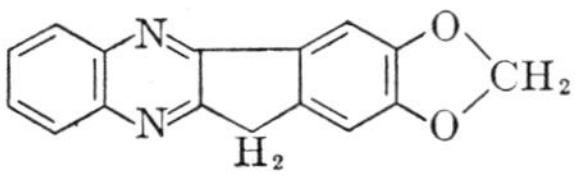

Yellow needles, m.p. 204–205°. Conc. H_2SO_4 gives blue-violet color; orange sulfate formed on dilution with water[17] (XXXV)(*R.I.* 2952)

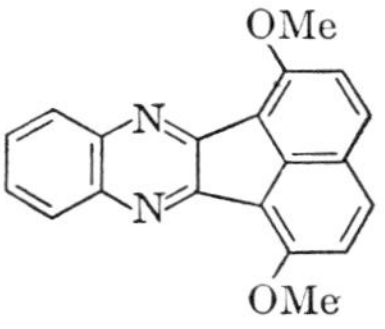

Yellow needles, m.p. 253° (corr.)[18] (XXXVI) (*R.I.* 3141)

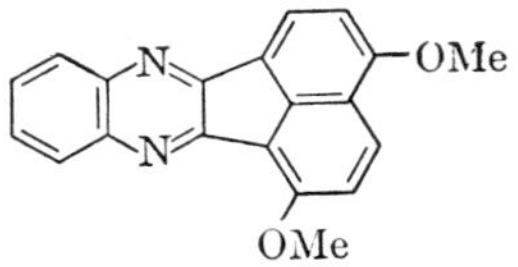

Yellow blades, m.p. 196–197° (corr.)[18] (XXXVII) (*R.I.* 3141)

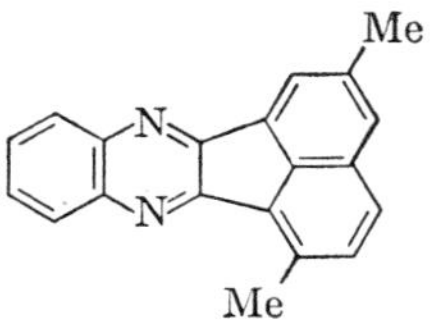

Yellow needles, m.p. 194° (corr.)[18] (XXXVIII) (*R.I.* 3141)

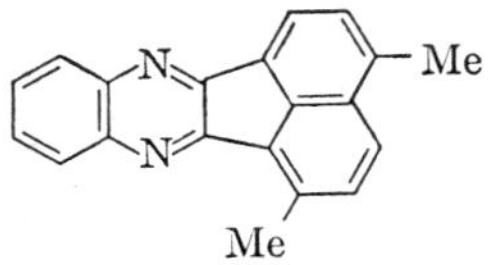

Yellow needles, mp. 198–199° (corr.)[18] (XXXIX) (*R.I.* 3141)

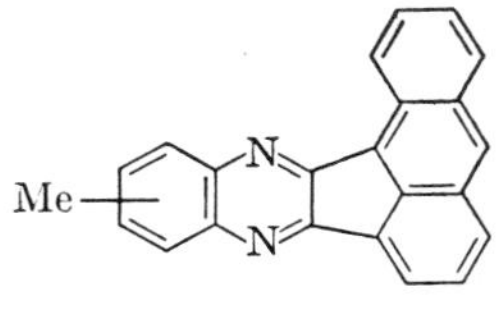

Orange-yellow cryst., m.p. 237°[19] (XL) (*R.I.* 3540)

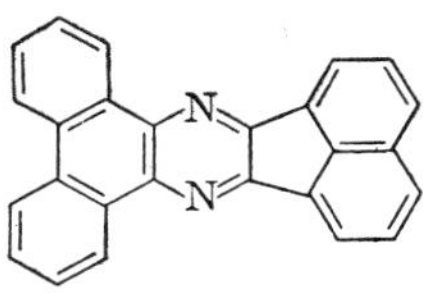

Yellow needles. Conc. H_2SO_4 gives purple color[20] (XLI)

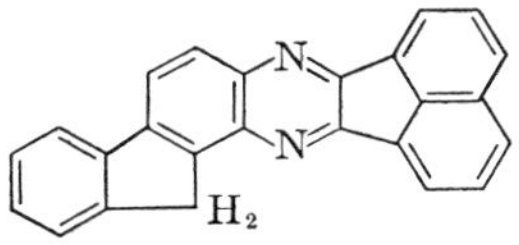

Orange-yellow needles, m.p. 288°[21] (XLII) (R.I. 3707)

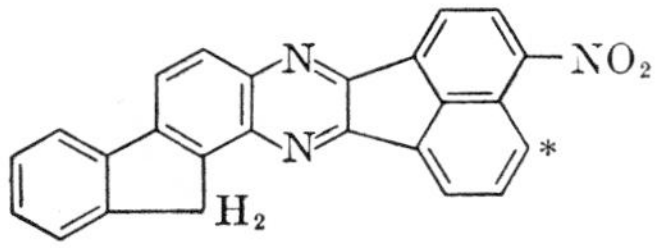

Red-brown solid, m.p. > 295°. An alternative structure with the NO_2 group at (*) is not excluded[21] (XLIII) (R.I. 3707)

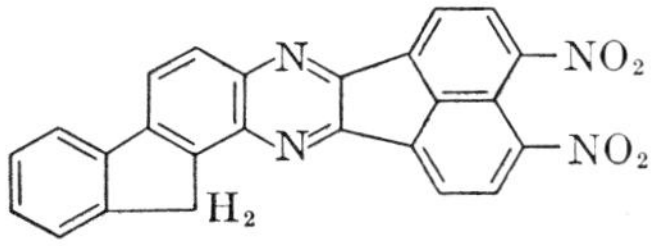

Chocolate-brown needles, m.p. > 295°[21] (XLIV) (R.I. 3707)

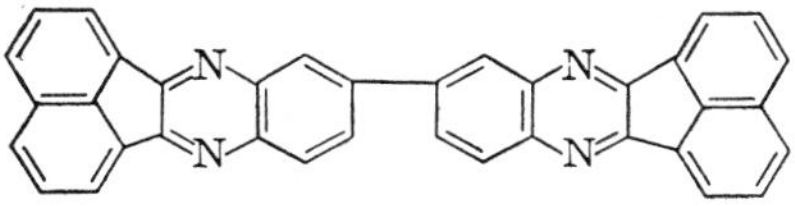

(XLV)[22] (R.I. 3141)

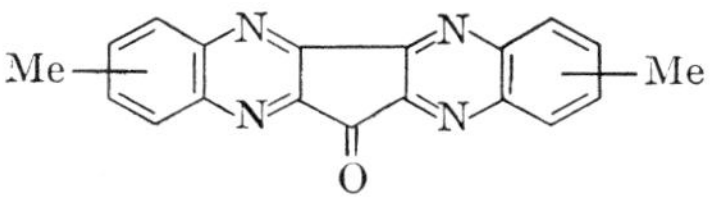

Yellow needles, m.p. > 300°[16] (XLVI) (R.I. 3140)

Treatment of 2,3-trimethylenequinoxaline with boiling benzaldehyde, and with p-nitrobenzaldehyde in boiling acetic anhydride, respectively, gives the compounds (XLVII) and (XLVIII):

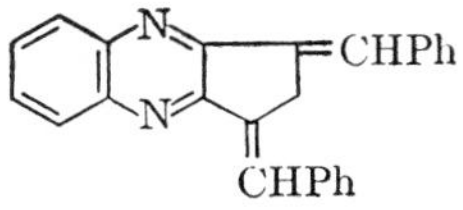

Brown cryst., m.p. 213°[23] (XLVII) (R.I. 1752)

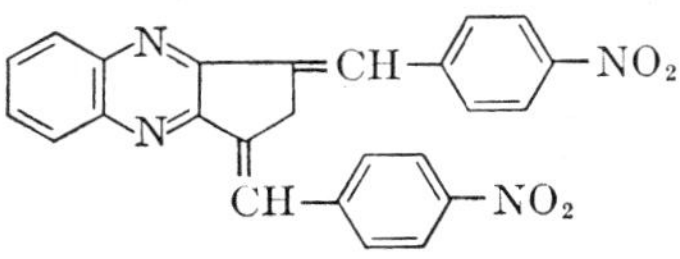

Yellow needles, dec. 268–270°[23] (XLVIII) (R.I. 1752)

Compounds (XLIX) and (L) are prepared from the 1,2-diketone (diphenylcyclopentanetrione) and the appropriate N-substituted-o-diamine:

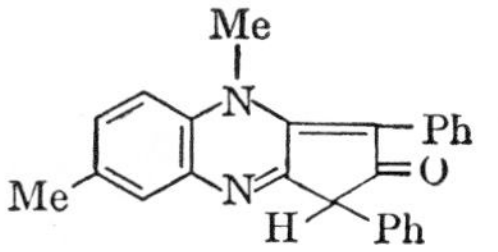

Yellow needles, m.p. 224–225°[15] (XLIX) (R.I. 1753)

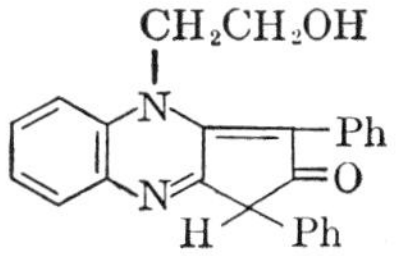

Yellow plates, m.p. 208–209°[15] (L) (R.I. 1753)

The following quaternary salts are prepared from acenaphthenquinone by condensation with the appropriate N-phenyl-1,2-diamine in acetic acid, followed by addition of mineral acid:

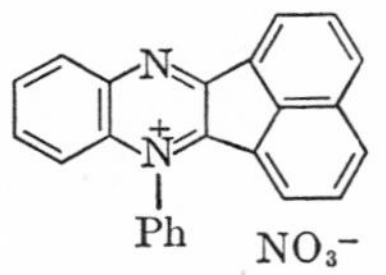

Yellow needles. Conc. H_2SO_4 gives red color. Ammonium hydroxide and methanol give the pseudo base methyl ether, $C_{25}H_{18}ON_2$, m.p. 180–185°[24] (LI) (*R.I.* 3141)

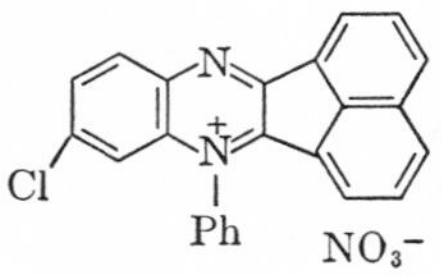

Yellow needles. Conc. H_2SO_4 gives red color. Pseudobase methyl ether (*cf* LI), $C_{25}H_{17}ON_2Cl$, m.p. 200–220°[24] (LII) (*R.I.* 3141)

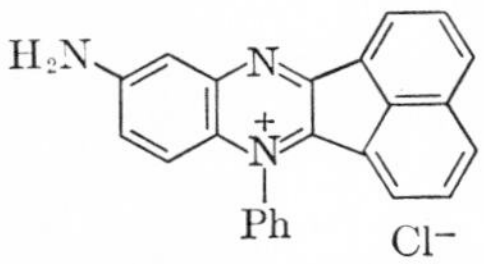

Violet needles. Conc. H_2SO_4 gives red-brown color. N-Ac deriv., red needles. Nitrate, violet plates[24] (LIII) (*R.I.* 3141)

Compound (LIV) (or tautomer) is prepared by condensing 1,4-dichloro-cyclopentene-3,5-dione with o-phenylenediamine:

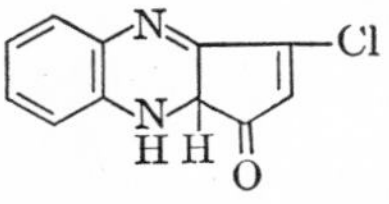

Yellow or red needles, m.p. 160–165° (dec.). NaOH gives a sparingly sol. yellow Na salt[25] (LIV) (*R.I.* 1753)

Compounds (LV) and (LVI) are formed from the diphthaloyl-o-diamines (as LVII) by reduction with zinc dust in acetic acid, followed by thermal dehydration of the initial reduction products.

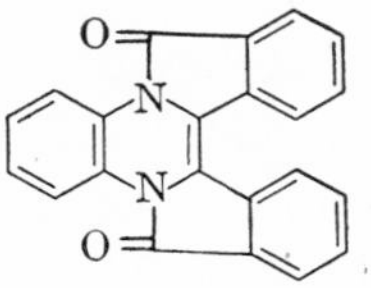

Red needles, m.p. 278°. Insol. in acids and dil. alk. With hot strong alk. gives the (?) dicarboxylic acid, m.p. 270–273°[26] (LV) (*R.I.* 3470)

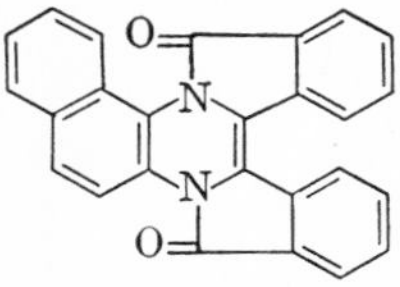

Red needles, m.p. 323–324°[26] (LVI) (*R.I.* 3697)

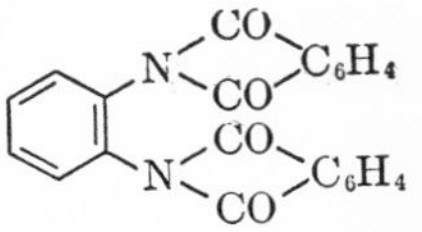

(LVII)

Compounds (LVIII) and (LIX) contain a 5-membered ring fused to the quinoxaline ring system at C_5-C_6, and are prepared from the appropriate o-diamine and 1,2-diketone:

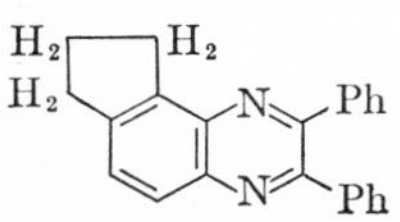

M.p. 162°[27] (LVIII) (*R.I.* 1754) 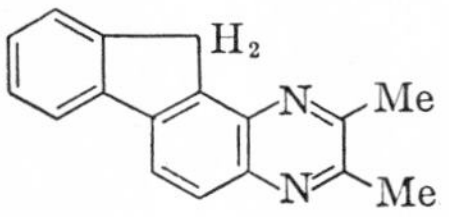   (LIX)[28]

The compounds (LX) and (LXI) are prepared from the nitroso derivatives (LXII) (Table XXXVII-3) and (LXIII) (Chapter XXXVII, Section 2B) by reduction to the corresponding amines which are then condensed with cyclohexanone, the final ring closures being analogous to the Fischer indole synthesis. Hydrolysis of (LX) with methanolic potassium hydroxide gives the acid (LXIV).

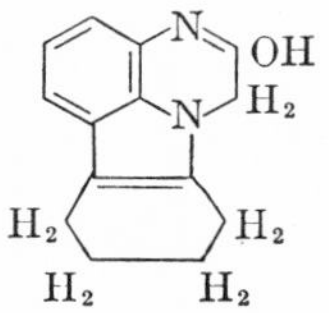

m.p. 285° (corr.)[29]
(LX)
R.I. 2418

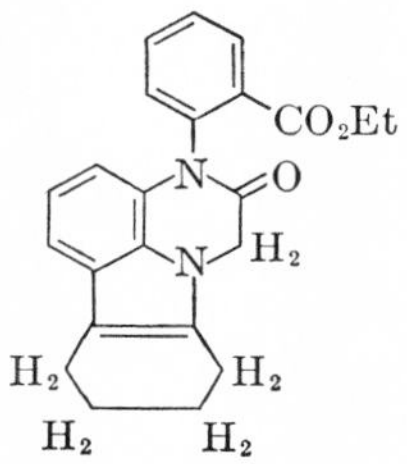

m.p. 171-172°[30]
(LXI)
R.I. 2418

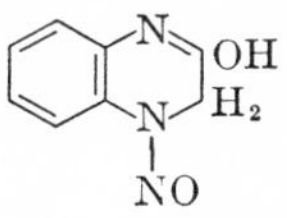

(LXII)

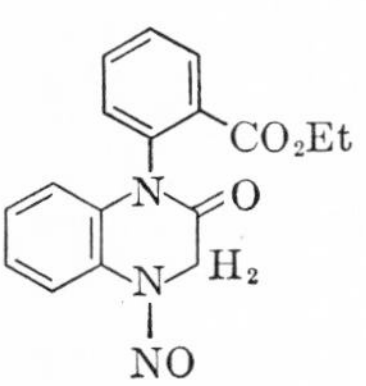

(LXIII) 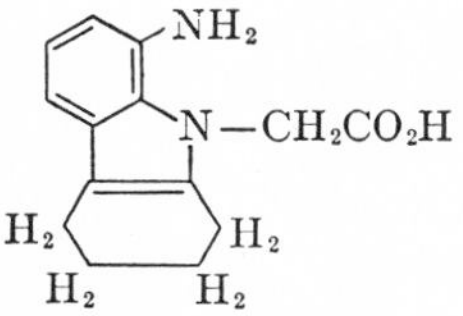   (LXIV)

Compounds (LXV) and (LXVI), having a 6-membered ring fused to N_1-C_8 of the quinoxaline nucleus, have been prepared from 8-amino-1,2,3,4-tetrahydroquinoline (LXVII) by heating with pyruvic acid and benzoin, respectively. In these reactions the quinoline component is functioning as an N-substituted-o-diamine; its usefulness in this sense, however, seems limited, as an analogous product was not obtained by condensation with diacetyl, and attempts to prepare quaternary salts by condensation with a dicarbonyl compound in presence of mineral acid (*cf.* Chapter XXXIV) were also unsuccessful.[31]

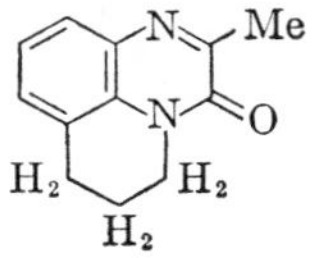

M.p. 113°[31] (LXV) (R.I.   Orange plates, m.p. 146°[31]   (LXVII)
         1896)   (LXVI) (R.I. 1896)

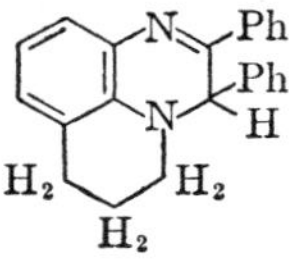

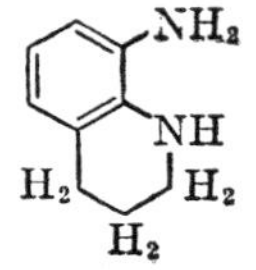

2. Quinoxalines Condensed with Nitrogenous Heterocyclic Rings

A. Pyrroloquinoxalines

Compounds (I)–(XIX) contain a pyrrole ring fused to a quinoxaline residue, the 2,3-positions of each ring system being involved. The compounds are prepared by conventional reactions between an *o*-diketone and the appropriate diamine. Obvious alternative structures are possible for compounds (XII)–(XVII), which are prepared from diaminofluorene and substituted isatins, and for (XVIII) and (XIX).

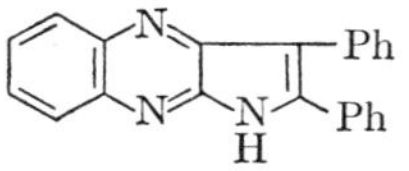

Yellow needles, m.p. 240–241°[14] (I)   Yellow needles, m.p. 258°[14] (II) (R.I.
         (R.I. 1626)   1626)

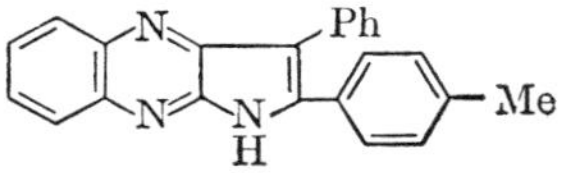

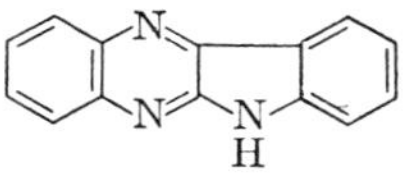

Yellow cryst. m.p. 295–297°[32–34] (III)   Yellow needles, m.p. 225°. OEt at 6
         (R.I. 2413)   or 7[35] (IV) (R.I. 2413)

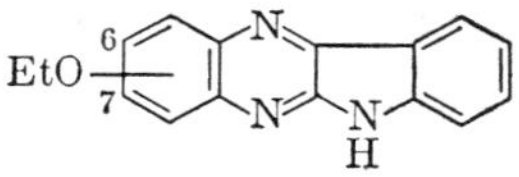

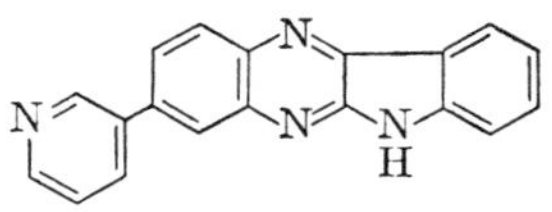

Yellow needles, m.p. 275–276°[36] (V)   Yellow needles, m.p. 307–308° (dec.)
         (R.I. 2413)   Positions of the pyridyl ring in this
                                              compd. and (V) should possibly be inter-
                                              changed[36] (VI) (R.I. 2413)

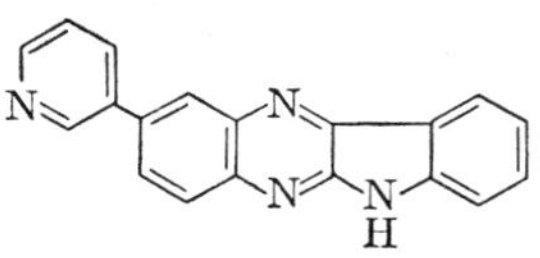

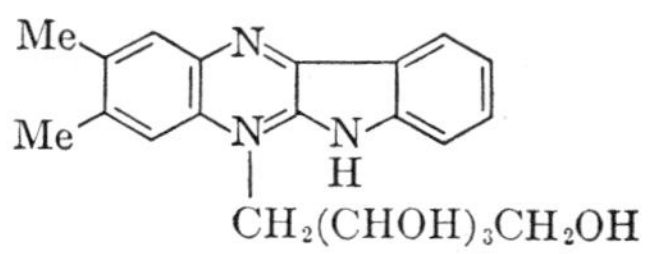

(VII)[32–34] (R.I. 2412) 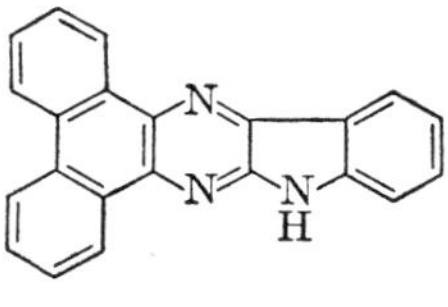   Pale orange needles, m.p. > 360°.
                                              Conc. H_2SO_4 gives red color[20] (VIII)

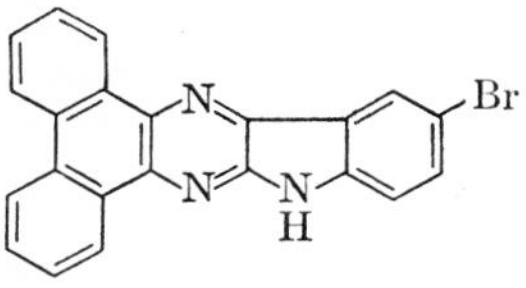

M.p. 360°. Conc. H_2SO_4 gives violet-red color[20] (IX)

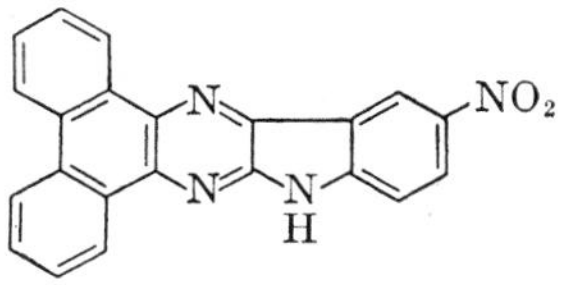

Ochre cryst., m.p. > 360°. Conc. H_2SO_4 gives violet color[20] (X)

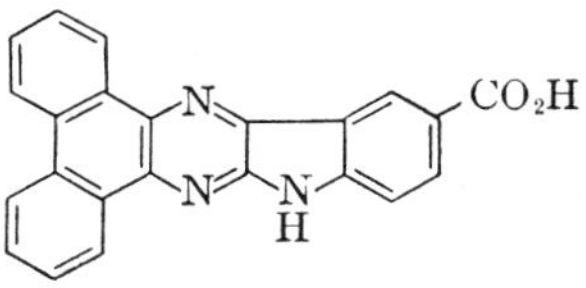

M.p. > 360°[20] (XI)

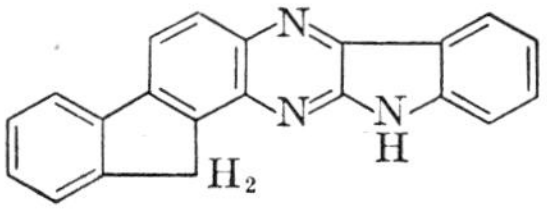

Yellow needles, m.p. > 295°[21] (XII) (R.I. 3475)

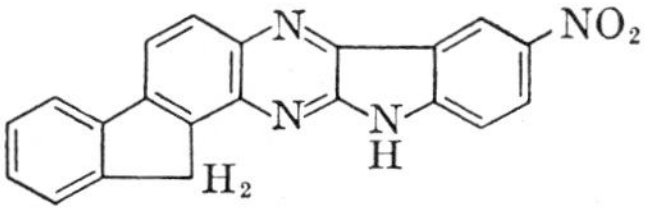

Brown-yellow cryst., m.p. > 295°[21] (XIII) (R.I. 3475)

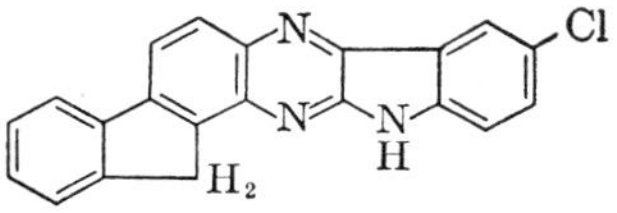

Brown cryst., m.p. > 295°[21] (XIV) (R.I. 3475)

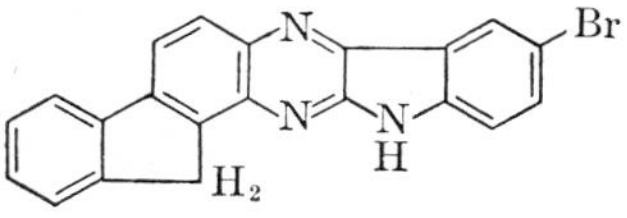

Brown plates, m.p. > 295°[21] (XV) (R.I. 3475)

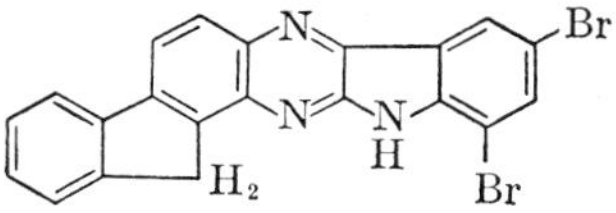

Brown powder, m.p. > 290°[21] (XVI) (R.I. 3475)

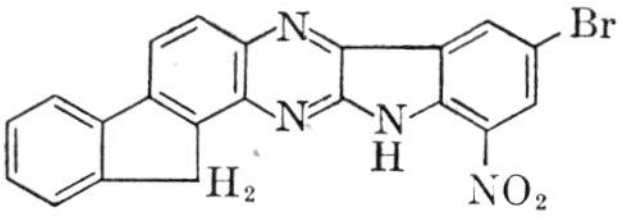

Violet needles, m.p. > 295°[21] (XVII) (R.I. 3475)

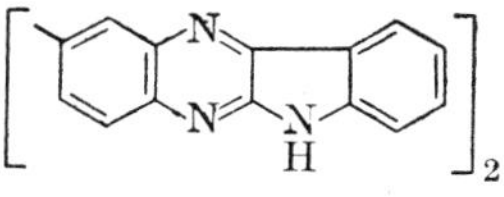

(XVIII)[22] (R.I. 2413)

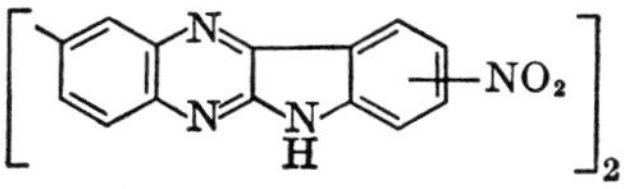

(XIX)[22] (R.I. 2413)

B. *Pyridoquinoxalines*

Compounds (XX)–(XXIa) are prepared from the appropriate diamino-quinoline and dicarbonyl compound.

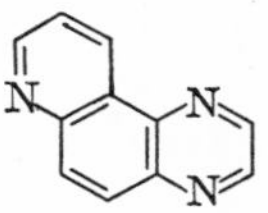

M.p. 135°. Picrate, m.p. 165–166°. Tri-*N*-oxide, m.p. > 400°[37] (XX) (*R.I.* 1892)

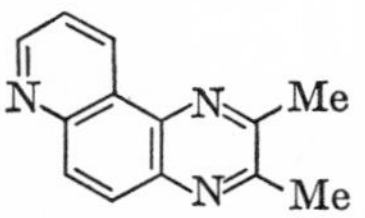

M.p. 142–144°. Tri-*N*-oxide, m.p. 255–257°[37] (XXI) (*R.I.* 1892)

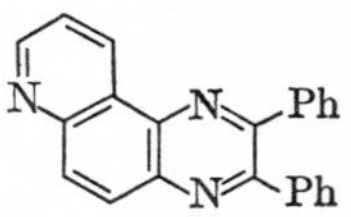

Yellow plates, m.p. 205–206°[15] (XXIa) (*R.I.* 1892)

Derivatives of the quaternary base (XXII) have been prepared from (XXIII) (Chapter XXXVII, Section 1B) by Usherwood and Whiteley.[38] If cold concentrated sulfuric acid is added to (XXIII), followed by dilution with water, the product is the sulfonate corresponding to (XXII), and on crystallization of this substance from chloroform and the appropriate alcohol the corresponding methoxide (yellow prisms, m.p. 276–278°) and ethoxide (yellow prisms, m.p. 240°) are formed. From their properties these "alkoxides" appear to be the methyl ether and ethyl ether, respectively, of the covalent pseudo base corresponding to (XXII).

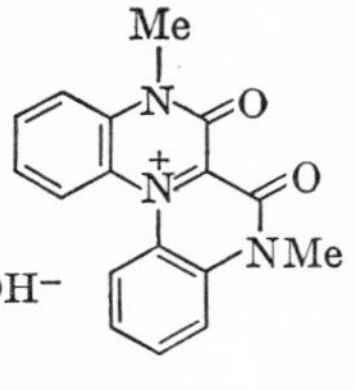

(XXII)
R.I. 2468

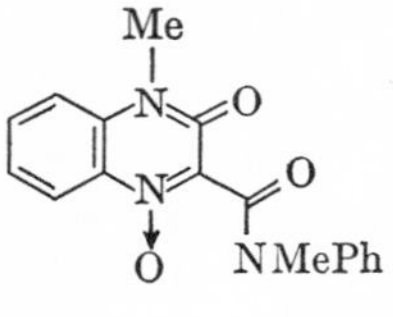

(XXIII)

C. *Pyrazoloquinoxalines* (*Flavazoles*) (*R.I. 1561*)

The compound (XXIV), which is the prototype of the group of substances discussed in this section, has been named *flavazole* and is numbered as shown[39]; it has been prepared, together with a variety of substituted

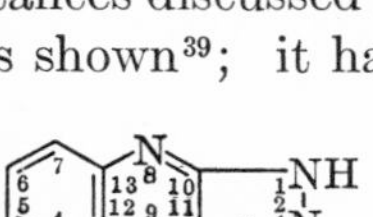

(XXIV) 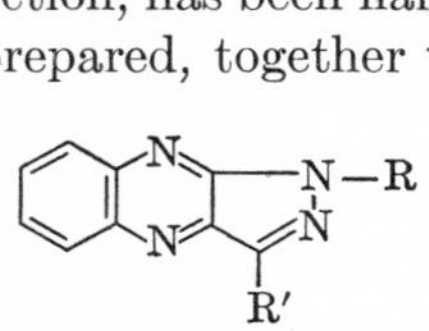   (XXV) 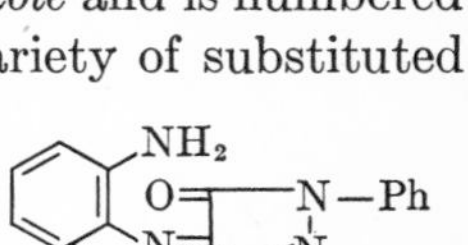   (XXVI)

derivatives, by Ohle and his associates. Substituted flavazoles are, however, more readily accessible than the parent base, and will therefore be described first.

1-Phenylflavazole (XXV; R = Ph, R' = H), m.p. 152.5–153.5°, is formed in poor yield by cyclization, in boiling N sodium hydroxide, of the anil (XXVI) derived from *o*-phenylenediamine and 1-phenyl-4,5-diketo-pyrazoline.[40] It is also obtainable by decarboxylation of 1-phenylflava-zole-3-carboxylic acid (XXV; R = Ph, R' = CO_2H) (*vide infra*).

1-Phenyl-3-methylflavazole (XXV; R = Ph, R' = Me) is prepared from the 3-methyl analog of (XXVI), the cyclization being effected in acetic acid[40]; it is to be noted that the anil was originally mistaken for the flavazole compound.[41] This flavazole is a yellow crystalline solid, m.p. 133.5–134°, and shows the fluorescence and the brown-red solution in sulfuric acid, which are typical of members of this group. The 3-methyl group is resistant to oxidation.

1,3-Diphenylflavazole (XXV; R = R' = Ph), m.p. 231°, gives a blood-red coloration in concentrated sulfuric acid, and is prepared by cyclizing the 3-phenyl analog of (XXVI) in boiling acetic acid.[42]

1-Phenyl-3-polyhydroxyalkylflavazoles. These compounds have the general structure represented by the expression (XXVIII). They may be prepared from 2-polyhydroxyalkylquinoxalines (XXVII) by reaction with phenylhydrazine under mild acid conditions; in practice, it is usually more convenient to work with a solution of (XXVII) prepared *in situ* (Table IV, method A), or to treat the sugar simultaneously with *o*-phenylenediamine and phenylhydrazine (Table XXXVIII-4, method B).[39,43,44] The synthesis has been studied by Ohle and his co-workers,[39,43,44] who consider

(XXVII) $+ 3PhNHNH_2 \longrightarrow$

$(CHOH)_{n-1}$
|
CH_2OH

(XXVIII)

that it may be applied to reducing sugars in general except to those substituted at C_3 and C_4. The reaction is of potential value as a method of diagnosing sugar configuration[44]; and the sparing solubility and good crystallizing power of the products are of practical value in demonstrating that quinoxaline formation has actually occurred with a given sugar on treatment with *o*-phenylenediamine, the alternative possibility of benzi-minazole formation (compare Chapter XXXVI, Section 1) being excluded by the isolation of the flavazole derivative.[44]

As indicated above, the reaction requires the use of 3 moles of phenyl-hydrazine for each mole of polyhydroxyalkylquinoxaline; the following mechanism has been suggested for the synthesis[39] and indicates that two moles of phenylhydrazine are reduced during the dehydrogenation of the tetrahydroderivative (XXXI), which is formed by isomerization of (XXX). The isomerization of (XXVII) to (XXIX) involves an Amadori type of shift (cf. Chapter XXXVI).

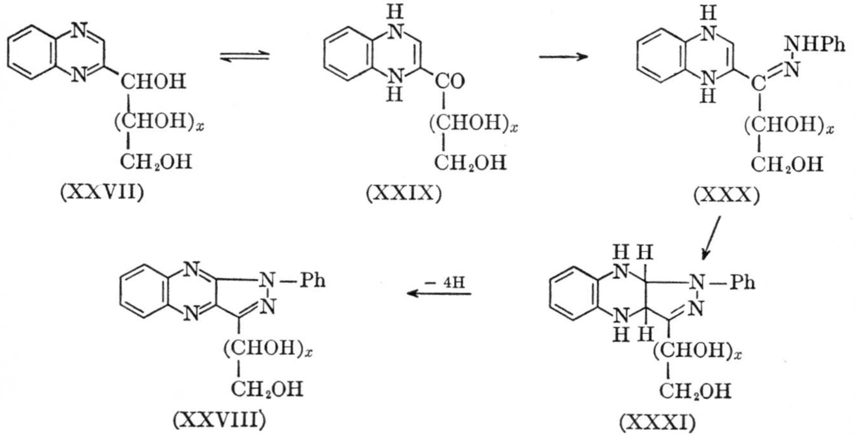

TABLE XXXVIII-4. 1-Phenyl-3-polyhydroxyalkylflavazoles

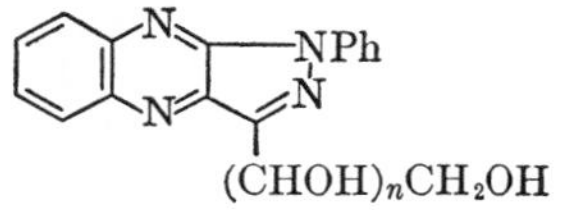

					Acetyl deriv.	
Substituent at C$_3$	Method of prep.[a] and yield[b]	Sugar used	M.p., °C.	[α]$_D$ in C$_5$H$_5$N	M.p., °C.	[α]$_D$ in CHCl$_3$
d-Threotrihydroxy-propyl	A(10%) B(33%)	d-Galactose	194	−53°	97	−38°
l-Threotrihydroxy-propyl	A(3.3) B(12)	l-Sorbose	194	+53.5°	97	+37.8°
d-Dihydroxyethyl	A(12) B(11.4)	d-Xylose	212	+8.0°	128	+80°
l-Dihydroxyethyl	A(10) B(10)	l-Arabinose	212	−8.0°	128	−82.5°
l-Erythrodihy-droxypropyl	A(25) B(14)	l-Rhamnose	211	+43.8°	173	−83.8°
d-Erythrotrihy-droxypropyl	See refs. 43 and 39	d-Glucose or d-Fructose	218	−19.1°	124	+64.4° +81.5° (C$_5$H$_5$N)

[a] A, an aqueous solution of the sugar (1 mole) is heated (95°, 4.5 hours, CO$_2$ atmosphere) with o-phenylenediamine, hydrazine hydrate, acetic acid (1 mole each) and boric acid (2 moles). A solution of phenylhydrazine (3.5 moles) in aqueous hydrochloric acid containing a little acetic acid is then added, and the whole is refluxed for 18–24 hours (CO$_2$ atmosphere). B, the sugar and o-phenylenediamine (1 mole each) are refluxed for 20–24 hours (CO$_2$ atmosphere) with phenylhydrazine (5 moles) in aqueous hydrochloric acid containing a little acetic acid.
[b] Reference 44 unless otherwise stated.

General Properties of 1-Phenyl-3-polyhydroxyalkylflavazoles. The physical constants of these compounds are given in Table XXXVIII-4. They crystallize extremely well, and are sparingly soluble in water. They are bright yellow if the side-chain hydroxyl groups are free, but pale greenish-yellow if these groups are alkylated, acylated, or converted into CO groups. They give more or less intense red or reddish-brown solutions in concentrated sulfuric acid.

Proof of Structure of 1-Phenyl-3-d-erythrotrihydroxypropylflavazole. The presence of the 1',2',3'-trihydroxypropyl side chain in this compound XXXII; R = 1-phenyl-3-flavazyl) has been established in the following manner.[39] The compound gives a trityl derivative, which in turn yields a diacetyl derivative; it thus contains three hydroxyl groups, of which one is a primary grouping. The compound readily gives an acetonyl derivative, which does not yield a trityl ester; it thus follows that the acetonyl compound (XXXIII) has been formed by condensation of the primary and one other hydroxyl group of (XXXII), which therefore contains the grouping $CHOHCH_2OH$. Benzoylation of (XXXII) gives a monobenzoate, which with lead tetraacetate is oxidized to a mixture of the monobenzoate (XXXIV) of glycolaldehyde and *1-phenylflavazole-3-aldehyde* (XXXV) (yellow plates, m.p. 144°). Benzoylation of the acetonyl derivative (XXXIII) gives a monobenzoate which with acetic acid is converted into a compound isomeric, and not identical, with the monobenzoate prepared from (XXXII); these two monobenzoates must therefore be represented by (XXXVI) and (XXXVII), respectively, and hence (XXXII) contains the grouping $(CHOH)_2CH_2OH$. Oxidation of (XXXVI) with lead tetraacetate gives the anticipated formaldehyde, together with the flavazole derivative (XXXVIII).

RCHOH	RCHOH	CHO	RCHO
CHOH	CH—O	CH₂OBz	
CH₂OH	| CMe₂		
	CH₂—O		
(XXXII)	(XXXIII)	(XXXIV)	(XXXV)

RCHOBz	RCHOH	RCHOBz	RCO₂H
CHOH	CHOH	CHO	
CH₂OH	CH₂OBz		
(XXXVI)	(XXXVII)	(XXXVIII)	(XXXIX)

Proof of the ring structure of (XXXII; R = 1-phenyl-3-flavazyl) was obtained[40] by oxidizing the aldehyde (XXXV) (with chromic anhydride in boiling acetic acid) to *1-phenylflavazole-3-carboxylic acid* (XXXIX) [yellow needles, m.p. 244° (dec.); ethyl ester, m.p. 168°], which loses carbon dioxide when heated at 260° under reduced pressure and yields 1-phenylflavazole (XXV; R = Ph, R' = H), the synthesis of which has already been described.

3-d-Erythrotrihydroxypropylflavazole (XL; R = CHOHCHOHCH$_2$OH) is prepared by condensing 2-*d*-arabotetrahydroxybutylquinoxaline with hydrazine. It forms light yellow needles, m.p. 225–226° (dec.), [α]$_D$ +15.04° (in 0.1 N NaOH), +30.2° (in borax), and −12.8° (in pyridine).[45]

(XL)   (XLI)

Flavazole-3-aldehyde (XL; R = CHO). This compound is prepared from the foregoing substance in poor yield by oxidation with lead tetraacetate, but with periodic acid in dilute acetic acid at 20° the yield is almost quantitative.[45] It has m.p. 256–258° (dec.), is soluble, and stable, in dilute alkalis, and is not attacked by atmospheric oxygen. With hydrazine hydrate it gives *3-methylflavazole*, m.p. 221–222°, and on boiling with concentrated alkali it undergoes a Cannizzaro reaction, yielding *3-hydroxymethylflavazole*, m.p. 244–246°, and the 3-carboxylic acid (*vide infra*).

Flavazole-3-carboxylic acid (XL; R = CO$_2$H). This acid may be prepared (*a*) by oxidation of 3-*d*-erythrotrihydroxypropylflavazole (XL; R = CHOHCHOHCH$_2$OH) with chromic anhydride in 50% sulfuric acid at 25–35°, or (*b*) from flavazole-3-aldehyde by oxidation with ammoniacal silver nitrate. It has m.p. 272–273° (efferv.), and is very sparingly soluble in water, insoluble in thionyl chloride, and difficult to esterify; the *methyl ester*, m.p. 257–258°, does not react with methanolic ammonia at 20°. The *acetyl derivative*, m.p. 213–214°, of the acid, however, reacts with thionyl chloride, and the *amide* (XL; R = CONH$_2$), m.p. 310–312°, is thence obtained by the action of methanolic ammonia accompanied by simultaneous deacetylation.[45]

Flavazole-3-carboxylic acid sublimes fairly readily at normal pressure with loss of carbon dioxide, the product being:

Flavazole (XL; R = H). This compound melts at 274–275° and is sparingly soluble in water, but dissolves easily in N sodium hydroxide and in concentrated mineral acid. It is best recrystallized from aqueous sodium carbonate. It readily yields an *acetyl derivative*, m.p. 160–162°, but does not react with diazomethane (in ether at 20°) or with methyl iodide (20 hours at 100°).

The contrast between the high melting point (275°) of this compound and the much lower melting point (165°) of *1-methylflavazole* (XLI) [prepared analogously to flavazole, starting with 2-*d*-arabotetrahydroxybutyl-quinoxaline and methylhydrazine] has led to the suggestion[45] that flavazole is either a zwitterion or a bimolecular associate of the type discussed by Hayes and Hunter[46] for simple pyrazoles.

The solubility of flavazole in caustic alkali (but not in alkali carbonate) is characteristic of flavazoles with a free 1-position, and is reminiscent of the behavior of pyrazole and indazole. In the case of (XL; R = CHOHCH-OHCH₂OH) the color in alkali is greatly intensified, a fact attributed by Ohle and Iltgen[45] to the formation of a flavazole anion stabilized by resonance of the type (XLII) ←→ (XLIII). These workers also draw attention to the similar deepening of color which occurs when the yellow phenylhydrazone of quinoxaline-2-aldehyde is converted into its sodium salt (Chapter XXVIII), and consider that the canonical forms (XLIII) and (XLIV), which are very similar in structure, make major contributions to the anions of flavazoles having a free 1-position, and of quinoxaline-2-aldehyde, respectively.

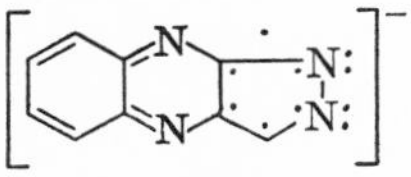

(XLII) 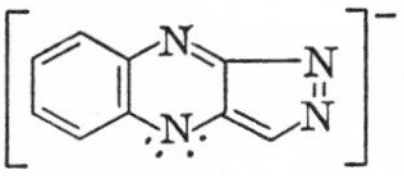   (XLIII) 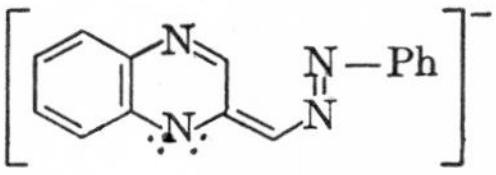   (XLIV)

D. *Glyoxalinoquinoxalines*

The compound (XLV) is prepared by condensing 3,4,3′,4′-tetraamino-diphenyl with parabanic acid in boiling acetic acid.[22]

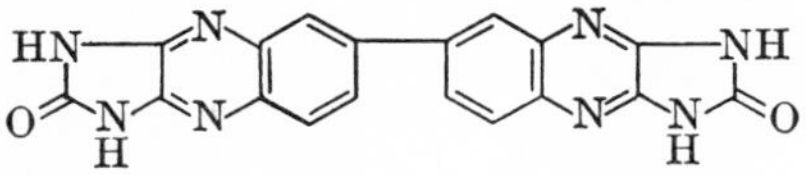

(XLV)
R.I. 1562

E. *Triazoloquinoxalines*

If 2,3-dichloroquinoxaline (Chapter XXX, Section 2) is boiled under reflux for several hours with sodium azide in alcohol, the substance (XLVI) is produced. This compound has m.p. 265° (after previous shrinking), and is converted into the hydroxy analog (XLVII), m.p. 288° (efferv.) by prolonged refluxing with the theoretical amount of sodium ethoxide in ethanol.[47]

(XLVI)   (XLVII)   (XLVIII)
R.I. 1475   R.I. 1475

F. Pyridazoquinoxalines

The compound (XLVIII), a yellow crystalline powder, m.p. > 330°, is formed in a somewhat impure condition by evaporating an alcoholic solution of hydrazine and the anhydride of quinoxaline-2,3-dicarboxylic acid, followed by heating the residual solid to 200°.[48]

References

1. Witt and Schmidt, *Ber.*, **25**, 1013 (1892).
2. Witt and von Helmolt, *Ber.*, **27**, 2351 (1894).
3. Crippa, *Gazz. chim. ital.*, **59**, 330 (1929).
4. Crippa, Cessi, and Perroncito, *Gazz. chim. ital.*, **63**, 251 (1933).
5. Fischer and Römer, *Ber.*, **41**, 2350 (1908).
6. Crippa, Axerio, and Long, *Gazz. chim. ital.*, **60**, 301 (1930).
7. Crippa and Long, *Gazz. chim. ital.*, **61**, 388 (1931).
8. Crippa and Long, *Gazz. chim. ital.*, **62**, 394 (1932).
9. Maurer and Sehiedt, *Ber.*, **67**, 1980 (1934).
10. Maurer, Schiedt, and Schroeter, *Ber.*, **68**, 1716 (1935).
11. Maurer and Schiedt, *Ber.*, **70**, 1857 (1937).
12. Kon, *J. Chem. Soc.*, **1922**, 513.
13. Bost and Towell, *J. Am. Chem. Soc.*, **70**, 903 (1948).
14. Ruhemann, *J. Chem. Soc.*, **1910**, 1438.
15. Hall and Turner, *J. Chem. Soc.*, **1945**, 699.
16. Nietzki and Benckiser, *Ber.*, **19**, 772 (1886).
17. W. H. Perkin, W. M. Roberts, and R. Robinson, *J. Chem. Soc.*, **1914**, 2405.
18. Lesser and Gad, *Ber.*, **60**, 242 (1927).
19. Liebermann and Zsuffa, *Ber.*, **44**, 202 (1911).
20. Buu-Hoï and Jacquignon, *Compt. rend.*, **226**, 2155 (1948).
21. Dutta, *Ber.*, **65**, 1793 (1932).
22. Tiwari and Dutt, *Proc. Natl. Acad. Sci. India*, **7**, 58 (1937).
23. Bennett and Willis, *J. Chem. Soc.*, **1928**, 1960.
24. Ullman and Cassirer, *Ber.*, **43**, 439 (1910).
25. Zincke and Fuchs, *Ber.*, **26**, 513 (1893).
26. Lieb, *Monatsh.*, **39**, 873 (1918).
27. Borsche and Bodenstein, *Ber.*, **59**, 1909 (1926).
28. Diels, Schill, and Tolson, *Ber.*, **35**, 3284 (1902).
29. W. H. Perkin and Riley, *J. Chem. Soc.*, **1923**, 2399.
30. Clemo, W. H. Perkin, Jr., and R. Robinson, *J. Chem. Soc.*, **1924**, 1751.
31. Hazlewood, Hughes, and Lions, *J. Proc. Roy. Soc. N. S. Wales*, **71**, 462 (1938).
32. Bednarczyk and Marchlewski, *Bull. intern. acad. polon. sci., Classe sci., math. nat.*, **1938A**, 529.

33. Marchlewski, *Roczniki Chem.*, **18,** 698 (1938).
34. Bednarczyk and Marchlewski, *Biochem. Z.*, **300,** 46 (1938).
35. Marchlewski and K. Radcliffe, *Ber.*, **32,** 1869 (1899).
36. Coates, A. H. Cook, Heilbron, Hey, Lambert, and Lewis, *J. Chem. Soc.*, **1943,** 404.
37. Linsker and R. L. Evans, *J. Am. Chem. Soc.*, **68,** 874 (1946).
38. Usherwood and Whiteley, *J. Chem. Scc.*, **1923,** 1069.
39. Ohle and Melkonian, *Ber.*, **74,** 279 (1941).
40. Ohle and Melkonian, *Ber.*, **74,** 398 (1941).
41. Sachs and Barschall, *Ber.*, **35,** 1437 (1902).
42. Sachs and Becherescu, *Ber.*, **36,** 1132 (1903).
43. Ohle and Hielscher, *Ber.*, **74,** 13 (1941).
44. Ohle and Liebig, *Ber.*, **75,** 1536 (1942).
45. Ohle and Iltgen, *Ber.*, **76,** 1 (1943).
46. Hayes and Hunter, *J. Chem. Soc.*, **1945,** 1.
47. Stollé and Hanusch, *J. prakt. Chem.*, **136,** 9 (1933).
48. Wegler, *J. prakt. Chem.*, **148,** 135 (1937).
49. F. E. King and Beer, *J. Chem. Soc.*, **1945,** 791.
50. Wolf, Beutel, and Stevens, *J. Am. Chem. Soc.*, **70,** 2572 (1948).
51. Hinsberg and Schwantes, *Ber.*, **36,** 4039 (1903).
52. Kühling, *Ber.*, **24,** 3029 (1891).
53. Dutt and Sen, *J. Chem. Soc.*, **1922,** 2663.
54. Kehrmann and Safar, *Helv. Chim. Acta*, **8,** 668 (1925).
55. Schönberg and Malchow, *Ber.*, **55,** 3746 (1922).
56. Schönberg and Kraemer, *Ber.*, **55,** 1174 (1922).
57. Weijlard and Tishler, *J. Am. Chem. Soc.*, **67,** 1231 (1945).

CHAPTER XXXIX

Azaquinoxalines

Azaquinoxalines are compounds in which a —CH= group in the benzene ring of the quinoxaline ring system has been replaced by a nitrogen atom. Examples are (*a*) 5-azaquinoxalines, *viz.*, (I) and its derivatives; (*b*) 5,7-diazaquinoxalines, containing the ring system (II); and (*c*) 5,8-diazaquinoxalines, derived from the system (III).

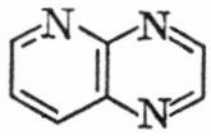

(I)
R.I. 968

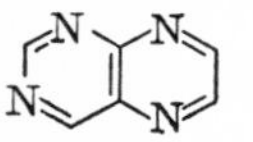

(II)
R.I. 959

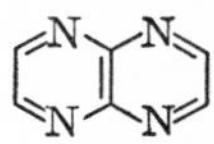

(III)

The method of preparation is the same for compounds of each of these types, namely, condensation of the appropriate diamino- heterocyclic compound (-pyridine, -pyrimidine, or -pyrazine, respectively) with a 1,2-dicarbonyl compound.

5-Azaquinoxalines. These compounds are listed in Table XXXIX-1.

TABLE XXXIX-1. 5-Azaquinoxalines

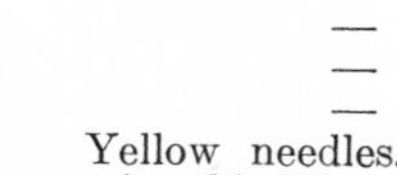

R_1	R_2	R_3	R_4	M.p., °C.	Remarks	Ref.
H	H	H	H	147–148	—	3
H	H	H	Br	167	*N*-Oxide, m.p. 286° (dec.)	3
H	H	NH_2	H	267	—	4
OH	OH	NH_2	H	>300	—	4
Me	Me	H	H	148–149	—	3
Me	Me	H	Br	150 (dec.)	—	3
Me	Me	NH_2	H	227–228	—	4
Ph	Ph	H	Br	156–158	Yellow needles. Gives a trimethiodide, red needles, m.p. 192° (dec.)	3
Ph	Ph	NH_2	H	273	Yellow needles. Ac deriv., m.p. 268–269°	3

5,7-Diazaquinoxalines. A simple example of this class is 2,3-diphenyl-5,7-diazaquinoxaline (IV) (yellow tablets, m.p. 170.5°).[1] Compounds containing this ring system are described as *pteridines.* A number of them occur naturally and are known as *pterins.* In recent years interest in this

356

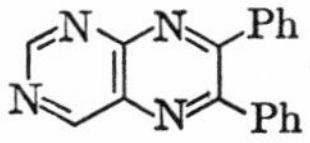

(IV)
R.I. 959

field has been greatly stimulated by the elucidation of the constitution of
the natural pterins and by the discovery that folic acid, one of the B-group
vitamins, contains the pteridine ring system. This group of compounds
is discussed fully in the volume on Compounds with Condensed Pyrimidine
Rings.

5,8-Diazaquinoxalines. 2,3-Dimethyl-5,8-diazaquinoxaline (V) forms
yellow needles, m.p. 219° (dec.), and may be prepared either from 2,3-
diamino-4,5-dimethylpyrazine and glyoxal, or from 2,3-diaminopyrazine
and diacetyl.[2]

2,3,6,7-Tetramethyl-5,8-diazaquinoxaline (VI) crystallizes in yellow
needles, m.p. 261° (corr.).[2]

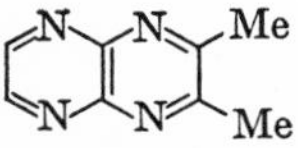

(V)

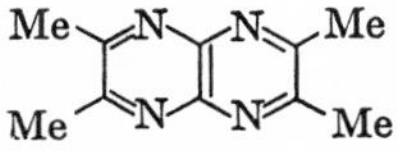

(VI)

References

1. Isay, *Ber.*, **39**, 250 (1906); F. Sachs and G. Meyerheim, *Ber.*, **41**, 3958 (1908).
2. Ellingson and Henry, *J. Am. Chem. Soc.*, **70**, 1257 (1948).
3. Petrow and Saper, *J. Chem. Soc.*, **1948**, 1389.
4. Bernstein, Stearns, Shaw, and Lott, *J. Am. Chem. Soc.*, **69**, 1151 (1947).

Ultraviolet Absorption Spectra of Cinnoline and Quinoxaline Derivatives

The tables show the positions of the principal maxima (in $m\mu$) and the molar extinction coefficients for the compounds in the solvents indicated.

TABLE AI-1. Cinnoline Derivatives

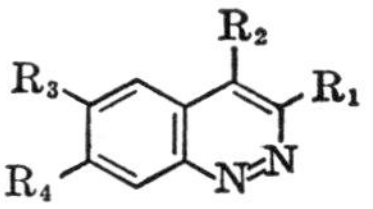

R_1	R_2	R_3	R_4	Solvent[c]	$\lambda_{max.}$	$E_{max.}$
H	H	H	H	A	276	187
					286	181
					308.5	127
					317	120
					322.5	142
					390	19.5
H	NH$_2$	H	H	B	240	12600
					345	11500
H	NHAc	H	H	B	226	42300
					303.5	8000
					328.5	7450
H	NHPh	H	H	B	248	14500
					364	15100
H	OH	H	H	B	284.5	2770
					296	2700
					338	13800
					352	12200
H	OMe	H	H	B	291	5500
					313	4500
H	OEt	H	H	A	280	6190
					290.5	6190
					310	2660
					318	2630
					321.5	3670
					362.5	468
H	OPh	H	H	A	282.5	6310
					292.5	6610
					310.5	4320
					323	4880
H	OAc	Cl	H	B	246	21500
					300	3510
					346.5	13000

TABLE AI-1. Cinnoline Derivatives (*continued*)

R_1	R_2	R_3	R_4	Solvent[c]	λ_{max}.	E_{max}.
H	NH$_2$	NO$_2$	H	B	255	15900
					269	14100
					327	4670
					405	7500
H	NHAc	NO$_2$	H	B	229.5	28200
					264	26700
					304.5	7020
					361	6460
H	NHPh	NO$_2$	H	B	247	24700
					278	11600
					343.5	6100
					418	11800
H	OH	NO$_2$	H	B	267	9420
					324.5	8710
					364.5	12300
H	OAc	NO$_2$	H	B	236	15700
					263	12600
					323.5	11200
					362	9080
II	OMe	NO$_2$	H	B	290.5	5520
					300	4790
					353	5370
H	OPh	NO$_2$	H	B	289.5	6120
					353.5	5730
H	OH	—OCH$_2$O—		B	256.5	17800
					265	16600
					292.5	2690
					341	14500
					348.5	11600
					358	15500
H	OH	Me	Me	B	289.5	2500
					347	9710
					362	8170
Me	OH	H	H	B	250	9360
					281	3300
					292	3340
					347.5	11500
					358.5	10700
Et	OH	H	H	B	249.5	10300
					282.5	3860
					291.5	4150
					344	11800
					357.5	11500
CO$_2$H	OH	H	H	B	263	7410
					339	12500
Cl	OH	Br	H	B	249.5	20500
					290	6000
					303	7330
					351	10200
					367.5	11000
Cl	OH	Me	H	B	243.5	14400
					288	4270
					299	4590
					351.5	11700
Cl	OAc	Me	H	B	247	20800
					264.5	15200
					351.5	11200

Table continued

TABLE AI-1. Cinnoline Derivatives (*continued*)

R_1	R_2	R_3	R_4	Solvent[c]	$\lambda_{max.}$	$E_{max.}$
Br	OH	Br	H	B	253	20400
					291	6670
					304	8670
					350	10300
					369	11300
Me	OH	NO_2	H	B	238.5	20700
					325.5	11000
					376	16000
CO_2H	OH	Me	H	B	254.5	20100
					352	11900
Cl	OAc	Me	Me	B	246	22000
					267.5	15700
					307.5	3880
					349	12300
CH_2CO_2Me [a]	OMe	OMe	OMe	B	234.5	24700
					262	20600
					270	22200
					294	2690
					351	13900
					364	13700

[a,c] See note at end of Table AI-4.

TABLE AI-2. Other Cinnoline Derivatives

Compound	Solvent[c]	$\lambda_{max.}$	$E_{max.}$
	B	251.5	8910
		352	12700
		369	12900
	B	269.5	8040
		328	9330
		370	12900
	B	240.5	37600
		273	14500
		281	14200
		363	13800
		379	15100
	B	258.5	15800
		322	3060
		335.5	3980
		399	12900

Table continued

TABLE AI-2. Other Cinnoline Derivatives (*continued*)

Compound	Solvent[c]	$\lambda_{max.}$	$E_{max.}$
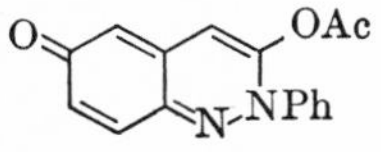 [structure: cinnoline with OAc and N-NPh substituents] *b*,†	B	235 330 413	44700 6300 4470
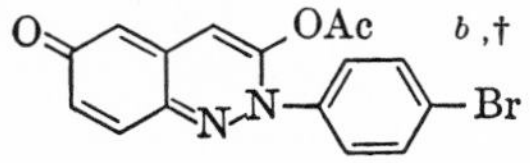 [structure: cinnoline with OAc and N-N–C₆H₄–Br] *b*,†	B	235 338 415	— — —
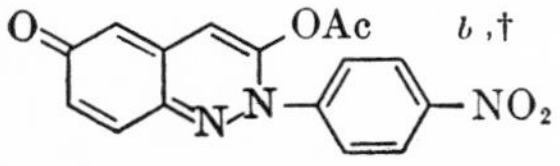 [structure: cinnoline with OAc and N-N–C₆H₄–NO₂] *b*,†	B	239 311 415	— — —

a,b,c See notes at end of Table AI-4.

TABLE AI-3. Quinoxaline Derivatives

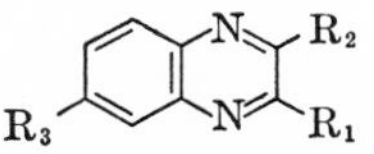

[structure: quinoxaline ring with R_2 and R_1 at 2,3 positions and R_3 at 6 position]

R_1	R_2	R_3	Solvent[c]	$\lambda_{max.}$	$E_{max.}$	Ref.
NH_2	Sulfanilamido	H	pH 6.6, C	250 355	25000 13500	1
NH_2	OH	H	pH 6.48, C	330	14000	1
Sulfanilamido	OH	H	pH 6.34, C	250 345	22000 17000	1
OH	OH	H	B D	310 316 327 341	12600 12200 15600 10600	2 3,4,5
OH	o-Aminophenyl	H	B	303.5 363.5	7100 8500	6,7,8
OH	CH_2Cl	H	D	238 254	23600 7400	9
OH	Me	Cl	D	240 345	27000 9100	9

References: (*1*) Stevens, Pfister, and Wolf, *J. Am. Chem. Soc.*, **68**, 1035 (1946). (*2*) Glotz, *Bull. soc. chim.*, **3**, 511 (1936). (*3*) Gowenlock, Newbold, and Spring, *J. Chem. Soc.*, **1945**, 622. (*4*) Newbold and Spring, *J. Chem. Soc.*, **1948**, 519. (*5*) Scudi and Silber, *J. Biol. Chem.*, **156**, 343 (1944). (*6*) Bednarczyk and Marchlewski, *Bull. intern. acad. polon. sci., Classe sci. math. nat.*, **1938A**, 529. (*7*) Marchlewski, *Roczniki Chem.*, **18**, 698 (1938). (*8*) Bednarczyk and Marchlewski, *Biochem. Z.*, **300**, 46 (1938). (*9*) Dawson, Newbold, and Spring, *J. Chem. Soc.*, **1949**, 2579.
c See note at end of Table AI-4.

TABLE AI-4. Quinoxaline Derivatives

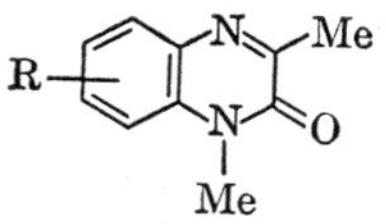

R	Solvent[c]	$\lambda_{max.}$	$E_{max.}$	Ref.*
H	B	229	21200	9
		280.5	5600	
		336.5	6700	
6-Cl	B	236	31000	9
		278	5200	
		342	5200	
7-Cl	B	232	24800	9
		281	6200	
		335	6600	

* For reference see Table AI-3.

[a] The structures of these two compounds should possibly be interchanged (see Chapter V, Section 2).

[b] Where no reference is given, data are from Professor R. A. Morton (private communication), except for compounds marked †, which are from Kornfeld, *J. Am. Chem. Soc.*, **70**, 1373 (1948).

[c] A = cyclohexane; B = alcohol; C = buffer of pH indicated; D = 0.1 N sodium hydroxide.

Basic Strengths of Cinnoline, Phthalazine, and Quinoxaline Derivatives

TABLE AII-1. Basic Strengths of Cinnoline Derivatives

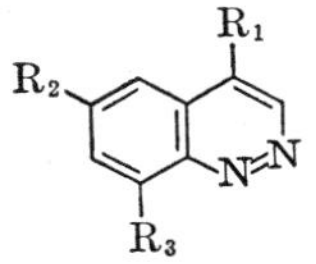

R_1	R_2	R_3	pK_a	Solvent[a]	Temp., °C.	Ref.
H	H	H	2.70	A	20	1
			2.51	B	21–22	2
Cl	H	H	2.08	B	21–22	2
NH_2	H	H	6.84	A	20	1
			6.26	B	25	2
NHPh	H	H	5.31	B	21–22	2
OH	H	H	1.77	B	21–22	2
OMe	H	H	2.71	B	21–22	2
OPh	H	H	2.27	B	21–22	2
NH_2	NO_2	H	5.08	B	25	2
OPh	NO_2	H	3.15	B	25 ± 2	2
NH_2	NH_2	H	6.86	B	25 ± 2	2
OPh	H	NO_2	2.49	B	25 ± 2	2

TABLE AII-2. Basic Strengths of Phthalazine Derivatives

Substituent	pK_a	Solvent[a]	Temp., °C.	Ref.
Nil	3.47	A	20	1
1-NH_2	6.60	A	20	1

TABLE AII-3. Basic Strengths of Quinoxaline Derivatives

Substituents	pK_a	Solvent[a]	Temp. °C.	Ref.
Nil	~0.8	H_2O	20	1
2-NH_2	3.96	H_2O	20	1
5-NH_2	2.62	H_2O	20	1
6-NH_2	2.95	H_2O	20	1
2,3-di-NH_2	4.70	H_2O	20	1

[a] A = Water. B = 50% aqueous alcohol.
References. (1) Albert, Goldacre, and J. Phillips, *J. Chem. Soc.*, **1948**, 2240. (2) Keneford, Morley, Simpson, and Wright, *J. Chem. Soc.*, **1949**, 1356.

Antibacterial and Parasiticidal Activities of Cinnoline and Quinoxaline Derivatives

Cinnolines. Trypanocidal activity (*Trypanosoma congolense* in mice) is displayed by crude reduction products prepared from 6-nitro-4-amino-1-methylcinnolinium iodide and from 6-nitro-4-amino-1,3-dimethylcinnolinium iodide.[1] Antimalarial activity (*Plasmodium gallinaceum* in chicks) is displayed by a number of Bz-substituted 4-dialkylaminoalkylaminocinnolines.[2]

Quinoxalines. In tests against *Staphylococcus aureus*, no noteworthy activity is shown by a number of 2-hydroxy- and other quinoxalines.[3] Certain 2,6-dichloro- and 6-substituted-2-chloro-3-dialkylaminoalkylaminoquinoxalines show antimalarial activity against *Plasmodium gallinaceum* in chicks[4,5]; in particular, 2,6-dichloro-3-diethylaminoethylaminoquinoxaline is more active in this respect than Mepacrine.[6] For further details regarding antimalarial activity of quinoxaline compounds, and for similar data relating to cinnoline and phthalazine derivatives, reference should be made to *A Survey of Antimalarial Drugs* (Wiselogle).

Table AIII-1 following records miscellaneous observations of biological activity for a number of quinoxaline derivatives.

TABLE AIII-1. Biological Data for Quinoxaline Derivatives

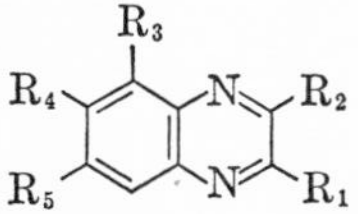

(Quinoxaline nucleus: positions R$_3$, R$_4$, R$_5$ on the benzene ring; R$_1$, R$_2$ on the pyrazine ring; R$_6$)

R$_1$	R$_2$	R$_3$	R$_4$	R$_6$	Remarks	Ref.
H	H	Sulfanilamido	H	H	Same order of bacteriostatic activity as sulfathiazole against type I pneumococcus	7
H	H	H	Sulfanilamido	H		
H	H	NH[CH$_2$]$_2$NEt$_2$	OMe	OMe	No antimalarial activity	8
H	H	Sulfanilamido	OMe	OMe	No antimalarial or antibacterial activity	8
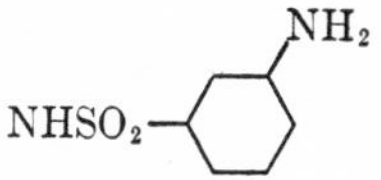 (cyclohexyl bearing NH$_2$ and NHSO$_2$)	H	H	H	H	Less than $1/10$ as effective as sulfadiazine against *P. gallinaceum* in chicks	9
Sulfanilamido	H	H	H	H	Has antibacterial and antimalarial (in birds) action. Is metabolized by rats and rabbits to 2-sulfanil amido - 3 - hydroxyquinoxaline, and by rabbits to 2-acetylsulfanilamidoquinoxaline	10–13
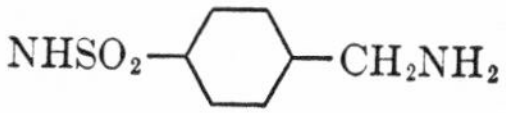 (NHSO$_2$-cyclohexyl-CH$_2$NH$_2$)	H	H	H	H	Has no action against several species of bacteria in concns. at which Marfanil is effective	14
Sulfanilamido	Me	H	H	H	Against *H. pertussis* in mice is much more active than, and only $1/6$ as toxic as, 2-sulfanilamido-quinoxaline	15
Me	H	H	H	H	The di-N-oxides of these compds. have some antibacterial action against *S. hemolyticus* and *C. diphtheriae*	16
Me	C$_5$H$_{11}^n$	H	H	H		

References

1. Keneford, Lourie, Morley, Simpson, Williamson, and Wright, *Nature*, **161**, 603 (1948).
2. Keneford and Simpson, *J. Chem. Soc.*, **1947**, 917.
3. Schales, Schales, and Friedman, *Arch. Biochem.*, **6**, 329 (1945).
4. Crowther, Curd, Davey, and Stacey, *J. Chem. Soc.*, **1949**, 1260.
5. Curd, Davey, and Stacey, *J. Chem. Soc.*, **1949**, 1271.
6. Haworth and S. Robinson, *J. Chem. Soc.*, **1948**, 777.
7. Jensen, *Acta Chem. Scand.*, **2**, 91 (1948).
8. Ehrlich and Bogert, *J. Org. Chem.*, **12**, 522 (1947).
9. English, Clark, Shepherd, Marson, Krapcho, and Roblin, *J. Am. Chem. Soc.*, **68**, 1039 (1946).
10. Stevens, Pfister, and Wolf, *J. Am. Chem. Soc.*, **68**, 1035 (1946).
11. Scudi and Silber, *J. Biol. Chem.*, **156**, 343 (1944).
12. D. G. Smith and H. J. Robinson, *Proc. Soc. Exptl. Biol. Med.*, **57**, 292 (1944)
13. Seeler, Mushett, Graessle, and Silber, *J. Pharmacol.*, **82**, 357 (1944).
14. Wolf, R. M. Wilson, and Tishler, *J. Am. Chem. Soc.*, **68**, 151 (1946).
15. Platt and Sharp, *J. Chem. Soc.*, **1948**, 2129.
16. McIlwain, *J. Chem. Soc.*, **1943**, 322.

SUBJECT INDEX

This index lists only the compounds of sufficient interest to be mentioned in the text, together with their reactions, etc. To locate any other compound (method of preparation, physical constants, references, derivatives, and characteristic reactions) the *table of the general group* to which the compound belongs should be consulted; reference to the general groups and tables is given in both the index and the table of contents. Polycyclic systems, most of which are not named in the text, are fully covered in the index; the nomenclature used is that of the *Ring Index* and the usual alphabetical arrangement of substituents has been applied.

A

Aceanthra[1,2-*b*]quinoxaline, deriv., 342.

Acenaphtho[1,2-*b*]dibenzo[*f,h*]quinoxaline, 343.

Acenaphthenequinone, cond. w. *o*-aminodiphenylamines, 344.

15-Acenaphth[1,2-*b*]indeno[2,1-*f*]quinoxaline, 343.

Acenaphtho[1,2-*b*]quinoxaline, derivs., 342-4.

3-Acetamidoaryl-1-ketophthalazines, sensitivity to light, 126.

2-Acetamidobenzo[*c*]cinnoline, 56.

3-Acetamidobenzo[*c*]cinnoline, 56.

3-Acetamido-2-carbamylquinoxaline, 253.

3-Acetamido-2-carbomethoxyquinoxaline, 253.

8-Acetamido-3,4-dihydro-1-hydroxy-4-keto-3-methylphthalazine, 164.

7-Acetamido-4-hydroxylaminocinnoline, 38.

3-Acetamidoquinoxaline-2-carboxylic acid, amide, 253.

6-Acetamidotetrazolo[*a*]phthalazine, 197.

Acetic anhydride-pyridine, action on 2-arylamino-*iso*indolinone-3-acetic acids, 109.

    action on 4-hydroxycinnoline-3-carboxylic acids, 24-28.

    action on 3,2'-nitroarylphthalazine-4-acetic acid derivs., 109.

2-Acetonyl*cyclo*hexanone, reaction w. phenylhydrazine, 48.

4-Acetonyl-3,4-dihydro-1-hydroxy-3(2'-methyl-4'-nitrophenyl)phthalazine, 128.

1-Acetoxy-3-acetyl-3,4-dihydro-4-keto-phthalazine, 145.

3-Acetoxy-2-aryl-2,6-dihydro-6-ketocinnolines, 49-50.

    table, 50.

    u.v. absorption spectra, 50.

4-Acetoxycinnolines, formn., 23.

4-Acetoxycinnoline-3-carboxylic acids, ethyl esters, 24.

1-Acetoxy-3,4-dihydro-4-keto-3-substituted phthalazines, *see* 1-Alkoxy derivs., 169-175.

1-Acetoxy-4-hydroxyphthalazine, 145.

4-Acetoxy-2-methylpyrimido[4,5-*b*]quinoxaline, 253.

4-*p*-Acetoxyphenylcinnoline, 44.

4-*p*-Acetoxyphenyl-*x*-iodocinnoline, 44.

Acetylation, of 4-aminocinnolines, 36.

    of 2-polyhydroxyalkyl quinoxalines, 302.

    of 3,4-dihydro-1-hydroxy-4-keto-3-substituted phthalazines, 169.

    of 4-hydroxycinnoline-3-carboxylic acid, 24-28.

    of 1-hydroxyphthalazines, 82.

4-Acetylcinnoline, 11.

    oxime, 11.

3-Acetyl-3,4-dihydro-1-hydroxy-4-keto-phthalazine, 145.

3-Acetyl-2,3β-dihydroxyquinoxaline, *o*-aminoanil, 237.

1-Acetyl-4-ethyl-1,2,3,4-tetrahydro-2-keto-6 (and 7)-nitroquinoxalines, 320.

7-Acetyl-4-hydroxylaminocinnoline oxime, 38.

1-Acetyl-2-methyl-3-phenyl-4-cyclopenta-[*b*]quinoxaline, 341.

367

7-Acetyl-4-phenoxycinnoline, reaction w. hydroxylamine, 38.

2-Acetyl-3-phenylquinoxaline, oxidn., 238

2-Acetylpyridine-3-carboxylic acid, reaction w. phenylhydrazine, 198.

3-Acetylsulfanilamido-2-aminoquinoxaline, hydrolysis, 263.

6-(or 7-)Acetylsulfanilamido-2-methylquinoxaline, 273.

Acridines, cf. Cinnolines, 35.

Acylation, of 2-aminoquinoxalines, 263.
   of 1,4-dihydroxyphthalazine, 144–5.
   of 2,3-dihydroxyquinoxaline, 243.
   of 1,2,3,4-tetrahydroquinoxalines, 326.

4-Acylcinnolines, 11.

Acyl derivs., of 1-hydroxyphthalazines, 84–105.

Acylhydrazones, cyclization, 72.

Acylquinoxalines, table, 207–224.

Addition reactions, of quinoxaline, 228.

o-Aldehydoarylhydrazone-C-sulfonate-cinnamic acids, conversion to phthalazine-4-acetic acids, 107–8.

o - Aldehydoarylhydrazone - C - sulfonate-cinnamic acids, conversion to 2-arylaminoisoindolinone-3-acetic acids, 108.

o-Aldehydobenzoic acid arylhydrazones, cyclization, 85, 95.

3-Aldehydo-1-phenylpyrazolo[3,4-b]-quinoxaline, 351.

Alkaline decomposition, of benzo[c]cinnolinium salts, 54.
   of cinnolinium salts, 43–4.
   of phthalazinium salts, 82.

4-Alkoxy-3-aryl-3,4-dihydro-1-methoxy-phthalazines, 130–3.
   by methylation then alkylation of 3-aryl-1-ketophthalazines, 127.
   prepn., 130.
   props., 130–3.
   table, 131–2.
   thermal decomp., 130.

3-Alkoxy-2-chloroquinoxalines, 261.

4-Alkoxycinnolines, 31–2.
   prepn., 31.
   props., 31–2.
   table, 31.

1-Alkoxy-3,4-dihydro-4-keto-3-substituted-phthalazines, 169–175.
   prepn., 169–170.

props., 170–3.
   table of Bz-substituted compds., 173.
   table of Bz-unsubstituted compds., 170–172.

4-Alkoxy-3,4-dihydro-1-methoxy-3-nitro arylphthalazines, thermal decompn. to 4-keto-derivs., 132.

8a-Alkoxy-8b-hydroxy-8a,8b-dihydrodiphenanthro[9,10-c,9',10'-e]pyridazine, 60.

4-Alkoxyphthalazines, table, 84.

2-Alkoxyquinoxalines, 270–2.
   table, 270–1.

1-Alkyl-3-aryl-4-keto-3,4-dihydrophthalazines, 95–6.

Alkylation, of N-arylaminophthalimides with rearrangement, 169–170.
   structure of products, 173–5.
   of 3,4-dihydro-1-hydroxy-4-keto-3-substituted phthalazines, 169.
      structure of products, 173–5.
   of 1,4-dihydroxyphthalazine, 144.
   of 1-hydroxyphthalazines, 82, 94.
   of 2-hydroxyquinoxalines, factors affecting, relative ease, 241.
   of 1,2,3,4-tetrahydroquinoxalines, 326.
   value of comparison with acylation in heterocyclics, 82.

Alkyl derivs., of 1-hydroxyphthalazines, 84–105.

1,4-endo-Alkylene-1,2,3,4-tetrahydroquinoxalines, 326–9.

1-Alkylphthalazines, 72–6.
   prepn., 72.
   props., 72–6.
   table, 73–5.

Alkylquinoxalines, table, 207–224.

Alloxan, cond. w. N-substituted o-phenylenediamines, 310–311.
   reaction w. o-phenylenediamines, 250.

Alloxazine(s), 2-aminoquinoxalines from, 263.
   from 3-carbethoxyaminoquinoxaline-2-carboxylic acid amide, 253.
   hydrolysis, 251.

Amadori rearrangement, during formn. of flavazoles, 349.

Amination, of 2-chloroquinoxalines, 263.
   of 4-phenoxycinnolines, 33–4.
   selective, of dichloroquinoxalines, 258, 269.

o-Aminoacetophenones, cinnolines from, 13.

5-Aminoacridines, *cf.* cinnolines, 43.

o-Amino-*N*-alkylanilines, reaction w. 1,2-diketones, 286–8.

6-Amino-7-anilino-2,3-diphenylquinoxaline, 287.

1-Amino-2-anilino-4-ethoxynaphthalene, quinoxaline quaternary salts from, 332.

α-(*o*-Aminoanilino)-α-hydroxy-α',α',β,β-tetramethylglutaric acid, quinoxaline deriv. from, 237

α-(*o*-Aminoanilino)-α-hydroxy-α',β,β-trimethylglutaric acid, 236–7.

α-(*o*-Aminoanilino)-α-hydroxy-α',β,β'-trimethylglutaric acid, quinoxaline deriv. from, 237.

2,2'-Aminoanilino-3-methylquinoxaline, hydrolysis, 264.

2,2'-Aminoanilinoquinoxalines, 264–5.

6-Amino-7-anilino-1,2,3-triphenylquinoxalinium chloride, anhydro base of, 290, 319.

o-Aminoarylamine salts, of quinoxaline-2,3-dicarboxylic acids, 254.

1-Amino-2-arylaminonaphthalenes, benzo-[*f*]quinoxalines from, 332.

2-Amino-1-arylazonaphthalenes, cond. w. aryl methylene ketones, mechanism, 336.

3,2'-Aminoaryl-3,4-dihydro-1-hydroxy-phthalazine-4-acetic acids, lactams, table, 116.

3,2'-Aminoaryl-3,4-dihydro-4-ketophthalazines, dehydration, 95, 191–2.

o-Aminoarylethylenes, cinnolines from, 6.

2-Aminoaryl-4-ketophthalazines, benziminazolo-3,4-dihydrophthalazines from, 191–2.

2-(*o*-Aminoaryl)-4-ketophthalazines, conversion to 2-(*o*-carboxyphenyl)benziminazoles, 86, 94.

2-Aminobenzo[*c*]cinnoline, 56.

3-Aminobenzo[*c*]cinnoline, 56.

3-Amino-2-carbamylquinoxaline, 253.

Aminocarbazoles, by redn. of acetamidobenzo[*c*]cinnolines, 56.

1-Amino-4,2'-carbethoxyphenyl-1,2,3,4-tetrahydro-3-ketoquinoxaline, cond. w. cyclohexanone, 345.

3-Amino-2-carbomethoxyquinoxaline, 253.

4-Amino-6-chlorocinnoline,quaternization, 43.

2-Amino-4-chloro-3-nitroacetophenone, group exchange in diazotized, 22.

2-Amino-4-chloro-5-nitroacetophenone, group exchange in diazotized, 17.

3-Amino-2-chloroquinoxalines, 261.

3-*sec*-Amino-2-chloroquinoxalines, 258.

4-Aminocinnolines, 35–8.
acetylation, 36.
basicity, 36.
cf. 4-aminoquinolines, 5-aminoacridines, 43.
prepn., 35–6.
props., 36.
quaternization, 36–9.
table, 35.

5-Amino-3,4-dihydro-1-hydroxy-4-keto-3-methylphthalazine, 162, 164.
proof of structure, 162–3.

5-(and 8)-Amino-3,4-dihydro-1-hydroxy-4-keto-3-methylphthalazine, 164.
diazotized, coupling with β-naphthol, 163.

1-Amino-1,2-dihydro-3-hydroxyquinoxaline, cond. w. cyclohexanone, 345.

5-Amino-1,4-dihydroxyphthalazine, 141, 143.
chemiluminescence, 153–5.
catalysis and inhibition of, 153–4.
effect of substitution, 154–5.
mechanism, 155.

6-Amino-1,4-dihydroxyphthalazine, 141, 143.

5-Amino-1,4-dimethoxyphthalazine, 168.

2-Aminodiphenylamine-2'-carboxylic acid, quinoxaline deriv. from, 329.

o-Aminodiphenylamines, cond. w. acenaphthenequinone, 344.
reaction w. 1,2-diketones, 286–8.

1-Amino-4-ethoxy-2-*p*-toluidinonaphthalene, quinoxaline quaternary salts from, 332.

Amino groups, hydrolysis of, in quinoxalines, cinnolines, phthalazines, 263.

2-Amino-ω-halogenoacetophenones, cinnolines from, 22.
group exchange in diazotized, 22.

8-Amino-4-hydroxycinnoline, diazotization, 64.

5-Amino-4-hydroxy-1-methoxyphthala-
zine, 157.
2-Amino-3-hydroxyquinoxaline, acylation,
263.
from 2,3-diamino-deriv., 263.
3-Amino-2-hydroxyquinoxaline, methylation, 241.
8-Amino-7-keto-3-phenylnaphtho-
[1,2,3-de]phthalazine, 193.
3-Amino-2-methoxyquinoxaline, 241.
6- (or 7-)Amino-2-methylquinoxaline, 273.
2-Amino-3-nitroacetophenone, cinnolines
from, 22.
group exchange in diazotized, 22.
2-Amino-5-nitroacetophenone, cinnolines
from, 17.
2-Amino-4-nitrodiphenylamines, abnormal
reactions w. benzil, 288.
2-Amino-1,3'-nitrophenylazonaphthalene,
cond. w. acetophenone, 336.
o-Aminophenol hydrochloride, reaction w.
2,3-dihydroxyquinoxalines, 243.
10-Amino-7-phenylacenaphtho[1,2-b]-
quinoxalinium chloride, 344.
2-Amino-1-phenylazonaphthalene, benzo-
[f]quinoxalines from, 336–8.
advantages over 1,2-diaminonaphtha-
lene as starting material, 336.
3α-(o-Aminophenylimino)ethyl-2,3β-di-
hydroxyquinoxaline, 237.
5-o-Aminophenylimino-hexahydro-2,4,6-
triketopyrimidines, 250.
4-o-Aminophenyl-5-keto-1-phenylpyrazo-
lines, dehydration, 349.
o-Aminophenylpropiolic acid, cinnolines
from, 16.
1-Aminophthalazines, 183.
table, 184–5.
N-Aminophthalimides, intermediates in
1,4-dihydroxyphthalazine formn., 142.
effect of substituents, 143.
isomerization to 1,4-dihydroxyphthal-
azines, 140.
N-Aminophthalimidines, by redn. of
phthalazines, 78.
4-Aminoquinolines, cf. cinnolines, 43.
2-Aminoquinoxaline, from 2-chloro-deriv.,
258.
2-Aminoquinoxalines, 263–9.
primary, prepn., 263.
props., 263–4.
table, 264.

secondary, 264.
table, 265.
tertiary, 265.
2-Aminoquinoxaline-3-carboxylic acid, action of acetylsulfanilyl chloride, 263.
hydrolysis, 263.
3-Aminoquinoxaline-2-carboxylic acid, amide, 253.
methyl ester, 253.
3-Aminoquinoxaline-2-carboxylic acids,
from alloxazines, 251.
8-Amino-1,2,3,4-tetrahydrocarbazole-9-
acetic acid, 345.
5-Amino-1,2,3,4-tetrahydro-1,4-diketo-
2,3-dimethylphthalazine, diazotized,
coupling w. 2-naphthol, 176.
11-Amino-5,7,12,14-tetrahydro-7,12-dike-
tophthalazino[2,3-b]phthalazine, 198.
8-Amino-1,2,3,4-tetrahydroquinoline, reaction w. benzoin, 345–6.
reaction w. pyruvic acid, 345–6.
6-Aminotetrazolo[a]phthalazine, 197.
5-Aminouracil, oxidn., 64.
3-n-Amyl-2-methylquinoxaline di-N-oxide,
redn., 232.
4-Anilino-1-chlorophthalazine, 182.
4-Anilinocinnoline, 31.
4-Anilinocinnolines, quaternization, 39.
4-Anilino-2,3-dihydro-3-keto-10-methyl-
2-phenylxantheno[9,1-cd]pyridazine,
193.
1-Anilino-2-methylnaphth[1,2]imidazole,
336.
Anilinovinyl heterocyclic quaternary salts,
cyanine dyes from, 290–1.
4-p-Anisylcinnoline, oxidn., 10.
salts, 7.
4-p-Anisylpyridazine-5,6-dicarboxylic
acid, 10.
Anthranils, 1,4-dihydroxyphthalazines
from, 141.
Anthraquinone-1-carboxylic acid, reaction
w. hydrazine, 192.
Aposafranine dyes, quinoxaline analogs,
290.
3-d-Arabotetraacetoxybutyl-2-hydroxy-
quinoxaline, O-methylation, 241.
2-d-Arabotetrahydroxybutyl-3-hydroxy-
quinoxaline, see 2-d-arabo-Tetra-
hydroxybutyl-3-hydroxyquinoxaline.
2-d-Arabotetrahydroxybutyl-3-phenyl-
quinoxaline, 301.

2-d-*Arabo*tetrahydroxybutylquinoxalines,
    see 2-d-*arabo*-Tetrahydroxybutylquin-
    oxalines.
Aromatic *o*-diamines, reaction w. 1,2-
    dicarbonyl compds., 203–227.
    products other than quinoxalines, 204–5.
Arylamines, diazotized, coupling with
    2-naphthol-1-sulfonic acid, 106–8.
4-Arylaminocinnolines, 36.
    basicity, 36.
    salts, 36.
    table, 37.
2-Arylamino*iso*indolinone-3-acetic   acids,
    cyclization to *iso*indolinopyrazolido-
    colines, 109.
    from intermediates in prepn. of phthal-
        azine-4-acetic acids, 108.
2-Arylamino-3-methylene*iso*indolinones,
    conversion to 2-aryl-1,2-dihydro-1-
    keto-4-methylphthalazines, 128.
    from   3-aryl-1-keto-4-methylphthal-
        azines, 127.
    effect of substituents, 128.
N-Arylaminophthalimides, alkylation and
    rearrangement, 169–170.
        structure of products, 173–5.
        isomerization to   3,4-dihydro-1-hy-
            droxy-4-keto-3-substituted phthal-
            azines, 158.
1-Arylazo-2-naphthaquinone-1-sulfonates,
    conversion to phthalazine derivs., 106–8.
2-Arylbenzo[*f*]quinoxalines, 336.
4-Arylcinnolines, prepn., 6.
    props., 7.
    quaternary salts, 9.
    quaternization, 39.
    reduction to 3-arylindoles, 10.
    table, 8–9.
4-Arylcinnoline *N*-oxides, prepn., 9.
    table, 9.
Aryl derivs., of 1-hydroxyphthalazines,
    84–105.
4-Aryl-2,3-dicarboxy-6-ethoxybenzo[*f*]-
    quinoxalinium chlorides, 332.
3-Aryl-3,4-dihydro-1,4-dimethoxyphthal-
    azines, action of heat, 169.
1-Aryl-1,2-dihydro-2-hydroxy-2,3-di-
    phenylquinoxalines, stability toward
    oxidation, 324–5.

3-Aryl-3,4-dihydro-4-hydroxy-1-methoxy-
    phthalazine, anhydro derivs., 131–2.
3-Aryl-3,4-dihydro-4-hydroxy-1-methoxy-
    phthalazines, characterization as per-
    chlorates, 133.
3-Aryl-3,4-dihydro-1-hydroxyphthala-
    zines, by redn. of 3-aryl-1-ketophthal-
    azines, 126.
3-Aryl-3,4-dihydro-1-hydroxyphthala-
    zine-4-acetic acids, 106–118.
    action of hot alkali, 119.
    action of sulfuric acid, 119.
    and functional derivs., table, 110–115.
    conversion to 3-aryl-1-ketophthalazines,
        119.
    conversion to 3-aryl-1-keto-4-methyl-
        phthalazines, 119.
    oxidation, 119, 158.
    prepn., 106–8.
    props., 108–118.
3-Aryl-3,4-dihydro-4-keto-1-methoxy-
    phthalazines, 169.
    table, 136.
3-Aryl-3,4-dihydro-1-methoxy-4(2′,4′-di-
    nitrobenzylidene)phthalazines, 135.
    table, 136.
3-Aryl-3,4-dihydro-1-methoxy-4-methyl-
    enephthalazines, 133–8.
    oxidn., 169.
    prepn., 133–5.
    props., 135–8.
    reaction w. 4-anilinomethylene-4,5-di-
        hydro-5-keto-3-methyl-1-phenyl-
        pyrazole, 136.
    reaction w. 2,4-dinitrochlorobenzene,
        135–6.
    table, 134–5.
1(2-Aryl-1,2-dihydro-4-methoxy-1-phthal-
    azylidene)-2(4,5-dihydro-5-keto-3-
    methyl-1-phenyl-4-pyrazolylidene)-
    ethanes, table, 136.
3-Aryl-2,5-diketo*iso*indolinopyrazolido-
    colines, from phthalazine derivs., 109.
4-Aryl-6-ethoxybenzo[*f*]quinoxalinium
    chloride-2,3-dicarboxylic acids, 332.
3-Aryl-4-ethoxy-3,4-dihydro-1-methoxy-
    phthalazines, action of heat, 169.
3-Aryl-4-keto-3,4-dihydro-1-hydroxy-
    phthalazines, by oxidation of phthala-
    zine-4-acetic acid derivs., 108.

3-Aryl-1-keto-4-methylphthalazines, by
oxidation of phthalazine-4-acetic acid
derivs., 108–9.
isomerization to 2-arylamino-3-methyl-
ene*iso*indolinones, 127.
effect of substituents, 128.
methylation, 127, 133.
table, 122–5.
2-Aryl-4-ketophthalazines, conversion to
3-aryl-3,4-dihydro-4-ketophthala-
zines, effect of substitution on, 86, 95.
3-Aryl-1-ketophthalazines, 119–129.
from phthalazine-4-acetic acid derivs.,
109, 116.
methylated derivs., 130–9.
methylation, 126–7, 130.
prepn., 119.
props., 126–8.
redn., 126.
redn. to 3-aryl-3,4-dihydro-1-hydroxy-
phthalazines, 189.
table, 120–2.
Arylhydrazines, reaction w. *o*-aldehydo
acids, 85, 95.
3-Aryl-1-methoxy-4-methylenephthala-
zines, by methylation of 3-aryl-1-
keto-4-methylphthalazines, 127.
4(3-Aryl-1-methoxyphthalazine)cyanines,
table, 137–8.
3-Aryl-1-methoxyphthalazinium perchlorates, 127.
oxidn., 169.
3-Aryl-1-methoxy-4-substituted methyl-
phthalazinium salts, table, 137.
Aryl methylene ketones, cond. w. 2-amino-
1-arylazonaphthalenes, 336.
anomalous behavior of pyruvic acid,
336.
1-Arylphthalazines, 72–7.
prepn., 72.
props., 72–6.
table, 73–5.
N-Arylphthalimides, reaction w. hydrazine, 140.
N-Arylphthalimidines, by redn. of 3-aryl-
1-ketophthalazines, 126.
Arylquinoxalines, table, 207–224.
Azaphthalazines, 198–200.
Azaquinoxalines (see appropriate Pyra-
zines), 356.
6-Azidotetrazolo[*a*]phthalazine, 196–7.

4-Azidotetrazolo[*a*]quinoxaline, 261, 353–
4.
Azobenzene and azoxybenzene, spectra,
cf. benzo[*c*]cinnolines, 57.
Azo compounds, conversion to benzo[*c*]-
cinnolines, 52–3.

B

"Balbiano's acid," *see* α-Keto-α',β,β'-
trimethylglutaric acid, 236.
Benzaldehyde arylhydrazone-*o*-carboxylic
acids, cyclization, 85, 95.
4,6'-Benzamido-1'-keto-*n*-hexylcinnoline,
11.
1-Benzeneazo-1(1',2'-dihydro-3'-hydroxy-
quinoxalylidene)-2,3,4-trihydroxybu-
tane, 309.
Benzil derivatives, failure to react w.
o-phenylenediamine, 205.
Benzil, quinoxaline quaternary salts from,
332.
Benzimidazo[2,1-*a*]phthalazines, *see* 1',-
2',3,4-benziminazolo-3,4-dihydro-
phthalazines, 191.
Benziminazole derivs., from 2-amino-4-
nitro-mono-*N*-substituted anilines,
288.
from phthalazine derivs., 86, 94, 96,
116.
1',2',3,4-Benziminazolo-3,4-dihydro-
phthalazines, 191–2.
prepn., 191–2.
table, 191.
Benzo[*h*]cinnoline deriv., 57.
3,4-Benzocinnolines, see Benzo[*c*]cinno-
lines, 52–7.
Benzo[*c*]cinnoline, 52.
cf. phenazines and cinnolines, 54.
basicity, 54.
oxidation, 54.
quaternary salts, 54.
reduction, 55.
Benzo[*c*]cinnoline di-*N*-oxide, 54.
Benzo[*c*]cinnoline *N*-oxide, 52.
nitration, 56.
Benzo[*c*]cinnolines, 52–7.
prepn., 52–3.
props., 54–7.
salts, 55.
systems of numbering formulas, 56.
table, 53.

Benzo[c]cinnoline-sulfonic acids, 56.
3-Benzo[de]cinnolines, see 3-Benzo[de]-phthalazines, 192.
3,4-Benzocinnolinium salts, 44.
5,6-Benzo-2,3-dichloroquinoxaline, 261.
7,8-Benzo-2,3-dimethyl-9-cyclopenta[f]-quinoxaline, 345.
[1,4]-Benzodioxino[2,3-b]quinoxaline, 261.
Benzo[f]naphtho[2,1-c]cinnoline, 57-8.
3-Benzo[de]phthalazines, 192.
Benzo[g]phthalazine deriv., 192.
Benzopyrano[4,3,2 - de,2',3',4' - ij]phthalazine deriv., 195.
Benzoquinone, adduct w. 2,3-dimethylquinoxaline, 283.
Benzo[f]quinoxalines, 332-8.
  from 1-amino-2-arylaminonaphthalenes, 332.
  from 2-amino-1-phenylazonaphthalene, 336-8.
  table, 337.
  oxidn., 337.
  prepn., 332.
  tables, 333-5, 337.
Benzo[f]quinoxaline-3-acetic acid, ethyl ester, structure, 337-8.
Benzo[b]quinoxalo[2,3-f][1,4]diazocine deriv., 254.
Benzo[h]thiaxantheno[10,1,2-cde]cinnoline deriv., 195.
3,4-Benzoisoxazoles, phthalazines from, 141.
Benzoyl formic acid, reaction w. 3,4-diaminotoluene, 237.
1-Benzoylphthalazine, 76.
2,N-Benzyldimethylaminoethylaminoquinoxaline, 265.
4-Benzyl-1-hydroxyphthalazine, redn., 78.
N-Benzylideneaminoisatin, cinnoline deriv. from, 11.
N-Benzylideneaminophthalimides, from 1,4-dihydroxyphthalazines, 143.
6-Benzyl-8-ketopyrido[1,2-a]quinoxaline, 339.
6-Benzyl-3-phenylpyridazine-5-carboxylic acid chloride, cyclization, 58.
2-Benzyl-3-phenylquinoxaline, acetylation, 277.
  reactivity of methylene group, 276.
1-Benzylphthalazine, from 4-chloro-deriv., 179.
  oxidn., 76.

2-Benzylquinoxaline, reactivity of methylene group, 276.
Bicyclo[2,2,1]heptan-3-one, cyclization of 2-acetylidenehydrazide, 61.
9,9'-Bis(acenaphtho[1,2-b]quinoxaline), 343.
Bisbenzo[h]cinnoline[9,1,2-cde,10,5,6-c'-d'e']anthracene, 196.
Bis[1]benzothiapyrano[4,3,2-de,2',3',4'-ij]phthalazine, 195.
  salts, 194-5.
2,3-Bis(dibromomethyl)quinoxaline, 277, 283.
3,3'-Bis(2,2'-dihydroxyquinoxaline)aldazine hydrate, 248.
Bis-2-(1,3-dimethylquinoxaline)trimethincyanine, 290-1.
2,2'-Bis(6-indolo[2,3-b]quinoxaline), 347.
Bis-2-(3-methyl-1-phenylquinoxaline)trimethincyanine, 290-1.
2,2'-Bis(x-nitro-6-indolo[2,3-b]quinoxaline), 347.
Bisphenanthro[1,2,3-de,3',2',1'-ij]phthalazine deriv., 195.
2,5-Bis-2'-quinoxalyl-1,4-diaryl-1,4-dihydropyrazines, 304-5.
6,6'-Bis(1,2,3-trihydro-2-ketoimidazo[b]-quinoxaline), 353.
Borsche synthesis, 17.
  effect of acid concn., 17.
  effect of substituents, 17.
  group exchange in, 17.
Bromination, of 2,3-dimethylquinoxaline, 283.
  of glucazidones, 339.
  of 2-methylquinoxalines, 277.
  effect of substituents, 277.
Bromoacetic acid, reaction w. o-diamines, 235.
6-Bromo-4-chlorocinnoline, prepn., 29.
2-Bromocoumaran-3-ones, conversion to quinoxalines, 296-8.
2-Bromodibenzo[fh]-5-indolo[2,3-a]quinoxaline, 346.
9-Bromo-12,14-dihydroindeno[2,1-f]indolo[3,2-b]quinoxaline, 347.
6-Bromo-4-hydroxycinnoline, chlorination, 29.
  chlorination with group exchange, 23.
3-Bromo-4-hydroxycinnolines, chlorination, 29.
  chlorination with group exchange, 23.

1-Bromo-4-hydroxyphthalazine, 182.
9-Bromo-11-nitro-12,14-dihydroindeno-
    [2,1-*f*]indolo[3,2-*b*]quinoxaline, 347.
6-Bromoquinoxaline-2,3-dicarboxylic acid,
    decarboxylation, 254.
6-Bromo-1,2,3,4-tetrahydro-2,3-diketo-
    1,4-dimethylquinoxaline, 241, 330.
3-*iso*Butyldihydro*iso*indole, from 1-chloro-
    4-*iso*butylphthalazine, 179.
Butyl glyoxylate, reaction w. *o*-diamines,
    235.
4-*iso*Butyl-1-hydroxyphthalazine,   redn.,
    78.
1-*iso*Butylphthalazine, from 4-chloro
    deriv., 179.

C

2-Carbamylquinoxaline-3-urethan, 253.
Carbazoles, from benzo[*c*]cinnolines, 56.
3-Carbethoxyaminoquinoxaline-2-carbox-
    ylic acid, 253.
o-Carbethoxyphenyl-9-fluorenylidenecar-
    binol, reaction w. hydrazine, 141.
4,2′-Carbethoxyphenyl-1,2,3,4-tetrahy-
    dro-3-keto-1-nitrosoquinoxaline,
    redn., 345.
3-*o*-Carbethoxyphenyl-7,8,9,10-tetrahy-
    dro-2-keto-1-pyrazino[3,2,1-*jk*]car-
    bazole, 345.
1,2′-Carbethoxyphenyl-1,2,3,4-tetrahy-
    dro-2-ketoquinoxaline, 329.
1-Carbethoxy-1,2,3,4-tetrahydro-2-keto-
    3,3-diphenylquinoxaline, 329–330.
1-Carbethoxy-1,2,3,4-tetrahydro-4-keto-
    2,3,3-triphenyl-1,2-diazete, 329.
3-*o*-Carbomethoxybenzoyl-3,4-dihydro-1-
    hydroxy-4-ketophthalazine, 144.
*N*α-Carbomethoxy-1,2,3,4-tetrahydrocin-
    noline-*N*β-carboxylic acid, potassium
    salt, 47, 63.
1-Carbomethoxytetrahydro-3-hydroxy-
    1-pyrazolo[4,3-*c*]cinnoline, 62–3.
1′-Carbomethoxy-1,2,3,4-tetrahydro-3′-
    keto-3,4,4′,5′-pyrazolinocinnoline,
    47, 63.
2-Carbonamido-1,2-dihydro-1-hydroxy-
    5,8-methano-1,4-diphenylphthalazine,
    196.
1,4-*endo*Carbonyl-1,2,3,4-tetrahydro-2-
    keto-3,3-diphenylquinoxaline, 330.
4-Carboxycinnolines, substituted, *see* sub-

stituent cinnoline-4-carboxylic acid,
    11.
3,2′-Carboxybenzoyl-1,2,3,4-tetrahydro-
    phthalazine, 198.
2-*o*-Carboxybenzoyl-1,2,3,4-tetrahydro-
    phthalazines, sodium salts, oxidn., 70.
2(*o*-Carboxyphenyl)-benziminazoles, from
    2(*o*-aminoaryl)-4-ketophthalazines,
    86, 94.
2(2′-Carboxyphenyl)-5-phenylpyrazine-
    2-carboxylic acid, 337.
Chlorination, of 2,3-dihydroxyquinoxa-
    lines, 260.
    of 4-hydroxycinnolines, 23, 29.
    group exchange during, 23.
    of 1-hydroxyphthalazine-4-carboxylic
        acid, 78.
    of 1-hydroxyphthalazines, 78, 178.
    of hydroxyquinoxalines, 258.
    of 2-hydroxyquinoxalines, 236.
4-Chloroacetylcinnoline, 11.
5-Chloroacridines, *cf.* 4-chlorocinnolines,
    35.
2-*p*-Chlorobenzyl-3-phenylquinoxaline,
    acetylation, 277.
4-Chlorocinnoline, basicity, 31.
    prepn., 29.
    redn., 4, 31.
    salts, 31.
4-Chlorocinnolines, 29–31.
    cf. 5-chloroacridines, 35.
    cf. 4-chloroquinolines, 29–31.
    conversion to alkoxy derivs., 31.
    conversion to phenoxy derivs., 32.
    formation, 23.
    hydrolysis, 30.
    prepn., 29.
    props., 29–31.
    table, 30.
7-Chloro-4-(4′-diethylamino-1′-methyl-
    butyl)aminocinnoline, 38.
2-Chloro-3-diethylaminopropylaminoquin-
    oxaline, 259–260.
    action of heat, 259–260.
3-Chloro-1,2-dihydro-2,2-diphenylquinox-
    aline, 330.
9-Chloro-12,14-dihydroindeno[2,1-*f*]in-
    dolo[3,2-*b*]quinoxaline, 347.
1-Chloro-3,11-dihydro-3-keto-4-*cyclo*-
    penta[*b*]quinoxaline, 344.
4-Chloro-2,3-dihydro-3-keto-10-methyl-

2-phenylxantheno[9,1-*cd*]pyridazine, 193.

6-Chloro-2,3-dihydroxyquinoxaline, reaction w. *o*-aminophenol hydrochloride, 243.

reaction w. *o*-phenylenediamines, 243.

4-Chloro-5,6-dimethoxyphthalazine, 71.

2-Chloro-6-ethyl-8,9-diphenylpteridine, 204.

2-Chloro-4-ethyl-6,7-diphenylpyrimido-[4,5-*b*]pyrazine, 204.

4-Chloro-1-ethylphthalazine, redn., 72.

Chloroglyoximes, reaction w. *o*-phenylenediamines, 264.

6-Chloro-2-hydrazinobenzoic acid, cinnoline deriv. from, 17.

7-Chloro-4-hydroxy-6-nitrocinnoline, chlorination, 29.

with group exchange, 23.

5-Chloro-4-hydroxy-3-phenylcinnoline, 17.

1-Chloro-4-hydroxyphthalazine, 182.

4-Chloroindazolone, formn., 17.

8-Chloro-7-keto-3-phenylnaphtho[1,2,3-*de*]phthalazine, 193.

2-Chloro-3-methoxyquinoxaline, amination, 266.

6-Chloro-1-methyl-4-cinnolone, from 4-amino-6-chlorocinnoline methiodide, 43.

2-Chloromethyl-3-hydroxyquinoxaline, from 3-ethoxy-2-methylquinoxaline-1-oxide, 318.

3-Chloromethyl-2-hydroxyquinoxaline, methylation, 241.

4-Chloro-1-methylphthalazine, redn., 72.

3(2′-Chloro-5′-nitrophenyl)-1-ketophthalazines, conversion to 3,4-dihydro-1,4-dihydroxy derivs., 128.

Chloro*iso*nitrosoketones, reaction w. *o*-phenylenediamines, 264.

Chloro-opiazone, see 4-chloro-5,6-dimethoxyphthalazine, 71.

1-Chlorophthalazine, redn., 70.

1-Chlorophthalazines, 78.

reaction w. amines, 178.

reaction w. sodium alkoxides, 178.

reduction, 72, 179.

4-Chloroquinoline, *cf.* Chlorocinnolines, 29–31.

6-Chloroquinoxaline-2,3-dicarboxylic acid, decarboxylation, 254.

2-Chloroquinoxalines, 258–262.

amination, 263.

prepn., 258.

props., 259.

reaction w. dialkylaminoalkylamines, 264.

reaction w. sodium alkoxides, 270.

table, 258–9.

6-Chloro-1,2,3,4-tetrahydro-2,3-diketo-1,4-dimethylquinoxaline, 241, 330.

6-Chloro-1,2,3,4-tetrahydropyrazino-[2,3-*b*]quinoxaline, 259–260.

6-Chlorotetrazolo[*a*]phthalazine, 197.

6-Chloro-1,2,3-triphenylquinoxalinium chloride, 288.

Cinnamaldehyde, reaction w. 1,4-dihydroxyphthalazine, 143.

Cinnoline, basicity, 5.

from cinnoline methiodide, 43.

prepn., 4–5.

props., 4–5.

ring system, historical, 3.

salts, 4–5.

syntheses, mechanism of, 22–23.

toxicity, 5.

Cinnoline-4-carboxylic acid, 4.

chloride, 11.

decarboxylation, 4.

ethyl ester, 11.

prepn., 11.

Cinnoline derivs., antibacterial and parasiticidal action, 364–5.

basic strengths, table, 363.

contg. additional aromatic rings, 57–60.

contg. additional fused rings, 52–65.

bridged rings, 61.

fused heterocyclic rings, 62–4.

general synthetic routes, 3.

occurrence, 3.

reduced, 46–51.

w. nonoxygenated rings, 46–8.

w. oxygenated rings, 48–51.

redn. to indoles, 10.

u.v. absorption spectra, table, 358–361.

Cinnoline quaternary salts, see Cinnolinium salts, 39–45.

action on *Trypanosoma congolense*, 364.

Cinnolinium salts, 39–45.

prepn., 39.

reactions, 43–5.

structure, 39–43.

table, 40–2.

Condensed quinoxalines, 332–355.
Configuration, of sugars, 1-phenyl-3-poly-
hydroxyalkylflavazole formn. in detn.
of, 349.
Corynebacterium diphtheriae, action of quinoxalines against, 365.
Coumaran-2,3-diones, quinoxalines from,
298.
reaction w. *o*-phenylenediamine, 237.
Coumaran-3-ones, conversion to quinoxalines, 296–8.
Cuminal, 4-methylcinnoline-7-carboxylic
acid from, 13.
Cyanines, contg. phthalazine nucleus,
table, 137–8.
2-Cyanomethyl-3-methylquinoxaline, reactivity of methylene group, 277, 283.
2-Cyanomethylquinoxaline, 276.
reactivity of methylene group, 277.
spiro[Cyclohexane-1,2'-[2]cyclopenta[*b*]-
quinoxaline], 342.
Cyclohexanediones, cyclization of monophenylhydrazones, 57.
*Cyclo*penta[*b*]quinoxaline derivs., 341–4.
*Cyclo*penta[*f*]quinoxaline derivs., 345.

D

Decarboxylation, of 1,2-dihydro-2-keto-1-
substituted quinoxaline-3-carboxylic
acids, 311.
of 2-hydroxyquinoxaline-3-carboxylic
acids, 235.
of quinoxaline-2,3-dicarboxylic acids,
254.
Decomposition, alk., of 3-methylphthal-
azinium iodides, 186.
thermal, of phthalazine pseudo-base
ethers, 130.
Dehydration, of 1,2-dihydro-1-methyl-3-
methylphenylcarbamidoquinoxaline,
317–8.
6-Diacetamidotetrazolo[*a*]phthalazine,
197.
2,2'-Diacetohydrazinodiphenyl, conversion to benzo[*c*]cinnoline, 52.
1,2-Diacylbenzenes, reaction w. hydrazine, 76.
Diacyl derivs., of 1,4-dihydroxyphthala-
zines, 168–177.
of 1,4-dihydroxyphthalazines, of unknown structure, 176.

2,3-Diacylquinoxalines, table, 207–224.
Dialkylaminoalkylaminobenzo[*c*]cinnol-
ines, 56.
4-Dialkylaminoalkylaminocinnolines, 36.
action on *Plasmodium gallinaceum*, 364.
table, 37.
3-Dialkylaminoalkylamino-2-chloro-6-sub-
stituted quinoxalines, action on *Plasmodium gallinaceum*, 364.
Dialkylaminoalkylaminoquinoxalines, 264.
2,3-Dialkoxyquinoxalines, 260.
table, 271.
Dialkyl derivs., of 1,4-dihydroxyphthal-
azines, 168–177.
of 1,4-dihydroxyphthalazines, of unknown structure, table, 176.
of 1,4-dihydroxyphthalazines, structure,
173–5.
1,3-Dialkyl-4-keto-3,4-dihydrophthala-
zines, 95–6.
2,3-Dialkylquinoxalines, table, 207–224.
2,3-Dialkyl-1,2,3,4-tetrahydro-1,4-diketo-
phthalazines, 175–6.
table, 175.
o-Diamines, reaction w. 2,3-dichloroquin-
oxaline, 261.
4,5-Diamino-2-chloro-6-ethylpyrimidine,
reaction w. benzil, 203–4.
4,6-Diamino-1,3-dimethylcinnolinium iodide, 39.
2,2'-Diamino-6,6'-dimethyldiphenyl, 56.
2,2'-Diamino-1,1'-dinaphthyl, 58.
2,2'-Diaminodiphenyl, conversion to benzo[*c*]cinnoline, 52.
4,6-Diamino-1-methylcinnolinium iodide,
39.
1,2-Diaminonaphthalene, cond. w. isonitrosoacetophenone, 336.
o-Diamino nitrogen heterocyclics, cond.
w. *o*-dicarbonyl compds., 356–7.
3,4-Diaminophenylarsonic acid, reaction
w. cyanogen, 267.
2,3-Diaminoquinoxaline, 265–7.
2,3-Diaminoquinoxaline derivs., 260.
disecondary, table, 268–9.
primary-secondary, table, 267–8.
fine structure, 267.
hydrolysis, 263.
reactions, 267.
2,3-Diaminoquinoxaline-6-arsonic acid,
267.

3,4-Diaminotoluene, reaction w. benzoylformic acid, 237.
reaction w. chloroacetone, 273.
reaction w. diacetyl, 283.
reaction w. ethyl chloroacetate, 320.
1,4-Dianilinophthalazine, 182.
2,2'-Diaryl-2,2'-dihydro-4,4'-dimethoxy-
1,1'-bisphthalazines, 132–3.
2,3-Diaryloxyquinoxalines, 260.
table, 271.
1,4-Diarylphthalazines, 76–7.
prepn., 76.
props., 76.
table, 77.
2,3-Diarylquinoxalines, table, 207–224.
Diazomethane, reaction w. 4-hydroxy-
cinnoline-3-carboxylic acid, 32.
Diazotization, of 8-amino-4-hydroxycinno-
line, 64.
4-Diazo-2,3,5-triphenylpyrrole, cyclization, 62.
Dibenzo[f,h]acenaphtho[1,2-b]quinoxa-
line, 343.
Dibenzo[f,h]cinnoline deriv., 57.
Dibenzo[1,2,3-de,4,5,6-d'e']diphthalazine
deriv., 194.
Dibenzo[fh]-5-indolo[2,3-a]quinoxaline,
346.
Dibenzo[fh]-5-indolo[2,3-a]quinoxaline-2-
carboxylic acid, 347.
Dibenzo[f,h]phthalazine deriv., 193.
Dibenzo[f,h]quinoxalines, table, 338.
3,4-Dibenzoylcinnoline, 11.
action, of hydroxylamine on, 63.
redn., 62.
1,3-Dibenzylidene-2,3-dihydro-1-cyclo-
penta[b]quinoxaline, 343.
9,11-Dibromodihydroindeno[2,1-f]indolo-
[3,2-b]quinoxaline, 347.
3-Dibromomethyl-1,2-dihydro-2-keto-1-
methylquinoxaline, 241.
2-Dibromomethyl-3-phenylquinoxaline,
277.
2-Dibromomethylquinoxaline, 277.
2,3-Di(bromomethyl)quinoxaline, 283.
1,4-Dibromophthalazine, 179, 182.
reaction w. sodium azide, 182.
2,3-Dibromoquinoxaline, 261.
Dicamphor, reaction w. hydrazine, 61.
Dicamphorquinone, reaction w. hydrazine,
61.

4,5-Dicarbethoxy-4,5-dihydro-3,6-dimeth-
ylpyridazine, reaction w. hydrazine,
199.
1,3-Dicarbethoxy-2,3-dihydrocyclopenta-
[b]quinoxaline, 341.
3,4-Dicarbethoxy-2,5-dimethylfuran, reaction w. hydrazine, 199.
1,2-Dicarbonyl compds., reaction w. aromatic o-diamines, 203–227.
reaction w aromatic o-diamines, products other than quinoxalines, 204–5.
2,6-Dichloro-3-diethylaminoethylamino-
quinoxaline, 364.
action of heat, 259–260.
2,2-Dichloro-2,3-dihydro-9-keto-3,3-di-
phenyl-1,4-methanoquinoxaline, 330.
1,4-Dichlorocyclopentene-3,5-dione, cond.
w. o-phenylenediamine, 344.
1,4-Dichlorophthalazine, 179, 182.
reaction w. sodium azide, 182.
stability, cf. 2,3-dichloroquinoxaline,
182.
2,3-Dichloroquinoxaline, amination, 265.
from 2-hydroxyquinoxaline, 236.
reaction w. o-diamines, 261.
reaction w. ethylenediamine, 260.
reaction w. methylmagnesium iodide,
227.
reaction w. sodium azide, 353–4.
reaction w. o-substituted phenols, 261.
selective amination of, 258.
stability, cf. 1,4-dichlorophthalazine,
182.
2,3-Dichloroquinoxalines, 260–1.
reactivity of chloro groups, 260–1.
table, 260.
2,6-Dichloroquinoxalines, action on Plasmodium gallinaceum, 364.
2,2-Dichloro-1,2,3,4-tetrahydro-9-keto-
3,3-diphenyl-1,4-methanoquinoxa-
line, 329–330.
4,4'-Dicinnolyl, 11.
N-Diethyl-Bz-dinitroanilines, reaction w.
zinc chloride and acetic anhydride,
320.
1,4-Dihalogenophthalazines, 179–182.
prepn., 179–182.
props., 182.
2,2'-Dihydrazinodiphenyl, conversion to
benzo[c]cinnoline, 52.

1,2-Dihydrocinnoline, 4.
  oxidation, 4.
  prepn., 46.
  props., 46.
1,2-Dihydrocinnoline hydrochloride, 46.
Dihydrocinnolines, 46–7.
3,4-Dihydro-1,4-dihydroxy-3(2'-chloro-
  5'-phenyl)phthalazines, from 3-aryl-
  1-keto-derivs., 128.
3,4-Dihydro-1,4-dihydroxy-3(2',4'-di-
  aminophenyl)phthalazine, from the 4-
  acetic acid lactam, 117.
6,7-Dihydro-1,4-dihydroxy-5,8-dimethyl-
  pyridazo[4,5-d]pyridazine, 199.
2,3-Dihydro-xy-dihydroxy-z-keto-Bz-
  methylcyclopenta[b]quinoxaline, 342.
3,4-Dihydro-1,4-dihydroxy-4-methyl-3-
  (2',4'-dinitrophenyl)phthalazine, 117.
  conversion to 1-keto-4-methyl-3(2',4'-
  dinitrophenyl)phthalazine, 118.
  conversion to 3-methyleneisoindolinone
  deriv., 118.
3,4-Dihydro-1,4-dihydroxy-3(2',4'-nitro-
  phenyl)phthalazine, from the phthala-
  zine-4-acetic acid, 117.
  4-methyl ether, 117.
  oxidn., 117.
2,7-Dihydro-3,7-diketo-2-phenylbenzo-
  [de]phthalazine, 192.
2,3-Dihydro-2,2-dimethylcyclopenta[b]-
  quinoxaline, 341.
2,3-Dihydro-1,3-di(p-nitrobenzylidene)-1-
  cyclopenta[b]quinoxaline, 343.
3,4-Dihydro-3(2',4'-dinitrophenyl)phthal-
  azine-4-acetic acid, conversion to 1-
  keto-4-methyl-2(2',4'-dinitrophenyl)-
  phthalazine, 118.
  oxidn., critical conditions for, 118.
1,4-Dihydro-4,4-diphenylcinnoline(?), 47.
1,4-Dihydro-4,4-diphenylcinnoline(?) hydrochloride, 47.
8,9-Dihydro-2,3-diphenyl-7-cyclopenta[f]-
  quinoxaline, 345.
3,4-Dihydro-2',5'-diphenyl-3,4,3',4'-pyr-
  rolocinnoline, 11.
6,11-Dihydro-4-hydroxy-6,11-diketo-1-
  phenylnaphtho[2,3-g]phthalazine,
  193.
1,2-Dihydro-3-hydroxy-2,2-dimethylquin-
  oxalines, stability to oxidn., 324–5.

4,5-Dihydro-5-hydroxy-2,5-diphenylfu-
  rans, conversion to quinoxalines, 293–
  6.
1,2-Dihydro-2-hydroxy-2,3-diphenyl-1-
  substituted quinoxalines, from quaternary salts, 319.
1,2-Dihydro-4,β-hydroxyethyl-2-keto-1,3-
  diphenyl-4-cyclopenta[b]quinoxaline,
  343.
5,6-Dihydro-9-hydroxy-8-keto-9-methoxy-
  6-phenylpyrido[1,2-a]quinoxaline,
  340.
3,4-Dihydro-1-hydroxy-4-keto-3-methyl-
  5-nitrophthalazine, 162, 164.
3,4-Dihydro-1-hydroxy-4-keto-3-methyl-
  8-nitrophthalazine, 164.
1,2-Dihydro-3-hydroxy-2-keto-1-methyl-
  quinoxaline, action of phosphorus
  pentabromide, 261.
  by redn. of 4-oxide, 317.
1,2-Dihydro-3-hydroxy-2-keto-1-methyl-
  quinoxaline-4-oxide, 317.
  ethyl ether, 317.
  redn., 317.
1,2-Dihydro-3-hydroxy-2-keto-1-phenyl-
  quinoxaline, cond. w. o-aminophenol,
  311.
  cond. w. o-phenylenediamine, 311.
3,4-Dihydro-1-hydroxy-4-keto-3-substi-
  tuted phthalazines, 158–167.
  acetylation, 169.
  alkylation, 169.
  structure of products, 173–5.
  unknown structures, 164–6.
  Bz-substituted, 162–6.
  prepn., 162–3.
  tables, 164–165, 166.
  unsubstituted in Bz ring, prepn., 158.
  props., 158–162.
  table, 159–161.
1,2-Dihydro-1-hydroxy-5,8-methano-1,4-
  diphenylphthalazine-2-carboxylic
  acid amide, 196.
3,4-Dihydro-1-hydroxy-4-methoxy-4-
  methyl-3(2',4'-dinitrophenyl)phthal-
  azine, 117.
1,2-Dihydro-2-hydroxy-1-methyl-6-nitro-
  2,3-diphenylquinoxaline, 288.
3,4-Dihydro-1-hydroxy-3-methylphthal-
  azyl-5(and 8), 1'-azo-2'-naphthol, 163.

1,2-Dihydro-3-hydroxy-1-methylquinox-
aline, 261.
reaction w. phosphorus pentabromide,
261.
1,2-Dihydro-3-hydroxy-6-methylquinoxa-
line, oxidn., 324.
3,4-Dihydro-1-hydroxy-3,2'-nitroaryl-
phthalazine-4-acetic acids, conversion
to 3-aryl-2,5-diketo*iso*indolinopyrazo-
lidocolines, 109.
3,4-Dihydro-1-hydroxy-3(4'-nitro-2'-
methoxyphenyl)phthalazine-4-acetic
acid, conversion to 3-aryl-1-keto-
phthalazine, 116.
3,4-Dihydro-1-hydroxy-3(2',4'-nitro-
phenyl)phthalazine-4-acetic acid, conversion to *iso*indolinone deriv., 117.
oxidn., 117.
1,2-Dihydro-3-hydroxy-1-nitrosoquinoxa-
line, oxidn., 324.
redn., 345.
1,2-Dihydro-2-hydroxy-6-nitro-1,2,3-tri-
phenylquinoxaline, 288.
3,4-Dihydro-4-hydroxy-3-phenylphthala-
zine, action of hydrogen chloride,
133.
ethers, 133.
prepn., 132–3.
1,2(or 3,4)-Dihydro-4(or 1)-hydroxy-2(or
3)-phenylpyrido[3,4-*d*]pyridazine,
198–9.
5,6-Dihydro-9-hydroxy-6-phenylpyrido-
[1,2-*a*]quinoxaline, 340.
3,4-Dihydro-2-hydroxyquinoxaline, 243.
oxidn., 324.
1,4-Dihydro-3-hydroxyquinoxaline-2-alde-
hyde, anil, 308, 319–320.
1,2-Dihydro-3-hydroxyquinoxalines, from
redn. of *o*-nitrophenylglycines, 318.
1,2-Dihydro-2-hydroxy-1,2,3-triphenyl-
quinoxaline, 290.
9,10-Dihydro-9-imino-10-ketophenan-
threne, 59.
12,14-Dihydroindeno[2,1-*f*]indolo[3,2-*b*]-
quinoxaline, 347.
Dihydro*iso*indole, from redn. of 1-chloro-
phthalazine, 179.
1,2-Dihydro-2-keto-4,7-dimethyl-1,3-di-
phenyl-4-*cyclo*penta[*b*]quinoxaline,
343.

1,2-Dihydro-2-keto-1,3-dimethylquinoxa-
line, 238, 310–311.
reactivity of 3-methyl group in, 311.
2,3-Dihydro-2-keto-1,3-diphenyl*cyclo*-
penta[*b*]quinoxaline, 342.
3,4-Dihydro-4-keto-1,3-disubstituted
phthalazines, 95–6.
tables, 97–100, 101–103.
3,4-Dihydro-4-keto-1-methoxy-3-substi-
tuted phthalazines, partial demethyl·
ation, 158.
1,4-Dihydro-4-keto-1-methylcinnolines,
48–9.
constitution, 48.
formation, 23.
table, 49.
1,2-Dihydro-2-keto-1-methyl-3,*N*-meth-
ylanilinoquinoxaline, 317.
1,2-Dihydro-2-keto-1-methyl-3-methyl-
phenylcarbamidoquinoxaline, chloro
derivs., suggested formn. of, 318.
3,4-Dihydro-3-keto-4-methyl-2-methyl-
phenylcarbonamidoquinoxaline-1-ox-
ide, dehydration, 348.
3,4-Dihydro-4-keto-1-methyl-3-phenylpy-
ridazo[4,5-*b*]quinoline, 199.
5,6-Dihydro-5-keto-8-methyl-6-phenylpy-
rido[2,3-*d*]pyridazine, 198–9.
1,2-Dihydro-2-keto-3-methyl-1-phenyl-
quinoxaline, reactivity of methyl
group in, 311.
1,2-Dihydro-2-keto-1-methylquinoxaline-
3-carboxylic acid, by hydrolysis of a
tetrahydro-3-carbamido deriv., 317.
1,2-Dihydro-2-keto-1-methylquinoxalines,
by methylation of 2-hydroxyquinox-
alines, 311.
3,4-Dihydro-4-keto-3-methyl-1-substi-
tuted phthalazines, from 3-methyl-
phthalazinium iodides, 186.
1,2-Dihydro-2-keto-3-methyl-1-substi-
tuted quinoxalines, basicity, 311.
quaternization, 311.
1,2-Dihydro-1-keto-4,3'-pentyl-2-phenyl-
benzo[*g*]phthalazine, 192.
5,10-Dihydro-5-keto-3-phenylbenzo[*g*]-
cinnoline, 57–8.
2,3-Dihydro-3-keto-2-phenylindeno[1,3-
de]phthalazine-7-carboxylic acid, 193.

3,4-Dihydro-4-keto-3-substituted-1-al-
    kylquinoxalinium salts, cyanine dyes
    from, 291.
3,4-Dihydro-4-keto-3-substituted phthala-
    zines, 85–105.
  unsubstituted at C_1, 85–95.
    prepn., 85–94.
    props., 94–5.
    table, 87–93.
1,2-Dihydro-2-keto-1-substituted quinox-
    alines, 310–318.
    prepn., 310–311.
    props., 311–318.
    table, 314–316.
1,2-Dihydro-2-keto-1-substituted quinox-
    aline-3-carboxylic acids, 310–311.
    decarboxylation, 311.
1,2-Dihydro-2-keto-1-substituted quinoxa-
    lyl-3-pyruvic acids, ethyl esters, 311.
1,2-Dihydro-2-keto-1,3,4-trimethylquinox-
    alinium iodide, 311.
1,2-Dihydro-1-methyl-3-methylphenyl-
    carbamidoquinoxaline-4-oxide, 311,
    317.
3,4-Dihydro-3-methyl-1-substituted
    phthalazines, from 3-methylphthala-
    zinium iodides, 186.
2,3-Dihydro*cyclo*penta[b]quinoxaline-1,3-
    dicarboxylic acid, ethyl ester, 341.
1,2-Dihydro-4-phenylcinnoline, prepn., 46.
    props., 46.
5,6-Dihydro-6-phenylpyrido[1,2-a]quinox-
    aline, 339.
5,11-Dihydro-5-phenylquinoxalo[2,3-b]-
    quinoxaline, 311, 317.
3,4-Dihydrophthalazines having "unre-
    active" 3,4-substituents, 186.
    prepn., 186–9.
    table, 187–8.
6,13-Dihydropyrazino[2,3-b,5,6-b']di-
    quinoxaline, 261, 267.
Dihydroquinoxalines (1,2- and 1,4-), 310–
    325.
  contg. hydroxyl or carbonyl group in
    hetero ring, 310–325.
  contg. *neither* hydroxyl or carbonyl
    groups in hetero ring, table, 312–3.
  w. hydroxyl groups at C_2 or C_3, 318–325.
    prepn., 318–324.
    props., 324–5.
    table, 321–3.

1,2-Dihydroquinoxalines, behavior as ac-
    ids and bases, 325.
    oxidn., 324.
3,4-Dihydroquinoxalines, oxidn., 235.
5,12-Dihydroquinoxalo[2,3-b]quinoxaline,
    261.
1,2-Dihydroquinoxalyl-2-hydroxyacetal-
    dehyde, 304–5.
    anils, 304–5.
3,4-Dihydro-2-tetrahydroxybutyl-3-keto-
    4-methylquinoxaline, reaction w.
    phenylhydrazine, 307.
5,6-Dihydro-1,5,6,10-tetramethylbenzo-
    [c]cinnoline, 55.
    dealkylation, 56.
    redn., 56.
1,4-Dihydroxy-2,3-dimethylphthalazine,
    conversion to 1,4-dihydroxyphthala-
    zine, 140.
4,6-Dihydroxy-1,9-diphenylpyridazo[4,5-
    g]phthalazine, 192.
1,6-Dihydroxy-4,9-diphenylpyridazo[4,5-
    g]phthalazine, 192.
4,6-Dihydroxy-1,9-dixylylpyridazo[4,5-g]-
    phthalazine, 192.
7,9-Dihydroxy-8-ketopyrido[1,2-a]quinox-
    aline, 340.
1,4-Dihydroxy-5-methylaminophthala-
    zine, 141.
2,3-Dihydroxy-6-methylquinoxaline, reac-
    tion w. phosphorus pentachloride,
    260.
1,4-Dihydroxy-5-nitrophthalazine, 146.
    methylation, 162.
1,4-Dihydroxy-6-nitrophthalazine, 146.
1,4-Dihydroxyphthalazine, acetylation,
    157.
    acylation, 144–5.
    alkylation, 144.
    fine structure, 145.
    formation mechanism, 142–3.
    from 1-hydroxy-4-methoxy deriv., 157.
    reaction w. aldehydes, 143.
    reaction w. *o*-bromomethylbenzyl bro-
      mide, 144.
    reaction w. *o*-carbomethoxybenzoyl
      chloride, 144.
    reaction w. phosphorus pentahalides,
      179–182.
    reaction w. phosphorus pentasulfide,
      144.

reaction w. phthaloyl chloride, 144.
5,6-Dihydroxyphthalazine, prepn., 71.
  props., 71.
7,8-Dihydroxyphthalazine, from 1-chloro-
  7,8-dimethoxyphthalazine, 179.
1,4-Dihydroxyphthalazines, 140–156.
  chemiluminescence of, 153–155.
  modified or polynuclear, table, 152–3.
  mono-acyl derivs., 157–167.
  mono-alkyl derivs., 157–167.
  props., 143–155.
  prepn., 140–3.
  reaction w. phthaloylchlorides, 197.
  table, 147–151.
2,3-Dihydroxypyrazino[2,3-b]quinoxaline,
  267.
1,4-Dihydroxypyridazo[4,5-b]quinoxaline,
  354.
2,3-Dihydroxyquinoxaline, 228.
  as reagent for alkaline earths, 243.
  derivs., chlorination, 260.
    methylation, 241, 330.
    prepn., 242.
    props., 243.
    table, 242.
  from 2-d-arabotetrahydroxybutyl-3-hy-
    droxyquinoxaline, 304.
  from 1,2-dihydro-3-hydroxyquinoxaline,
    324.
  from 3-ethoxyquinoxaline-1-oxide, 233.
  from 2-hydroxyquinoxaline, 236.
  from 3-methoxy-2-sulfanilamido deriv.,
    263.
  use in photography, 243.
Dihydroxytartaric acid, quinoxaline quaternary salts from, 332.
3,12-Diketobisbenzo[h]cinnolino[9,1,2-
  cde,10,5,6-c'd'e']anthracene, 196.
5,6-Diketobisbenzo[h]cinnolino[9,1,2-cde,-
  3,4,10-e'd'c']anthracene, 196.
7,10-Diketobisphenanthro[1,2,3-de,3',-
  2',1'-ij]phthalazine, 195.
5,14-Diketobenzo[f]diisoindolo[2,1-a,1',-
  2'-c]quinoxaline, 344.
5,6-Diketobenzo[f]quinoxaline derivs.,
  337.
  phenazines from, 337.
α,β-Diketobutyric acid lactone, reaction
  w. o-phenylenediamine, 237.
5,9-Diketo-3,11-dimethyldinaphtho[1,2,-
  3-de,3',2',1',-ij]phthalazine, 194.

7,14-Diketodinaphtho[1,2,3-de,1',2',3'-
  ij]phthalazine, 194.
5,8-Diketodinaphtho[1,2,3-de,3',2',1'-ij]-
  phthalazine, 194.
5,8-Diketodinaphtho[1,2,3-de,3',2',1'-ij]-
  phthalazine-10-carboxylic acid, 194.
2,3-Diketogluconic acid lactone, reaction
  w. o-phenylenediamine, 301.
5,12-Diketoisoindolo[2,1-a,1',2'-c]quin-
  oxaline, 344.
5,8-Diketo-2-methylnaphtho[1,2,3-de]-
  phenanthro[3,2,1-ij]phthalazine, 195.
6,8-Diketo-5-methylpyrido[1,2-a]quinox-
  aline, 339.
1,2-Diketones, reaction w. 2,3-diamino-
  quinoxaline, 267.
  reaction w. mono-N-substituted o-phen-
    ylenediamines, 286–8.
1,4-Diketones, condensed phthalazines
  from, 192–6.
5,6-Diketo-3-phenylbenzo[f]quinoxaline,
  oxidn., 337.
5,10-Diketo-1-phenyl-1-pyrazolo[1,2-b]-
  phthalazine, 197.
  from 1,4-dihydroxyphthalazine, 144.
  5(3-)phenylpyrazoline from, 197.
Diketosuccinic acid, reaction w. o-phenylenediamines, 254.
12,13-Diketo-α,β,α',β'-thiophenebisthio-
  chrome, reaction w. hydrazine, 64.
1a,2a-Diketo-α,β,α',β'-thiophenebis[thio-
  chrome]azine, 64.
1,4-Dimercaptophthalazine, 144.
1,4,7,10-Dimethanobenzene[c]cinnolines,
  61.
  salts, 61.
1,6-Dimethoxyacenaphtho[1,2-b]quinoxa-
  line, 342.
3,6-Dimethoxyacenaphtho[1,2-b]quinoxa-
  line, 342.
2,3-Dimethoxy-11-indeno[1,2-b]quinoxa-
  line, 342.
1,4-Dimethoxy-5-nitrophthalazine, 168.
1,4-Dimethoxyphthalazine, 168.
3,6-Dimethylacenaphtho[1,2-b]quinoxa-
  line, 342.
2,6-Dimethylacenaphtho[1,2-b]quinoxa-
  line, 342.
N-Dimethylaminophthalimide, reaction
  w. hydrazine. 140.

4-*p*-Dimethylaminostyrylcinnolinium salts, 39.
2-*p*-Dimethylaminostyryl-1-quinoxalinium salts, 290–1.
Dimethyl azodicarboxylate, reaction w. styrene, 47.
1,10(or 4,5)-Dimethylbenzo[*c*]cinnoline, methylation, 55.
6,6'-Dimethyl-2,2'-dimethylaminodiphenyl, 56.
3,5-Dimethyl-11-*iso*propyldibenzo[*f,h*]-cinnoline-4-carboxylic acid, ethyl ester, 57–8.
5,6-Dimethylpyrazine-2-carboxylic acid, 283.
2,3-Dimethylpyrazino[2,3-*b*]pyrazine, 357.
2,3-Dimethylpyrido[3,2-*f*]quinoxaline, 348.
2,6-(or 2,7-)Dimethylquinoxaline, 206, 273.
2,3-Dimethylquinoxaline, 277–283.
    adduct w. diacetyl dioxime, 277–8.
    cond. prod., table, 279–282.
    derivs., 261.
    reaction w. quaternizing agents, 286.
    reactivity of methyl groups, 283.
        steric configuration and, 283.
    structure, 278.
2,3-Dimethylquinoxaline methiodide, 286.
2,3-Dimethylquinoxalinium salts, reaction w. aldehydes, 290–1.
2-(1,3-Dimethylquinoxaline)-2-(1,3,3-trimethylindoline)trimethincyanine, 290–1.
Dinaphthophthalazines, 194.
3,4,2',1',5,6,1',2'-Dinaphthopyridazine, 58.
10,11-Dinitro-15-acenaphth[1,2-*b*]indeno-[2,1-*f*]quinoxaline, 343.
2(2',4'-Dinitroanilino)-3-methylene*iso*indolinone, conversion to 1-keto-4-methyl-2(2',4'-dinitrophenyl)phthalazine, 118.
2,2'-Dinitrodiphenyls, redn., 52.
N(2,4-Dinitrophenyl)aminophthalimide, 117, 118.
2(2',4'-Dinitrophenyl)*iso*indolinone-3-acetic acid, 117.
Dioximes, 2-*o*-aminoanilinoquinoxalines from, 206.

11-[1,3]-Dioxolo[5,6]indeno[1,2-*b*]quinoxaline, 342.
3,4,9',10',5,6,9'',10''-Diphenanthropyridazine, props., 59–60.
Diphenanthro[9,10-*c*,9'10'-*e*]pyridazine, 57–9.
    deriv., 60.
2,3-Diphenoxyquinoxaline, action of methyl iodide, 286.
1,4-Diphenylbutane-1,2,4-triones, reaction w. *o*-phenylenediamine, 293–6.
1,4-Diphenyldibenzo[*f,h*]phthalazine, 193.
Diphenyleneazone, see Benzo[*c*]cinnoline, 52.
1,3-Diphenylfuro[3,4-*c*]cinnoline, 62.
Diphenylhydroxyacetaldehyde phenylhydrazone, cyclodehydration of, 47.
Diphenylketene, adduct w. ethyl benzeneazocarboxylate, rearrangement of, 330.
3,10-Diphenylperylo[3,4-*cd*,9,10-*c'd'*]dipyridazine, 195.
2,5-Diphenylpyrazine, 338.
2,3-Diphenylpyrazino[2,3-*b*]quinoxaline, 267.
1,3-Diphenylpyrazolo[3,4-*b*]quinoxaline, 348–9.
1,4-Diphenylpyridazo[4,5-*c*]cinnoline, 62–3.
2,3-Diphenylpyrido[3,2-*f*]quinoxaline, 348.
6,7-Diphenylpyrimido[4,5-*b*]pyrazine, 356–7.
1,3-Diphenyl-2-pyrrolo[3,4-*c*]cinnoline, 62.
    oxidn., 11.
2,3-Diphenyl-1-pyrrolo[2,3-*b*]quinoxaline, 346.
2,3-Diphenylquinoxaline di-*N*-oxide, stability to redn., 233.
1,3-Diphenylthieno[3,4-*c*]cinnoline, 62–3.
Diphthaloyl-*o*-phenylenediamines, redn., 344.
2,3-Di-*n*-propylquinoxalines, 261, 278.
Dipyridazino[4,5-*a*,4'5'-*c*][9*a*]quinolizine deriv., 199–200.
Dipyrimido[5,4-*c*,4'5'-*e*]pyridazine deriv., 62–64.
Diquinoxalines, table, 225.
6,6'-Diquinoxalyl, 229.

N,N'-Disubstituted hydrazines, reaction
w. phthalic anhydride, 175–6.
3,4-Di(thiobenzoyl)cinnoline, 11, 63.
3,9-Dixylylbenzo[1,2,3-*de*,4,5,6-*d'*,*e'*]di-
phthalazine, 194.
Dodecahydro-4,7,11,11,12,12-hexa-
methyl-1,4,7,10-dimethanobenzo[*c*]-
cinnoline, 61.

E

1,2-Epoxy-1,4-dihydro-3-hydroxy-4-
methylquinoxaline, 319–320.
8b,8c-Epoxydiphenanthro[9,10-*c*,9',10'-
e]pyridazine, 59.
3-*d-Erythro*trihydroxypropyl-1-phenylpy-
razolo[3,4-*b*]quinoxaline, structure,
351.
3-*d-Erythro*trihydroxypropylpyrazolo[3,4-
b]quinoxaline, oxidn., 351.
2-*d-Erythro*trihydroxypropylquinoxaline-
3-carboxylic acid lactone, 301.
1,4-Ethano-6-methyl-1,2,3,4-tetrahydro-
quinoxaline, 326.
4-Ethoxycinnoline, 31.
6-Ethoxy-2,3-diphenyl-4-*p*-tolylbenzo[*f*]-
quinoxalinium chloride, 332.
2-Ethoxy-3-hydroxyquinoxaline, hydrolysis, 270.
(?)-Ethoxy-6-indolo[2,3-*b*]quinoxaline,
346.
2-Ethoxy-3-methylquinoxaline, hydrolysis,
270.
3-Ethoxy-2-methylquinoxaline-1-oxide,
233.
action of alc. hydrochloric acid, 318.
2-Ethoxyquinoxaline, from 2-chloro deriv.,
258.
3-Ethoxyquinoxaline-1-oxide, 233.
6-Ethoxytetrazolo[*a*]phthalazine, 197.
6-Ethoxy-2,3,4-triphenylbenzo[*f*]quinox-
alinium salts, 332.
Ethyl 3-acetylquinoline-2-carboxylate
phenylhydrazone, cyclization, 199.
Ethyl benzeneazocarboxylate, adduct w.
diphenylketene, rearrangement, of,
330.
Ethyl 4,5-dihydro-3,6-dimethylpyridazine
dicarboxylate, reaction w. hydrazine,
199.
1-Ethyl-1,2-dihydro-3-hydroxy-7-nitro-
quinoxaline, 320.

1-Ethyl-1,2-dihydro-3-hydroxyquinoxa-
line, from *Bz*-nitroderivs., 320.
3-Ethyldihydro*iso*indole, from 1-chloro-4-
ethylphthalazine, 179.
Ethyl 1,2-dihydro-2-keto-1-methylquinox-
aline-3-carboxylate, 241.
Ethyl 1,2-dihydro-2-keto-1,6,7-trimethyl-
quinoxaline-2-carboxylate, 241.
2-Ethyl-1,2-dihydro-1,2,3-triphenylquin-
oxaline, 290.
Ethyl α,β-diketobutyric acid, reaction w.
o-phenylenediamine, 237.
1-Ethyl-*p*-dimethylaminostyrylcinnolin-
ium iodides, 14.
Ethyl 2,5-dimethylfuran-3,4-dicarboxy-
late, reaction w. hydrazine, 199.
Ethyl heptahydro-9-keto-9a-quinolizine-1-
carboxylate, reaction w. hydrazine,
199.
4-Ethyl-1-hydroxyphthalazine, redn., 78.
Ethyl 2-keto*cyclo*hexylglyoxylate, cond.
w. phenylhydrazine, 51.
3-Ethyl-7-ketonaphtho[1,2,3-*de*]phthala-
zine, 193.
1-Ethyl-3-methyl*iso*indazole, 46.
Ethyl 2-methylquinoxaline-3-carboxylate,
237.
1-Ethylquinoxalino[2,3-*b*][1,4]diazepine,
259–260.
Ethyl 3-methyl-2-quinoxalylpyruvate,
283.
reactivity of methylene group, 276.
1-Ethylphthalazine, from 4-chloro deriv.,
179.
salts, 72.
Ethyl 2-quinoxalyl pyruvate, 276.
1-Ethyl-1,2,3,4-tetrahydrocinnoline (?),
47.
1-Ethyl-1,2,3,4-tetrahydropyrazino[2,3-
b]quinoxaline, 259–260.

F

Flavazoles, see Pyrazoloquinoxalines, 348–
353.
Fluoflavin, 261.
Fluorenone-1,5-dicarboxylic acid phenylhydrazone, dehydration, 192.
Fluorubin, 261.
dipotassium salt, 228.
Folic acid, 357.
quinoxaline analog, 253.

Furo[3,4-c]cinnoline deriv., 62.
Furo[3,4-b]quinoxaline deriv., 300.
spiro[Furo(3,4-b)quinoxaline-1(3),9'-xanthenes], 254–5.

G

Glucazidones, see 8-Ketopyrido[1,2-a]
quinoxalines, 338.
d-Glucosonic acid, reaction w. o-phenylenediamine, 301.
Glyoxalinoquinoxalines, 353.
Group exchange, in Borsche synthesis, 17.
in diazotized o-aminoketones, 17–23.
in 4-hydroxycinnolines during chlorination, 23.
in nitration of glucazidones, 340.

H

Halochromy, of quinoxalines, 203.
of styryl quinoxalines, 283.
α-Halogenoketones, reaction w. aryl o-diamines, 206.
1-Halogenophthalazines, 178–9.
prepn., 178.
props., 178.
reactions, 178–9.
table, 180–1.
2-Halogeno-6,7,12,13-tetrahydro-6,13-diketobenzo[b]quinoxalo[2,3-f][1,4]-diazocine, 254.
Hemophilus pertussis, action of quinoxalines against, 365.
Heterocyclic o-diamines, quinoxalines from, 203.
Hetero ring, stability in 1-hydroxyphthalazines, 78.
Hexahydrocinnolines(?), 48.
2,3,5,6,7,8-Hexahydro-4-hydroxy-2-phenyl-3-ketocinnoline, 51.
4,5,6,8,9,10-Hexahydro-3-hydroxypyridazo[ij]quinolizine, 199.
1,4,5,6,7-Hexahydro-3-methyl-1-phenyl-cinnoline(?), 48.
Hydrazine, effect of on formation of 2-d-arabotetrahydroxybutylquinoxaline, 302.
reaction w. phthalic acid derivs., 140.
reactivity, cf. substituted derivs., toward arylphthalimides, 140.
Hydrazine salts, of 1,4-dihydroxyphthalazines, 142.

9a-Hydrazino-1a,4a,10a,13a-tetrahydro-1,4,10,13-tetrahydroxydipyridazino-[4,5-a,4',5'-c][9a]quinolizine, 199.
6-Hydrazinotetrazolo[a]phthalazine, 197.
Hydrolysis, of 2-alkoxyquinoxalines, 270.
of 2-amino group in quinoxalines, (primary) 263, (secondary) 264.
of 2-amino group in quinoxalines, cf.
amino-cinnolines and -phthalazines, 263.
3,2'-Hydroxyarylquinoxalines, table, 297–8.
Hydroxybenzo[c]cinnolines, 56.
3-Hydroxycinnoline, 16.
reduced, 48.
oxindole from, 10, 48.
4-Hydroxycinnoline, nitration, 24.
reduced, 48.
4-Hydroxycinnoline-3-carboxylic acid, 24.
esterification, 24.
reaction w. pyridine-acetic anhydride, 24–28.
4-Hydroxycinnoline-3-carboxylic acids, prepn., 16.
4-Hydroxycinnolines, 16–28.
acetylation, 23.
chlorination, 23, 29.
group exchange during, 23.
methylation, 23.
prepn., 16–23.
props., 23.
table, 18–21.
2-Hydroxycoumaran-3-ones, conversion to quinoxalines, 296–8.
4-Hydroxy-6,7-dimethoxycinnoline-3-acetic acid, ether esters, 32.
methylation, 23.
1-Hydroxy-7,8-dimethoxy-5-nitrophthalazine, alkylation, 82.
1-Hydroxy-7,8-dimethoxyphthalazine, acetylation, 82.
benzylation, 82.
demethylation, 82.
methylation, 82.
2-Hydroxy-3,2'-hydroxyarylquinoxalines, 237.
3-Hydroxy-7-ketonaphtho[1,2,3-de]-phthalazine, 193.
6-Hydroxy-8-ketopyrido[1,2-a]quinoxaline, 341.

9-Hydroxy-8-ketopyrido[1,2-*a*]quinoxaline, prep., props., 340–341.
4-Hydroxy-6-methoxycinnoline-3-carboxylic acid, 24.
ethyl ester, 24.
4-Hydroxy-1-methoxy-5-nitrophthalazine, 157.
1-Hydroxy-4-methoxyphthalazine, 157.
4-Hydroxy-7-methylcinnoline, nitration, 24.
4-Hydroxy-8-methylcinnoline, nitration, 24.
2-Hydroxy-3-methyl-1,4-naphthaquinone, metallic derivs., as chemiluminescence catalysts, 154.
4-Hydroxy-8-methyl-5(or 7)-nitrocinnoline, formn., 24.
chlorination, 29.
4-Hydroxy-7-methyl-8-nitrocinnoline, chlorination, 29.
formn., 24.
4-Hydroxy-3-methyl-6-nitrocinnoline, methylation, 23.
2-Hydroxy-6(or 7)-methyl-3-phenylquinoxaline, 237.
4-Hydroxy-1-methylphthalazine, 72.
O-methylation, 82.
redn., 78.
2-Hydroxy-3-methylpyrazine[2,3-*b*]quinoxaline, 267.
3-Hydroxymethyl-1-pyrazolo[3,4-*b*]quinoxaline, 352.
2-Hydroxy-3-methylquinoxaline, from 2-aminoanilino deriv., 264.
quaternization, effect of reagent on position of, 286.
3-Hydroxy-6-methylquinoxaline, by redn. of 4-methyl-2-nitrophenylglycine, 324.
3-Hydroxy-6(or 7)-methylquinoxaline, from 1,2-dihydro deriv., 324.
4-Hydroxynaphthalic acid, coupling with benzene diazonium chloride, 192.
3-Hydroxy-2,4′-nitrobenzenesulfonamidoquinoxaline, 263.
4-Hydroxy-6-nitrocinnoline, 17.
methylation, 23.
4-Hydroxy-6-nitrocinnolines, methylation, 49.
4-Hydroxy-8-nitrocinnolines, chelation, 23.
m-Hydroxyphenylacetic acid, coupling with diazotized arylamines, 49.

4-*p*-Hydroxyphenylcinnoline, from the ethiodide, 44.
salts, 7.
4-*p*-Hydroxyphenylcinnoline ethiodide, alk. decomp., 44.
4-*p*-Hydroxyphenyl-3-phenylcinnoline, 44.
1-Hydroxy-4-phenylphthalazine, acetylation, 82.
ring fission, 78.
3-Hydroxy-2,1′-phenylpyridazylquinoxaline-1′-hydroxide, 309.
2-Hydroxy-3-phenylquinoxaline, 238.
1-Hydroxy-4-*n*-propylphthalazine, redn., 78.
1-Hydroxyphthalazine, attempted nitration, 82.
ring fission, 78.
1-Hydroxyphthalazine-4-carboxylic acid, attempted nitration, 82.
chlorination, 78.
redn., 78.
1-Hydroxyphthalazines, 78–82.
acetylation, 82.
acyl derivs., 84–105.
of unknown structure, 96.
table, 104.
alkylation, 94.
alkyl derivs., 84–105.
aryl derivs., 84–105.
chlorination, 78, 178.
prepn., 78.
props., 78–82.
redn., 78.
table, 79–81.
4-Hydroxyquinazolines, *cf.* 4-Hydroxycinnolines, 23.
4-Hydroxyquinoline-3-carboxylic acids, *cf.* cinnolines, 24.
4-Hydroxyquinolines, *cf.* 4-Hydroxycinnolines, 23.
2-Hydroxyquinoxaline, reaction w. phosphorus pentachloride, 258.
3-Hydroxyquinoxaline-2-aldehyde, 246–8.
from 2-*arabo*- or 2-*l-xylo*-tetrahydroxybutylquinoxaline, 307.
3-Hydroxyquinoxaline-2-aldehyde *N*′-acetyl-*N*′-phenylhydrazone, 248.
3-Hydroxyquinoxaline-2-aldehyde phenylhydrazone, 308.
effect of *p*H on formn., 308–9.

2-Hydroxyquinoxaline-3-carboxylic acid, from 2-amino deriv., 263.
2-Hydroxyquinoxaline-3-carboxylic acids, decarboxylation, 235.
from alloxazines, 251.
Hydroxyquinoxalines, methylation, 238.
2-Hydroxyquinoxalines, alkylation, 241.
having no other hetero substituent, 235–6.
prepn., props., table, 235–6.
methylation, 311.
3(3'-Hydroxy-2'-quinoxalyl)-1-phenyl-pyridazinium hydroxide, 309.
3-Hydroxy-2-tetrahydroxybutylquinoxaline, reaction with phenylhydrazine, effect of configuration on, 307–8.
of substitution on, 308.
mechanism, 308.
6-Hydroxytetrazolo[a]phthalazine, 197.
chlorination, 197.
4-Hydroxytetrazolo[a]quinoxaline, 261, 353–4.
2-Hydroxy-3-substituted quinoxalines, 236–244.
prepn., 236–238.
props., 238–241.
table, 238–240.

I

Iminazoles, from aldehydes and 2-amino-1-phenylazonaphthalene, 336.
Imidazo[b]quinoxaline deriv., 353.
dispiro[isoIndene-2,2'(3')-quinoxaline-3',-2''-isoindene] deriv., 326.
Indeno[2,1-f]indolo[3,2-b]quinoxaline derivs., 347.
Indeno[1,3-de]phthalazine deriv., 193.
Indeno[1,2-b]quinoxaline derivs., 342.
Indoles, from cinnolines, table, 10.
IsoIndolinopyrazolidocolines, from phthalazine derivs., 109.
6-Indolo[2,3-b]quinoxaline, 346.
7-Indolo[2,3-b]quinoxalo[2,3-e]pyrazine, 267.
4-Iodo-1-methylphthalazine, 72.
1-Iodophthalazines, from 1-chlorophthalazines, 178.
Isonitrosomalondimethylanilide, oxidative cyclization to quinoxaline deriv., 311, 317.

K

α-Keto acids, cond. w. N-substituted o-phenylenediamines, 310.
o-Ketobenzoic acids, reaction w. hydrazine, 78.
8-Ketobenzopyrano[1,2,3-de]benzthiapyrano[2',3',4'-ij]phthalazine, 195.
8-Ketobenzo[h]thiaxantheno[10,1,2-cde]-cinnoline, 195.
3-Ketobicyclo[2,2,1]heptanylidene-2-acethydrazide, cyclization, 61.
11-Ketoindeno[1,2-b]quinoxaline, 342.
4-Keto-1-methoxy-3-nitroarylphthalazines, by thermal decomp. of 4-alkoxy-3,4-dihydro derivs., 132.
8-Keto-9-methoxy-6-phenylpyrido[1,2-a]-quinoxaline, 340.
1-Keto-3(2'-methyl-4'-nitrophenyl)-phthalazine, reactions w. acetone, 128.
8-Keto-6-methylpyrido[1,2-a]quinoxaline, 339
12-Ketocyclopenta[1,2-b,3,4-b']di(bz-methylquinoxaline), 343.
8-Keto-6-phenylpyrido[1,2-a]quinoxaline, prepn., props., 339.
8-Ketopyrido[1,2-a]quinoxaline, prepn., 338.
props., 339.
8-Ketopyrido[1,2-a]quinoxaline-9-sulfonic acid, prepn., props., 340.
3-Keto-1-substituted-[4,5]-benzisooxazole-4-carboxylic acid,1,4-dihydroxy-5-substituted aminophthalazines from, 141.
α-Keto-α',α',β,β-tetramethylglutaric acid, reaction w. o-phenylenediamine, 237.
6-Ketotriazolo[4,5,1-ij]cinnoline, 62, 64.
α-Keto-α',β,β'-trimethylglutaric acid, reaction w. o-phenylenediamine, 236–7.

L

Lactobacillus casei, action of quinoxaline analog of folic acid, 253.
Luminol, see 5-Amino-1,4-dihydroxy-phthalazine, 146.

M

Maleic anhydride, adduct w. 2,3-dimethyl-quinoxaline, 283.

Mesoxalic acid, ethyl ester, cond. w. N-
substituted o-phenylenediamines, 311.
reaction w. o-phenylenediamines, 251.
5,8-Methanocinnoline derivs., 61.
5,8-Methano-1,4-diphenylphthalazine,
196.
1,4-Methano-6-methyl-1,2,3,4-tetrahy-
droquinoxaline, 326.
1,4-Methanoquinoxaline derivs., 330.
2-p-Methoxybenzyl-3-phenylquinoxaline,
acetylation, 277.
4-Methoxycinnoline, basicity, 31–2.
3-Methoxyquinoxaline-2-aldehyde, from
2-d-arabotetrahydroxybutyl-3-meth-
oxyquinoxaline, 307.
3-Methoxy-2-sulfanilamidoquinoxaline,
hydrolysis, 263.
6-Methoxytetrazolo[a]phthalazine, 197.
Bz-Methylaceanthra[1,2-b]quinoxaline,
342.
Methyl anthranilates, 13.
Methylation, of 3-aryl-1-ketophthalazines,
126–7.
    of 3-aryl-1-keto-4-methylphthalazines,
    126–7, 133.
    of 7,9-dihydroxy-8-ketopyrido[1,2-a]-
    quinoxaline, 340.
    of 1,4-dihydroxy-5-nitrophthalazine,
    162.
    of 2,3-dihydroxyquinoxalines, 330.
    of 4-hydroxycinnolines, 23.
    of 4-hydroxy-8-methyl-5(or 7)-nitrocin-
    noline, 49.
    of 4-hydroxy-6-nitrocinnolines, 49.
    of hydroxyquinoxalines, 238.
    of 2-hydroxyquinoxalines, 311.
2-(1-Methylbenzoxazole)-2-(1,3-dimethyl-
quinoxaline)trimethincyanine, 291.
2-Methylbis[1]benzopyrano[4,3,2-de,2′,-
3′,4′-ij]phthalazine, 195.
4-Methylcinnoline, nitration, 15.
4-Methylcinnoline-7-carboxylic acid, 6.
4-Methylcinnolines, 13–15.
    basic center, 13.
    conversion to skatole, 10.
    formn., 13.
    quaternary salts, 13.
    quaternization, 39.
    table, 14.
1-Methylcinnolinium iodide, alk. decomp.,
43.

4-Methylcinnolinium salts, reaction w. p-
dimethylaminobenzaldehyde, 39.
1-Methyl-4-cinnolones, 48–9.
    table, 49.
Methyl-4,6-dihydro-4-ketocinnolyl-6-ni-
tronates, 49.
2,3-Methylenedioxy-11-indeno[1,2-b]-
quinoxaline, 342.
Methyl l-glucosonate, reaction w. o-
phenylenediamine, 301.
Methyl group, reactivity in 1,2-dihydro-2-
keto-3-methyl-1-substituted
quinoxalines, 311.
1-Methylisoindole, by redn. of phthalazines, 72, 76.
3-Methylisoindole, from 1-chloro-4-meth-
ylphthalazine, 179.
Methyl 2-methoxy-5-methylphenylglyox-
ylate, reaction w. o-phenylenediamine, 296.
4-Methyl-8-nitrocinnoline, 15.
3-Methyl-2-phenacylquinoxaline, 283.
3-Methyl-2-phenylbenzo[f]quinoxaline-
N-oxide, 234.
3-Methyl-4-phenylcinnoline, chloroplatinate, 7.
    ethiodide, alk. decomp., 44.
    oxidn., 10.
    N-oxide, nitro derivs., 9.
N-Methyl-o-phenylenediamine, reaction
w. pyruvic acid, 310–11.
Methylphenyloxamic acid, 317.
3-Methyl-1-phenylpyrazolo[3,4-b]quinox-
aline, 348–9.
3-Methyl-4-phenylpyridazine-5,6-dicar-
boxylic acid, 10.
6(or 7)-Methyl-2-phenylquinoxaline, 206.
2-Methyl-3-phenylquinoxaline, methio-
dides, 286.
    reactivity of methylene group, 277.
1-Methylphthalazine, 72.
    from 4-chloro deriv., 179.
    reaction w. benzaldehyde, 76.
    reaction w. chloral, 76.
    reaction w. phthalic anhydride, 76.
    redn., 76.
3-Methylphthalazinium iodides, alk. decomp., 186.
5-Methylpyrazine-2,3-dicarboxylic acid,
277.

3-Methyl-1-pyrazolo[3,4-*b*]quinoxaline, 352.
2-(1-Methylquinoline)-2-(1,3-dimethyl-quinoxaline)trimethincyanine, 291.
2-Methylquinoxaline, 276.
  cond. prod., table, 274–5.
  of substituted, table, 276.
  derivs., 273–285.
  di-*N*-oxide, 232.
    redn., 232.
  oxidn., 276, 277.
  reactivity of methyl group, 276.
    effect of substituents, 276.
6-Methylquinoxaline, quaternization, 286.
1-Methyl-3,9,10-triazophenanthrene   (?), derivs., 27.
Monoacyl derivs., of 1,4-dihydroxyphthal-azines, see monoalkyl derivs., etc., 157–167.
Monoalkyl derivs. of 1,4-dihydroxyphthal-azines, 157–167.
  N-derivs., see 3,4-dihydro-1-hydroxy-4-keto-3-substituted phthalazines, 158.
  O-derivs., 157.
  unknown structures, 165–166.
  table, 166.
Monoximes, use in quinoxaline synthesis, 206.

N

Naphtho[1,2,3-*de*]phenanthro[3,2,1-*ij*]-phthalazine, deriv., 195.
Naphtho[1,2,3-*de*]phthalazine derivs., 193.
Naphtho[2,3-*g*]phthalazine deriv., 193.
2-Naphthol-1-sulfonic acid, reaction w. diazotized prim. arylamines, 106–8.
Nitration, of glucazidones, 339.
  of 4-hydroxycinnolines, 24.
  of 4-methylcinnoline, 15.
10(or 11)-Nitro-15-acenaphth[1,2-*b*]indeno-[2,1-*f*]quinoxaline, 343.
o-Nitroarylglycines, redn. to 1,2-dihydro-3-hydroxyquinoxalines, 324.
2-Nitrobenzo[*c*]cinnoline-6-oxide, 56.
3-Nitrobenzo[*c*]cinnoline-6-oxide, 56.
2-Nitrodibenzo[*fh*]-5-indolo[2,3-*a*]quinox-aline, 346.
9-Nitro-12,14-dihydroindeno[2,1-*f*]indolo-[3,2-*b*]quinoxaline, 347.
5-Nitro-1,2-diphenylbenziminazole, 288.

8-Nitro-4-hydroxycinnoline, formn., 24.
3(?)-Nitro-4-hydroxycinnoline, formn., 24.
Nitromalonodimethylanilide, action of sul-furic acid, 319–320.
2-Nitronaphthalene, redn., 58.
Nitronates, methyl, by methylation of 6-nitro-4-hydroxycinnolines, 23.
6-Nitro-4-phenoxycinnolines, 32.
o-Nitrophenylglycines, redn., 235, 318.
3-Nitrophenyl-1-methoxyphthalazinium perchlorates, 133.
5-Nitro-2-phenyl-1-*p*-tolylbenziminazole, 288.
3-Nitrophthalic anhydride, reaction w. hy-drazines, 162.
*iso*Nitrosomalondimethylanilide, oxidative cyclization to quinoxaline deriv., 311, 317.

O

Octahydro-4,7,11,11,12,12-hexamethyl-1,4,7,10-dimethanobenzo[*c*]cinnoline, 61.
Opiazone, see 1-Hydroxy-7,8-dimethoxy-phthalazine, 82.
Oxidation, comparative facility of, 3,4-dihydro-1,4-dihydroxy- and 1-keto-4-methyl-3-nitroarylphthalazines, 118.
  critical conds. for phthalazine-4-acetic acid derivs., 118.
  of 2-*d*-*arabo*tetrahydroxybutyl-3-hy-droxyquinoxaline, 246–7.
  of 3-aryl-3,4-dihydro-1-hydroxyphthal-azine-4-acetic acids, 108–9, 117, 158
  of 3-aryl-3,4-dihydro-1-methoxy-4-methylenephthalazines, 169.
  of 3-aryl-1-methoxyphthalazinium per-chlorates, 169.
  of benzo[*f*]quinoxalines, 337.
  of 1,2-dihydro-3-hydroxyquinoxalines, 324.
  of 1,2-dihydro-1-methyl-3-methylphen-ylcarbamidoquinoxaline-4-oxide, 317.
  of 1,2-dihydroquinoxalines, 324.
  of 3,4-dihydroquinoxalines, 235.
  of 2,3-dimethylquinoxaline, 283.
  of 1,3-diphenyl-2-pyrrolo[3,4-*c*]cinno-line, 11.
  of 3-*d*-*erythro*trihydroxypropylpyrazolo-[3,4-*b*]quinoxaline, 351.

of glucazidones, 339.
of 8-ketopyrido[1,2-*a*]quinoxaline-9-sulfonic acid, 340.
of 2-methylquinoxaline, 276, 277.
of phenazine, 254.
of 3-phenyl-2-substituted quinoxalines, 238.
of 2-polyhydroxyalkylquinoxalines, 302–4.
of quinoxaline, 228.
of quinoxaline-2,3-dicarboxylic acid, 255.
N-Oxides, of 4-arylcinnolines, table, 9.
of quinoxaline, 232–4.
of quinoxalines and cinnolines, comparison, 9.

P

spiro[*cyclo*Pentane-1,2′-[2]cyclopenta[*b*]quinoxaline], 342.
*cyclo*Penta[*b*]quinoxaline derivs., 341-4.
*cyclo*Penta[*f*]quinoxaline derivs., 345.
Peroxidic props. of quinoxaline *N*-oxides, 232.
Perylo[3,4-*cd*,9,10-*c′d′*]dipyridazine deriv., 195.
Phenanthraquinone imine, reaction w. acetic anhydride, 60.
Phenanthro[9,10-*b*]quinoxalo[2,3-*e*]pyrazine, 267.
Phenazines, from 5,6-diketobenzo[*f*]quinoxalines, 337.
oxidn. of, 254.
Phenazone, see Benzo[*c*]cinnoline, 52.
Phenazonium salts, *cf.* cinnolinium salts, 44.
Phenolphthalein, possible quinoxaline analogs, 254-5.
4-Phenoxycinnoline, basicity, 33.
conversion to 4-amino-derivs., 33–4.
hydrolysis, 33.
4-Phenoxycinnolines, 32–4.
prepn., 32–3.
props., 33–4.
table, 33.
Phenoxylation, of 4-chlorocinnolines, 32.
4-Phenoxyphthalazines, table, 84.
7-Phenylacenaphtho[1,2-*b*]quinoxalinium salts, 344.
2-Phenylbenzo[*f*]quinoxaline, 336.

4-Phenylcinnoline, from 1,2-dihydro deriv., 46.
oxidn., 10.
redn. to 3-phenylindole, 10.
salt, 7.
3-Phenylcinnoline-4-carboxylic acid, 11.
o-Phenylenediamine, by redn. of quinoxaline or the di-*N*-oxide, 232.
cond. w. 1,4-dichloro*cyclo*pentene-3,5-dione, 344.
cond. w., 4,5-diketo-1-phenylpyrazoline, 349.
cond. w. *iso*nitrosoacetone, 276.
diphthaloyl deriv., redn., 344.
failure to react w. diketones, 205.
reaction w. aldoses, 300.
reaction w. 6-chloro-2,3-dihydroxyquinoxaline, 243.
reaction w. coumaran-3-ones, 296–8.
reaction w. cyanogen, 265.
reaction w. diacetyl, 277.
reaction w. 2,3-dichloroquinoxaline, 261.
reaction w. 4,5-dihydro-5-hydroxy-2,5-diphenylfurans, 293–296
table, 294–5.
reaction w. 3-hydroxyglucazidone, 340.
reaction w. 5-hydroxy-2-hydroxymethyl-4-pyrone, 341.
Schiff base formation instead of quinoxalines from, 204–5.
o-Phenylenediamines, reaction w. alloxan, 250.
reaction w. bromoacetic acid, 235.
reaction w. chloro*iso*nitroso ketones, 264.
reaction w. diketosuccinic acid, 254.
reaction w. glyoxylic esters, 235.
reaction w. α-halogeno esters, 318–9.
reaction w. α-keto acids (esters), 236.
reaction w. mesoxalic acid (ester), 251.
reaction w. monochloroglyoximes, 264.
reaction w. oxalic acid (ester), 243.
N-substituted, condensation w. alloxan, 310–311.
condensation w. *o*-keto acids, 310.
1,2′-Phenylethylphthalazine, 76.
1-Phenyl-*d*-fructosone, reaction w. *o*-phenylenediamine, 301.
3-Phenylindole, 46.
1-Phenylphthalazine, from 4-chloro deriv., 179.

Phenylphthalazinium salts, 133.
5(3)-Phenylpyrazoline, 197.
1-Phenylpyrazolo[3,4-*b*]quinoxaline, 348–9.
1-Phenylpyrazolo[3,4-*b*]quinoxaline-3-aldehyde, 351.
1-Phenylpyrazolo[3,4-*b*]quinoxaline-3-carboxylic acid, 351.
  decarboxylation, 349.
4-Phenylpyridazine-5,6-dicarboxylic acid, 10.
2-Phenylquinoxaline, 206.
3-Phenylquinoxaline, from *o*-phenylenediamine and phenacyl bromide, 324.
3-Phenylquinoxaline-2-carboxylic acid, oxidn., to 2-hydroxy deriv., 238.
11-Phenylquinoxalo[2,3-*b*][1,4]benzoxazine, 311, 317.
2-Phenyl-3-*p*-tolyl-1-pyrrolo[2,3-*b*]quinoxaline, 346.
Photosensitivity, of quinoxaline di-*N*-oxide sodium salts, 233.
Phthalaldehydic acid arylhydrazones, cyclization, 85, 95.
Phthalazine, from 1-chlorophthalazine, 179.
  prepn., 69–70.
  props., 70.
  alkiodides, alk. decomp., 94.
Phthalazines, antimalarial action of, 364.
  basic strengths, 363.
  condensed, 191–8.
  redn., 189.
  unsubstituted in hetero ring, 69–71.
Phthalazino[2,1-*a*][1,5]benzodiazepine, derivs., 116, 117.
Phthalazino[2,3-*b*]phthalazine derivs., 197–8.
Phthalazino[2,3-*b*]phthalazine derivs., 144, 190.
Phthalaz-4-ones, see 3,4-Dihydro-4-ketophthalazines, 85.
2,1′-Phthalazylacrylic acid, 76.
  salts, 76.
1-Phthalazylphthalone, 76.
Phthalic acid derivs., reaction with hydrazine, 140.
Phthalic acid dihydrazides, intermediates in 1,4-dihydroxyphthalazine formn., 142–3.

Phthalic anhydrides, reaction with hydrazines, 162.
  reaction with hydrazine, 140.
  mechanism, 142–3.
Phthalide derivs., conversion to 1,4-dihydroxyphthalazines, 141.
Phthalimide, from 1-hydroxyphthalazine, 82.
Phthalimidines, by redn. of phthalazines, 78, 95.
asym-Phthalylideneacetylacetone, reaction w. hydrazine, 141.
asym-Phthalylidenefluorene, reaction w. hydrazine, 141.
asym-Phthalylideneglycine, reaction w. hydrazine, 141.
Phthiocol, see 2-Hydroxy-3-methyl-1,4-naphthaquinone, 154.
Plasmodium gallinaceum, action of cinnolines against, 36, 364.
  of quinoxalines against, 364–5.
2-Polyhydroxyalkylbenziminazoles, 300.
3-Polyhydroxyalkyl-1-phenylpyrazolo[3,-4-*b*]quinoxaline, 349.
  formn. mechanism, 350.
  props., 351.
  table, 350.
2-Polyhydroxyalkylquinoxalines, 300–9.
  alk. decomp., 304–6.
  prepn., 300–2.
  props., 302–9.
  reaction w. phenylhydrazine, 306–9.
  reaction w. phenylhydrazine, 349.
  table, 303.
1,4-Propano-6-methyl-1,2,3,4-tetrahydroquinoxaline, 326.
3-*n*-Propyldihydro*iso*indole, from 1-chloro-4-*iso*propylphthalazine, 179.
Pteridines, see Pyrimido[4,5-*b*]pyrazines, 356–7.
Pyrazine-2,3-dicarboxylic acid, 228.
Pyrazinetetracarboxylic acid, 255.
Pyrazino[3,2,1-*jk*]carbazole derivs., 345.
Pyrazino[2,3-*b*,5,6-*b*′]diquinoxaline deriv., 261, 267.
Pyrazino[2,3-*b*]pyrazine, 357.
Pyrazino[2,3-*b*]quinoxaline derivs., 260–1, 267.
Pyrazolo[4,3-*c*]cinnoline deriv., 62–3.
1-Pyrazolo[5,1-*a*]*iso*indoles, from phthalazine, derivs., 109.

Pyrazolo[1,2-*b*]phthalazine deriv., 197.
1-Pyrazolo[3,4-*b*]quinoxaline, prepn., props., 352–3.
1-Pyrazolo[3,4-*b*]quinoxaline-3-aldehyde, prepn., props., 352.
1-Pyrazolo[3,4-*b*]quinoxaline-3-carboxylic acid., prepn., props., 352.
Pyrazoloquinoxalines, 348–53.
Pyridazine, from 4-arylcinnolines, 10.
Pyridazine-4,5-dicarboxylic acid, 70–1.
Pyridazine-1,2,3,4-tetracarboxylic acid, 54.
Pyridazo[4,5-*c*]cinnoline, deriv., 62–3.
Pyridazo[4,5-*g*]phthalazine derivs., 192.
Pyridazo[4,5-*b*]quinoline deriv., 199.
Pyridazo[*ij*]quinolizine deriv., 199.
Pyridazoquinoxalines, 354.
Pyridine-3,4-dicarboxylic acid diphenylhydrazide, cyclization, 199.
Pyrido[2,3]pyrazines, table, 356.
Pyrido[2,3-*d*]pyridazine, derivs., 198–9.
Pyrido[3,4-*d*]pyridazine, deriv., 198–9.
Pyrido[3,2-*f*]quinoxaline, 348.
Pyrido[1,2-*a*]quinoxaline derivs. (*see also* Glucazidones), 338–340.
Pyrido[1,2,3-*de*]quinoxaline derivs., 346.
4,2′-Pyridylcinnoline, 26.
2,3′-Pyridyl-6-indolo[2,3-*b*]quinoxaline, 346.
3,3′-Pyridyl-6-indolo[2,3-*b*]quinoxaline, 346.
Pyrimido[4,5-*b*]pyrazine deriv., 356–7.
Pyrimido[4,5-*b*]quinoxaline deriv., 253.
2-Pyrrolo[3,4-*c*]cinnolines, 11, 47, 62.
Pyrrolo[2,3-*b*]quinoxaline derivs., 346.
Pyruvic acid, anomalous reaction w. 2-amino-1-phenylazonaphthalene, 336.
o-methylaminoanil of, 310–11.

Q

Quaternary salts (*see also* Cinnolinium salts, etc.), of 4-arylcinnolines, 9.
of benzo[*f*]quinoxalines, 332.
of 4-methylcinnolines, 13.
Quaternization, of 4-aminocinnolines, 36.
of cinnolines, 39–45.
of 1,2-dihydro-2-keto-3-methyl-1-substituted quinoxalines, 311.
of phthalazine, 70.
Quinoxaline, prepn., 228.

props., 228–229.
reaction w. Grignard reagents, 326.
Quinoxaline-2-aldehyde, 276.
Quinoxaline-2-aldehydes, 246–9.
from 2-tetrahydroxybutylquinoxalines, 306–8.
prepn., 246.
props., 246.
table, 247.
Quinoxaline alkiodides, alk. decomp., 290.
Quinoxaline analogs, of aposafranine dyes, 290.
Quinoxaline-2-carboxylic acid, from 2-*d*-*arabo*tetrahydroxybutylquinoxaline, 304.
aryl esters, 254.
chloride, reaction with *N*-*p*-aminobenzoylglutamic acid, 253.
Quinoxaline-2-carboxylic acids, 250–3.
by oxidn. of glucazidones, 339.
prepn., 250–2.
props., 253.
table, 251–2.
Quinoxaline cyanines, 290–1.
Quinoxaline derivs., substituted in *Bz* ring, table, 220–224.
unsubstituted in *Bz* ring, table, 207–219.
Quinoxaline-2,3-dicarboxylic acid, anhydride, reaction w. hydrazine, 354.
reaction w. phenols, 254.
derivs., table, 255–6.
oxidn., 255.
Quinoxaline-2,3-dicarboxylic acids, 254–7.
prepn., 254.
props., 254–5.
tables, 255–6.
Quinoxaline nucleus, bathochromic effect in cyanine dyes, 291.
Quinoxaline *N*-oxides, 232–4.
cf. cinnoline oxides, 9.
prepn., 232.
props., 232–4.
Quinoxalines, action on *Staphylococcus aureus*, 364.
antibacterial and parasiticidal action, 364–5.
basic strengths, table, 363.
biol. data, table, 365.
by oxidn. of 1,2-dihydro derivs., 324.
condensed with carbocyclic rings, 332–46.

Quinoxalines (*continued*):
  condensed with nitrogenous hetero
    rings, 346–54.
  from aromatic *o*-diamines and 1,2-di-
    carbonyl compds., 203–27.
  from aromatic *o*-diamines and 1,2-dicar-
    bonyl compds., abnormal reactions,
    204–5.
  from compds. contg. furan ring, 293–9.
  quaternization of, 286.
    effect of quaternizing agent, 286.
    effect of substituents, 286.
  reaction w. peracetic acid, 232.
  reduced, 310–331.
  u.v. absorption spectra, table, 361–2.
  unsubstituted in hetero ring, 228–231.
    table, 229–231.
Quinoxalinium salts, 286–292.
  prepn., 286–8.
  props., 288–292.
  table, 289.
Quinoxalo[2,3-*b*]acenaphtho[1,2-*e*]pyra-
  zine, 267.
Quinoxalo[2,3-*b*][1,4]benzoxazine deriv.,
  261, 311, 317.
11-Quinoxalo[2,3-*b*][1,4]benzthiazine, 261.
Quinoxalo[2,3-*b*][1,4]diazepine deriv.,
  259–260.
Quinoxalo[1,2-*a*]quinoxaline deriv., 348.
Quinoxalo[2,3-*b*]quinoxaline derivs., 261,
  311, 317.
Quinoxalo[1,2-*a*]quinoxalinium hydroxide
  deriv., 317.
2-Quinoxalylacetoxyacetaldehyde, 304–5.
p-(2'-Quinoxalylcarbamyl)benzoylglu-
  tamic acid, 253.
2-Quinoxalylhydroxyacetaldehyde, 304–5.

R

Reduction, of 3-aryl-1-ketophthalazines,
  126.
  of benzo[*c*]cinnolines, 55.
  of 4-chlorocinnoline, 4.
  of 4-chlorophthalazines, 72, 179.
  of 3,4-dihydro-1-hydroxy-3-nitroaryl-
    phthalazines, 158.
  of 1,2-dihydro-3-hydroxy-1-nitrosoquin-
    oxaline, 345.
  of 3,4-dihydro-4-keto-3-substituted
    phthalazines to phthalimidines, 95.
  1,2-dihydro-1-methyl-3-methylphenyl-
    carbamidoquinoxaline-4-oxide, 317.
  of 2,3-dihydroxyquinoxaline, 243.
  of 2,2'-dinitrodiphenyls, 52.
  of diphthaloyl-*o*-phenylenediamines,
    344.
  of 3-ethoxy-2-methylquinoxaline-1-ox-
    ide, 233.
  of 1-hydroxyphthalazines, 78.
  of 1-methylphthalazine, 76.
  of *o*-nitroarylglycines, 324.
  of *o*-nitrophenylglycines, 235, 318.
  of phthalazine, 70.
  of phthalazines to 1,2,3,4-tetrahydro
    derivs., 189.
  of quinoxaline to 1,2,3,4-tetrahydro
    deriv., 228.
  of quinoxaline di-*N*-oxide, 232.
  of quinoxalines to tetrahydro derivs.,
    325.
Retenequinone, cond. w. acetoacetic ester,
  58.
Richter synthesis mechanism, 16.

S

Sodium azide, reaction w. 1,4-dihalogeno-
  phthalazines, 182.
Sodium benzaldehydearylhydrazone-*C*-
  sulfonate-2-*β*-acrylic acids, conversion
  to phthalazine-4-acetic acids, 107–8.
Spectra, of benzo[*c*]cinnolines, 57.
  of cinnoline and quinoxaline derivs.,
    358–62.
Stability, of hetero ring in 1-hydroxy-
  phthalazines, 78.
Staphylococcus aureus, action of quinoxalines against, 364.
Stereoisomerism, of 1,2,3,4-tetrahydro-
  quinoxalines, 326.
Streptococcus hemolyticus, action of quinoxalines against, 365.
Styrene, reaction w. dimethyl azodicarboxylate, 47.
4-Styrylcinnoline, 14.
  oxidation, 11.
1-Styrylphthalazine, 76.
  redn., 76.
Sugars, relation of configuration to flavazole formation from, 349.
Sulfanilamidoquinoxalines, biol. data, table, 365.

Sulfonation, of glucazidones, 339, 340.
2-Sulfonamidoquinoxalines, 265.
  table, 266.

T

3-d-arabo-Tetraacetoxybutyl-2-hydroxy-
  quinoxaline O-methylation, 241.
3,3',4,4'-Tetraaminodiphenyl, 229.
  condensation w. parabanic acid, 353.
N_1,N_2,N^α,N^β-Tetracarbomethoxy-4-hy-
  drazino-1,2,3,4-tetrahydrocinnoline,
  47.
Tetrachloro-o-xylene, reaction w. hydrazine, 69.
1,2,3,4-Tetrahydro-1-alkylphthalazines,
  76.
1,2,3,4-Tetrahydrobenzo[c]cinnolines, 57.
Tetrahydrocinnolines, 47-8.
1,4,6,9-Tetrahydro-4,6-diketo-3,7-di-
  methyl-1,9-diphenylpyridazo[4,3-g]-
  cinnoline, 62-3.
1,2,3,4-Tetrahydro-1,4-diketo-2,3-di-
  methylphthalazine,   1,4-dihydroxy-
  phthalazine from, 140.
1,2,3,4-Tetrahydro-1,4-diketo-2,3-di-
  methylphthalazyl-5,1'-azo-2'-naph-
  thol, copper deriv., 176.
1,2,3,4-Tetrahydro-2,3-diketo-1,4-di-
  methylquinoxalines, 330.
5,6,7,8-Tetrahydro-6,7-diketo-5,8-dimeth-
  ylquinoxalo[1,2-a]quinoxalinium-13-
  hydroxide, 317, 348.
1,2,3,4-Tetrahydro-2,9-diketo-3,3-di-
  phenyl-1,4-methanoquinoxaline, 329-
  330.
1,2,3,4-Tetrahydro-2,3-diketo-6-methoxy-
  1,4-dimethylquinoxaline, 241.
1,2,3,4-Tetrahydro-2,3-diketo-1-methyl-
  quinoxalines, 241.
5,7,12,14-Tetrahydro-7,12-diketo-11-nitro-
  phthalazino[2,3-b]phthalazine, 198.
5,7,12,14-Tetrahydro-7,12-diketophthalaz-
  ino[2,3-b]phthalazine, 197-8.
1,2,3,4-Tetrahydro-2,3-diketo-1,4,6-tri-
  methylquinoxaline, 241.
3,5,6,7-Tetrahydro-2,3-diphenylpyrido[1,-
  2,3-de]quinoxaline, 346.
4,5,6,13-Tetrahydro-3-hydroxy-5-phenyl-
  benzo(h)cinnoline, 57-8.
7,8,9,10-Tetrahydro-2-hydroxy-1-pyra-
  zino[3,2,1-jk]carbazole, 345.

5,6,7,8-Tetrahydro-3-hydroxy-5,9,9-tri-
  methanocinnoline, 61.
1,2,3,4-Tetrahydro-2-keto-1-methyl-3-
  methylphenylcarbamidoquinoxaline,
  317.
3,5,6,7-Tetrahydro-3-keto-2-methylpy-
  rido[1,2,3-de]quinoxaline, 346.
1,2,3,4-Tetrahydro-2-keto-6(or 7)-methyl-
  quinoxaline-1-acetic acid, ethyl ester
  (presumed), 319-320.
1,2,3,4-Tetrahydro-1-keto-3-phenylnaph-
  thalene-2-acetic acid, reaction w. hydrazine, 58.
1a,4a,10a,13a-Tetrahydro-1,4,9a,10,13-
  pentahydroxydipyridazino[4,5-a,4',-
  5'-c][9a]quinolizine, 200.
1,2,3,4-Tetrahydro-4-phenylcinnoline, 46.
  prepn., 47.
  props., 47.
  salts, 47.
4,5,6,7-Tetrahydro-2-phenylindazole,   51.
1,2,3,4-Tetrahydrophthalazine, 70.
  "diazotization," 190.
  reaction w. phthaloyl chlorides, 190.
1,2,3,4-Tetrahydrophthalazine-3-o-ben-
  zoylbenzoic acids, sodium salts, oxidn.,
  70.
1,2,3,4-Tetrahydrophthalazine hydrochloride, reaction w. phthaloyl chloride,
  198.
1,2,3,4-Tetrahydrophthalazines, 189-190.
  table, 189.
5,7,12,14-Tetrahydrophthalazino[2,3-b]-
  phthalazines, 144, 190.
1,2,3,4-Tetrahydro-2-phthaloylphthala-
  zine, sodium salt, oxidn., 70.
1,2,3,4-Tetrahydropyrazino[2,3-b]quin-
  oxaline, 260-1.
1,2,3,4-Tetrahydroquinoxalines, 325-330.
  having no oxygen atom attached to
    hetero ring, 325-9.
  having oxygen atom attached to hetero
    ring, 329-330.
  stability to redn., 232.
  stereoisomers, 326.
  table, 329.
  table, 327-8.
5,7,12,14-Tetrahydro-5,7,12,14-tetraketo-
  phthalazino[2,3-b]phthalazine, 197-8.
2-d-arabo-Tetrahydroxybutyl-3-hydroxy-
  quinoxaline, 301.

2-*d-arabo*-Tetrahydroxybutyl-3-hydroxy-quinoxaline (*continued*):
dehydration, 341.
oxidn., 246–7.
reaction in acid soln. with phenylhydrazine, 308–9.
2-*d-arabo*-Tetrahydroxybutyl-3-phenyl-quinoxaline, 301.
2-*d-arabo*-Tetrahydroxybutylquinoxaline,
cond. w. hydrazine, 352.
form. from glucose derivs., mechanism, 301–2.
glucazidone from, 304.
3-*d-erythro*-1′,2′,3′-trihydroxypropyl-1-phenylflavazole from, 308.
2-*d-arabo*-Tetrahydroxybutylquinoxalines,
oxidn., 304.
reaction w. phenylhydrazine, 306–9.
2,4,7,9-Tetrahydroxydipyrimido [5,4-*c*, 4′,5′-*e*]pyridazine, 62, 64.
5-Tetrahydroxypentyl-2,3-dimethylin-dolo [2,3-*h*]quinoxaline, 346.
2,3,6,7-Tetramethylpyrazino [2,3-*b*]pyra-zine, 357.
Tetrazolo [*a*]phthalazine derivs., 196–7.
Tetrazolo [*a*]quinoxaline deriv., 261.
Tetrazolo [*a*]quinoxalines, 353–4.
Thieno [3,4-*c*]cinnoline deriv., 62–3.
α,β,α′,β′-Thiophenebis [thiochrome]az-ine, 62, 64.
2-*p*-Toluenesulfonamidobenzo [*c*]cinnoline, 56.
1,2,4-Triaminobenzene, reaction w. acetyl-sulfanilyl chloride, 273.
reaction with methylglyoxal, 273.
2,4,5-Triaminodiphenylamine, competitive
formn. of 6,7-diamino-1,2,3-triphen-ylquinoxalinium chloride and 6-am-ino-7-anilino-2,3-diphenylquinoxaline
from, 287.
Triazolo [4,5,1-*ij*]cinnoline deriv., 62, 64.
Triazoloquinoxalines, 353–4.
2-Tribromomethylquinoxaline, 277.
1,2,3-Tricarbomethoxyquinolizine-4-car-boxylic acid betaine, reaction w. hy-drazine, 200.
1-(3′-Trichloro-2′-hydroxy)propylphthal-azine, 76.

2,3,*x*-Trichloro-6-methylquinoxaline, 260.
2,4,6-Triethylphenylglyoxal, abnormal re-action w. *o*-phenylenediamine, 204–5.
1,2,3-Trihydroxy*cyclo*penta [*b*]quinoxaline,
reaction w. aldehydes, 343.
1,7,8-Trihydroxyphthalazine, acetylation, 82.
Trihydroxypropyl-3-hydroxyquinoxal-2-yl ketone, phenylhydrazone, 309.
3-Trihydroxypropyl-1-phenylpyrazolo [4, 5-*b*]quinoxaline, 309.
3-*d-erythro*-Trihydroxypropyl-1-phenyl-pyrazolo [3,4-*b*]quinoxaline, structure, 351.
3-*d-erythro*-Trihydroxypropylpyrazolo [3,-4-*b*]quinoxaline, oxidn., 351.
2-*d-erythro*-Trihydroxypropylquinoxaline-3-carboxylic acid lactone, 301.
2,3-Trimethylenequinoxaline, reaction w. aldehydes, 343.
2-(1,3,3-Trimethylindoline)-2-(3-methyl-1-phenylquinoxaline)trimethincya-nine, 290–1.
2,4,6-Trimethylphenylglyoxal, abnormal
reaction w. *o*-phenylenediamine, 204–5.
2,3,6-Trimethylquinoxaline, 283.
cond. prod., table, 284.
1,2,3-Trimethylquinoxalinium iodide, cya-nine dyes from, 290–1.
1,2,3-Triphenylquinoxalinium bromide, re-action with ethylmagnesium iodide, 290.
1,2,3-Triphenylquinoxalinium chloride, 287.
2,4,6-Tri*iso*propylphenylglyoxal, abnormal
reaction w. *o*-phenylenediamine, 204–5.
Triquinoxalines, table, 225.
Trypanosoma congolense, action of cin-nolines against, 364.

W

Widman-Stoermer synthesis, mechanism, 6–7.

X

Xantheno [9,1-*cd*]pyridazine derivs., 193.